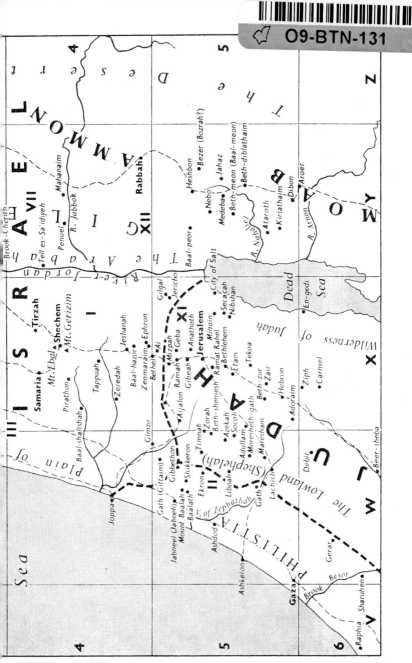

THE NEW CLARENDON BIBLE

OLD TESTAMENT

VOLUME III

———

THE HEBREW KINGDOMS

THE HEBREW KINGDOMS

BY

E. W. HEATON

FELLOW OF ST. JOHN'S COLLEGE
OXFORD

OXFORD UNIVERSITY PRESS

1968

Oxford University Press, Ely House, London W. 1

GLASGOW NEW YORK TORONTO MELBOURNE WELLINGTON
CAPE TOWN SALISBURY IBADAN NAIROBI LUSAKA ADDIS ABABA
BOMBAY CALCUTTA MADRAS KARACHI LAHORE DACCA
KUALA LUMPUR HONG KONG TOKYO

PRINTED IN GREAT BRITAIN

PUBLISHER'S PREFACE

When it became necessary, a year or two ago, to contemplate revision of the Old Testament volumes of the Clarendon Bible series, the publishers were faced with two important decisions: first, on what text the revision should be based, and second, whether any significant change should be made in the form and plan of the series.

It seemed to them, after taking the best available advice, that the Revised Version could not expect to hold the field for much longer in face of the developments in scholarship which have taken place since its publication in the eighteen eighties, and which have been reflected in more recently published versions. On the other hand, the New English Bible Old Testament is not yet published, and even after its publication it will be some little time before its usefulness for schools and universities can be evaluated. In these circumstances, the Revised Standard Version has seemed the obvious choice, the more particularly because of the recent decision by the Roman Catholic hierarchy to authorize the use of their own slightly modified version in British schools. The publishers would like to express their gratitude to the National Council of Churches of Christ in the United States of America for the permission, so readily given, to make use of the RSV in this way.

With regard to the form of the series, the success of the old Clarendon Bible over the years has encouraged them to think that no radical change is necessary. As before, therefore, subjects requiring comprehensive treatment are dealt with in essays, whether forming part of the introduction or interspersed among the notes. The notes themselves are mainly concerned with the subject-matter of the books and the points of interest (historical, doctrinal, etc.) therein presented; they deal with the elucidation of words, allusions, and the like only so far as seems necessary to a proper comprehension of the

459 44

author's meaning. There will, however, be some variations in the content and limits of each individual volume, and in particular it is intended that a fuller treatment should be given to Genesis, and to the Psalms.

The plan is to replace the volumes of the old series gradually over the next few years, as stocks become exhausted.

AUTHOR'S PREFACE

This volume has been written to provide an introduction to the principal features of Israel's life, literature, and faith during the period which began with the establishment of two independent Hebrew kingdoms after the death of Solomon in 922 B.C. and ended with the fall of Jerusalem in 587 B.C. It covers, therefore, the last part of the period presented in *From Moses to Elisha* by L. Elliott-Binns (1929) and the whole of the period presented in *The Decline and Fall of the Hebrew Kingdoms* by T. H. Robinson (1926).

When these two early volumes of *The Clarendon Bible* were written forty years ago, there was a large measure of agreement among students of the Old Testament about the conclusions of critical scholarship and the character of Israel's religion, whereas today opinions differ considerably and generalization has become much more difficult. This change has been brought about partly by the access of new knowledge, but primarily by new ways of approaching the familiar evidence as it is found in the Old Testament. The discovery of the Ras Shamra texts (and through them the cultural and religious legacy of Canaan) brought the greatest single gain in our knowledge during the last forty years, but their most significant influence, like that of many other archaeological finds, has been on the general presuppositions with which the Old Testament is studied. It is now taken for granted, to a degree hardly dreamed of a generation ago, that Israel was a part of the ancient Near East and, therefore, that the Old Testament must be considered in this wide cultural and religious context.

This fundamental shift in perspective is reflected throughout the present volume, but most obviously, in two main ways. First, as a comparison with T. H. Robinson's treatment of the period will indicate, the biggest innovation is the inclusion of separate sections on Worship and Wisdom. The former is demanded by far-reaching developments in the study of the Psalms, from which there has emerged almost universal agreement that many of them are pre-exilic compositions used in the worship of Solomon's Temple. In addition to providing documentary evidence for an aspect of Israel's life too important to be neglected, the Psalms throw a flood of light on the character of religious thought in Jerusalem during the period of the monarchy. It is much to be hoped, therefore, that no out-of-date examination syllabuses will deter the teacher and student from recognizing the importance of the Psalms for a proper understanding of the pre-exilic period. It is probably too much to hope that a comparable recognition will be accorded as readily to the tradition of Wisdom during the monarchy. Although most scholars accept the pre-exilic origin of much of the Book of Proverbs, few, until quite recently, have investigated the implications of this conclusion, or related it to a growing body of evidence which points to the existence and pervasive influence of a school of wisdom established by Solomon in Jerusalem. The justification for including the section on Wisdom will, therefore, be found, if it is found at all, not so much in an established consensus of academic opinion on the subject as in the contribution it makes to the picture as a whole.

The second main way in which the changed outlook in Old Testament studies is reflected in this volume will be found in its constant concern to elucidate what was distinctive in Israel's faith and theological insight. The urgency of this task clearly increases the more it is acknowledged that the people of God was deeply involved in the culture of other peoples in the ancient Near East. Although the task is urgent, in the present unsettled climate of scholarly opinion, everyone who essays it inevitably places himself in a highly exposed position.

If, however, one is to attempt to wrest from the complexity of the Old Testament evidence any coherent picture of its main religious traditions, to plot their interrelationship, and, above all, evaluate their theological significance, it is impossible to avoid making up one's mind about many controversial issues which academic prudence might suggest were better left as open questions. I have tried to make amends for my temerity in a fairly extensive bibliography, which, I hope, may guide the student to more cautious considerations of disputed topics and also serve as an acknowledgement of my deep indebtedness to scholars of many and diverse points of view.

As the book leaves my hands, however, I am more immediately aware of the debt I owe to those who have helped during the final stages of its preparation. With characteristic generosity Mr. Vernon Pratt sacrificed many hours of his last weeks in Oxford as a graduate student to compiling the Index of Subjects, and for the production of the Index of Biblical References my wife and three children cheerfully converted our dining-room into a sorting office to bring order out of a chaos of record cards. What is more, they allowed me to neglect them over long periods without complaint.

E. W. HEATON

St. John's College, Oxford

CONTENTS

LIST OF ILLUSTRATIONS   xv–xvi

LIST OF SELECTED PASSAGES   xvii–xx

I. INTRODUCTION   1–59

  I. THE CO-EXISTENCE OF THE KINGDOMS   1

  II. THE INTERNATIONAL RELATIONS OF THE KINGDOMS   9

     (i) Damascus
     (ii) Assyria
     (iii) Egypt and Babylon

  III. THE ECONOMIC AND SOCIAL DEVELOPMENT OF THE
       KINGDOMS   21

     (i) Phoenician enterprise
     (ii) Royal enterprise
     (iii) Private enterprise and private poverty

  IV. THE RELIGIOUS TRADITIONS OF THE KINGDOMS   42

     (i) The religion of Canaan
     (ii) Mosaic Yahwism
     (iii) The theology of Jerusalem
     (iv) Prophetic Yahwism

II. HISTORY   60–132

  THE DEUTERONOMIC HISTORY OF 1 AND 2 KINGS   60

     (i) The sources and the framework
     (ii) The theological viewpoint
     (iii) The occasion and date

  I. THE DIVIDED KINGDOMS (922–876)   69
     Notes on selections from 1 Kings 11^{26}-15^{22}

II. THE HOUSE OF OMRI (876-842)   78
   Notes on selections from 1 Kings 16^{15}-22^{40}

III. THE REVOLT OF JEHU (842)   89
   Notes on selections from 2 Kings 9^{1}-10^{27}

IV. THE KINGDOMS IN PEACE AND PROSPERITY
   (783-742)   96
   Notes on 2 Kings 14^{23}-15^{7}

V. THE DECLINE AND FALL OF ISRAEL (746-721)   99
   Notes on selections from 2 Kings 15^{8}-17^{33}

VI. THE KINGDOM OF JUDAH ALONE (715-587)   108
   Notes on selections from 2 Kings 18^{1}-25^{30}

III. WORSHIP   133-64
   (i) Worship at the local sanctuaries
   (ii) Worship at the Temple
   Notes on selected Psalms

IV. WISDOM   165-96
   (i) The Counsellor and the Scribe
   (ii) Schools of Wisdom
   (iii) Wisdom and Prophecy
   (iv) The Wisdom of the Schools
   (v) The Book of Proverbs
   Notes on selections from the Book of Proverbs

V. LAW   197-230
   (i) The Book of the Covenant
   (ii) Law in the courts and in the sanctuaries
   (iii) Teaching and Law in Deuteronomy
   (iv) Deuteronomy's interpretation of Law
   (v) The origin of Deuteronomy
   Notes on selections from Deuteronomy

VI. PROPHECY 231-389

 (i) The institutional prophets
 (ii) The independent prophets
 (iii) From prophetic oracle to prophetic book

ELIJAH AND ELISHA 247
 Notes on selections from 1 Kings 17^1–2 Kings 5^{19}

AMOS 264
 Notes on the Book of Amos

HOSEA 285
 Notes on selected passages

MICAH 306
 Notes on selected passages

ISAIAH 315
 Notes on selected passages

JEREMIAH 348
 Notes on selected passages

CHRONOLOGICAL TABLES 391

BIBLIOGRAPHY 396

INDEX OF SUBJECTS 403

INDEX OF SCRIPTURE REFERENCES 415

LIST OF ILLUSTRATIONS

Fortifications for Civil War. Model of the east gate of Tell
    en-Nasbeh. *Palestine Institute, Berkeley, California*   7

Imperial Power. Statue from Nimrud. *British Museum*   14

The Influence of Egypt. Ivory panel from Nimrud. *Directorate
    General of Antiquities, Baghdad*   19

Canaanite Craftsmanship. Gold plate from Ras Shamra.
    Louvre   22

A Mythological Text from Ras Shamra. *Louvre*   26

Solomon's Fortifications. Reconstruction of the Gate at
    Megiddo. *By courtesy of the Oriental Institute, University of
    Chicago*   31

Town-planning in the Jordan Valley. Excavated street at Tell
    es-Saʿidiyeh. *University Museum, Pennsylvania*   35

The Neighbour's Landmark. Babylonian boundary-stone.
    Staatliche Museum, Berlin   40

Agents of God's Judgement. Relief from Nimrud. *British Museum*   57

Storm-god on a bull. Stele from Arslan-Tash. *Louvre*   74

Palatial Luxury in Samaria. Ivory plaque. *Palestine Archaeo-
    logical Museum. Copyright reserved*   79

The Royal Phoenician Style. Capitals from Hazor and Ramat
    Raḥel. *Professor Yigael Yadin, The Hebrew University of Jeru-
    salem and the Israel Department of Antiquities and Museums*   80

The Humiliation of Jehu. Black Obelisk from Nimrud. *British
    Museum*   90

Jerusalem before the Exile. Plan of the city.   112

Divination: a Student's Teaching-aid. Clay model from
    Nimrud. *Directorate General of Antiquities, Baghdad*   117

Babylonian Record of the First Deportation from Jerusalem.
    Babylonian Chronicle tablet. *British Museum*   128

A Canaanite Prototype of Solomon's Temple. Temple at Hazor. *Professor Yigael Yadin, The Hebrew University, Jerusalem*   134

Solomon's Temple. Reconstruction by C. F. Stevens. *American Schools of Oriental Research, Cambridge, Massachusetts*   140

Sacral Kingship. Statue from Nimrud. *Directorate General of Antiquities, Baghdad*   144

The Office of a Scribe. Scribal Chamber at Nimrud. *Directorate General of Antiquities, Baghdad*   168

A School Exercise. Egyptian writing-board. *British Museum*   194

A forbidden Canaanite Altar. Altar at Hazor. *Professor Yigael Yadin, The Hebrew University, Jerusalem*   198

The Alien Culture of the Nations. Ivory head from Nimrud. *Directorate General of Antiquities, Baghdad*   216

A King like all the Nations. Ivory plaque from Megiddo. *By courtesy of the Oriental Institute, University of Chicago*   226

Baal of the Lightning. Stele from Ras Shamra. *Louvre, M. Chuzeville*   252

Beds of Ivory. Ivory from Nimrud. *Directorate General of Antiquities, Baghdad*   278

Fertility Cult Symbols. Ivory from Nimrud. *Directorate General of Antiquities, Baghdad*   292

Sennacherib: King of Kings. Relief from Nineveh, after Layard. *Ashmolean Museum, Oxford*   340

The Babylon of Nebuchadrezzar. Excavation of the Ishtar Gate. *Directorate General of Antiquities, Baghdad*   353

Map of the Kingdoms of Israel and Judah   *front end paper*

Map of the Imperial Powers of the Near East   *back end paper*

LIST OF SELECTED PASSAGES

1 & 2 KINGS

I KINGS

11^{26-40}	Jeroboam—rebel and refugee (922)	69
12^{1-20}	The revolt of the northern tribes (922)	71
12^{25-33}	Jeroboam I of Israel (922–901)	72
14^{21-31}	Rehoboam of Judah (922–915)	75
15^{16-22}	War between Asa of Judah and Baasha of Israel (c. 900–875)	76
16^{15-28}	Omri of Israel (876–869)	78
16^{29-34}	Ahab of Israel (869–850)	81
17^{1-24}	Elijah the Man of God	250
18^{1-46}	Elijah's contest on Mount Carmel	251
19^{1-18}	Elijah's confrontation on Mount Horeb	257
19^{19-21}	Elijah calls Elisha	260
20^{1-34}	Ahab and the wars with Damascus	83
21^{1-20}	Elijah at Naboth's vineyard	259
22^{1-40}	Ahab's last battle (850)	85

2 KINGS

2^{1-18}	Elisha succeeds Elijah	261
5^{1-19}	Elisha converts Naaman	263
9^{1-13}	Jehu is anointed king (842)	91
9^{14-28}	Jehu's assassination of Joram and Ahaziah (842)	92
$9^{30}-10^{27}$	Jehu's final massacres (842)	93
14^{23-29}	Jeroboam II of Israel (786–746)	96
15^{1-7}	Uzziah (Azariah) of Judah (783–742)	98
15^{8-31}	The decline of Israel (746–732)	99
16^{1-20}	Ahaz of Judah's subjection to Assyria (735–715)	102
$17^{1-6, \, 24-33}$	The fall of Israel (732–721)	105
$18^{1}-19^{37}$	Hezekiah's reform and rebellion (715–687)	108
21^{12-6}	The apostasy of Manasseh (687–642) and Amon (642–640)	115
$22^{1}-23^{30}$	Josiah's rebellion and reformation (640–609)	118
$23^{31}-25^{30}$	Judah's decline and fall (609–587)	126

PSALMS

2	A hymn for the king's coronation	151
5	An individual's lament	152
20	A prayer for the king before battle	153
29	A hymn to Yahweh as Creator and King	154
47	A hymn for the celebration of Yahweh's Kingship	155
48	A hymn celebrating the beauty and security of Zion	157
72	A prayer for the king and his people	158
80	A communal lament from the Northern Kingdom	160
84	A pilgrim's praise for the Temple	161
132	A processional liturgy of commemoration	162

PROVERBS

3^{21-32}	A lesson on neighbourliness	186
4^{20-27}	A lesson on vigilance	187
8^{1-36}	The authority of wisdom	188
$22^{17}-23^5$	The words of the wise in Egypt and Israel	192
25^{1-10}	Proverbs from the school of Hezekiah	195

DEUTERONOMY

6^{1-9}	The Great Commandment	213
7^{1-11}	The Holy War of the People of God	215
12^{1-19}	The abolition of the local sanctuaries	219
15^{1-18}	Two sabbatical laws for the protection of the poor	222
17^{14-20}	A king like all the nations	225
20^{1-9}	Israel's good fight of faith	227
22^1-25^3	Laws of humanity	228

AMOS

1^1-2^{16}	Yahweh's judgement of crimes against common humanity	266
3^{1-8}	Israel's election and the prophet's authority	270
3^9-4^3	Samaria doomed to destruction	271
4^4-5^{15}	Rites and righteousness	272
5^{16-27}	The Day of the Lord	274
6^{1-14}	A corrupt people on the brink of disaster	277
7^1-8^3	Divine patience and prophetic insight	280
8^{4-14}	Destroyers destroyed	282
9^{1-8a}	The conclusion	283
9^{8b-15}	A later appendix	284

HOSEA

1^1	Hosea and his ministry	289
1^{2-9}	The marriage of Hosea	289
2^{2-15}	Yahweh's dealing with his unfaithful wife	293
3^{1-5}	The discipline of redeeming love	295
4^{1-3}	Yahweh's charge against his people	297
4^{4-19}	Yahweh's charge against the priests	298
5^{8-15}	Yahweh's judgement on Israel and Judah	300
6^{1-6}	Israel's confession and Yahweh's reply	301
$6^{11b}-7^{12}$	Israel's political failure	302
11^{1-11}	The kindness and severity of God	304

MICAH

1^1	Micah and his ministry	308
1^{2-9}	Yahweh's judgement on Samaria and Jerusalem	308
2^{1-11}	The prophet denounces the exploiters of the poor	309
3^{1-12}	The fate of Jerusalem's ruling classes	312
6^{6-8}	The old religion and the new faith	314

ISAIAH

1^1	Isaiah and his ministry	323
1^{2-9}	Judah's rebellion and terrible plight	323
1^{10-17}	Rites and righteousness	324
1^{18-20}	The choice which faces the accused	324
1^{21-26}	Yahweh's purge of Jerusalem	325
2^{6-22}	The Day of the Lord	326
5^{1-7}	The parable of the vineyard	326
5^{8-24a}	Cry havoc!	328
6^{1-13}	The prophet's inaugural vision	329
7^{1-9}	Isaiah counsels Ahaz	331
7^{10-17}	The sign of Immanuel	333
8^{5-8a}	Ahaz's false choice	335
8^{16-18}	Isaiah's withdrawal	335
9^{2-7}	The Man born to be King	336
10^{5-15}	The arrogant boasting of Assyria	338
20^{1-6}	Isaiah's sign against reliance on Egypt	341
22^{1-14}	The judgement on Jerusalem	342
28^{1-13}	Jerusalem's leaders will learn their lesson	344
28^{14-22}	Yahweh's strange work of judging his own people	345

29^{1-8} A judgement on Jerusalem reversed   346
31^{1-3} The wisdom of men and the wisdom of God   348

JEREMIAH

1^{1-3} Jeremiah and his ministry   354
1^{4-12} Jeremiah's call and inaugural revelation   355
2^{1-13} Israel's appalling apostasy   356
$3^{1}-4^{4}$ A plea for true repentance   357
4^{5-31} Disaster from the North   358
5^{1-14} A nation such as this   361
7^{1-26} The Temple and its alien religion   363
$8^{18}-9^{1}$ The prophet's sympathy with his people   365
11^{1-8} Jeremiah and Josiah's reform   366
$11^{18}-12^{6}$ The plot of Jeremiah's kinsmen   368
15^{10-21} Jeremiah's lament and Yahweh's reply   369
17^{9-18} Taunts and self-torture   371
18^{18-23} The prophet's bitter prayer for vengeance   371
20^{7-18} Jeremiah's vocation and its cost   372
22^{13-19} Jeremiah on Josiah and Jehoiakim   373
23^{9-32} Concerning the prophets   374
26^{1-24} Jeremiah's Temple sermon and its sequel   377
$29^{1-7, 24-32}$ Jeremiah's letter to the exiles   379
31^{31-34} The New Covenant   381
32^{1-15} Jeremiah's confidence in Judah's future   383
36^{1-32} Baruch's scroll   384
$37^{1}-45^{5}$ The last years of Jeremiah   387

I. INTRODUCTION

1. *The Co-existence of the Kingdoms*

THE period of the Divided Monarchy (922–587) begins not so much with the disruption of a kingdom as with the collapse of an empire. With the exception of Damascus in the far north and Edom in the far south, Solomon had succeeded in keeping intact the hard-won territories of his father David and these extended far beyond the tribal confines of Israel and Judah. For a brief but brilliant period, the Davidic Empire was undoubtedly the most considerable power in Palestine and Syria and held in allegiance, whether by governors or vassal kings, all the surrounding minor states—the Philistines, Moabites, Arameans, Edomites, and Ammonites (1 Kgs. 4²¹; cf. 2 Sam. 8¹⁻¹⁴). In this vast imperial complex, kept in hand by David's own army of mercenaries, Israel and Judah still had pride of place, but there was little to encourage them to think that together they constituted a single kingdom.

The death of Solomon removed, therefore, not only the powerful bolt which held together the diverse states of David's empire, but also the personal link which David had originally forged between the tribes of the north and the south. Without it, Israel and Judah simply went their separate ways.

There never was a *united* kingdom, except in the sense that Israel and Judah, for two momentous reigns, shared a king in common. David and Solomon reigned over a *dual* monarchy. David, himself a Judean, began his rule first in Hebron, when 'the men of Judah came, and there they anointed David *king over the house of Judah*' (2 Sam. 2⁴). This independent move on the part of Judah is less surprising when we recall that, among the tribes of Israel, it always seems to have walked alone. Judah is not even mentioned, for example, in the roll-call of the ancient Song of Deborah, where absent tribes are named and castigated for failing to turn up to fight the Canaanites of the north (Judg. 5¹³⁻¹⁸). It was only after some years that David, king of Judah, was chosen by the northern tribes to become also the *king of Israel*: 'So all the elders of Israel came to the king at Hebron; and King David made a convenant with them at Hebron before the Lord, and they anointed David king over Israel. . . . At Hebron he reigned over Judah seven years and six months; and at Jerusalem he reigned over all Israel and Judah thirty-three years' (2 Sam. 5³, ⁵). David now belonged to both Israel and Judah, but their joint capital, Jerusalem, being an independent city-state and David's own personal possession (cf. 2 Sam. 5⁶⁻⁹), belonged to neither of them and, constitutionally, they did not belong to each other.

The dual character of David's monarchy is constantly noted (2 Sam. 3¹⁰; 24¹⁻⁹; 1 Kgs. 1³⁵) and at one point it came ominously near to its later disruption. This happened after the failure of Absalom's rebellion, when Israel accused Judah (who, despite their part in the uprising, had responded to David's appeal for reinstatement: 2 Sam. 19¹¹⁻¹⁵) of trying to monopolize *their* king: 'We have ten shares in the king, and in David also we have more than you. Why then did you despise us? Were we not the first to speak of bringing back our king?' (2 Sam. 19⁴³). The significance of this cleavage between the two kingdoms is high-lighted in the biblical narrative by the immediate sequel of Sheba's revolt, with its ringing watchword:

> We have no portion in David,
> and we have no inheritance in the son of Jesse;
> every man to his tents, O Israel! (2 Sam. 20¹)

This was the cry which re-echoed when, after Solomon's death, Israel rejected his son for a king of their own choosing (1 Kgs. 12¹⁶).

After the disruption, the two kingdoms developed very differently. Judah continued to live a life apart from the great world, quietly soaking up the Canaanite culture in which David and Solomon had immersed it and modifying by degrees its social structure and religious inheritance. Judah became a sacral and highly centralized society and its slow-moving conservatism enabled it to retain a single dynasty throughout the three and a half centuries of its independent existence, with the city of David the focus of its national and religious life.

By contrast, Israel lacked a centre and was all excess. Without the stability which recognized institutions give, it oscillated between extremes of zeal and extremes of apostasy, extremes of wealth and extremes of poverty, extremes of grandeur and extremes of degradation. The northern kingdom exploited its exposure to the outside world, did nothing by halves and everything in a hurry. After a mere two centuries, it hastened to its extinction.

The history of Israel is a fantastic record of unscrupulous adventurers and unrestrained violence. In two hundred years, it ran through no less than nineteen kings, of whom nine were usurpers, seven were murdered, and one committed suicide. Of the ten kings who inherited the throne legitimately, seven are accounted for by the two dynasties of Omri and Jehu alone (and these usurpers are unconvincing witnesses to the right of succession!). It is obvious that Israel differed from Judah in never having accepted the settled hereditary idea of monarchy and in having retained something of the older and more episodic notion of leadership, which dominated the age of the 'judges' and survived to the time of Saul. It is now customary to describe this concept as 'charismatic' in view of the fact that the leaders are said to have been chosen and endowed by 'the Spirit of Yahweh' (Judg. 3^{10}; 6^{34}; 11^{29}; 13^{25}; cf. 1 Sam. 11^6). This grandiose term should not, however, be allowed to conceal the evidence that the 'judges' were bellicose tribesmen and that their possession of 'the Spirit of Yahweh' is no more than a theological way of evaluating their zeal and energy in delivering Yahweh's people from the hands of the heathen. Of this old order (if order it may be called), what chiefly survived in the northern kingdom was its instability and violence. The ancient idea that Yahweh chose and endowed his national champions as circumstances demanded is probably reflected in the anointing of some of Israel's kings by prophets (1 Kgs. 19[16]; 2 Kgs. 9[1-6]; cf. 1 Sam. 9[16]; 10[1]), but it must be admitted that kingship in the north was much more obviously military than 'charismatic'. The loss of the religious (if barbarous) sanctions of the old tribal rule and the rejection of Judah's newly adopted dynastic system exposed the northern kingdom to the lawless opportunism of military usurpers.

The record speaks for itself. Baasha (900–877), despite the record of his choice by Yahweh (1 Kgs. 16[1, 2]), gained the throne by murdering Nadab in his army camp (1 Kgs. 15[27, 28]). Baasha's son, Elah (877–876), was assassinated within two years by Zimri, his chariot-commander, who then found time as king-for-a-week to exterminate the family of his predecessor before finally committing suicide (1 Kgs. 16[8-20]). Omri (876–869), the commander-in-chief of the Israelite forces, having first disposed of Tibni, seized the throne in a military *coup d'état* (1 Kgs. 16[15-22]). The dynasty which he founded, more on the basis of military power than hereditary principle, was overthrown thirty-five years later by Jehu, another officer, who was anointed by a prophet in the middle of a session of the army council (2 Kgs. 9[1-6]). The dynasty which Jehu established, with such distinguished prophetic backing and bloody brutality, lasted (largely because of the long, untroubled reign of Jeroboam II) for nearly a century (842–745). Zechariah, the last of Jehu's line, was murdered by Shallum after a reign of only six months. In the final chaos of Israel's national existence from 746–721 B.C., there were six kings and five of them lost the throne by violence (see pp. 100 ff.). Before we attempt to read any constitutional theory into this lawless succession, we should weigh the bitter comment of the northern prophet Hosea: 'They made kings, but not through me. They set up princes, but without my knowledge' (8[4]). It is clear, at least, that the men of Israel set great store by their independence.

The contrast between the stability of the throne of David and the chronic instability of the throne in Israel would almost certainly be illuminated if we possessed more information about the character and strength of the army in the two kingdoms. It

is at least clear that Israel inherited the bulk of Solomon's
chariot force in the garrison towns of Hazor, Gezer, and
Megiddo (fig. p. 31) (1 Kgs. 9¹⁵⁻¹⁹), to the latter of which (as
recent excavations reveal) substantial additions were made in
the time of Ahab (869–850). Solomon is reported to have owned
no less than 1,400 chariots (1 Kgs. 10²⁶) and, according to the
Assyrian record, Ahab was able to field an astonishing force of
2,000 at the battle of Qarqar in 853 B.C. The Israelite establishment was much reduced, however, before the end of the ninth
century (2 Kgs. 13⁷), and when the kingdom fell in 721 B.C.,
the Assyrians were able to loot a mere fifty chariots from
Samaria (as against, for example, 300 from Hamath). Chariotry
in Israel was one of Solomon's Canaanite innovations, like the
professional army of which it was a part. Many of Israel's
professional soldiers were also from a Canaanite background.
Zimri, the military usurper of Elah's throne, and Omri, the
army commander-in-chief, another usurper, were both, probably, non-Israelite mercenaries, as the absence of any reference
to their fathers suggests. It is, therefore, highly unlikely that
their military *coups*, whatever may be true of Jehu (see pp. 89 f.),
were inspired by any such noble 'Free Israelite' sentiments as
opposition to the hateful institution of monarchy and its
heathen abolition of the ancient practice of 'holy war'.

If national religious feeling came to be associated with the
army anywhere after the disruption of the monarchy, it was,
paradoxically, in Judah, where the military establishment can
never have been very influential. In the middle of the ninth
century, the southern kingdom still possessed a few horses and
chariots (2 Kgs. 3⁷; 8²¹), but at the end of the next century, we
find Hezekiah being mocked by Sennacherib's envoy (2 Kgs.
18²⁴) and rebuked by the prophet Isaiah (Isa. 31¹⁻³), because
he relied for them on Egypt. After the devastation of 701 B.C.,
Judah could never afford to re-form its professional army and
began to depend exclusively (as Nebuchadrezzar's records confirm) on an army conscripted by compulsory military service.
It is possible (but by no means certain) that this development,
viewed as a revival of the people's militia (as in the good old

days of the Judges), awakened a new national consciousness among all those liable for military service. These men, who were called 'the people of the land' (see notes on 2 Kgs. 22¹), secured the throne for Josiah against a conspiracy in the Jerusalem court (2 Kgs. 21²³, ²⁴) and, again, for his son, Jehoahaz, in a final and unsuccessful bid to safeguard the nation's independence (2 Kgs. 23³⁰, ³³⁻³⁵). This resurgent nationalism among the citizens of Judah, it has been suggested, was one of the factors underlying Josiah's religious reformation.

Judah's dreams of independent sovereignty and dominion over the nations, to which the royal psalms bear striking witness (see pp. 151 f., 158 f.), were far removed from the reality of its situation. The southern kingdom was nearly always too weak to be independent even of the northern kingdom and, as for dominion over the nations, the imperial age had ended for both houses of Israel with the death of Solomon. At the disruption of the dual monarchy, the Davidic Empire simply dissolved, neither Israel nor Judah being in the least capable of holding its constituent states together. From extra-biblical evidence, it is reasonably certain that Ammon, Moab, the Aramean states, the Philistines (cf. 1 Kgs. 15²⁷; 16¹⁵), and, in some measure, the Edomites (1 Kgs. 22⁴⁷), rapidly claimed their independence (cf. 2 Sam. 8¹⁻¹⁴). Israel and Judah, therefore, were left as two of the half-dozen or so minor kingdoms in Palestine, whose fortunes during the succeeding centuries were to be determined by greater powers from outside—Damascus, Assyria, Egypt, and Babylon.

It is true that Israel and Judah shared a common faith and, as the scope of the prophets' ministries and the unified history of 1 and 2 Kings remind us, the two kingdoms were, from a religious point of view, two halves of a single whole—'both houses of Israel' (Isa. 8¹⁴; see further, pp. 62 f.). Politically, however, they were independent. The northern kingdom, with greater natural resources, more money, and more man-power (see pp. 21, 101), stood in relation to Judah (in the contemptuous phrase of one of Israel's kings) as the cedar to the thistle (2 Kgs. 14⁹). With insignificant exceptions, when the two kingdoms

FORTIFICATIONS FOR CIVIL WAR. The photograph shows a model of the excavated remains of the great east gate of Tell en-Nasbeh, eight miles north of Jerusalem, which is generally (but not unanimously) identified with Mizpah, the border fortress between Judah and Israel. The point of view is outside the city gate facing south. On the left is the base of the massive east tower, 30 ft. square, with which the city wall from the south terminated. On the right, the wall from the north is seen overlapping the inner side of the southern wall to a distance of about 33 ft., thus forming the extra-mural enclosure (33 by 30 ft.) in the centre of the photograph. In peacetime, this enclosure, which was paved and drained, was used as a meeting-place and court-room, and long stone benches are still in position at the bottom of the outer tower (centre). In wartime, the enclosure was a dangerous trap for attacking enemy forces, who were compelled to advance up the road of the city mound (top left) and in turning left round the outer tower expose their unprotected right side to the defenders on the inner wall of the city (right). If the attackers survived this ordeal, they were impeded by the gate proper, which had two sets of piers jutting out from each side, leaving a roadway into the city 14 ft. wide and forming two guardrooms (6 by 8 ft.), which were also supplied with benches, in the space between them (cf. fig. p. 31). From the outer piers (the nearer pair in the picture) hung two great doors, the central stone stop for which is still clearly visible. The long slot in the left pier was the rest for the bar of the gates when they were open. It is illuminating to recall that the enemy against whom this Judean border town was so heavily fortified was none other than the kingdom of Israel and that in all probability the work was accomplished by Asa of Judah (913–873) with stones taken from Ramah (cf. 1 Kgs. 15$^{16-22}$).

were allies, whether in war or peace, Israel was the leader, and
when they were enemies, Israel was almost invariably the
aggressor and the victor.

The relationship between the two kingdoms falls roughly
into four successive periods—of hostility, alliance, toleration,
and separation. The period of *hostility* was the half-century
following the disruption (922–876), when there was continual
border fighting over the disputed territory of the tribe of
Benjamin, the no-man's-land between the two states (1 Kgs.
14^{30}; 15^{16}). The feud was dropped when Judah, having bribed
Damascus to march against Israel, succeeded in pushing its
border far enough north to safeguard Jerusalem (1 Kgs. 15$^{16-22}$).
The period of *alliance* lasted throughout the dynasty of Omri
(876–842), when Israel deliberately fostered friendly relations
with Judah and the two royal families were even united in
marriage (2 Kgs. 8$^{18, 26, 27}$). In these years, we find Judah being
called upon twice to help Israel against Damascus (1 Kgs.
22$^{1-40}$; 2 Kgs. 8$^{25-29}$) and once against Moab (2 Kgs. 3$^{4-27}$),
although, apparently, its contribution to the joint war-effort
was not considered worthy of notice, either on the Moabite
Stone, or in Shalmaneser's list of Assyria's enemies at the battle
of Qarqar (see p. 11). The period of *toleration* began with
Jehu's revolt in the northern kingdom and lasted for sixty
years (842–783), when, for the most part, both kingdoms were
too enfeebled for anything else. Jehu's blood-purge was extended to the royal house of Judah (2 Kgs. 9^{27}; 10$^{12-14}$) and put
an end to Omri's policy of friendship. For forty years, Israel,
weak internally and oppressed by Damascus, crawled along in
a state of exhaustion. This explains why Judah suddenly threw
down a foolhardy challenge to Israel, sometime after 801 B.C.
It was answered in an expedition without parallel, when Israel
marched south, ravaged Jerusalem, and plundered the Temple
(2 Kgs. 14$^{8-14}$). Judah was reduced to abject vassalage, now
without exaggeration a mere thistle under Israel's cedar. The
period of *separation* covered the last sixty years of the coterminous
life of the kingdoms (783–721). At first both of them exploited
independently, with Jeroboam II in Israel and Uzziah in

Judah, the stalemate in international affairs, and concentrated on extending their frontiers and expanding their economy (see pp. 96-99). These boom years, however, came to an abrupt end with the resurgence of Assyrian power after 745 B.C. In this new and threatening situation, Judah opted to become vassal to Assyria rather than join Israel in a defensive alliance of minor states, and so it was that it outlived the northern kingdom by nearly a century and a half (see pp. 102-5). Without this respite, during which the literature and traditions of the kingdom of Israel were brought south and joined with those of Judah, we should know a good deal less than we do about either of these unequal houses and their brief experiment with monarchy.

II. *The International Relations of the Kingdoms*

The kingdoms of Israel and Judah were never strong enough to pursue any independent foreign policy and their names occur in the historical records of the great powers only among references to the minor states of Palestine and Syria. This extra-biblical evidence is of great value, not only in amplifying the Old Testament history, but also in reducing it to size, since it is easy to forget that by secular standards the people of God was of small significance in the international politics of the ancient Near East. The occupation and control of Israel or Judah might be useful in helping to finance the imperial war-machines, or necessary as part of some larger scheme of military or commercial expansion, but the two kingdoms rarely held a key position in the major policies of their powerful neighbours.

If, however, Israel and Judah mattered little to the great powers, their own fortunes were almost entirely determined by them. When the nations round about were preoccupied with their own problems, the Hebrew kingdoms were free to develop their commerce and expand their territory—occasionally, as we have seen, at each other's expense. When, however, they were threatened by external aggression, they agreed to sink their differences and enter an alliance, which was frequently extended to include others among the minor states in Palestine and Syria. At times, this basic pattern was complicated by an insolent attempt on the part of one of the minor states to involve one of the great powers in its own disputes, from which, almost invariably, it ended up the loser, paying heavily either way—to victorious foe or victorious friend. Throughout their history, the two Hebrew kingdoms were trapped in a complex international situation, rather like the smallest specimens in a collection of Chinese boxes, covered by the next in size and so on, until finally all are encased by the biggest in the set. At the beginning of the period of the divided kingdoms, there was, in fact, no really big power to dominate the rest, since the glory of Egypt had already faded and Assyria was only just beginning to stir from its long period of lethargy. For well over a century, it was one of the minor states which kept Israel and Judah in their place—the powerful Aramean kingdom of Damascus.

(i) DAMASCUS, 922–732 B.C.

The kingdom which had its capital in Damascus[1] was founded in the reign of Solomon (1 Kgs. 11$^{23-25}$). To the end of the ninth century B.C., Damascus remained the head of a group of city-states, which were established (about 1050 B.C.) in the region north-east of the sea of Galilee, by Arameans who had migrated to the west. During this period, it dominated the affairs of the northern kingdom and provides the key to Israel's external history.

We first become aware of the importance of Damascus, when Asa of Judah (913–873) bribed the Aramean king, Ben-hadad I (? 900–860), now known to us directly from the 'Milqart Stele' (see p. 77), to come to his rescue against Baasha of Israel (900–877), who was then challenging Judah's northern border (1 Kgs. 15$^{16-22}$). It is improbable that Ben-hadad needed much persuading, since already in the reign of David the Arameans had declared their interest in the great

---

[1] This Aramean kingdom and its inhabitants are often called 'Syria' and 'Syrians' (following the Greek version of the Old Testament). The name of the territory of these northern city-states is properly Aram.

caravan route from Damascus, which ran along the east side of Jordan, to Edom and Arabia (2 Sam. 10[16, 17]; cf. Num. 20[17]). On this first brush with Israel, Ben-hadad I deprived it of 'all the land of Naphtali' (1 Kgs. 15[20]) and it seems likely that he retained his dominant position throughout the reign of Omri (876–869), who is reported to have ceded to him cities and trading rights in Samaria (1 Kgs. 20[34]). His son, Ben-hadad II (? 860–843), relentlessly kept up the pressure on Israel in the time of Ahab (869–850), probably with the aim of reducing Israel to an Aramean satellite before the rising power of Assyria began its conquest of the west. The sober narrative of 1 Kgs. 20 recounts how Ben-hadad II and his vassal kings marched south and besieged Samaria (see pp. 83 ff.). His failure seems to have provoked a far-reaching reorganization (now reflected in 1 Kgs. 20[24, 25]), by which the kings of the petty Aramean states were replaced by governors owing allegiance directly to himself. Thus, Ben-hadad II converted a loose confederation into a united kingdom with its capital at Damascus. If we may trust the order of events in the biblical narrative, the success of the new kingdom was not immediate, since Ahab again defeated the Aramean army at Aphek. The subsequent treaty, however, was concluded on such friendly terms as to provoke hostile prophetic comment and to make the historian wonder how real a victory Ahab actually won (1 Kgs. 20[26–43]).

The pact, in any case, was demanded by the arrival of Assyria on the scene. In 853 B.C., Shalmaneser III (859–824) marched west and met a coalition of twelve kings, including Ben-hadad II and Ahab, now fighting as allies, at the battle of Qarqar (fig. p. 144). This famous engagement is not mentioned in the Old Testament, but the Assyrian records report '1,200 chariots, 1,200 cavalrymen, 20,000 foot soldiers of Adad-'idri [Ben-hadad II] of Damascus . . . 2,000 chariots and 10,000 foot soldiers of Ahab, the Israelite' (J. B. Pritchard, *Ancient Near Eastern Texts*, pp. 278–9). Although Assyria claimed the victory at Qarqar, it is significant that in the next few years its forces never ventured far from home. It was probably in this period of Assyrian recuperation that Ben-hadad II reasserted his power in the south. He routed the allied forces of Israel and Judah in the strategic region of Ramoth-gilead (1 Kgs. 22$^{1-36}$; see pp. 85 f.) and reduced Samaria to a state of famine and cannibalism (2 Kgs. 6^{24}–7^{20}). Worse was to follow. In 843 B.C., Hazael, 'the son of a nobody', usurped Ben-hadad's throne (2 Kgs. 8$^{7-15}$) and brought the kingdom of Damascus to the zenith of its power. For Israel, the reign of Hazael (843–796) was a reign of terror (2 Kgs. 13$^{3, 22}$).

The strength of Damascus at this time is clear from its repeated victories over Assyria between 849 and 841 B.C. It was Hazael's resistance which diverted the Assyrian forces to a campaign further south in 841 B.C., as a result of which Jehu of Israel was compelled to pay tribute. After an account of his engagement with Damascus, Shalmaneser's record on the famous 'Black Obelisk' continues laconically: 'I marched as far as the mountains of Ba'ali-ra'si, a headland by the sea [? Mount Carmel], and put up on it a representation of my royal person. At that time I received the tribute of the people of Tyre, Sidon, and of Jehu, son of Omri' (fig. p. 90; see p. 91). Assyria, however, did not immediately pursue her ambitions in the west, so that Hazael was free to deal wth Israel. Since his accession in 843 B.C., he had already engaged Joram of Israel (2 Kgs. 8^{28}), and now it was the turn of Jehu (842–815). Jehu lost to Hazael all his territory east of Jordan, as far south as the Arnon valley (2 Kgs. 10$^{32, 33}$), and in the reign of his son, Jehoahaz (815–801), Israel was reduced to a state of complete subjection: 'There was not left to Jehoahaz an army of more than fifty horsemen and ten chariots and ten thousand footmen; for the king of Syria had destroyed them and made them like the dust at threshing' (2 Kgs. 13^7; cf. 13^{22}). Hazael even penetrated as far south as Gath, which he seized, and Jerusalem itself was spared a similar fate only at the cost of an immense payment (2 Kgs. 12$^{17, 18}$).

With the death of Hazael about 796 B.C., the power of Damascus began to decline. Assyria started its campaigns in the west again and the king of Hamath, now supported by Assyria, assumed the leadership of the Aramean states. It is ironical that the armies of Assyria should have brought relief to Israel and that in 2 Kgs. 13⁵ the 'saviour' given by the Lord is none other than the Assyrian king Adad-nirari III (811–783)! But it was this significant shift in the balance of power which enabled Jehoash (801–786) to recover from Ben-hadad III (? 796–770), the new king of Damascus, the cities which his father had lost so recently (2 Kgs. 13²⁵). In the reign of his successor, Jeroboam II (786–746), Damascus, after a further Assyrian attack in 773 B.C., lay impotent and Israel was able to extend its northern frontier into Aramean territory and enjoy a period of peace and prosperity (2 Kgs. 14²⁵, ²⁸; see pp. 96 ff.).

The tailpiece to the story of Damascus and the Hebrew king-doms has a characteristic twist. Just as Judah had sought the help of Damascus against Israel at the very beginning, so now, at the bitter end, Israel united with her age-long enemy against Judah (2 Kgs. 15³⁷; 16⁵⁻⁸; Isa. 7¹⁻⁹). The purpose of this unnatural alliance was to force Ahaz of Judah (735–715) into an alliance against Assyria, but Ahaz decided to submit to Assyria instead (see pp. 315 f.). By his choice he spared Judah the fate which awaited the allies (2 Kgs. 16⁹). In 732 B.C., Tiglath-pileser III captured Damascus, deported its inhabitants, and turned the Aramean kingdom into four Assyrian provinces (Jer. 49²³⁻²⁷). Israel became an Assyrian province ten years later.

(ii) ASSYRIA, 883–609 B.C.

Israel just outlived the Aramean kingdom of Damascus, which had dominated its history for more than a century. Similarly, Judah just outlived Assyria, under whose dominion for nearly two centuries the people of God were confronted by imperial power on the grand scale and began to learn from their prophets how world history is to be understood.

Assyria's impact on the Hebrew kingdoms is directly related to five periods of the empire's history: (1) Revival (883–828), (2) Revolt and Recovery (828–783), (3) Impotence (783–746), (4) Resurgence and Imperial Rule (745–640), and (5) Decline and Fall (640–609).

(1) *Revival* (883–828). The revival of Assyrian power began with that nauseating sadist Ashur-nasirpal II (883–859), and, as we have seen (p. 11), made its first impact on Israel at the battle of Qarqar (853) in the reign of his more diplomatic and intelligent son, Shalmaneser III (859–824). During the two following periods, Assyrian development influenced the fortunes of Israel and Judah less directly, but by no means less considerably.

(2) *Revolt and Recovery* (828–783). The reign of Shalmaneser III ended in a disastrous revolt of Assyrian vassal rulers and, until about 800 B.C., the empire was in a state of decline. This weakness was, of course, the underlying reason for the vigour of Damascus and the subjection of Israel in the reign of Hazael (843–796). During the next twenty years, however, Assyria recovered sufficiently under king Adad-nirari III (811–783) to demolish Damascus.

(3) *Impotence* (783–746). On the death of Adad-nirari III, the empire was torn by internal revolts and under the rule of his three weak sons sank to the nadir of its power. This forty-year period of impotence in Assyria almost exactly coincided with the confident reigns of Jeroboam II in Israel and Uzziah in Judah (see pp. 96–99).

(4) *Resurgence and Imperial Rule* (745–640). When Tiglath-pileser III (745–727) threw out the last of the three brothers and took the throne himself, a new policy was inaugurated in

---

IMPERIAL POWER. This colossal limestone statue, 10½ ft. high, was one of a pair which guarded the doorway of the palace of Ashur-nasirpal II (883–859) at Nimrud, one of the four major cities of Assyria and known in the Old Testament as Calah. The creature is basically a bull, but it has the head of a man, the wings of an eagle, and on its breast, flanks, and hindquarters the curly hair of a lion. The animal's five legs represent an Assyrian sculptor's convention which is thought to indicate that it was intended to be seen either at rest from the front or striding out from the side. As the king's guardian against evil spirits, the sphinx has been given a benevolent facial expression, but as a whole it communicates a conception of assurance and power of the kind the Hebrew kingdoms often had good reason to fear. The monument also helps us to visualize the two cherubim which stood 17 ft. high in the 'holy of holies' of Solomon's Temple.

Assyria and the empire entered its last great period of power (fig. p. 14). Tiglath-pileser was not content to make raids on the west for the sake of loot and trade; his aim was nothing less than conquest and dominion. Assyria's new foreign policy affected the Hebrew kingdoms immediately. In his first great campaign to the west (743–738), Tiglath-pileser exacted tribute from Menahem of Israel (2 Kgs. 15^{19}) and (on one reading of his own record) from Uzziah of Judah (see pp. 98 f.). In the second campaign of 734–732 B.C., Assyria answered the impertinent coalition led by Damascus and Israel (see p. 13), by capturing a number of Philistine cities and exacting tribute from Ahaz of Judah, Ammon, Edom, and Moab. Israel, however, fared worst and lost not only most of its territory but also the bulk of its population (see notes on 2 Kgs. 15^{29}). Like Jerusalem later, the northern kingdom suffered a devastating first deportation a decade before its final collapse. In 732 B.C., Damascus became part of the Assyrian empire and the remnant of Israel was given Hoshea, an Assyrian puppet, as king. Ten years later, it fell to Sargon II (722–705) to claim the fall of Samaria and make the second deportation from the northern kingdom (see pp. 105–8).

When Ahaz became an Assyrian vassal in 733 B.C., Judah escaped the fate of Israel only at the cost of its independence (see pp. 102–5). Hezekiah (715–687), his son and successor, was tempted to kick over the traces at the very outset of his reign. Assyria was preoccupied in the north, where Sargon II was engaged in suppressing rebellions, and in 712 B.C. Ashdod, aided and abetted by Egypt (cf. Isa. 18$^{1-6}$, 20$^{1-6}$), was recruiting an anti-Assyrian coalition in Palestine. It seems, however, that Hezekiah had the sense to postpone his bid for independence until Sennacherib (705–681), Sargon's foolish and big-mouthed son, came to the Assyrian throne. Hezekiah then made a decisive move. He stopped paying tribute, cleared his kingdom of Assyrian cults, and organized, with the help of Egypt and Babylon, a considerable coalition of the smaller states (see notes on 2 Kgs. 18$^{1-8}$). As was only to be expected, this flagrant provocation brought the Assyrian down like a wolf on the fold, and in the crushing campaign of 701 B.C. Sennacherib completely subjugated the rebels. Most of Judah's territory was given away to pro-Assyrian Philistine kings and Hezekiah was left, 'like a bird in a cage', with little more than the city of Jerusalem (see notes on 2 Kgs. 18¹³). Although there is some doubt about the immediate sequel (see pp. 108–15), the end of the eighth century saw Judah reduced to a state of complete impotence in which it remained for sixty years. The kingdom's age of humiliation, when Manasseh (687–642) kept his throne so long by Assyrian permission, significantly coincided with the reign of the last Assyrian king of any consequence, Ashurbanipal (699–633 ?), who ground Egypt in the dust and left his empire in an impressive (if extremely precarious) condition.

(5) *Decline and Fall* (640–609). Obviously, Judah was not free to move until Assyria lost its grip, but this happened with dramatic suddenness. In the later years of Ashur-banipal's reign, Assyrian supremacy was seriously threatened on a great number of fronts—by the Medes, the Scythians, and, above all, by the Chaldeans, who after a bloody civil war seized power and soon established the independent neo-Babylonian monarchy. This happened in 626 B.C., when Nabopolassar, a Chaldean prince, defeated the Assyrians and took the throne. This momentous shift in the balance of power was reflected in the kingdom of Judah, where Josiah (640–609) took advantage of the imminent collapse of the Assyrian empire to make a brave attempt to restore not only the religious and political independence of his own people, but the lost glories of the empire of David (see pp. 118–25). Before the end of Josiah's reign, Nineveh, the proud capital of Assyria, had fallen in 612 B.C. to the Babylonians (see p. 239), who proceeded to wipe out the last remnant of Assyrian resistance in 609 B.C. It was in that final engagement that Josiah, in trying to block Egyptian forces on their way to help Assyria against the Babylonians, lost his life. There could have been no more ominous portent, for in the next twenty years, Judah became a vassal of Egypt and was liquidated by the Babylonians.

(iii) EGYPT AND BABYLON (*mainly* 609–587 B.C.)

Between Egypt and Babylon, Judah was brought to disaster.
So far, it has been possible to sketch the international relations
of the two kingdoms with no more than a passing reference to
Egypt, because until its brief revival in Judah's last years, the
once-glorious empire of the Pharaohs was, in the words of the
Assyrian officer's famous jibe, no more than a 'broken reed . . .
which will pierce the hand of any man who leans on it' (2 Kgs.
18[21]). The five centuries which ended as the Hebrew monarchy
began had witnessed the zenith of Egypt's grandeur and greatness, when Palestine and Syria were part of its empire and its
rule was paramount in the ancient Near East. With the XXIst
Dynasty (1065–935), Egypt, now split internally, began to
decline. This growing weakness, however, did not prevent her
from exercising a treacherous influence in Palestinian politics
by incessant intrigue, nor from attempting occasionally a more
direct kind of military intervention.

During the first decade of the divided monarchy, Shishak
(935–914), the aggressive founder of the XXIInd Dynasty,
planned to liquidate his immediate neighbours and in 918
B.C. overran both Israel and Judah. The immediate shock was
devastating (1 Kgs. 14[25–28]), but, since Egyptian pressure could
not be maintained, of short duration. It is even possible that
during the dynasty of Omri (876–842) Egypt was so weakened
as to seek an alliance with Israel. At least, it was to Egypt that
Israel turned in its last agony (724–721), although, characteristically, no help came to save Samaria from its fate (see notes
on 2 Kgs. 17[1–6]). Shortly afterwards, however, the Egyptian
forces met and were defeated by the Assyrian army in 716 B.C.
at the battle of Raphia near their own border in the south.
This encounter, insignificant in itself, was the first direct engagement between Egypt and the new Assyrian master of
Palestine; between the two there was constant friction for a
century.

In Hezekiah's reign (715–687), the part played by Egypt
is obscure and was probably devious. Although Egyptian

THE INFLUENCE OF EGYPT. This spectacular ivory panel, nearly $7\frac{1}{2}$ in. high and 6 in. wide, is one of a great Assyrian collection excavated at Fort Shalmaneser, Nimrud, between the years 1957 and 1963. Designed to decorate an elaborate chair or throne, it depicts a winged sphinx with the body of a lion and the head of a man, set in a framework originally overlaid with gold. The style shows a mixture of three artistic traditions: quasi-Egyptian in the Pharaonic head-cloth and crown, Phoenician in the apron (with stylized serpent's head) between the lion's legs, and Syrian in the broad features of the face. The voluted palmettes above and below the body may be compared to the Phoenician-style 'proto-Ionic' capitals familiar in Palestine (see fig. p. 80). The ivory illustrates the wide influence of Egypt in the ancient Near East and may be dated in the eighth century B.C. (see M. E. L. Mallowan, *Nimrud and its Remains,* vol. ii, pp. 560–4).

promises seem to have encouraged Ashdod in her revolt against Assyria in 712 B.C., when it came to the point, the Pharaoh treacherously handed over the rebel leader to the Assyrian king. There is no ambiguity, however, about Egyptian meddling later in Hezekiah's reign. In 701 B.C., the Pharaoh joined forces with Judah and other minor states against Sennacherib and met with a resounding defeat. Assyria was now determined to put an end to Egypt's insolent scheming. A major expedition installed Assyrian governors in Egypt in 672 B.C., and in 663 B.C. Ashur-banipal finally sacked the ancient capital city of Thebes (cf. Nahum 3^{8-10}).

That might well have been the end of Egypt's interference in Palestine, had there not emerged a new (the XXVIth) Dynasty (663–525), which succeeded in restoring the country's internal unity and began to pursue a new and subtle foreign policy. This involved switching its support to its old enemy Assyria, in order to counter-balance the new powers (especially the Babylonians) which looked like taking over its empire. Thus, the first Pharaoh of the new dynasty, Psammetichus I (663–609), fought on the side of Assyria against the Babylonians in 616 B.C., and his successor, Necho II (609–593), was marching to relieve all that the Babylonians had left of the Assyrian forces, when he met and killed Josiah in 609 B.C. (2 Kgs. 23^{29}).

From this point, for the next twenty years, the relations between Egypt and Babylon are inextricably entwined with the fate of Judah and explain just how and why the southern kingdom came to be strangled. Although the Babylonians were victorious in 609 B.C., Necho II was able to justify his new foreign policy by annexing Judah. He replaced its king, Jehoahaz, by his own nominee, Jehoiakim, and exacted crippling tribute (see p. 127). This ludicrous attempt to pick up the crumbs of Assyria's fallen empire had no hope of success and after skirmishes across the river Euphrates, the Babylonians in 605 B.C. routed the Egyptian forces at the battle of Carchemish (Jer. 46^2). This defeat shattered any residual Egyptian illusions about reviving its Asiatic empire.

The death of Nabopolassar (626–605) delayed the Baby-
lonian follow-up, but this was undertaken by his successor,
Nebuchadrezzar (605–562), who marched south and subju-
gated almost the whole of Palestine. Judah exchanged her
Egyptian yoke for that of Babylon. Unfortunately, however,
Jehoiakim could not bring himself to accept the fact that
Egypt was a spent force (cf. 2 Kgs. 24⁷) and that the Babylonians had, without a doubt, inherited Assyria's former supremacy in Palestine. Heavy but inconclusive fighting between
Babylonian and Egyptian forces in 601 B.C. encouraged
Jehoiakim to rebel against Nebuchadrezzar (2 Kgs. 24¹). This
fatal step led directly to the Babylonian invasion of Judah and
the first deportation of its people in 597 B.C. (see pp. 126 ff.). On
this occasion, Necho II of Egypt wisely kept his distance, but
one of his headstrong successors, Hophra (588–569), whom the
Greeks called Apries, gave Judah false encouragement in its
death throes by advancing against the second and final Babylonian invasion. Jeremiah, at least, was not deceived (Jer.
37⁶⁻¹⁰) and, sure enough, Hophra returned in haste to Egypt
and left Judah to its fate.

III. *The Economic and Social Development of the Kingdoms*

David and Solomon inaugurated a process of economic
development and rapid social change which the loss of their
empire at the disruption of the monarchy did little to halt. In
contrast to the recurrent international and political crises in
which the two kingdoms were involved, in their internal affairs
this period of three hundred years is one of steady material
progress. The population continued to rise and probably
touched nearly a million (800,000 in Israel and 200,000 in
Judah) by the end of the eighth century B.C., when the kingdoms reached the peak of their prosperity. But as society expanded, it became less homogeneous. The distinctive existence
and power of court circles in the capital, the emergence of a
new bureaucracy and a new nobility, the development of both
royal and private commercial enterprise, and the consequent

CANAANITE CRAFTSMANSHIP. This magnificent gold plate, 7½ in. in diameter, was discovered at Ras Shamra and is dated 1450–1350 B.C. It depicts a charioteer with drawn bow hunting wild bulls, of which three are represented, with a gazelle and two dogs, in the main composition. Four wild goats occupy the centre of the plate. The piece illustrates the excellence of the Canaanites' metal work and their indebtedness to a diversity of artistic traditions from Egypt, the Aegean, and Asia Minor.

uneven distribution of wealth, all tended towards the break-up of Israel's traditional society. It is clear that the pastoral calm of Judah and the agricultural life of Israel were exposed in this period to nothing less than an economic and social revolution, by which the two kingdoms were made to approximate (at least on the surface) to the older and more sophisticated civilization of the Canaanites. For two centuries and more, the active representative and bearer of the Canaanite heritage was Phoenicia, which, it is now possible to see, must rank with Damascus and Assyria as a major influence in Israel's development.

(i) *Phoenician enterprise*

Phoenicia, which takes its name from *phoinix*, the Greek translation of Canaan, meaning 'land of purple [dye]', is an ancient area of civilization known to us from its principal city-states—Tyre, Sidon, and Byblos (Gebal). Although the Old Testament often refers to Phoenicia and its inhabitants as 'Sidon' and 'the Sidonians', the dominant city-state in this period was, in fact, Tyre. With the accession of Hiram to the throne in 981 B.C., Tyre entered a golden age, throughout which it remained one of Israel's influential friends. Already in the reign of David, whose kingdom extended as far north as 'the fortress of Tyre' (2 Sam. 24[7]), we are told that 'Hiram king of Tyre sent messengers to David, and cedar trees, also carpenters and masons who built David a house' (2 Sam. 5[11]). This was the beginning of Israel's reliance on Phoenician craftsmanship and technical skill which continued during its extended period of 'modernization'. Solomon's Temple was designed and built by Phoenicians (1 Kgs. 5[1-12]) and its phenomenally advanced metal work was carried out by Phoenician technicians (1 Kgs. 7[13-47]), all in the best Canaanite tradition (fig. p. 22). The biblical account was confirmed by the excavations in 1957 at Hazor, where a Canaanite temple was discovered built on the plan we find in Solomon's Phoenician building (fig. p. 134). The excavation of Solomon's garrison city of Megiddo has also revealed the same Phoenician craftsmanship and design, in the excellence of its masonry and in the use of 'proto-Ionic' capitals (cf. figs. pp. 31, 80; 1 Kgs. 9[10, 11, 15]).

Phoenician architectural influence reappears during the reigns of Omri and Ahab in the middle of the ninth century B.C., when the *entente cordiale* between the two countries developed to the point of Ahab's marrying Jezebel, the king of Tyre's daughter (1 Kgs. 16³¹). At Ahab's citadel of Hazor, the excavators in 1958 discovered two further 'proto-Ionic' capitals, which have, incidentally, the distinction of being the first found in Palestine with the design on both sides and belonging, therefore, to a free-standing column and not a mere pilaster (fig. p. 80). Similar capitals have been found yet again at Ahab's magnificent and privately-owned city of Samaria, together with hundreds of fragments of carved ivory inlay (fig. p. 79), which once decorated the luxurious panels and furniture of Ahab's 'ivory house' (1 Kgs. 22³⁹; Amos 3¹⁵, 6⁴). These ivories display the same mixture of stylistic influences (with Egyptian *motifs* predominating) as is found in an earlier collection of beautiful ivory pieces from Canaanite Megiddo, which admirably illustrate the decoration of Solomon's 'great ivory throne' (1 Kgs. 10¹⁸⁻²⁰) and, indeed, the Canaanite conception of kingship which was now being copied in Judah and Israel (fig. p. 226).

One source for the ivory used in these carvings is indicated by the note that Solomon 'had a fleet of ships of Tarshish at sea with the fleet of Hiram. Once every three years the fleet of ships of Tarshish used to come bringing gold, silver, ivory, apes, and peacocks' (1 Kgs. 10²²). It is unnecessary to decide whether the term 'Tarshish ship' derives from the name of a port (such as Sardinia or Tartessus in southern Spain), or (with much less probability) from a word meaning 'metal refinery', since both derivations point unmistakably to the type of mercantile vessel operating from the copper-town of Ezion-geber on the Gulf of Aqaba. As the Israelites were afraid of the sea and knew nothing about sailing, the fleet was not only built but manned by experts from Tyre (1 Kgs. 9²⁶⁻²⁸; see p. 33). It is uncertain how long this joint enterprise prospered. Although the fleet came to grief in the reign of Jehoshaphat (873–849) (1 Kgs. 22⁴⁸), in the following century, Judah won back control over Ezion-geber (Elath) from Edom and, presumably, used it again as a port (2 Kgs. 14²²).

There can be no doubt, however, that Tyre continued to exploit its position as the leading mercantile people, heaping up 'gold like the dirt of the streets' (Zech. 9³), and that some of its prosperity splashed over into Israel and Judah. We have, at least, positive evidence of the continuing influence of Phoenician design and craftsmanship in Judah from the time of Jeremiah. At an unidentified site called Ramat Raḥel on the southern outskirts of Jerusalem, what appears to be a royal fortress, built from scratch in the seventh century B.C., shows close connexions with the style and techniques of Ahab's Samaria. The excavators claim that it is one of the finest examples of masonry from the period of the monarchy and their fourth season on the site in 1961 brought the number of 'proto-Ionic' capitals found there up to ten—the first to be unearthed in the southern kingdom (fig. p. 80).

From the sixth century B.C., we have the splendid allegorical dirge against 'the good ship Tyre' in Ezek. 27¹⁻³⁶, which shows that Israelite interest in the power of Tyre continued into the Exile. The prose section which now interrupts this allegory (Ezek. 27¹⁰⁻²⁵) reveals the astounding range of Tyre's commercial empire. Beginning in the western Mediterranean, the list of importers and exporters using Phoenician ships moves east to Greece and Asia Minor, and then from Edom in the south through Palestine to Damascus in the north, and then again from Arabia to Assyria. Among the motley of exotic imports which Tyre received in exchange for its own merchandise (silver, iron, tin, lead, bronze, slaves, horses, mules, ivory tusks, ebony, emeralds, purple, embroidered work, linen, coral, agate, wine, white wool, wrought iron, cassia, calamus, saddlecloths, lambs, rams, goats, spices, clothes, and carpets), Judah and Israel stand out quite uniquely in contributing plain agricultural products only: '. . . wheat, olives and early figs, honey, oil and balm' (Ezek. 27¹⁷; cf. 1 Kgs. 5¹¹). Palestine is relatively poor in mineral resources and it looks as though the copper mined in the Arabah region was not worth mentioning (see p. 33). For their imports—gold, silver, tin (for making bronze), and timber (not to speak of ivory, apes, and peacocks)—the two kingdoms, of course, depended largely on the merchant shipping of Tyre.

Phoenicia, however, brought to Palestine more than gold and it would be a mistake to confine its influence to the economic development of Israel and Judah. We have already noted that the Phoenicians were 'middle-men' in the sphere of art and architecture, introducing to Israel foreign designs and technical skills. It is highly probable that they were also important carriers of the ancient social and religious heritage of Canaan. Until quite recently the Canaanites were known to us only from scattered references in the Old Testament and meagre traditions about Phoenicia in much later documents. This situation has changed beyond recognition, however, since the discovery, deciphering, and interpretation of the Ras Shamra texts, which are much more revolutionary in their implications for our understanding of the Bible than the more widely publicized Dead Sea Scrolls. These texts first came to light in 1928 at Ras Shamra, the site of the ancient city of Ugarit, situated at the northern end of the Phoenician coast some two hundred miles north of Tyre (fig. p. 22). For centuries before its fall about the end of the thirteenth century B.C., Ugarit was a cosmopolitan Canaanite capital city, port, and centre of commerce for trade between Egypt, Asia Minor, and Babylon, and its general prosperity is clear from the discovery of such details as the fact that some of its private houses had up-to-date bathrooms. Among the more important buildings brought to light, there were two temples dedicated to Dagon and Baal, an immense palace, and the house and

---

A MYTHOLOGICAL TEXT FROM RAS SHAMRA. This small clay tablet, dated 1400–1350 B.C., is part of one of the mythological texts discovered at Ras Shamra in a new Semitic language, which since its decipherment in 1930 has been known as Ugaritic. The cuneiform (wedge-shaped) characters were written with a stylus on soft clay which was subsequently hardened by firing. The photograph shows a small section of the legend of Aqhat, son of the righteous king Danel, in which Anat, the consort of Baal and principal goddess of love and war in the Canaanite pantheon, threatens the supreme god El and extorts from him permission to wreak her jealous rage on Aqhat (see G. R. Driver, *Canaanite Myths and Legends*, pp. 54–57, III, R. vi. 1–32). The damage at the top and bottom of this tablet illustrates the difficult problem which faces scholars in determining the sequence of the Ras Shamra texts.

library of the chief priest, which also, apparently, served as a
school for scribes. Further discoveries at Ugarit fall roughly
into three groups. First, a great quantity of artefacts, such as
tools, weapons, weights, and ivories (among the latter being a
three-foot panel of carved ivory from the king's bed), many
of which reveal the now familiar mixed 'Phoenician' style.
Second, hundreds of clay tablets in several different languages,
largely consisting of official transactions and diplomatic correspondence. Third, and most important, a collection of longer
literary texts written about 1400 B.C. in an unknown alphabetic
language, which was deciphered with impressive speed within
a year of its discovery and is now called Ugaritic. These texts
include two legends about the ancient king Keret and Aqhat,
the son of Danel, another king, and a number of myths in epic
style recounting the life and activities of Baal and his fellow
gods and goddesses of the Canaanite pantheon (fig. p. 26).
This material gives us direct access for the first time to the
religion and society of the ancient Canaanites and it has already
thrown a flood of light on much that was previously obscure in
the Old Testament. It has, however, done much more than
that. In the light of this dramatic discovery, it is plain to see
that *the central drama of the Old Testament is the conflict and accommodation between Mosaic Yahwism and Canaanite civilization, in the
closely connected spheres of religion and social order.*

Although it is wise to avoid jumping to hasty conclusions
about detailed parallels and connexions, there can be no doubt
that the Ugaritic texts reveal the *kind* of Canaanite culture,
which, under the influence of the monarchy, provided the
model for most of the economic and social developments in
the Hebrew kingdoms. A great deal of this culture, especially
the religion of the Canaanites, was encountered through the
ancient sanctuaries, which the Israelites took over along with
agriculture from their predecessors in the land (see pp. 133–9).
The evidence, however, points to more direct contact with
Canaanite life during the period of the monarchy, by which
time the city-state of Ugarit had fallen into decay. Much
of this, we may surmise, was provided by Tyre. Tyre had

inherited the Canaanite legacy of Ugarit and was still a vigorous Canaanite city-state. In the light of the Ugaritic discoveries, we can see more clearly that what Israel borrowed from Tyre was not merely a number of masons and metal-workers, but a distinctive cultural legacy, which revived and reinforced much that survived in Palestine from its Canaanite past. Solomon's Phoenician Temple, built by men from Tyre, was designed on the same model as those dedicated to Dagon and Baal at Ugarit and as the temple at Hazor, which was once the royal city of Jabin, who headed the coalition of northern Canaanite kings against Joshua (Josh. 11$^{1-15}$). When the house of Omri became related by marriage to the royal house of Tyre, the religion which Jezebel brought with her and promoted in Israel was a version of what is found at Ugarit (see p. 83). When, as late as the sixth century B.C., the Hebrew prophet spoke his oracle against the king of Tyre, he taunted him with aspiring to the wisdom of king Danel of the ancient Ugaritic legend (Ezek. 28^3). This isolated reference is a reminder that we know nothing of Tyre's contribution to Israel's knowledge of Canaanite literature, but since the Phoenicians may well have been responsible for teaching the early Hebrews the art of alphabetic writing, it is not impossible that in this later period the men of Tyre imported literature, as well as other luxuries, to satisfy the growing pretensions of the king and his court.

(ii) *Royal enterprise*

The institution of the monarchy on the model of a Canaanite city-state fundamentally dislocated the traditional pattern of Israel's life (fig. p. 226). The economic and social repercussions of this innovation are conveniently summarized for us by a later critic, who uses Samuel as his mouthpiece:

These will be the ways of the king who will reign over you: he will take your sons and appoint them to his chariots and to be his horsemen, and to run before his chariots; and he will appoint for himself commanders of thousands and commanders of fifties, and some to plough his ground and to reap his harvest, and to make his implements of war and the equipment of his chariots. He will take your daughters to be perfumers and cooks and bakers. He will take the best of your fields and vineyards and olive orchards and give them to his servants. He will take the tenth of your grain and of your vineyards and give it to his officers and to his servants. He will take your menservants and maidservants, and the best of your cattle [Hebrew: *young men*] and your asses, and put them to his work. He will take the tenth of your flocks, and you shall be his slaves (1 Sam. 8^{11-17}; cf. Deut. 17^{14-20}).

The emphasis of this impassioned indictment falls on the loss of the liberty and dignity of the subject, which the alien despotism of the monarchy and its centralized bureaucracy entailed. Most of these changes (presented here as charges) may be readily documented under five main topics.

(1) *Military Service*. The shepherds of Judah and the farmers of Israel frequently found themselves having to abandon their flocks and fields to fight in wars, which may have served the king's political or commercial interests, but which were of no concern to them. They deeply resented being conscripted by the king's officer (cf. 2 Kgs. 25^{19}) and billeted in great garrison cities like Hazor, Megiddo, and Gezer, which the king had simply taken over from the Canaanites and where they were compelled to live and train alongside his foreign mercenaries (see fig. p. 31 ; pp. 4 f.).

(2) *Forced Labour*. An even greater indignity and infringement of the subject's freedom was his regular conscription for forced labour. Most of the evidence for the detested *corvée* comes from the reign of Solomon, when the king raised a levy of 30,000, who were sent off in relays to cart timber from Lebanon, and a levy of 70,000 labourers and 80,000 quarry-men, who were set to work on his monstrous building projects in Jerusalem (1 Kgs. 5^{13-18}). At a conservative estimate, this forced labour involved a quarter of the total population of the kingdom (cf. 1 Kgs. $12^{4, 18}$). In the next century, we are told, all the men of Judah were drafted to fortify Geba and Mizpah (1 Kgs. 15^{22}), and in the last days of the monarchy Jeremiah denounced Jehoiakim for making 'his neighbour serve him for nothing' on his new and luxurious palace (Jer. $22^{13, 14}$). Although direct

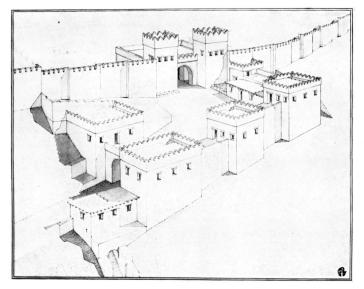

SOLOMON'S FORTIFICATIONS. This reconstruction gives an artist's impression of the massive city gate which Solomon built at Megiddo, the capital of his fifth administrative district. The approach to the gate was either by road or by a flight of steps up the mound on which the city stood (bottom left-hand corner). You first passed through a gate-house, with two sets of piers jutting out from the towers on either side, and then entered a fortified courtyard. On your left, set into the city wall, was the great gate itself, with two flanking towers (top middle). Through the first door-way (which ought to have a straight beam at the top and not an arch), you entered a passage about 67 ft. long and 14 ft. wide running between three pairs of evenly spaced piers built out from the side walls. Between each set of piers on each side were small rooms 10 by 17 ft. The plan and dimensions of this gate at Megiddo so closely resemble those of gates also built in Solomon's reign at Hazor in the north and Gezer in the south that all three may be attributed to the royal (probably Phoenician) architect (cf. 1 Kgs. 9^{15}). It is also interesting to observe that they correspond remarkably to the east gate into the main court of the Jerusalem Temple as it is described in Ezek. 40$^{5-16}$.

evidence is lacking, it is virtually certain that throughout this period gangs of forced labour were employed on the king's estates, 'to plough his ground and to reap his harvest' (1 Sam. 8^{12}).

(3) *Crown Property.* The kings of Israel and Judah were large property owners in their own right (Jerusalem belonging personally to David and Samaria to Omri) and their estates were managed by a special officer called the 'Master of the Household' (1 Kgs. 18³; cf. 1 Chron. 27²⁵⁻³¹). It was, presumably, to his department that a collection of dockets found in the palace of Samaria were once delivered. These inscribed pieces of pottery from the eighth century B.C. seem to have been used as invoices or labels for wine and oil sent from some sixteen villages and crown vineyards near the capital. Many of the officials mentioned on them have Canaanite names compounded with Baal. The method by which much of the king's property was acquired is suggested by Ahab's treatment of Naboth (1 Kgs. 21¹⁻¹⁶; see pp. 259 f.), which amply justifies the warning that 'he will take the best of your fields and vineyards and olive orchards' (1 Sam. 8¹⁴). To add insult to injury, family property seized by the king was often given to his allies, henchmen, and favourites at court (cf. 1 Kgs. 9¹¹). Even in the rustic days of Saul, the king had distributed land to his officers (1 Sam. 22⁷), and as the professional army and civil service increased both in size and power (cf. Jer. 38²⁴⁻²⁸; 2 Kgs. 21²³), the rewards and privileged position given to their staff must have been deeply resented outside the capital.

(4) *Taxation.* Solomon had divided his kingdom (with the exception of Judah) into twelve administrative districts for taxation purposes (1 Kgs. 4⁷⁻¹⁹) and, according to a list now to be found in the book of Joshua (Josh. 15²¹⁻⁶²), it appears that at a later date Judah was similarly organized. Tithes of grain and wine were exacted for maintaining, among other things, the immense burden of the court (cf. 1 Kgs. 4²², ²³). They continued, as the evidence of Ezek. 45¹³⁻¹⁶ makes clear, up to the end of the monarchy. In addition to this regular annual taxation, there was always the possibility of a levy to help the king buy off one of the great powers. We know, for example, that in the northern kingdom Menahem exacted money for Assyria (2 Kgs. 15¹⁹, ²⁰) and that Jehoiakim taxed the people of Judah to pay the tribute demanded by Egypt (2 Kgs. 23³⁵).

The alternative was for the king to make free with the treasure of the Temple (1 Kgs. 15^{18}; 2 Kgs. 16$^{8, 17, 18}$, 18$^{15, 16}$).

(5) *Royal Monopolies*. In so far as any business existed in this period, it was in the hands of the king. Solomon's most imaginative enterprise was the building of a merchant navy with Hiram of Tyre at Ezion-geber, for trade in the Red Sea with comparable royal tycoons like the Queen of Sheba (1 Kgs. 9$^{26-28}$, 10$^{1-13, 22}$; see p. 24). By this astute move, Solomon broke the monopoly of the Midianite caravans which brought goods overland from Arabia and, in order to have the best of both worlds, he also collected toll from the merchants as they moved north along the 'King's Highway' east of Jordan to Damascus (1 Kgs. 10^{15}; cf. Num. 20^{17}).

The royal monopoly of King Solomon's mines at Ezion-geber is undoubtedly the best known. The idea of a large state-owned smelting plant, drawing on mines in the Arabah, worked in an intolerable climate by foreign slave labour, and producing lucrative exports of copper in exchange for the gold of Ophir (cf. 1 Kgs. 9$^{26-28}$, 10^{11}), established itself in the popular imagination as soon as it was proposed. The facts, however, are more modest. The excavator who first spoke of elaborate furnaces for smelting the copper ore at Ezion-geber published a revised report in 1965. In it, he accepted the view that smelting in the whole Arabah region was done in quite primitive open hearths fired with charcoal and that the metal-working at Ezion-geber was probably little more than the final processing of copper into ingots. Although Solomon was capable of most things (especially with the Phoenicians near at hand), his royal monopoly in metals for export, must remain, like his wisdom, a matter for debate.

There is no reason to doubt, however, that at a later date and in the northern kingdom, Ahab, who obviously modelled himself on Solomon, acquired royal trading-rights in Damascus (1 Kgs. 20^{34}). In addition, the Crown may have had extensive interests in the manufacture of pottery. In 1 Chron. 4^{23}, there is an isolated reference to a royal pottery and it may well throw light on hundreds of jar handles excavated in the southern kingdom with seal impressions bearing the puzzling inscription *lmlk*—'(belonging) to the king'. They evidently came from the last two centuries of the monarchy. It is suggested that this stamp both indicates the manufacture of the jar in a royal pottery and guarantees its capacity. An alternative but less probable explanation is that the jars were used for collecting taxes of wine and oil. If this were correct, however, it would equally illustrate the concentration of economic resources in the hands of the king.

According to the indictment of the monarchy now ascribed to Samuel, Israel had asked for a king 'like all the nations' (1 Sam.8⁵) and this is more or less what Israel got. As we now know from the Ugaritic texts, it was the Canaanite city-state which provided the pattern and inspiration for most of the economic and social developments in the two kingdoms. The king's claim to absolute rights over the land, the persons and the property of his subjects, his organization of the realm into districts for better central control, and the development of a ruling class drawn from the professional army, court establishment, and civil service, are all paralleled in the texts from Canaanite Ugarit. Even so small a detail as the office of Queen Mother in Israel (1 Kgs. 2¹⁹, 15¹³), which accounts for Athaliah's power to seize the throne and promote the cult of Baal (2 Kgs. 11¹⁻²⁰), has its Ugaritic counterpart.

Prophets and fanatical groups like the Rechabites and Nazirites (see pp. 95, 269) condemned this new order on religious grounds, but even their strictures are no more devastating than the social ridicule of the fable of Jotham, with which he greeted Abimelech's establishment of his Canaanite kingdom at Shechem in the days of the Judges (Judg. 9⁷⁻¹⁵). The olive, fig, and vine have something better to do than lord it over the other trees; it is left to the good-for-nothing bramble to play the ludicrous role of king. Here the proud and responsible country folk of Israel speak with an unmistakable voice.

(iii) *Private enterprise and private poverty*

Our fragmentary information, both from the Old Testament and from archaeological excavations, makes it difficult to say with any precision just how far the affluence of the king was shared by his subjects. There can be no doubt, however, that an appreciable number of Israelite citizens became men of

TOWN-PLANNING IN THE JORDAN VALLEY. The photograph shows a street of the eighth century B.C. at Tell es-Saʿidiyeh (see p. 36 and J. B. Pritchard, *The Biblical Archaeologist*, vol. xxviii, no. 1, 1965). The interesting feature of the residential part of the town so far excavated is the symmetrical arrangement of the houses along a straight paved street and their conformity to a standard pattern. The inside measurements of each house were about 28 by 16 ft., the bulk of the area being taken up by a large front room, of which two-thirds were covered by a roof supported on four columns of mud brick, with the rest left open and paved as a courtyard. There was a smaller room at the back of each house.

means. From the northern kingdom in the time of Jeroboam II, for example, we have the testimony of Amos and Hosea that such people built 'palaces' and 'houses of hewn stone' (Amos $3^{15}, 5^{11}, 6^4$; Hos. $8^{14}, 12^8$) and from Isaiah in the reign of Uzziah, Jeroboam II's southern contemporary, we learn that 'their land is filled with silver and gold, and there is no end to their treasures' (2⁷). The prophets were not exaggerating. Large private houses of this period have been excavated in the northern cities of Tirzah, Hazor, and Shechem, including one mansion at Shechem with a central courtyard and an elaborate drainage system. The economic prosperity which such evidence suggests was by no means confined to the larger and more famous cities. For example, at a site as yet unidentified (Tell es-Sa'idiyeh), east of Jordan and mid-way between the Sea of Galilee and the Dead Sea (near Zaphon and Zarethan on the map), excavators in 1964 discovered a residential street of ten almost identical houses and courtyards belonging to the eighth century B.C. Their standard pattern, the near-by cooking area and the orderly street clearly suggest a measure of town-planning and economic stability (fig. p. 35).

The recent excavation of the Judean city of Gibeon, six miles north of Jerusalem, has given another fascinating revelation of provincial prosperity in this period (during which, incidentally, the city is totally ignored by the Old Testament). Gibeon's magnificent 'pool', a vast circular pit made by hewing 3,000 tons out of the solid limestone, shows how this progressive community coped with the problem of its water-supply (cf. Jer. 41¹²). The pool itself is now ascribed to a date before the ninth century B.C., but some time later the local authorities were still sufficiently go-ahead to cut a stepped tunnel 167 feet long through the solid rock, in order to gain access from inside the city wall to a spring in the village below. Comparable feats of hydraulic engineering have been found at Megiddo, Gezer, Lachish, and, of course, Jerusalem, where, in the reign of Hezekiah (715–687), the remarkable Siloam Tunnel was cut (see pp. 111 ff.). As Gibeon looked after its water, so it looked after its wine. In 1959, the excavators of the city made the unexpected discovery of 38 vats; on the average, they were about seven feet deep and six feet in diameter, some of them being covered with a stone slab and containing fragments of a uniform type of ten-gallon storage jar. When all the evidence was put together, it became clear that the vats were used as wine cellars (keeping a steady 65 degrees Fahrenheit in the heat of the summer) and that their total capacity came to about 40,000 gallons. A large number of stamped handles from smaller jars were also found and these suggest that Gibeon was not only a large-scale producer of wine but also a local exporter of some consequence.

Gibeon is not an isolated example of the growth of private enterprise and specialization. As excavations at Lachish and Debir have disclosed, these two cities in the sheep-farming country of south Judah were centres of weaving and dyeing. It is tempting to speak of their 'textile industry', but for all their specialization and prosperity, these cities by modern standards worked on a very small scale. Although Lachish was one of the largest cities of Judah, it covered only 18 acres and Debir a mere $7\frac{1}{2}$ acres (with which we may compare Gibeon with 16 acres, and Shechem, Jericho, Gezer, and Jerusalem with between 8 and 12 acres, noting in passing that the city of Bristol covers 27,000 acres and that 640 acres are needed to cover a square mile). The weaving and dyeing of Debir, then, was hardly more than a 'cottage industry', carried on by about a thousand inhabitants occupying some two hundred houses.

In technique, however, if not in scale, the manufacture of pottery underwent a minor revolution towards the end of the monarchy. From about the eighth century B.C., in towns like Jericho, Megiddo, Gezer, Lachish, and Hazor, where potters' wheels have been excavated (cf. Jer. 18[3, 4]), bowls and jars became standardized in shape and size for mass-production methods and the employment of unskilled labour. Such cooperative private enterprises, sometimes proudly using a trademark, suggest the possibility that trade-guilds, which we know existed after the Exile for metal-workers, wood-workers, linenworkers, goldsmiths, and perfumers (1 Chron. 4[14, 21]; Neh. 3[8], 11[35]), came into being during the period of the monarchy (cf. Jer. 24[1]).

Recent excavations clearly confirm the prophets' evidence of economic growth; equally, they confirm the prophets' evidence of the social disintegration which was its consequence. In

the eighth century B.C., Amos bitterly condemned the callous
and luxurious excesses of the privileged women of Samaria:

> Hear this word, you cows of Bashan,
>   who are in the mountain of Samaria,
>   who oppress the poor, who crush the needy,
>   who say to their husbands, 'Bring that we may drink!' (4¹)

And Isaiah is no less outspoken about the new nobility in the
southern capital:

> The Lord enters into judgement
>   with the elders and princes of his people:
> 'It is you who have devoured the vineyard,
>   the spoil of the poor is in your houses.
> What do you mean by crushing my people,
>   by grinding the face of the poor?' (3¹⁴, ¹⁵)

'My people' for the prophet were part of one indivisible people
of Yahweh; in this new aggressively materialistic society, there
were two kinds of people—the rich and the poor.

At Tirzah, for example, for forty years the capital of the
northern kingdom until it yielded pride of place to Samaria,
the uniform houses of the tenth century B.C. suggest that every
family lived much like its neighbour, but two hundred years
later, despite the city's drop in status, there is a marked division
between the 'west-end' of well-built residences and the 'east-
end' of wretched slums. Similarly, there was a 'better' part of
the town in eighth-century Shechem, where a fine mansion has
already been noted. On a different part of the site, however,
the excavators also discovered slum houses, which had been
haphazardly patched in the prosperous days of Jeroboam II.
By contrast, the excavation of houses in the Judean wool town
of Debir shows that between the middle of the eighth century
B.C. and the end of the monarchy no such disparity developed.
The lack of any marked social division in Debir may mean
simply that it was a conservative little place far removed from
the life of the capital, or, it may point to the fact that in the
southern kingdom private enterprise developed less rapidly,
and with less violation of the traditional social structure, than
was the case in the northern kingdom. Certainly, there is

nothing in Judah comparable to the economic and social tensions which underlie Jehu's bloody revolution (see pp. 89–95) and it is intrinsically probable that in the southern kingdom, with its limited natural resources and its relatively isolated cantons in the mountains, fewer individuals were in a position to exploit their countrymen and get rich quick.

Those who succeeded, however, both in the north and in the south, were anxious to be buried as splendidly as they had lived. It was during this period that the wealthy began to construct elaborate tombs for themselves, characteristically consisting of a small courtyard leading down steps to a rock-hewn chamber. Shebna, Hezekiah's prime minister, had made such provision (Isa. 22¹⁶) and tombs of this type have been unearthed at Megiddo in the north and at Beth-shemesh, Lachish, and Mizpah in the south. The poor, on the contrary, have left no such memorials, since they were simply buried in the ground, or laid in 'the burial place of the common people' (Jer. 26²³).

Just as the poor have left little for the spade of the excavator, so, inevitably, the farming community is inadequately represented in archaeological discoveries. And yet, despite the growth of urban life in this period, the economy of the two kingdoms remained basically pastoral and agricultural. Even the latest priestly law presupposes only the simplest forms of commercial transaction and 'Canaanite' continued in use as a word for trader (Zeph. 1¹¹; Hos. 12⁷; Ezek. 17⁴; cf. Isa. 23⁸; Zech. 14²¹). The only explicit evidence we possess about the exports of Israel and Judah implies an agricultural community (Ezek. 27¹⁷) and the clever Assyrian war propaganda aimed at the ordinary *town-dweller* in eighth-century Jerusalem points to the same conclusion:

Make your peace with me and come out to me; then every one of you will eat of his own vine, and every one of his own fig tree, and every one of you will drink the water of his own cistern; until I come and take you away to a land like your own land, a land of grain and wine, a land of bread and vineyards, a land of olive trees and honey, that you may live, and not die (2 Kgs. 18³¹, ³²; cf. Mic. 4⁴; Zech. 3¹⁰).

THE NEIGHBOUR'S LANDMARK. This black marble boundary-stone, 18 in. high, concerned the property of the official shown (on the right) receiving his charter of possession from Merodach-baladan, king of Babylon (722–703). Above the two figures, both of whom are depicted as being (? fashionably) corpulent, there are the emblems of four Babylonian gods, who safeguard the charter against violation. Originally, such boundary-stones were used, as the Old Testament evidence suggests (cf. Deut. 19¹⁴), as actual landmarks, but later they were formalized into legal records of landed property. The removal of your neighbour's landmark was a serious offence and indifference to its authority became a proverbial way of describing social disintegration (cf. Hos. 5¹⁰; Job 24²).

It is clear that the small farmer remained the backbone of Israelite society and was deeply attached to his ancestral property. Its boundaries were strictly defined and sacrosanct (Deut. 19[14]) and careful provision was made to prevent its passing out of the family (Num. 27[2-11]; see notes on Jer. 32[6-15]). This well-established rural existence was ruinously disturbed by the new Canaanite development of the kingdoms. By constitution, commerce, and corruption, wealth and power were concentrated in the hands of the king and his new nobility. The terrible consequences for the landed peasantry are vividly presented in the scandalous affair of Naboth's vineyard (1 Kgs. 21[1-24]; see pp. 259 f.), and Elijah's denunciation of this violation of traditional morality is taken up with unabated fury by the prophets of the succeeding century:

> Woe to those who devise wickedness
>   and work evil upon their beds;
> When the morning dawns, they perform it,
>   because it is in the power of their hand.
> They covet fields, and seize them;
>   and houses, and take them away;
> they oppress a man and his house,
>   a man and his inheritance (Mic. 2[1, 2]; cf. Isa. 5[8]).

As Micah indicates, power was in the hands not of the king only, but of a new wealthy class, who snapped up the land of the peasant proprietor the moment he fell into debt. And the evidence suggests that this happened often. The later law of the Jubilee Year, which ruled that every fiftieth year land taken over should be returned to its original owners (Lev. 25[25-28]), represents a brave but hopeless attempt to counteract the abuses which went on during the period of the divided kingdoms.

If poverty meant the loss of the family farm for some people, for others it meant the loss of personal freedom. Many an Israelite was compelled to sell his children and then himself into slavery to one of his neighbours, simply because he was unable to pay his debts (cf. 2 Kgs. 4[1-7]; Neh. 5[1-5]; Amos 2[6]). The law recognized this appalling situation and tried to limit the period of slavery to six years (Exod. 21$^{2-11}$; Deut. 15$^{12-18}$), but the incident described in Jer. 34$^{8-16}$ and the evasive, highly theoretical regulations of Lev. 25$^{39-43}$ show how difficult it was to control ruthless power in this new money-based society. Traditionally, of course, a man's family was expected to rally round any of its members who had fallen on hard times, but, as constant pleas for the widow and orphan prove (Jer. 22^3; Deut. 14^{29}), family solidarity was breaking up under the impact of economic development and rapid social change. Even the earliest Hebrew law had been forced to acknowledge that Israelites often found it necessary to borrow money from outside the family and had attempted to mitigate the evil by enjoining generosity and forbidding any charge of interest on the loan (Exod. 22$^{25-27}$; Deut. 23$^{19, \ 20}$; 24$^{6, \ 12, \ 13}$; Lev. 25$^{35-38}$; cf. Pss. 15^5; 112^5). But the ancient law was ruthlessly violated, as we learn from Ezekiel's indictment of Jerusalem at the time of its fall: 'In you men take bribes to shed blood; you take interest and increase and make gain of your neighbours by extortion; and you have forgotten me, says the Lord God' (22^{12}; cf. Amos 2^8). Bribery, of which Ezekiel also accuses Jerusalem, had become the new order of the day and by it the very courts of law were corrupted (Isa. 1^{23}, 5^{23}, 10$^{1, \ 2}$; Mic. 3^{11}, 7^3). Faced with this brave new world, well might the deuteronomic writer plead: 'You shall not be partial in judgement; you shall hear the small and the great alike' (Deut. 1^{17}). At the disruption of the dual monarchy, Israel had been divided into two kingdoms. By the time of their collapse, each kingdom was divided into two classes—'the small and the great'.

iv. *The Religious Traditions of the Kingdoms*

The period of the Hebrew kingdoms was a time of acute crisis and crucial development for the faith of Israel. As soon as the tribes exchanged their semi-nomadic life for a settled agricultural economy and their distinctive covenant confederation for an 'international' kind of monarchy, it was inevitable that their faith in Yahweh should have undergone profound change. Mosaic Yahwism, originating in the desert and shaped by the needs of military conquest, was ill fitted to serve a social order and daily existence so radically different. To survive at all, therefore, Mosaic Yahwism had to come to terms with its new peasant environment.

Palestine, however, was far from being a religiously neutral ground on which the reformulation of Mosaic Yahwism could proceed peacefully and by slow degrees. For centuries, there had been entrenched in its ancient sanctuaries the sophisticated religion of Canaan, which had been developed with the express purpose of securing fertility and prosperity for farming communities. Not only was this religion apparently relevant to the immediate needs of the peasant, it was also seductively attractive in other, less utilitarian, ways. The licentiousness of some of its rituals had an obvious appeal; its mythology and culture were exciting to men of intelligence and imagination; and its close association with royal authority and privilege won the favour of those who sought personal aggrandizement and power.

The confrontation of Yahwism with this indigenous religious culture, ending in Yahwism's triumphant victory, despite every degree of syncretism and wholesale apostasy, is undoubtedly the major drama of the Old Testament between the time of Solomon and the destruction of the Temple. It is a drama, however, of which the action and location cannot now be traced in detail. The evidence from biblical and archaeological sources indicates what was happening in particular places at particular periods, but it leaves large gaps in our knowledge which only conjecture can bridge. We are better informed, for example, about the southern than the northern kingdom, while in the southern kingdom nearly all the evidence relates to Jerusalem. Just as the extent of our information differs from time to time and from place to place, so it differs for the various levels of the population. Records exist of the apostasies and reformations of kings, but, inevitably, we lack adequate evidence for assessing accurately the influence of Canaanite religious practices on the population as a whole, or the significance of factors like family tradition and education in keeping Israel's Yahwistic faith alive. In these circumstances, it is important to avoid the kind of over-simplified account of religion in the period of the Hebrew kingdoms which could be represented by the ups-and-downs of a single line on a graph; there is more than one line and none is so clear that we may speak with confidence of its development.

(i) *The religion of Canaan*

Our knowledge of the agricultural religion of the native Canaanite population which Israel encountered in Palestine has been enriched beyond recognition since the discovery of the Ras Shamra texts (see pp. 27 f.). It is now clear that the gods of the Canaanite pantheon were mythological personifications of forces operating in the natural order and that their struggles for power, representing characteristically the conflicting seasons of winter rain and summer drought, were dramatically enacted in the rituals of the sanctuaries. By this imitative magic, it was supposed that blessing and fertility were secured for the land and the peasants who depended on it.

Although officially El was the supreme god of the Canaanite pantheon, the most prominent god was undoubtedly Baal, the giver of rain and fertility, who is represented on a stele discovered at Ras Shamra holding a thunderbolt in his left hand and wearing a helmet significantly decorated with the horns of a bull (fig. p. 252). Baal is described in the Ras Shamra texts as the 'Son of Dagon', Dagon (whose name means corn) being an ancient Amorite fertility god, known to Old Testament writers as a god of the Philistines (Judg. 16²³; 1 Sam. 5²⁻⁷; 1 Chron. 10¹⁰). Baal is also identified with Hadad, the old Semitic god of rain and storm (fig. p. 74). His consort in the Ras Shamra texts is Anat, the ferocious goddess of war and love, but he is also closely associated with the goddess, Asherah (or, Astarte), who was properly the wife of the supreme god, El (fig. p. 292).

The influence of the cults of Baal and Asherah on Israelite religious practice during the period of the monarchy is immediately obvious from the explicit condemnations of them in the Old Testament. The mother of the Judean king Asa (913–873), we are told, 'had an abominable image made for Asherah' (1 Kgs. 15¹³) and later Jezebel, the wife of Ahab (869–850), introduced to Samaria the worship of Baal and Asherah (1 Kgs. 16³¹⁻³³), against whose raving prophets Elijah contended on Mount Carmel (see notes on 1 Kgs. 18). Two centuries afterwards, it was in Jerusalem that Manasseh (687–642) 'erected altars for Baal, and made an Asherah, as Ahab king of Israel had done' (2 Kgs. 21³) and they remained a part of the worship of the Temple until Josiah (640–609) cleared them out (2 Kgs. 23⁴; cf. Jer. 23²⁷).

In the light of these unambiguous references, it is possible to identify further evidence of Canaanite influence. For example, it is not without significance that many personal names during the monarchy were compounded with Baal (including some given to members of the royal family) and that the editor of the books of Samuel often replaced 'Baal' by *bōsheth*, the Hebrew word for 'shame'. Thus, Merib-*baal*, the name given both to one of Saul's sons and to the son of Jonathan, was changed to Mephi-*bosheth* (2 Sam. 21⁸, 4⁴; cf. 1 Chron. 9⁴⁰) and Esh*baal*, the name of another son of Saul, to Ish-*bosheth* (2 Sam. 2⁸; cf. 1 Chron. 8³³; see p. 97). Similar compound names were common among the Phoenicians; Jezebel's father, the king of Tyre, for example, was called Eth*baal* (1 Kgs. 16³¹). Further, the many references to Baal in Hosea (2⁸, ¹³, ¹⁶, ¹⁷, 9¹⁰, 11², 13¹) and Jeremiah (2⁸, ²³, 7⁹, 19⁵, 23¹³) are now seen to reflect not, as was once supposed, local problems provoked by local gods, but, rather, the life-and-death battle which was still being fought in the later monarchy between Yahwism and the Canaanite fertility cult.

The fundamental connexion of the Canaanite cult with fertility is best illustrated by the myth of Baal's conflict with Mot, the god of death and drought. It is recorded at length in the Ras Shamra texts and was probably recited as part of the liturgy of the New Year festival celebrated at Canaanite sanctuaries in the autumn. The myth runs as follows. Mot insists that Baal should descend into his realm of death, where he will lose his vital power. Baal's wife, Anat, knowing that his time has come, bids him accept the invitation and take with him everything that belongs to the season of fertility—wind, cloud, and rain. Baal's descent thus inaugurates the rule of Mot and the summer season of drought:

> and thou, take thou
> thy clouds and thy wind, thy bucket
> (and) thy rains, with thee . . . and go down
> (to) the lowest depths of the earth . . .
> for thou wilt have died.

When the news of Baal's death is brought to El, the supreme god, he leaves his throne and begins a ritual of mourning—of the kind we may suppose was enacted annually in the cult (cf. 1 Kgs. 18[28]):

> he strewed straw
> of mourning on his head, dust in which a man wallows
> on his pate; he tore the clothing
> of his folded loin-cloth; he set up a bloody pillar
> on a stone, two pillars in the forest;
> he gashed his (two) cheeks and (his) chin,
> thrice harrowed the upper part of his arm, ploughed
> (his) chest like a garden, thrice harrowed (his) belly
> like a vale. He lifted up his voice and cried:
> 'Baal is dead. What (will become of) the people of Dagon's
> son, what of the multitudes belonging
> to Baal?'

The importance of this mourning-rite for Baal is shown by the fact that Anat repeats it before going to bring her husband's corpse for burial on the mountain in the far north, where formerly he had lived and reigned (see p. 157). The sacrifices she then offers again reflect cultic usage:

> She slew seventy
> wild oxen as a funeral offering (?) for the victor
> Baal; she slew seventy oxen
> [as] a funeral offering (?) for the victor Baal;

> [she] slew seventy sheep
> [as] a funeral offering (?) for the victor Baal;
> [she] slew seventy harts
> [as a funeral offering (?)] for the victor Baal . . .

A new king ('one that knows and has understanding') is now needed and, on El's instructions, his wife, Asherah, nominates her son, Athtar. He, however, proves incompetent to take Baal's throne. Meanwhile, the sun is scorching the parched land:

> Shapash the luminary of the gods was burning hot
> without (rain from) heaven on account of Mot son of El.

Finally, Anat makes a decisive move; she seizes Mot and hope for Baal begins to revive. In a dream, El foresees the end of the drought:

> in a vision of the creator of creatures
> the heavens rained oil,
> the ravines ran with honey,
> and I knew that the victor Baal was alive.

The resurrection of Baal is disclosed, first, by his driving Athtar, the substitute king, from his throne and, finally, by his victory in a ferocious fight with Mot. Anat is then instructed to proclaim to the hosts of heaven that life and fertility have once again returned:

> do thou] fly over the hills
> [and tell], that the son(s) of El may know
> (and) [that] the host of the stars [may understand],
> [that] the downpour of rain will [again] come down;
> [for] the victor Baal [is alive],
> [for] the rider on the clouds [exists].
> [El Hadad] will come among (?) the peoples
> [and Baal] will return to the earth,
> [moreover] the dead [will come to life]
> [and] the herbs [will be saved by] the hand of the warrior;
> [for] he will graciously send [rain] from the clouds
> [and] give plentiful [showers of rain].

Baal is once more secure on his throne and peace and goodwill

(even between wild beasts; cf. Isa. 11^{6–9}) are now established
in his kingdom:

> Baal shall sit on the throne of [his kingdom]
> and Dagon's son on the seat of [his dominion],
> (when) the ox shall have the voice of the gazelle,
> (and) the hawk the voice of the sparrow . . .

(Quotations from G. R. Driver, *Canaanite Myths and Legends*,
pp. 103–19.)

Although Yahwism never admitted this pagan concept of
the dying and rising god, many other elements of Canaanite
mythology were, as we shall see, adopted and adapted for use
in the official worship of the Temple in Jerusalem. In the
northern kingdom, the evidence suggests that borrowing was
less discriminating and controlled. If Jeroboam I is correctly
interpreted as having approximated Yahwism in the royal
sanctuaries of Dan and Bethel to the cult of Baal the Bull (see
notes on 1 Kgs. 12^{25–33}), it is hardly surprising that sexual
orgies, of the kind associated with the celebration of Baal's
victory and marriage in the Canaanite cult, found their way
into the religious practice of other northern sanctuaries (cf.
Hos. 4^{12–14}, 9¹; Jer. 2²⁰, 3²).

(ii) *Mosaic Yahwism*

The Yahwistic faith which was threatened by the religion of
Canaan had four principal and highly distinctive features: (*a*)
it was a faith which originated in response to Yahweh's self-
disclosure to Moses and the conviction that it was Yahweh who
had delivered the Israelites from their bondage in Egypt; (*b*) it
was a faith which discerned the grace of Yahweh in the creation
of Israel as a covenant people and in his guidance and protection through all the vicissitudes of its history; (*c*) it was a faith
which demanded total trust in Yahweh's purpose and power;
(*d*) it was a faith which demanded absolute moral obedience.
In brief, whereas the religion of Canaan belonged to the world
of nature, myth, and cult, Mosaic Yahwism was rooted in
historical revelation, covenant community, and personal

response. The preservation of this faith in the Canaanite environment of Palestine bears witness to its intrinsic vitality in a way comparable to the preservation of Christian faith from its cradle in Judaism, through the Graeco-Roman world, to the present day.

The resilience of Mosaic Yahwism is nowhere more clearly demonstrated than in the faith of the deuteronomists during the last years of the monarchy. It retains all the essential features of Israel's distinctive tradition with a remarkable degree of detachment from the Temple and the 'royal theology' of Jerusalem and yet it is perceptibly different. The Yahwism of the deuteronomists is Mosaic Yahwism grown to maturity. So far from being a primitive 'desert' faith unable to illuminate the life of an agrarian society, or the zealous fanaticism represented by Jehu and his prophetic supporters (see pp. 89–95), the reformed Yahwism of the deuteronomists, while still emphatically Mosaic and rooted in the historical tradition of the Exodus deliverance, is a humane and moral conviction capable of winning the allegiance of responsible and intelligent citizens (see pp. 205–13).

Precisely where and how this Mosaic tradition survived and matured during the period of the monarchy, it is impossible to say. Recent Old Testament scholarship has emphasized the significance in this respect of such ancient sanctuaries as Shechem and Gilgal, which were important cult centres of the twelve-tribe confederation (the 'amphictyony') in the days of the Judges. Shechem, for example, was the first central sanctuary of the confederation (Josh. 24), and it is thought that some form of covenant renewal ceremony was regularly held there both before and after the beginning of the monarchy. For this reconstruction, appeal is made to such records as Deut. 27^{11-26}, 31^{9-13}, and Josh. 8^{30-35} (cf. 1 Kgs. $12^{1, 25}$; Hos. 6^9). Gilgal, the first sanctuary in Palestine at which the tribes of the Exodus encamped, is particularly associated with the tradition of Israel's entry into the Promised Land and it has been conjectured that Josh. 3 and 4 reflect a celebration of the conquest which was held regularly at this sanctuary. Gilgal was clearly

E

of outstanding importance in the time of Samuel (1 Sam. 7¹⁶) and Saul (1 Sam. 10⁸) and remained a place of pilgrimage as late as the eighth century B.C. (Hos. 4¹⁵).

It is, indeed, possible that Mosaic Yahwism was preserved in covenant renewal festivals at such sanctuaries as Shechem and Gilgal and, in this connexion, it is worth noting that the oldest account of the making of the covenant on Sinai (Exod. 19²⁻²⁰, 24¹⁻¹¹) is probably itself the literary deposit of a festival recital. The evidence, however, does not allow any very firm conclusions to be drawn and some of it unambiguously suggests that even these venerated centres of Yahwism had lapsed into Canaanite idolatry (Hos. 4¹⁵, 9¹⁵, 12¹¹; Amos 5⁵). Nevertheless, the great prophets' own clear Yahwistic tradition points conclusively to the fact that there existed in both kingdoms sources of religious instruction more authentically Israelite than the sanctuaries they themselves condemn (cf. Amos 2¹⁰, 3¹⁻², 9⁷; Hos. 11¹, 12⁹, 13⁴; Jer. 2¹⁻⁸).

By its very nature, Yahwism demanded for its proper understanding and transmission a tradition which was didactic rather than cultic (see pp. 138 f.). Since it was a moral faith arising in response to Yahweh's gracious self-revelation in history and not a religion which by magical rituals purported to give men power over nature, Yahwism was essentially concerned with commitment to God in the present on the basis of 'remembering' his mighty works in the past (see pp. 211 f.). These considerations direct our attention to the 'Law of Moses' and the teaching function of the priest. We may safely surmise that the continuity of Israelite tradition was greatly indebted to the work of priests, faithful men at obscure sanctuaries, who, week by week and year after year, taught their countrymen how Israel became the people of the covenant and brought home to them the moral obligations which this privilege involved (see pp. 203 ff.). It was from them and from local 'men of God' like Samuel (cf. 1 Sam. 9¹⁻10¹⁶) that we may suppose the early prophetic bands also learnt their zeal for Yahweh (see pp. 232–7).

There is a danger that students of the Old Testament by

concentrating exclusively on the famous sanctuaries and the great festivals, may overlook the most vital factors in keeping Israel's faith alive in Canaan. Of these, religious instruction in the circle of the family is probably the most important, as it is certainly the most difficult to trace. It should be noted, however, that Deuteronomy takes for granted a father's responsibility for giving religious instruction to his son (see p. 209) and that in the society with which Jeremiah was familiar each man taught his neighbour and each his brother, saying, 'Know the Lord' (see notes on Jer. 31³¹⁻³⁴). About other teachers, we can only speculate. There can be no doubt, however, that the writer known as the Yahwist ('J') was a man of outstanding ability, who well deserves his distinguished name, and it is improbable that he was in fact the isolated and unique figure he now appears to be (see pp. 172 f.).

(iii) *The theology of Jerusalem*

Any representation of the encounter between Mosaic Yahwism and the religion of Canaan as a simple conflict between truth and falsehood is seriously challenged by the ambiguous character of the Jerusalem tradition. It is important to recognize that the religion of Canaan offered for Israel's acceptance not only a polytheistic nature cult which was fundamentally alien to Mosaic Yahwism, but also a range of concepts, embodied in symbolism and mythology, of a kind which the worshippers of Yahweh had never encountered before and which invited them to develop the potential of their faith and so discover more fully its theological significance. There can be no doubt that Canaanite ideas enabled Israel to draw out the implications of Yahwism, just as Greek ideas enabled the Church in its formative years to discover more of the meaning of the Christian gospel.

This important theological development took place in Jerusalem and is widely reflected in the psalms sung in the worship of Solomon's Temple (see pp. 139–64). Two main concepts, closely related in Canaanite mythology, were adopted by Yahwism with permanent consequences for all subsequent

Jewish-Christian thought. First, Yahweh came to be thought of as *God the Creator*. Although the approximation of Yahweh to Baal played its part in this development (see pp. 154 f., 285 f.), the major influence probably came from the cult of 'El-'Elyôn, the supreme deity of pre-Israelite (i.e. Canaanite) Jerusalem, who is succinctly described as 'God Most High, maker of heaven and earth' (Gen. 14[19, 22]; Num. 24[16]; Ps. 73[11], 107[11]). Yahweh's power over the natural order was also proclaimed by the cosmic symbolism of the architecture and fittings of the Temple, which, of course, were Canaanite in origin (fig. p. 140; see p. 23). The second major theological development was that Yahweh came to be thought of as *King of all the earth* (Ps. 47[2]). The fact that a theology without the idea of the sovereignty of God is now almost unthinkable, alongside the fact that Yahwism was ignorant of it before it entered Jerusalem, indicates the extent of Israel's indebtedness to the city's Canaanite heritage (see pp. 149 f.). Even the prophets, who were of all men the most uncompromisingly hostile to Canaanite syncretism, freely adopted the concepts of God as Creator and King and put them to distinctive use in expressing their conviction that Yahweh's aboriginal purpose would in the end be fulfilled (Isa. 6[5], 43[15], 52[7]; Jer. 10[6, 7, 10]; Zech. 14[9]; see, further, pp. 152, 154 f.).

Canaanite influence on the theology and worship of the Temple was, however, deleterious as well as beneficial. The spokesmen of Yahwism concentrate their attack on two main perversions. First, the elaboration of the sacrificial cult, they held, entirely misrepresented both Yahweh's character as expressed in the covenant and Israel's required response in faith and moral obedience (Isa. 1[10-17]; Jer. 7[21-23]; see p. 314). Secondly, the complacent belief that Yahweh had his dwelling in the Temple (see pp. 148 f.) and so guaranteed Jerusalem against all disasters (see pp. 157 f.) engendered a pernicious sense of security. When the prophets were proclaiming that Assyria and Babylon had become the agents of Yahweh's righteous judgement on Jerusalem (see pp. 56 ff.), the psalmists of the Temple were celebrating the certain defeat of the nations outside its walls (see p. 158). Students of the Old Testament have recently come to recognize that this 'doctrine of the inviolability of Zion', so far from being a new insight of prophetic theology, had been taken over from an age-old Canaanite belief about 'holy places' (see p. 157). It was totally incompatible with the great prophets' conviction that Yahweh's covenant with Israel was conditional upon the people's response and that, indeed, the time for their judgement had come:

> Therefore because of you
>   Zion shall be ploughed as a field;
> Jerusalem shall become a heap of ruins,
>   and the mountain of the temple a wooded height.
>
> (Mic. 3¹²)

The privileged position of Zion in the theology of Jerusalem was inextricably connected with the privileged position of the dynasty of David (see p. 149). It is obvious, both from the psalmists' exaltation of the Davidic monarchy and from the Yahwists' denigration of it, that kingship in Jerusalem was modelled on and continued to propagate Canaanite concepts strange to Israelite tradition (see pp. 29–34). The crucial question is whether or not the new 'royal theology' of Court and Temple obliterated the distinctive features of Yahwistic faith (see pp. 65 f.). The issue is still regarded by students of the Old Testament as a delicate one and will, no doubt, continue to be debated, if only for the reason that any decision so much depends on highly speculative reconstructions of the worship of Temple and, in particular, of the autumnal Feast of Ingathering (see pp. 147 f.). Many scholars are now trying to demonstrate that Yahweh's covenant with the dynasty of David (cf. 2 Sam. 7⁴⁻¹⁷, 23⁵; Ps. 89¹⁻⁴, ¹⁹⁻³⁷; Jer. 33¹⁹⁻²²; Isa. 55³), so far from being incompatible with the Mosaic covenant (because its promises were unconditional and eternally guaranteed), represented, in fact, a legitimate reinterpretation and extension of it. Convincing evidence for this comfortable compromise is not easy to find. The case for Jerusalem's loyalty to the old tradition of the twelve-tribe confederation can scarcely rest, as some argue, on the presence in the Temple of so highly ambiguous a symbol as the Ark (see p. 163). What, however, can be established satisfactorily is that the theology and practice of the Temple did not so completely monopolize Jerusalem as to make it secure from the reforming zeal of local Yahwists. Four major cultic reforms are recorded as having been initiated from within the capital itself—by *Asa* (913–873) (1 Kgs. 15$^{9-15}$), *Jehoiada*, the priest, at the beginning of the reign of Joash (837–800) (2 Kgs. 11$^{17, 18}$), *Hezekiah* (715–687) (2 Kgs. 18$^{1-8}$; see pp. 108 ff.), and *Josiah* (640–609) (2 Kgs. 22^{1}–23^{30}; see pp. 118–25). This evidence, to which we may add the witness of Isaiah, Jeremiah, and the deuteronomic historian (see pp. 342–8, 363 ff., 65 f.), indicates that the tradition of Jerusalem was neither wholly Yahwist nor wholly Canaanite and that even the practice of the Temple, firmly entrenched though it was in the predominantly Canaanite culture of the court, was exposed from time to time to reforming kings.

The other significant factor which contributed to the diversity of the theology of Jerusalem was the capital's school of wisdom (see pp. 171–5). Its most remarkable feature seems to have been the cultivation of a high degree of intellectual detachment from all the various spheres in which its members exercised their influence. For example, the professional objectivity shown by the brilliant writer of the Court History of David is quite astonishing, especially in view of the close connexion between higher education and the service of the king (see pp. 166 f.). It is almost certain, however, that in the final analysis the work of the educated men of Jerusalem was far from neutral in relation to the city's two conflicting traditions. If it is true that Yahwism as a historical and moral faith was capable of theological development in a way which was intrinsically impossible for the cultic religion of Canaan and if, therefore, Yahwism had everything to gain and the religion of Canaan everything to lose by being exposed to trained, critical, and secular minds, it follows that Jerusalem's wisdom tradition was ranged on the side of the Law and the Prophets and that, in all probability, its men of learning made an immense, if anonymous, contribution to the preservation and growth to maturity of Israel's distinctive heritage.

(iv) *Prophetic Yahwism*

The Yahwistic faith of the great pre-exilic prophets—Amos, Hosea, Micah, Isaiah, and Jeremiah—can be appreciated fully only as it is found in their individual preaching and studied in relation to their particular historical context (see pp. 264–389). Since, however, these spokesmen for Yahweh were far from being, as once was thought, isolated spiritual geniuses, each of whom taught the essence of his own religious experience, it is possible to consider what was common to their faith as one of the traditions—indeed, the most powerful and illuminating tradition—of Israel's religion in the time of the monarchy.

The core of the prophets' faith was Mosaic Yahwism, but a Mosaic Yahwism radicalized to the point of apparent rejection. Thus Amos, nurtured though he was in the tradition of Yahweh's choice and protection of his people ($2^{9, 10}$), nevertheless totally reversed its orthodox interpretation (3^2), and with unprecedented daring cast it into the maelstrom of secular history to make it speak of Israel's judgement:

> 'Are you not like the Ethiopians to me,
>   O people of Israel?' says the Lord.
> 'Did I not bring up Israel from the land of Egypt,
>   *and* the Philistines from Caphtor
>   *and* the Syrians from Kir?
> Behold, the eyes of the Lord God
>   are upon the sinful kingdom,
> and I will destroy it from the
>   surface of the ground.'   ($9^{7, 8}$; see p. 284)

By the eighth century B.C., the Yahwistic tradition had obviously become a secure religious refuge for a backward-looking people. The prophets effected a stupendous change by using the tradition as a spring-board to precipitate them into contemporary history, where they discovered the 'new thing'

which Yahweh, the living God of the Exodus (cf. Hos. 12⁹),
was doing *now*:

> Remember not the former things,
>   nor consider the things of old.
> Behold, I am doing a new thing;
>   now it springs forth, do you not perceive it?
>   (Isa. 43¹⁸, ¹⁹; cf. Jer. 23⁷, ⁸)

Prophetic Yahwism was orientated not towards the past, but
towards the imminent future as it bore down upon the present.
It ruthlessly demolished a traditional distinction (and with it
an old security) by interpreting contemporary *secular* history
as Israel's *sacred* history; that is to say, it found Yahweh active
and dealing directly with his chosen people in the imperialist
policy of Assyria (Isa. 7²⁰, 10⁵; see pp. 338 f.) and the devastating power of Babylon (Jer. 25⁹, 27⁶; cf. 43¹⁰; see pp. 384–7),
just as Mosaic Yahwism had found Yahweh's 'mighty acts' in
the Exodus from Egypt and the conquest of Canaan (1 Sam.
12⁷, ⁸; see pp. 218 f.). It was always through history that
Yahweh came to his people. The old sacred history, now heard
by Israel with only half an ear as it was recited in the sanctuary
festivals, brought, it was believed, the assurance of blessing
(Mic. 3¹¹). The new 'sacred' history of world politics, to which
the prophets relentlessly directed their contemporaries' attention, brought the certainty of judgement:

> Therefore thus I will do to you, O Israel;
>   because I will do this to you,
>   prepare to meet your God, O Israel!   (Amos 4¹²)

Of course, Mosaic Yahwism, through its distinctive tradition of
law, had always spoken of God's 'curse' as well as his blessing
(cf. Deut. 27¹¹⁻²⁶), but the curse of the law was addressed to
disobedient individuals. The 'new thing' in Prophetic Yahwism is the terrifying declaration that the whole people is disobedient and now under sentence of death (Amos 5¹, ²).

The startling novelty of the prophets' teaching, which is
found not only in what they say but in the way they say it (see

AGENTS OF GOD'S JUDGEMENT. This gypsum relief, about 40 in. high, comes from Nimrud in the time of Tiglath-pileser III (745–727). It depicts the kind of siege warfare which Judah suffered at the hands of the Assyrians and which Sennacherib described in his annals: 'But as for Hezekiah, the Jew, who did not bow in submission to my yoke, forty-six of his strong walled towns and innumerable smaller villages in their neighbourhood I besieged and conquered by stamping down earth-ramps and then by bringing up battering rams, by the assault of foot-soldiers, by breaches, tunnelling and sapper operations' (D. Winton Thomas, *Documents from Old Testament Times*, p. 67). As is usual in the Assyrian siege sculptures, the bowmen, protected by huge wicker shields, carried by a second soldier, dominate the scene. By contrast, the representation of the specially constructed earth-ramp, battering ram, and city wall is disproportionately small. The battering ram, or (more accurately in this case) siege engine, is the type used for tumbling the flimsy parapets and high wooden galleries constructed on the outer rim of the city wall, rather than the type with the heavy swinging pole designed to bulldoze the massive masonry below. These siege engines were essentially wooden frames mounted on wheels, often covered (as here) with hide, and propelled by the crew inside, one or two of whom worked the long projecting 'spears' from the rounded turret at the front. It is possible, however, that in this relief the two 'spears' represent a pair of siege engines. On the top left, three of the city's inhabitants are seen impaled outside the walls, as another makes a gesture of surrender.

pp. 244 f.), forces us to ask whether we may properly speak of 'Prophetic *Yahwism*' at all. In answering this question, it is useful to distinguish between three types of innovator—the reformer, the revolutionary, and the radical. The reformer seeks to introduce change, while maintaining continuity with the existing tradition; the revolutionary seeks to overthrow tradition and substitute something entirely new; while the radical seeks to uncover the roots of tradition and abandon everything which does not spring from them directly. In these terms, the deuteronomists were more like reformers than were the prophets (see pp. 207–12); the promoters of pagan cults, like Ahaz (see pp. 102–5) and Manasseh (see pp. 115–18), were more revolutionary even than Amos and Micah. It is the term 'radical' which best describes the prophets' unprecedented relationship to the Mosaic tradition.

What, then, does this radical Prophetic Yahwism retain of Mosaic Yahwism to deserve the name? The answer, quite simply, is the root of the tradition: *Yahwism*. It is Yahweh—and none other—who is active in secular history and, moreover, active (as Mosaic Yahwism had always maintained) in direct and special dealings with his own particular people. The prophets do not merely announce that Israel must abandon its false assurance of salvation and then go into voluntary liquidation. On the contrary, they proclaim that Yahweh is about to *punish* his people for all their iniquities (Amos 3^2) and that the great world powers are themselves subservient to this very purpose (Isa. 10^{5-15}; see pp. 338–41). The iniquities which they catalogue in their diatribes, as the grounds for Israel's punishment, also show unmistakably how much they were indebted to the *moral* insight and emphasis of Mosaic Yahwism (see pp. 265, 307).

If judgement is the first, paradoxical, and most characteristic word of Prophetic Yahwism, it is by no means the last. Some of its spokesmen explicitly include as the climax of Yahweh's new and direct dealing with his people promises of their restoration to that relationship he had intended from the beginning of their history (see pp. 287 f.). It is in these visions of salvation beyond judgement that the prophets most clearly disclose the Mosaic form of their faith. Hosea, for example, sees Yahweh bringing Israel as his bride back to the 'honeymoon' period which followed the Exodus:

> Therefore, behold, I will allure her,
>> and bring her into the wilderness,
>> and speak tenderly to her.
> And there I will give her her vineyards,
>> and make the Valley of Achor
>> a door of hope.
> And there she shall answer as in the days of her youth,
>> as at the time when she came out of the land of Egypt.
>>
>> (Hos. 2$^{14, 15}$; see p. 295)

Jeremiah, similarly, in looking beyond judgement, draws on the tradition of Mosaic Yahwism for his promise of a New Covenant (Jer. 31$^{31-34}$; see pp. 381 ff.), as does Second Isaiah, the last of the great prophets, in his vision of a Second Exodus (Isa. 43$^{5-7, 16-21}$, 45^{13}, 48$^{20-22}$, 49$^{8-13}$, 55$^{12, 13}$).

Another way of characterizing the radicalism of Prophetic Yahwism is to say that it is 'eschatological'. The description is a useful one if eschatology is defined in terms wide enough to include the prophets' preaching of judgement as well as their promises of salvation. Such a definition might run as follows: 'Eschatology denotes that complex of teaching which arose from the prophets' conviction that Yahweh, the living God, was inaugurating a new action in history in relation to his people and to the consummation of his purpose.' The essence of Prophetic Yahwism is that the old order of Yahweh's dealing with Israel is being done away with and that a new one is about to take its place. As an historical phenomenon, the independent prophets of the eighth and seventh centuries were as new as their message. They embodied what they preached.

II. HISTORY

THE DEUTERONOMIC HISTORY OF
1 AND 2 KINGS

OUR primary source for the history of the kingdoms of Israel and Judah from the death of Solomon to the fall of Jerusalem is the (originally single) book of 1 and 2 Kings. The disruption of the united monarchy and the vicissitudes of the Israelite and Judean kings up to the fall of the northern kingdom in 721 B.C. are narrated in 1 Kgs. 12 to 2 Kgs. 17, and 2 Kgs. 18–25 recounts the story of the surviving southern kingdom until the fall of Jerusalem in 587 B.C.

The difficulties we encounter in trying to keep the thread of the narrative are largely the result of the writer's remarkable ambition, both as an historian and as a theological interpreter, for which, indeed, there is no parallel in the ancient Near East. He was not content simply to compile a list of kings interspersed with miscellaneous extracts from the royal archives; on the contrary, he drew selectively from a very wide range of sources, brought together what he had chosen within a carefully devised chronological framework and, by editorial arrangement and comment, offered an interpretation of these centuries as *the history of Yahweh's active intervention in judgement on his people's disobedience*.

(i) *The sources and the framework*

In 1 and 2 Kings, no less than eight sources may be distinguished, of which three are expressly named: 'the Book of the Acts of Solomon' (1 Kgs. 11[41]), consisting apparently of court records and biographical material in praise of the king's wisdom, 'the Book of the Chronicles of the Kings of Israel' (1 Kgs. 14[19]), and 'the Book of the Chronicles of the Kings of Judah' (1 Kgs. 14[29]). These last two books of chronicles, to

which the reader is referred over thirty times, have no connexion with the biblical books of Chronicles; they are much
earlier works and seem to have originated in well-informed
scribal circles in the two kingdoms. They evidently included
brief, bald statements of fact in the manner of annals ('In the
fifth year of King Rehoboam, Shishak king of Egypt came up
against Jerusalem', 1 Kgs. 14^{25}; cf. 2 Kgs. 15^{19}) and accounts of
public works like Ahab's buildings (1 Kgs. 22^{39}) and Hezekiah's
hydraulic engineering projects (2 Kgs. 20^{20}), but their frank-
ness (cf. 1 Kgs. 16^{20}) and evident availability to the general
public suggest that they were privately published rather than
official records. Another good historical source underlies the
appreciative account of Ahab's wars with Damascus in 1 Kgs.
20 and 22, but it is impossible to discover how far this northern
document extended beyond these two chapters. The four remaining sources are all prophetic in character. A cycle of
stories about Elijah, originally independent and circulating
orally among his disciples in the northern kingdom, has been
drawn on for 1 Kgs. 17–19, 21 and 2 Kgs. 1$^{2-17}$ and a second,
quite separate, cycle about Elisha is found in 2 Kgs. 2–13.
These Elisha stories, while embodying reliable traditions about
military and political affairs, are dominated by a preoccupation
with miracle, which evidently reflects the uncritical veneration
accorded to the great man of God by the northern prophetic
guilds (see further, pp. 248 f.). Legendary developments are
also obvious in the source material about the prophet Isaiah in
2 Kgs. 18^{13}–20^{19}, which is much more popular in character
than anything to be found in the biographical sections of the
prophetic book. Finally, traditions about the prophet Ahijah
have been used (1 Kgs. 11$^{29-39}$, 12^{15}, 14$^{1-18}$, 15^{29}).

The historian brought all this diverse material under control
and made it serve his purpose by means of a rigid editorial
framework. The record of the reign of each of the kings is
introduced and concluded by a standard formula. For the kings
of Judah the introductory formula runs as follows: 'In the ***
year of *** the son of ***, king of Israel, *** the son of ***,
king of Judah, began to reign. He was *** years old when he

began to reign, and he reigned *** years in Jerusalem. His mother's name was ***. And he did what was right/evil in the eyes of the Lord . . .' (cf. 2 Kgs. 14$^{1-3}$; 1 Kgs. 22$^{41,\ 42}$). For the kings of Israel, the formula is similar but omits the age of the new king and the name of his mother (cf. 2 Kgs. 14$^{23,\ 24}$). The concluding formula for each reign may be illustrated by that for Ahab: 'Now the rest of the acts of Ahab, and all that he did, and the ivory house which he built, and all the cities that he built, are they not written in the Book of the Chronicles of the Kings of Israel? So Ahab slept with his fathers; and Ahaziah his son reigned in his stead' (1 Kgs. 22$^{39,\ 40}$). It will be seen that the introductory formula contains two chronological references: the date of the king's accession in terms of the regnal year of the ruler of the *other* kingdom and the length of the king's reign. Before the establishment of any absolute chronological system (like the Christian B.C./A.D.), this synchronizing device, perhaps copied from Assyrian historians, shows great ingenuity. It is carried through the period from the disruption to the fall of Samaria with remarkable regularity, although, as differing dates used by different scholars still indicate, discrepancies exist and many detailed chronological problems remain unsolved. The writer's two-fold determination to preserve the reign of each king as a unit and, despite the varying lengths of the reigns, to keep the history of the two kingdoms in step with each other, led him to adopt another convention which at first seems confusing but is, in fact, orderly and precise. It goes like this. Having begun, for example, his account of a king of Judah, he takes it to its conclusion and follows it up with the reigns of all the kings of Israel who came to the throne during that Judean king's reign. He completes the reign of the last Israelite king of the period and then switches back to the Judean king who had by that time succeeded to the throne and so on. Thus, for example, the forty-one years of the reign of Asa in Judah (1 Kgs. 15$^{9-24}$) is followed by the reigns of the six Israelite kings who came to the throne during this period: Nadab, Baasha, Elah, Zimri, Omri, and (according to the historian's chronology) Ahab (1 Kgs. 15^{25}–22^{40}). The long account of Ahab's reign having been completed, a switch is made back to the reign of Jehoshaphat of Judah, which had, in fact, begun over twenty years earlier. The inevitable disadvantage of this method is that, as in the case of Jehoshaphat, a king may be mentioned in relation to his contemporary in the other kingdom (1 Kgs. 22²) before his accession to the throne has been announced (1 Kgs. 22⁴¹).

(ii) *The theological viewpoint*

Although, for its period, 1 and 2 Kings is a monumental achievement simply considered as a factual history of the kingdoms, its author was primarily interested in how the facts could be interpreted in terms of Yahweh's purpose for his people. What he intended to write was a work of historical theology. His outlook was dominated by the conviction that there could be no compromise between traditional Yahwistic faith and any other religion, whether the indigenous nature religion of Canaan, or the religion of neighbouring peoples. Israel, as the people of God, was under an obligation to make a clear-cut choice and failure to do so led not only to apostasy, but to disaster and defeat. Such defeat was more than political misfortune; it was, rather, the judgement of Yahweh active in contemporary events. This approach to the writing of history is greatly in advance of the confident boasting and national pride which characterize so many historical records of the ancient Near East, and it is important that we should not allow its profound sincerity to be obscured by the stereotyped and tedious formulas in which it is given expression throughout the book.

Of these recurrent theological formulas, the most obvious is the judgement passed upon all the kings of *Israel* (including the zealous Jehu but excluding Shallum, who reigned for only one month): 'He did what was evil in the sight of the Lord, and walked . . . in the way of Jeroboam the son of Nebat, who made Israel to sin' (1 Kgs. 22⁵²; cf. 15²⁶, ³⁴). The sin of Jeroboam, the first king of independent Israel, was, of course, his repudiation

of the single legitimate sanctuary of the Temple in Jerusalem by
setting up the rival northern sanctuaries of Dan and Bethel (see
notes on 1 Kgs. 12²⁵⁻³³). Similarly, most of the kings of *Judah* are
condemned for allowing worship at sanctuaries other than the
Temple: '. . .he sacrificed and burned incense on the high places,
and on the hills, and under every green tree' (2 Kgs. 16⁴; cf.
8¹⁸, ²⁷, 21²⁻⁹, ²⁰⁻²²). Even those Judean kings who win the
historian's general approval are (with two exceptions) judged,
because 'the high places were not taken away' (1 Kgs. 15¹⁴,
22⁴³; 2 Kgs. 12³, 14⁴, 15⁴, ³⁵). The two exceptions are Hezekiah and Josiah, who zealously destroyed the local sanctuaries
(2 Kgs. 18³⁻⁵, 23⁴⁻²⁵). It is obvious from this and much other
evidence that the historian was a member of the theological
school represented by the book of Deuteronomy, in which the
law of the single sanctuary is promulgated (see notes on Deut.
12¹⁻¹⁴), and that we shall misinterpret his rigid dogmatism
about the high places, unless we understand it in relation to
the deuteronomic school's vigorous campaign at the end of the
seventh century B.C. to restore the distinctive character of
Yahwistic faith.

Superficially, it is true that the kings are unjustly blamed
for disregarding a law promulgated only in 621 B.C. and of
which, therefore, nearly all of them were ignorant. But they had
no excuse for being ignorant of the apostasy from Yahwism
which the alien cults of the local sanctuaries encouraged and,
from this point of view, they were guilty of disobedience. The
deuteronomic historian (as we may now describe the author)
is more concerned about obedience to Yahweh than obedience
to an isolated (and late) legal provision, and this he makes
clear by his references to the Mosaic origin of Israel's distinctive faith. In one of his longer editorial comments, he declares
that the northern kingdom came to grief,

because the people of Israel had sinned against the Lord their God,
who had brought them up out of the land of Egypt from under the
hand of Pharaoh king of Egypt, and had feared other gods and walked
in the customs of the nations whom the Lord drove out before the
people of Israel, and in the customs which the kings of Israel had

introduced . . . and they served idols, of which the Lord had said to them, 'You shall not do this' (2 Kgs. 17⁷⁻¹²).

For the deuteronomist, the law of the single sanctuary was the law of Moses (cf. 2 Kgs. 18¹², 21⁸, 23²⁵) and, so far from being an innovation, was an attempt to restore the purity of primitive Yahwism.

In one major respect, the historian departs from the theology of the book of Deuteronomy and that is in his setting David alongside Moses as a criterion of authentic faith. Thus, Josiah is praised not only because he was faithful to the law of Moses (2 Kgs. 23²⁵), but also because he 'walked in all the way of David his father' (2 Kgs. 22²) and the Davidic ideal is referred to constantly throughout the book (1 Kgs. 11⁴, ³³, 14⁸, 15³, ⁵, ¹¹; 2 Kgs. 14³, 16², 18³). The importance accorded to David in 1 and 2 Kings raises the question as to whether the historian shared that 'royal theology', which was well established in Jerusalem, and which claimed that Yahweh had promised unconditionally the permanence of David's dynasty and the inviolable security of Zion (see further, pp. 148 f.). Clearly, such a belief would be difficult to reconcile with the dominant theme that Israel's continued existence was conditional upon her obedient response to Yahweh's demands. The evidence is ambiguous and hard to interpret with confidence. Although a number of references considered in isolation might suggest that the historian had inconsistently and uncritically accepted the claims made for Zion and the dynasty of David (cf. 2 Kgs. 8¹⁹, 19³⁴), they may well have been embodied in his sources and, in any case, are chiefly invoked to explain why Judah for all its disobedience survived as long as it did. Although, for example, Abijam 'walked in all the sins which his father did before him', it is explained that '*nevertheless* for David's sake the Lord his God gave him a lamp in Jerusalem, setting up his son after him, and establishing Jerusalem' (1 Kgs. 15³, ⁴; cf. 11¹², ¹³, ³⁶). On the other side, however, and more characteristic than this saving 'nevertheless', is the historian's warning 'only if', which frequently qualifies the promises of the 'royal theology' and affirms that David's dynasty and city will be allowed to survive *only if* they are obedient to Yahweh's law (1 Kgs. 8²⁵, 9⁴⁻⁹; 2 Kgs. 21⁷, ⁸). Although, therefore, the historian goes further than the book of Deuteronomy in recognizing the monarchy as a divine institution (see notes on Deut. 17¹⁴⁻²⁰), he remains a good deuteronomist, both in judging the Judean kings by the standard of a David idealized on thoroughly deuteronomic principles, and in subordinating the Davidic promise to the condition of the Mosaic law. There is no ambiguity in his insistence that the disaster which finally overcame Judah was Yahweh's righteous judgement: 'And the Lord said, "I will remove Judah also out of my sight, as I have removed Israel, and I will cast off this city which I have chosen, Jerusalem, and the house of which I said, My name shall be there" ' (2 Kgs. 23²⁷; cf. 24³, ⁴).

The end of the southern kingdom could be seen either as the fulfilment of the curse of the law on Israel's disobedience (cf. Deut. 27¹¹⁻²⁶, 28¹⁶⁻¹⁹), or as the fulfilment of prophecy; both affirmed the basic Old Testament conviction that Yahweh was sovereign and active in history. Prophecy, even though of a rather limited kind, obviously occupied a major place in the historian's theology. In addition to the considerable body of tradition about Elijah and Elisha (see pp. 247–50), many named prophets (Ahijah, Shemaiah, Micaiah, Jehu, Jonah, Josiah, Huldah) and anonymous prophets bear witness to Yahweh's part in the decline and fall of the kingdoms. In line with the book of Deuteronomy, which regards the fulfilment of prophecy as one of the criteria of its genuineness (Deut. 18²²), 1 and 2 Kings is criss-crossed by prophetic predictions and their carefully noted fulfilment in historical event. Thus, the disruption of Solomon's kingdom was the fulfilment of Ahijah's prophecy (1 Kgs. 12¹⁵; cf. 1 Kgs. 11²⁹⁻³⁹), the annihilation of the house of Ahab was the fulfilment of Elijah's prophecy (2 Kgs. 10¹⁰; cf. 1 Kgs. 21²¹, ²²), and Josiah's defiling of the altar of Bethel happened 'according to the word of the Lord which the man of God proclaimed, who had predicted these things' (2 Kgs. 23¹⁶; cf. 1 Kgs. 13²). It was, however, the destruction of Judah by the Babylonians which stood pre-eminently as the historical fulfilment of Yahweh's explicit purpose—'according to the word of the Lord which he spoke by his servants the prophets' (2 Kgs. 24²; cf. 21¹⁰⁻¹⁵).

(iii) *The occasion and date*

The fall of Jerusalem and the urgent need to understand it in a way which made continued faith in Yahweh possible provide the clue to the historian's purpose in undertaking his work. This disaster did not mean, as the Israelites' fears and the taunts of the heathen suggested, that Yahweh was dead. On the contrary, it meant that he was very much alive and active in righteous judgement:

I will cut off Israel from the land which I have given them; and the house which I have consecrated for my name I will cast out of my sight; and Israel will become a proverb and a byword among all peoples. And this house will become a heap of ruins; every one passing by it will be astonished, and will hiss; and they will say, 'Why has the Lord done thus to this land and to his house?' Then they will say, 'Because they forsook the Lord their God who brought their fathers out of the land of Egypt, and laid hold on other gods, and worshipped them and served them; therefore the Lord has brought all this evil upon them (1 Kgs. 9⁷⁻⁹).

From beginning to end, 1 and 2 Kings is a sustained attempt to teach the Israelites in exile that it was they themselves and not Yahweh who had failed and, therefore, that faith was still a possibility and that the future was in their hands. In their alienation, the proper response was not cynicism or despair but repentance—a new and whole-hearted 'turning' to Yahweh, in the confidence that he was compassionate and would forgive (1 Kgs. 8³³, ³⁴, ⁴⁶⁻⁵³; cf. 2 Kgs. 17¹³; Deut. 4²⁵⁻³¹).

Although the book as it now stands is so clearly related to the religious crisis of Israel in exile, and although the history is continued up to the end of the monarchy and in many earlier sections has the fall of Jerusalem explicitly in view (1 Kgs. 8⁴⁶⁻⁵³, 9⁶⁻⁹; 2 Kgs. 21¹⁰⁻¹⁵), some scholars maintain that the bulk

of the work was written before the Exile and originally ended
with 2 Kgs. 23^{25a}—that is, before the tragic death of Josiah, the
historian's hero and exemplar, in 609 B.C. (2 Kgs. 23$^{29, 30}$). It
is argued: (i) that the inclusion of Josiah's death would have
made nonsense of the prophecy of Huldah (2 Kgs. 22^{20}) and of
the deuteronomic thesis that righteous men prosper; (ii) that
the references to the permanence of the dynasty and city of
David (1 Kgs. 11^{36}; 2 Kgs. 8^{19}) could not have been included
after the fall of Jerusalem; (iii) that the existence of the Temple
'to this day' is presupposed in 1 Kgs. 8^8 (cf. 1 Kgs. 9^{21}). These
arguments are far from conclusive. It may be observed: (i) that
Huldah prophesied not only Josiah's peaceful death, but the
doom of Jerusalem (2 Kgs. 22$^{16, 17}$), of which, equally, a book
ending at 2 Kgs. 23^{25a} would make nonsense; (ii) that the tragic
death of Josiah was evidently not an insurmountable obstacle
to the unmistakably deuteronomic editor who included it (cf.
2 Kgs. 23$^{26, 27}$); (iii) that the references to the permanence of
the dynasty and city of David were not necessarily understood
by the historian in so unconditional a sense as to exclude
Yahweh's judgement, and, in any case, now stand in a work
which was at least thoroughly edited after the fall of Jerusalem;
(iv) that the survival of religious and civil institutions 'to this
day' may indicate no more than the date of the sources on
which the historian drew. It may be doubted, therefore,
whether any compelling reason has been given for postulating
a pre-exilic edition of 1 and 2 Kings. Those who do so must
either postulate an early compiler coming from the same
deuteronomic school and facing roughly the same religious
crisis as the final editor, or accept the immense difficulty of
explaining why a non-deuteronomic writer decided in the first
place to undertake the work, and why, in doing so, he made
selections from Israel's history which were so well fitted to
serve the later deuteronomic editor's theological purpose. It
seems preferable to regard the selection, compilation, and,
interpretation of the sources underlying 1 and 2 Kings as the
work of a single deuteronomic historian (or historical school),
who was also responsible for editing what the Hebrew Bible

calls 'The Former Prophets' (Joshua, Judges, 1 and 2 Samuel, 1 and 2 Kings). This great literary complex, possibly beginning with the book of Deuteronomy itself, is a magnificent and sustained attempt to record and interpret the story of Israel from the people's entry into Palestine to their deportation from it. Viewed in this light, 1 and 2 Kings contains the historical conclusion, which *theologically* was the starting-point, of a remarkable work of interpretation.

If the deuteronomic historian was primarily concerned to interpret the decline and fall of the kingdoms to his contemporaries in exile, we are primarily concerned to discover what actually happened. Because he selected only what was relevant to his religious purpose, he omitted a great deal we should like to know, such as the political involvements of important rulers like Omri, Manasseh, and Josiah. He provided, however, enough authentic information for a reconstruction of the main outline of events and it is to attempt such an exploitation of his theological achievement that the following selections have been made.

I. THE DIVIDED KINGDOMS
(922–876)

11. 26-40 *Jeroboam—rebel and refugee* (922)

The long and fabulous reign of Solomon (961–922) strained the dual monarchy to breaking-point and it held together only as long as he continued to exercise his ruthlessly autocratic rule. His success as a commercial tycoon, the splendour of his buildings, and the opulent culture of his court were enjoyed by relatively few of his subjects. For most Israelites, the glories of the reign meant crippling taxation, humiliating forced labour, and hateful bureaucracy. The new measure of unification imposed by Solomon's twelve administrative districts was a poor substitute for the old unity of the twelve tribes about their central sanctuary. The weakness of Egypt and Assyria at this time gave the king a golden opportunity of developing the

economic potentialities of his new kind of state, but this opportunity, so vigorously exploited, exposed too soon and too
blatantly the character of the innovation to which Israel had
only recently been introduced (see pp. 21–42). Outside government circles in Jerusalem the independent spirit of an older
order was not yet crushed and it reasserted itself in rebellion
and schism as soon as Solomon was dead.

The man who was chosen to be the first king of Israel in 922
B.C. had already won a reputation as an opponent of Solomon's
regime and a sympathizer with his own northern kindred. This
account does not explain in what way Jeroboam 'lifted up his
hand against the king' (v. 26), so that he was compelled to seek
political asylum in Egypt (v. 40), but the more elaborate Greek
version of this chapter says explicitly that he made an unsuccessful attempt to oust Solomon from the throne. The
emphasis of the deuteronomic historian falls on the initiative
of Ahijah, a prophet from the northern sanctuary of Shiloh (vv.
29–31), which may well reflect an authentic tradition of the
northern tribes' hostility to the debased religion and despotic
injustice of Solomon's rule.

26. *Jeroboam* means 'May the people be great' and is, perhaps,
a throne name, deliberately chosen as a counterblast to that of
his rival Rehoboam, which means 'May the people expand'.
Jeroboam was an *Ephraimite*, that is, a member of the most
powerful of the northern tribes. *Zeredah* has been identified
with a village south-west of Shechem.

27. The *Millo* was part of the fortifications of Jerusalem built
by forced labour (cf. 1 Kgs. 9¹⁵), over the northern element of
which Jeroboam had been put in charge (v. 28).

29. *Shiloh*, the home of the prophet Ahijah, was Israel's central
shrine from the time of Joshua to that of Samuel and, therefore,
a centre of zealous Yahwistic faith.

30, 31. Ahijah's action with the new (and so more potent)
garment is an example of prophetic symbolism; see pp. 239 f.

32–39. These verses, with their qualified 'Davidic theology' (see pp. 65 f.), are clearly the work of the deuteronomic historian. The *one tribe* of v. 32 is Benjamin, which Rehoboam retained for Judah (cf. 1 Kgs. 12[17, 21]). For *Ashtoreth*, *Chemosh*, and *Milcom* (v. 33), see notes on 2 Kgs. 23[13].

40. *Shishak* is the Egyptian Pharaoh, Sheshonk I (935–914), the powerful founder of the XXIInd Dynasty; see p. 18.

12. 1–20 *The revolt of the northern tribes* (922)

On the death of Solomon, his son, Rehoboam, succeeded to the throne of Judah without question, but the independent spirit of the northern tribes was such that his succession as their king could not be taken for granted. The last thing they were prepared to tolerate was a second Solomon, and so they met Rehoboam in solemn assembly at Shechem to demand a change of policy and negotiate terms. The negotiations broke down, because Rehoboam was a fool. He rejected the advice of his father's elder statesmen and, at the instigation of his arrogant young contemporaries, adopted a high-handed line which cost him the throne and disrupted the dual monarchy. His final act of folly was to send his chief of forced labour to pacify the rebels. After Rehoboam had fled to Jerusalem, the assembly at Shechem made Jeroboam the first king of the independent kingdom of Israel.

1. *Shechem*, situated at the eastern end of the pass between Mount Gerizim and Mount Ebal, was deeply embedded in the early traditions of Israel (cf. Gen. 33[18]; Judg. 9[1–6]) and was the sanctuary at which Joshua called his covenant assembly (Josh. 24[1–28]). Its importance as a northern centre of pilgrimage continued to the eighth century B.C.

2, 3. It is probable (as v. 20 implies) that Jeroboam, on his return from Egypt (cf. 1 Kgs. 11[40]), was called to the Shechem assembly only after the rejection of Rehoboam.

10. It is in character that 'the boys' (as the Hebrew puts it) should be slick with a proverb.

15. Rehoboam's obstinacy and rejection are represented by the deuteronomic historian as the fulfilment of prophecy (cf. 1 Kgs. 11²⁹⁻³⁹).

16. The people's reply recalls an earlier Israelite revolt against Judah (2 Sam. 20¹; see p. 2). *To your tents* is an archaic expression meaning 'Go home!'

17. This verse is probably a gloss, referring either to Israelites of the tribe of Benjamin who lived in the south (cf. 1 Kgs. 11³²), or to northern Israelites piously fled to the south (cf. 2 Chron. 11¹⁶).

18. *Adoram* was Solomon's minister of forced labour (1 Kgs. 4⁶, 5¹⁴). The common ancient Near Eastern practice of levying labour gangs was greatly developed by Solomon, who needed a large force for his grandiose building projects (1 Kgs. 5¹³⁻¹⁸). Despite 1 Kgs. 9²², Solomon's own Israelite subjects were conscripted (cf. 1 Kgs. 5¹³, 11²⁸) and this 'heavy yoke' (v. 4) was a major factor in the revolt of the northern tribes (see pp. 30 f.).

12. 25–33 *Jeroboam I of Israel* (922–901)

Jeroboam's first task was to consolidate his new kingdom and establish its independence of Judah (vv. 26, 27). He therefore fortified Shechem as his capital and chose Dan and Bethel as alternative sanctuaries to Jerusalem. In each of these sanctuaries, strategically situated at the northern and southern extremities of the kingdom, he placed a golden bull to serve as a rival cult symbol to the Ark in Jerusalem. At Bethel, in addition, he revived a northern version of the Feast of Ingathering, the harvest festival at the end of the agricultural year, which in the southern kingdom had become intimately associated with the Davidic monarchy. Thus, the political disruption of Solomon's kingdom was sealed and perpetuated by a religious schism.

25. *Shechem*: see notes on 1 Kgs. 12¹. *Penuel* was a remote city on the River Jabbok east of the Jordan and may have been occupied by Jeroboam, either to secure his territory from Judah's

influence, or because he was forced to withdraw from Shechem under pressure from an Egyptian invasion.

28. The *two calves of gold* were representations of bulls made of wood and overlaid with gold. It is debatable whether they are best understood as images of Yahweh, or as the throne or pedestal on which Yahweh was thought to rest invisibly and, therefore, comparable to the cherubim above the Ark in the Jerusalem Temple (cf. 1 Kgs. 6^{23-28}; 2 Kgs. 19^{15}; see p. 156). There are many pictorial representations from the ancient Near East of a god standing on the back of a young bull (fig. p. 74). Since Jeroboam's policy demanded the revival of what was already familiar, rather than the introduction of something that was completely novel, it is just possible that the bull symbolism had already become part of the religion of the northern tribes. It is unlikely, however, that it derives from the introduction of the golden calf by Aaron, since the narrative of Exod. 32^{1-8} was itself written to condemn the golden calves of Jeroboam (notice the parallel and inappropriate plural of Exod. $32^{4, 8}$: 'These are your *gods* . . .'. The calves of the northern kingdom were also condemned by the prophet Hosea ($8^{5, 6}$, 10^{5}, 13^{2}), for the obvious reason that (whatever Jeroboam's intention) the Israelites had succumbed to the danger inherent in the bull symbolism and come to identify Yahweh with the fertility cults of Canaanite religion.

29. *Bethel*, an Israelite sanctuary of great antiquity (cf. Gen. 28^{10-22}; Judg. $20^{18, 26-28}$), lay in the south of the kingdom and was still 'the king's sanctuary' (Amos 7^{13}) in the eighth century B.C. *Dan*, in the far north, never attained the significance of Bethel.

30, 31. These verses disclose the viewpoint of the deuteronomic historian in three ways: (*a*) it is said that the worship of Bethel and Dan *became a sin* (cf. 2 Kgs. 10^{29}); (*b*) Jeroboam is judged for contravening the law of the single sanctuary by establishing a multiplicity of *high places* (see pp. 219-22); (*c*) it is implied that Jeroboam deliberately rejected the Levitical priesthood, who were noted for their zealous Yahwism (cf. Exod. 32^{25-29}).

32, 33. Jeroboam finally asserted the independence of his king-dom by instituting at Bethel a northern counterpart to Judah's Feast of Ingathering. It is suggested that the date of the feast in *the eighth month* was a deliberate change from that of the seventh month in Jerusalem (1 Kgs. 8²). The precise dating, however, is evidence of a much later point of view, and it is improbable that the king did, in fact, introduce an innovation. On the suggestion that this celebration was Israel's New Year Festival, see pp. 147 f.

14. 21–31 *Rehoboam of Judah* (922–915)

The reign of Rehoboam, Jeroboam's contemporary in Judah, is a sorry story of religious apostasy and military defeat. Reho-boam was Solomon's eldest son by an Ammonite princess and continued in the southern kingdom the paganizing policy of his parents (vv. 21–24). His military losses are confirmed by the Pharaoh Shishak's own record of his campaign in Palestine in 918 B.C., which lists many towns captured from Israel as well as Judah. It has been suggested that Jeroboam sought the aid of his former Egyptian protector (1 Kgs. 11⁴⁰), but it is clear that the northern suffered no less than the southern kingdom.

21. The queen-mother is almost invariably named in the intro-duction to the reigns of Judean kings, because she held an official position in the kingdom (cf. 1 Kgs. 2¹⁹, 15¹³).

23, 24. *pillars* means the standing stones erected at local sanc-tuaries as symbols of the presence of deity and as objects of worship (by anointing). They are frequently associated with the *Asherim* (singular form, Asherah), which appear to have

STORM-GOD ON A BULL. This Assyrian basalt stele, 4½ ft. high, comes from the reign of Tiglath-pileser III (745–727) and was discovered in the ruins of the palace at Arslan-Tash, the site of the Assyrian frontier town of Hadatu. It depicts the god of the storm, probably Hadad, standing on the back of a bull and holding forked lightning in each hand. Gods are frequently repre-sented as standing or enthroned on the backs of animals in the ancient Near East and this artistic convention may shed light on the two golden bulls set up in Dan and Bethel by Jeroboam I.

been wooden poles symbolizing Asherah, the mother-goddess of the Canaanite fertility cult, now known to us from the Ras Shamra texts (cf. Judg. 3⁷, 6²⁵⁻³²; 1 Kgs. 18¹⁹; 2 Kgs. 21⁷; see further, pp. 44 f.). The Ras Shamra texts also confirm that *male cult prostitutes* were part of the establishment at Canaanite sanctuaries.

25. *Shishak*: see notes on 1 Kgs. 11⁴⁰.

26. *he took away everything*. Jerusalem escaped destruction at the hands of the Egyptian invader only by the payment of an enormous tribute, which included Solomon's ceremonial *shields of gold* (cf. 1 Kgs. 10¹⁷).

15. 16–22 *War between Asa of Judah and Baasha of Israel* (*c*. 900–875)

After a reign of seven years, Rehoboam was succeeded on the throne of Judah by his son Abijam (915–913), sometimes called Abijah. Abijam continued the lax religious policy of his father and the border warfare with the northern kingdom (1 Kgs. 15¹⁻⁸; 2 Chron. 13¹⁻²²). After less than three years, he was followed by his son Asa (913–873), who won high praise from the deuteronomic historian for his zealous prohibition of Canaanite practices (1 Kgs. 15⁹⁻¹⁵). Meanwhile, in the northern kingdom, Jeroboam I had been succeeded by his son Nadab (901–900), who was soon murdered in a military revolt by Baasha (1 Kgs. 15²⁵⁻³²). This usurper exterminated the family of Jeroboam and contrived to keep the throne of Israel for nearly a quarter of a century (900–877). In the reigns of Asa and Baasha, warfare over the definition of the frontier between the two kingdoms continued, and in this passage it is recorded that for the first (but not the last) time in Israel's history civil conflict was exploited by foreign intervention. The powerful Aramean kingdom of Damascus, of which Ben-hadad I was ruler, now enters the history of the kingdoms, called in by Asa of Judah to help him in his petty struggle with Israel (see pp. 10 f.).

17. Since *Ramah* was only five miles north of Jerusalem, Israel's fortifying of the town clearly reveals Judah's weakness at this time. Under pressure from Damascus, Baasha was forced to abandon the outpost (v. 21).

18. It is almost certain that *Ben-hadad* here is not identical with, but the father of, the Ben-hadad referred to in the time of Ahab (1 Kgs. 20, 22). Although the period is not too long for a single reign, the reference in 1 Kgs. 20³⁴ is most naturally interpreted as implying that there were two kings of the same name. The name itself means 'son of Hadad', Hadad ('the thunderer') being the god of Damascus, worshipped as Rimmon (cf. Hadad-rimmon in Zech. 12¹¹; see p. 104 and fig. p. 74). *Tabrimmon*, the father of Ben-hadad, is also named after the god. Both father and son are mentioned in the so-called 'Milqart Stele', a bas-relief of the god Milqart, which bears the following inscription in Aramaic: 'The monument which Bar-hadad, son of Tab-Rammon son of Hadyan, King of Aram, set up for his Lord Milqart' (D. Winton Thomas, *Documents from Old Testament Times*, pp. 239–40). It is dated about the middle of the ninth century B.C. and is ascribed by some scholars to Ben-hadad II (? 860–843). The fact that the stele was discovered near Aleppo does not necessarily provide evidence of the northward expansion of the Aramean kingdom, since it may have been taken there in Roman times. On its importance as an Aramaic inscription, see notes on 2 Kgs. 18²⁶.

19. This verse indicates: (*a*) that Abijam of Judah had had an agreement with Damascus; (*b*) that Baasha of Israel had ousted Judah from favour; (*c*) that Asa of Judah was bribing Damascus to change its allegiance once again, which, with characteristic opportunism, Ben-hadad did.

20. All these towns occupied by the Aramean forces are in the upper Jordan valley north of the Sea of Chinnereth (Galilee). *Naphtali* is the name of the area.

21. *Tirzah*, seven miles north-east of Shechem, was the capital

of the northern kingdom from early in the reign of Jeroboam I
(1 Kgs. 14¹⁷), until Omri moved it to Samaria (1 Kgs. 16²³, ²⁴).

22. Asa took advantage of Israel's withdrawal to use Baasha's
building material for fortifying Judah's frontier slightly north
of Ramah at *Mizpah* (fig. p. 7) and the strategic town of *Geba*,
which for long remained Judah's northern border (cf. 'from
Geba to Beer-sheba', 2 Kgs. 23⁸).

II. THE HOUSE OF OMRI
(876–842)

16. 15–28 *Omri of Israel* (876–869)

The limited interests of the deuteronomic historian are nowhere more clearly revealed than in his account of the reign of
Omri. To judge by these few verses, Omri was merely the
successful contender for the throne over his rivals in the army
command, who built himself a new capital and, otherwise, 'did
what was evil in the sight of the Lord'. In fact, as we know from
extra-biblical sources, Omri was one of the most powerful of
the kings of Israel and the founder of a dynasty which went far
towards realizing the northern kingdom's potential greatness.
He rescued his country from civil anarchy and put an end to
half a century of ruinous conflict with Judah. He revived
valuable trade relations with Phoenicia and sealed the alliance
by the fateful marriage of his son, Ahab, to Jezebel of the
Phoenician royal house. The economic prosperity and confidence of his reign are appropriately symbolized by his new
capital in Samaria, the splendour of which has recently been
confirmed by archaeological excavation. As we know from the
Moabite Stone (dated about 830 B.C.), Omri (like David,
2 Sam. 8²) was also successful in subjugating Moab: 'Omri, king
of Israel, he oppressed Moab many days, for Chemosh was
angry with his land. . . . And Omri had taken possession of the
land of Medeba and [Israel] dwelt in it his days and half the
days of his son, forty years' (D. Winton Thomas, *Documents from*

PALATIAL LUXURY IN SAMARIA. This pierced ivory plaque depicting a sphinx standing in a thicket of lotus plants was excavated in Samaria and is generally ascribed to the reign of Ahab and 'the ivory house which he built' (1 Kgs. 22³⁹) in the new capital of the northern kingdom. Intended as a piece of decoration for furniture or panelling, the carving is relatively small (3½ in. high) and unsophisticated (note, for example, the treatment of the wings) in comparison with the eighth-century ivories discovered at Nimrud, although it clearly comes from the same Egyptian-Phoenician artistic tradition (cf. fig. p. 19).

THE ROYAL PHOENICIAN STYLE. The style of the volute capitals illustrated is known as 'proto-Ionic' or 'proto-Aeolic' and may be regarded as characteristically Phoenician (cf. fig. p. 19). It is well represented by lime-stone capitals of the seventh and sixth centuries B.C. excavated in Cyprus. Phoenician artists and craftsmen brought the style to Palestine, where 'proto-Ionic' capitals dating from the tenth to the seventh centuries B.C. have been

Old Testament Times, pp. 195–8). Even more eloquent of Omri's achievement and fame is the fact that the Assyrian designation for northern Israel from the ninth to the seventh century B.C. was 'the house (or land) of Omri'.

15, 16. The Israelite dynasty which the usurper Baasha had tried to establish was overthrown with the murder of his son, Elah (877–876), by the chariot-commander, *Zimri* (1 Kgs. 16⁸⁻¹⁴), who committed suicide after a week (v. 18). *Omri*, whose parentage is not given, was probably a professional soldier of Canaanite extraction.

17. *Tirzah*: see notes on 1 Kgs. 15²¹.

21. *half of the people followed Tibni*, who (with Zimri and Omri) was one of three army officers fighting for the throne. His backers failed, *so Tibni died, and Omri became king* (!)

24. Omri *bought the hill of Samaria* as a personal possession, which he hoped to bequeath to his successors, although the dynastic idea never seems to have established itself in the northern kingdom (see pp. 3 f.). Samaria's splendid royal buildings and fortifications were completed by Ahab and the city remained the capital of Israel until the fall of the kingdom in 721 B.C.

25. Omri's success has earned him the title of the 'David of the north', which suggests many good reasons for the severity of the Judean historian's condemnation.

16. 29–34 *Ahab of Israel* (869–850)

The undoubted significance of Ahab's twenty years' reign is

found at Megiddo, Samaria, and (more recently) Hazor and Ramat Raḥel. The upper photograph shows two capitals from Hazor, which were made for the citadel of Ahab (869–850), but by the end of the ninth century B.C. were being used as a shelter for a clay oven—one (centre) lying upside down and the other (top right) on its side. The lower photograph shows one of many capitals found at Ramat Raḥel, the site of a royal fortress near Jerusalem built (probably) in the seventh century B.C. Excavations here prove for the first time that this Phoenician style penetrated to the southern kingdom.

far from easy to grasp, because our information is distributed between three sources in the Old Testament narrative: (*a*) the unfavourable account given by the deuteronomic historian in I Kgs. 16²⁹⁻³⁴ and 22³⁹, ⁴⁰; (*b*) the sober history of I Kgs. 20 and 22; and (*c*) the prophetic saga of Elijah in I Kgs. 17–19 and 21 (see pp. 249–60).

Omri had put Israel on the map of the ancient Near East and Ahab carried further his father's policies. Internally, his reign was a period of economic expansion and growing affluence. Excavations have revealed something of the magnificence of his capital at Samaria and (as we learn quite casually in I Kgs. 21¹) he had a second palace at Jezreel. Jericho, apparently, was only one of 'all the cities that he built' (v. 34; cf. I Kgs. 22³⁹). Ahab's alliance with Tyre no doubt greatly contributed to the country's material prosperity, although (through the pagan fanaticism of his wife Jezebel) it ultimately brought about the downfall of his dynasty. The dramatic conflict between Jezebel and Elijah so dominates our record that Ahab's character is unfairly represented as weak and his achievement modest. Fortunately, extra-biblical evidence is again available to redress the balance. During his reign, Assyria began to reassert itself in the west, but (as we learn from the record left by Shalmaneser III) 'Ahab the Israelite', with the kings of Hamath and Damascus as allies, succeeded in holding the major power in check. The military strength of Israel is suggested by the fact that it fielded 2,000 chariots and 10,000 infantry at the battle of Qarqar in 853 B.C., when the Assyrians (although claiming a victory) were forced to withdraw.

Ahab faced other external problems. Moab won her independence and a fair amount of Israelite territory in the later years of his reign, as the Moabite Stone (against 2 Kgs. 3⁵) makes clear. In Syria, Ahab was more successful. After nearly twenty years' domination from Damascus, he not only repelled Ben-hadad's two invasions (I Kgs. 20), but later was strong enough to take the initiative against the Aramean kingdom (I Kgs. 22; see pp. 85 f.). It is noteworthy that in this last war with Damascus, Ahab's ally was Judah, with whom good relations had now been established (see p. 8).

31. *Jezebel* was the daughter of Ethbaal, king of Tyre. Both names embody the name of the god *Baal*, *zebul* ('prince') being one of his regular titles in the Ras Shamra texts. *Sidonians* is the name given to the Phoenicians, whose principal cities were Tyre and Sidon.

32, 33. Jezebel's god was Baal-Milqart, the tutelary deity of Tyre, the character of which is now better known from the Ras Shamra texts. There, Baal is the most active god of the Canaanite pantheon and Asherah, the wife of El, the most prominent goddess (see p. 44). The *Asherah* of v. 33 is the cult-object of the goddess (see notes on 1 Kgs. 14²³). The Phoenician cult introduced to Samaria by Jezebel was similar to the popular religion which the Israelites had inherited from their Canaanite predecessors in Palestine (see pp. 44–48).

34. It is probable that *Hiel* offered his sons as foundation sacrifices, although the archaeological evidence claimed for this practice in Palestine is at best ambiguous. Their death is interpreted as fulfilling the curse on any one who dared to rebuild *Jericho* (Josh. 6²⁶).

20. 1–34 *Ahab and the wars with Damascus*

The struggle with Damascus recorded in this sober historical narrative is probably to be dated three years before the battle of Qarqar in 853 B.C. The Old Testament makes no reference to this famous clash between Assyria and a coalition of Aramean states, but in the annals of Shalmaneser III, Ahab appears as the ally of Damascus against the Assyrian invader (see p. 11). The Aramean attacks on Israel recounted in this chapter may represent an attempt to force Ahab to join the anti-Assyrian alliance.

1. *Ben-hadad*: probably Ben-hadad II (? 860–843); see notes on 1 Kgs. 15¹⁸. *thirty-two kings* suggests a loose military coalition

of petty rulers, who were soon to be replaced by governors (cf. v. 24).

3–9. To the demand for the surrender of Ahab's personal property in v. 3, Ben-hadad adds the humiliation of an unrestricted search and confiscation by his officers. It has been suggested, however, that the difference between the first and second requests (v. 9) is that between surrendering *your silver and your gold* and surrendering *your wives and your children*. This interpretation, which requires an emendation of the Hebrew text in vv. 3 and 7, finds some support in the Greek version of v. 7: 'He has [now] sent to me for my wives and children, [while] my silver and gold I did not [earlier] refuse.'

10. Samaria will be reduced to dust by so large a force of men that they will each have less than a handful to take away.

13. *a prophet came near to Ahab*. The favourable attitude of the unnamed prophet shows that this account comes from a source different from that of the Elijah stories.

14–21. The 232 *servants of the governors of the districts* (v. 14) were a small picked body of young commandos. The plan was that they should raid Ben-hadad's camp during the lunch hour and be followed up by the main force of 7,000 (vv. 14, 19).

23. The Arameans believed the Israelites to be proficient in mountain warfare, but inferior in flat country, where chariots counted (cf. Judg. 1¹⁹). Furthermore, they ascribed this limitation to Israel's God (cf. v. 28).

24. *remove the kings*. It has been suggested that this verse reflects a fundamental constitutional reorganization, by which Ben-hadad II replaced the vassal kings by governors and turned a loose confederation into the united Aramean kingdom of Damascus.

26. *Aphek*, the scene of the second Aramean attack, is probably to be identified with a town just east of the lake of Galilee on the main route from Damascus to Israel.

29, 30. Comparison with the number of infantrymen at the battle of Qarqar (see p. 11) warns us against taking these popular statistics too solemnly.

32, 33. The men responded to Ahab's use of the word *brother*.

34. *I will restore.* This is the only record of Omri's having lost cities and granted trading quarters to the father of Ben-hadad II. The pact between Israel and Damascus prepared the way for their alliance against Assyria in 853 B.C.

22. 1–40 *Ahab's last battle* (850)

This vivid narrative evidently comes from the same source as 1 Kgs. 20¹⁻³⁴, although it is probable that the section on Micaiah (vv. 5–28), which is hostile to Ahab, has been drawn from an independent prophetic tradition. It records Ahab's death in an unsuccessful attempt, in alliance with Jehoshaphat of Judah, to regain Ramoth-gilead from Damascus. More significant, however, is its account of the distinction and tension between two types of prophecy, represented, on the one hand, by Ahab's institutional prophets and, on the other hand, by the isolated figure of Micaiah, the son of Imlah, who proclaims the word of the Lord whether his hearers like it or not. Like his contemporary Elijah, Micaiah is represented as anticipating that great succession of independent prophets which begins with Amos (see pp. 237–44).

2. *Jehoshaphat* (873–849) succeeded his father Asa on the throne of Judah. In a reign of some twenty-five years, he maintained the stability of the Davidic dynasty, held control over Edom, and, therefore, commanded the caravan trade from Arabia (1 Kgs. 22⁴⁷⁻⁴⁹). If 2 Chron. 17–20 is a reliable historical witness, he also initiated important judicial and administrative reforms. Reversing his father's policy, he entered an alliance with the northern kingdom and married his son, Jehoram, to Ahab's daughter, Athaliah (2 Kgs. 8¹⁸). Just how dangerous this was, subsequent events were to prove (see pp. 88 f.).

3. *Ramoth-gilead*, in northern Transjordan some thirty miles east of the river, had been the centre of Solomon's sixth administrative district, but had since fallen into the hands of Damascus. Ben-hadad II had probably ceded it after his pact with Ahab (1 Kgs. 20³⁴), but some years had elapsed (cf. v. 1) without its being returned to Israel.

5. *Inquire first for the word of the Lord*. This represents a vestigial relic of the practice of 'holy war', before which Yahweh was consulted (Judg. 20²³, ²⁷, ²⁸) by means of the sacred lot cast by a priest (1 Sam. 14³⁶⁻⁴², 23²⁻⁴, ⁹⁻¹², 30⁷, ⁸). Although there are occasional references to kings' inquiring of the Lord through prophets in the narrative of 1 and 2 Kings (2 Kgs. 3¹¹, ¹²), the monarchy had secularized the conduct of war and kings like Ahab used their court prophets simply to rubber-stamp their own decisions.

6. Ahab's 400 prophets assure their patron that his proposed expedition against Ramoth-gilead will be successful. On this kind of prophecy, see pp. 232–7.

7, 8. The deuteronomic historian shows his Judean bias by representing Jehoshaphat as being on the side of authentic prophecy (cf. 2 Kgs. 3¹¹).

10–12. That the *prophesying* of this large assembly was an ecstatic group demonstration of fervent nationalism may be judged from Zedekiah's crude act of prophetic symbolism (see pp. 239 f.). *horns* were a symbol of power (cf. Deut. 33¹⁷; Zech. 1¹⁸⁻²¹).

13–17. After first giving a favourable answer like the rest of the prophets, and being rebuked for doing so, Micaiah speaks the truth directly and prophesies the king's death and the scattering of his people (v. 17). It is difficult to avoid the conclusion that his initial favourable answer was a deliberate attempt to accomplish Yahweh's will by enticing Ahab to his death (cf. v. 20).

19–23. These verses attempt to explain why there was no discrepancy between Micaiah's disclosure of Ahab's imminent death and the institutional prophets' prediction of his triumph. Both came from Yahweh—Micaiah's directly in vision (v. 17), that of the institutional prophets deviously through *a lying spirit* (vv. 20–23); both meant that Ahab's death was Yahweh's will. The explanation comes to Micaiah in a vision of Yahweh sitting in his heavenly council. This conception, familiar from the assemblies of gods in Canaanite and other mythologies, occurs frequently in the Old Testament (Job 1–2; Ps. 82¹, 89⁷; Isa. 6¹⁻¹³, 40¹⁻¹¹; Dan. 7⁹⁻¹³). The *host of heaven* (v. 19) means heavenly beings, Yahweh's 'privy councillors', who even engage in debate (v. 20), and not (as in 2 Kgs. 17¹⁶) stars. In the heavenly council, earthly events are determined and revealed in advance (cf. Jer. 23¹⁸; Amos 3⁷). What is determined in this case is Ahab's death, which Micaiah, the authentic prophet, knows by direct disclosure (v. 17), but which is concealed from the professional prophets. They are to be used to serve Yahweh's will by enticing Ahab to his death (v. 20), by means of prophetic assurances put into their mouth by one of the members of the heavenly council, who volunteers to act as *a lying spirit* (vv. 22, 23). Their message will be false, although its inspiration and purpose come from Yahweh himself (v. 20). The *lying spirit* is an agent of Yahweh, as even 'the Satan' still is as he appears in the heavenly court at the beginning of the book of Job (Job 1–2; cf. Zech. 3¹, ²; 1 Chron. 21¹). The phenomenon of false prophecy remained an intractable problem in Israel and led to explanations as devious and theologically intolerable as that given in these verses, as long as it was believed that ecstatic behaviour gave undeniable proof of divine inspiration.

24, 25. Zedekiah was not flattered to be called a lying agent of Yahweh's purpose. His question means: 'How do you know that you are right and I am wrong?'; and Micaiah's answer: 'You will find out.' The question of authority would be decided by what happened (v. 28).

26. It has been suggested that *the king's son* is the title of an official who was responsible for prisoners (cf. Jer. 36²⁶).

30. The fact that Ahab disguised himself and Jehoshaphat wore Ahab's clothes (reading 'my robes' with the Greek, cf. v. 32) shows that Ahab was the superior partner and extremely nervous.

38. This verse betrays the hand of the deuteronomic historian (cf. 1 Kgs. 21¹⁹).

39. *the ivory house* refers to a palace equipped with ivory-decorated furniture (cf. Amos 3¹⁵, 6⁴). Excavations at Samaria and elsewhere have unearthed many specimens of Egyptian design and Phoenician execution (figs. pp. 19, 79, 216, 278).

The successors of Ahab and Jehoshaphat (849–842)

The death of Jehoshaphat of Judah (849), a year after Ahab of Israel, brought to an end a period of relative stability in the two kingdoms, which had lasted nearly a quarter of a century. The next seven years was a time of deterioration and confusion which culminated in Israel with Jehu's bloody reassertion of the religion of Yahweh, and in Judah with Athaliah's bloody reassertion of the religion of Baal. The difficulty of charting this period is increased by the fact that both kingdoms had rulers called Ahaziah and Joram.

In Israel, Ahab was succeeded by his son Ahaziah (850–849), who died childless (2 Kgs. 1). He was followed by his brother Joram (849–842), who had to face a rebellion in Moab, which he was unable to crush (2 Kgs. 3⁴⁻²⁷), and further warfare with Damascus (2 Kgs. 8²⁸). He was the last king of the house of Omri and the first victim of Jehu's revolt.

In Judah, Jehoshaphat had been succeeded by his son Jehoram (the form used to distinguish him from Joram of Israel), who reigned 849–842 B.C. He was unable to prevent Edom's gaining its independence, with the result that Judah lost control of the southern trade routes (2 Kgs. 8²⁰⁻²²). Jehoram was followed by his son Ahaziah in 842 B.C. (2 Kgs. 8²⁵⁻²⁷), who fell victim to Jehu in less than a year. The real power in Judah after the death of Jehoshaphat was, however, exercised by Athaliah, the daughter of Ahab, who had married

Jehoram and dominated both her husband and her son. True to the zeal of Jezebel, her mother, she promoted the cult of the Phoenician Baal in Jerusalem and after her son's murder occupied the throne for six years herself (2 Kgs. 11$^{4-20}$).

III. THE REVOLT OF JEHU
(842)

The revolt of Jehu was a military *coup d'état* in which three forces hostile to the Omri dynasty exploded simultaneously. The one about which the Old Testament is most explicit was undoubtedly the most influential—that powerfully represented by Elijah's devotion to Yahweh and his utter repudiation of the religion of Baal (see pp. 247–60). The accommodation of Israel's Mosaic faith to the fertility cults of Canaan was an almost inevitable consequence of the people's adoption of a settled agricultural life and their exploitation of the cultural and economic possibilities of their new environment. The establishment of the monarchy accelerated their growing approximation to the life and manners of the surrounding nations and 'progressive' kings like Omri and Ahab most obviously compromised Israel's distinctive and traditional character. Jezebel's fanatical promotion of her Phoenician religion was the last straw and roused the conservative worshippers of Yahweh, who found their champions and spokesmen in the prophets, to overthrow the house of Ahab and have done with foreign influence.

The second force behind Jehu's revolt was social and economic discontent. Under the dynasty of Omri, Israel had pursued the development begun by Solomon and grown from being a society of small peasant farmers into a trading nation with competitive opportunities. With commercial expansion, there emerged a class-structure such as Israel had never previously known. Glaring inequalities of wealth and power outraged the conscience of all who cared for equity (see pp. 34–42).

The third force behind the revolt came, not for the last time in history, from discontent in the army. Jehu was an army officer and his revolt was conducted as a military *coup d'état*.

THE HUMILIATION OF JEHU. This panel from the four-sided black lime-stone obelisk, 6½ ft. high, which Shalmaneser III (859–824) caused to be erected in the main square of Nimrud, shows Jehu making his submission to the Assyrian king and offering tribute. The superscription of the panel, magnificently engraved in cuneiform writing, reads: 'The tribute of Jehu, son of Omri. Silver, gold, a golden bowl, a golden vase, golden cups, golden buckets, tin, a staff for the royal hand (?), *puruhati*-fruits' (D. Winton Thomas, *Documents from Old Testament Times*, p. 48). These token gifts, carried by thirteen Israelites, are represented on the three other panels which make up the row running round the obelisk next to the top. Jehu is depicted prostrate before Shalmaneser, bearded and wearing a sleeveless mantle over an ankle-length tunic; behind him are two Assyrian attendants. Shalmaneser stands holding a bowl (presumably just received from Jehu) and is attended by two servants, one holding a parasol, the other a club. Above (top centre) are the winged sun-disc and the star of Ishtar. The scene has unique interest in that it gives the only contemporary representation of any Israelite king.

Although the Old Testament provides little direct information, we may safely assume that the army was demoralized by Israel's long and costly war with Damascus, dissatisfied with the weak leadership of Joram, and resentful of the luxurious indolence of the court in Samaria (see p. 88).

Jehu's revolt attained its immediate objectives. The hated house of Ahab was wiped out and religious syncretism was temporarily halted. He destroyed one kind of society without, however, having anything to put in its place. His long reign (842–815) left the northern kingdom more isolated and desolate than ever before. Inevitably, Israel's alliances with Phoenicia and Judah were broken, and at a time when she was in danger of her life from Assyria and Damascus.

In 841 B.C., Assyria pressed south and exacted tribute from Tyre, Sidon, and 'Jehu, son of Omri'. Our information about this incident comes not from the Old Testament but from Shalmaneser III's Black Obelisk, on which Jehu, the furious charioteer (2 Kgs. 9[20]), is depicted in a humiliating act of submission before the Assyrian king. Incidentally, this is the earliest 'picture' of Israelites we possess and the only 'picture' of a Hebrew king which has survived (fig. p. 90). The Assyrians, however, withdrew from the west and left Damascus in undisputed possession (see pp. 12 f.). Jehu lost the whole of his Transjordan territory (2 Kgs. 10[32, 33]) to Hazael, who had seized the throne of Damascus. Jehoahaz, Jehu's son and successor (815–801), was so thoroughly dominated by the Aramean kingdom that he was allowed no more than a bodyguard of a mere 10 chariots, 50 horsemen, and 10,000 infantry —a contrast to Israel's 2,000 chariots at Qarqar only forty years earlier (2 Kgs. 13[3–7]).

9. 1–13 *Jehu is anointed king* (842)

The remarkable feature of this first scene of the drama of Jehu's revolt is its reticence. Later the action takes place in Jezreel and Samaria, but it begins quietly in the officers' mess at Ramoth-gilead, an insecure northern outpost of Israel threatened at the time by Damascus. It is not Elisha who goes to Jehu, but merely a young prophet of his community and the anointing takes place privately in an inner room. Jehu shows great reluctance to reveal to his fellow officers what has happened and (cf. v. 15) insists on strict secrecy. Nevertheless, the prophets' role in launching the revolt emphasizes its religious motivation and looks forward to the pent-up fury and implacable hatred of the house of Ahab with which it was carried out (cf. vv. 7–10).

1. On *Elisha*, see pp. 247 ff. The *sons of the prophets* were members of the prophetic guilds (see pp. 261 ff.). On *Ramoth-gilead*, see notes on 1 Kgs. 22³.

2. *Jehoshaphat*, the father of Jehu, is not to be confused with his namesake, the king of Judah.

6. *I anoint you king over the people of the Lord, over Israel*. The identification of Israel with *the people of the Lord* represents both a northern point of view and a desire to emphasize the religious significance of the revolt. The sacred rite of anointing the king was originally performed by a prophet (cf. 1 Sam. 10¹, 16³; 1 Kgs. 19¹⁶); see, further, pp. 3 f., 151.

7–10a. *And you shall strike down . . . and none shall bury her*. This command to exterminate the house of Ahab destroys the dramatic reticence of v. 10b and clearly comes from the deuteronomic historian.

11. *mad fellow* represents the plain man's judgement of the ecstatic prophet (cf. Hos. 9⁷; Jer. 29²⁶).

13. Jehu's brother officers improvised a throne on the steps, sounded the accession fanfare and proclaimed him king (cf. 2 Sam. 15¹⁰; 1 Kgs. 1³⁴).

9. 14–28 *Jehu's assassination of Joram and Ahaziah* (842)

This brutal and vigorous narrative splendidly conveys a sense of the speed with which Jehu carried out his revolt. The kings of Israel and Judah were conveniently together at Jezreel, Joram of Israel having retired there after being wounded in the Aramean war and Ahaziah of Judah having come to visit him (2 Kgs. 8²⁸, ²⁹). Jehu sets out from Ramoth-gilead for Jezreel, detains two successive messengers sent out by Joram, and is identified as he approaches the city by the furious speed of his driving. The two kings, quite unsuspecting, go out to meet him and get his news of the situation across the Jordan.

Jehu immediately makes his purpose clear. Joram turns and is shot in flight. Ahaziah tries to escape but is mortally wounded in his chariot and dies at Megiddo.

14. It has been suggested that Jehu should be substituted for Joram to make the note read, 'Now Jehu with all Israel had been on guard at Ramoth-gilead . . .', defending it against the army of Damascus. *Hazael* had just murdered Ben-hadad and seized the throne of Damascus (2 Kgs. 8⁷⁻¹⁵; see p. 12).

15. *the news* of his having been anointed king (2 Kgs. 9¹³).

22. Jehu's motive is opposition to the Canaanite paganism which *Jezebel*, the wife of Ahab and mother of Joram, had promoted in Israel; see p. 225.

25, 26. The scene of Joram's end, *the property of Naboth the Jezreelite* (v. 21), is taken as fulfilling Elijah's prophecy against his father Ahab (1 Kgs. 21¹⁹); see pp. 259 f.

27. *Beth-haggan* is seven miles and *Ibleam* eight miles south of Jezreel. *Megiddo*, Ahab's splendid chariot-centre, is, however, some nine miles to the north-west of Jezreel (fig. p. 31).

9. 30–10. 27 *Jehu's final massacres* (842)

A century later Hosea was to condemn Jehu's bloody excesses (1⁴); the writer of this narrative recounts them with evident relish. The only moral value of the story lies in its warning against the horrors of religious fanaticism. With the exception of the forty-two wretched Judeans who were casually slaughtered and flung into a pit (10¹²⁻¹⁴), all the characters of this four-act drama are fanatics—either for Yahweh or for Baal. First, Jezebel, the evil genius of her easy-going husband, was thrown to her death and devoured by dogs in Jezreel (9³⁰⁻³⁷). Second, Jehu cunningly terrified the hard core of the loyalists in Samaria into exterminating Ahab's family and sending their heads to be piled in heaps at the city-gate of Jezreel (10¹⁻¹¹). Third, Jehu *en route* for Samaria gratuitously murdered the kinsmen of Ahaziah of Judah and found an ally in the reactionary zealot Jehonadab (10^{12-17}). Finally, in Samaria, by the despicable deceit of posing as an enthusiast for the cult of Baal to the extent of offering pagan sacrifices himself, Jehu enticed its leaders to their destruction and enjoyed the satisfaction of turning their temple into a latrine (10^{18-27}). Jehu's triumph seemed complete, but his blood-letting in fact reduced the northern kingdom to a state of weakness which was unparalleled since the disruption of the monarchy (cf. 2 Kgs. $10^{32, 33}$).

30. *Jezebel*, splendidly depicted as calm and arrogantly masterful to the very end, had pursued her paganizing policy during three reigns in Israel (Ahab, Ahaziah, Joram), and through her daughter Athaliah continued to exercise her malign influence in Judah even after her death.

31. *Zimri*, with whose name Jezebel taunts Jehu, was an earlier army officer who gained the throne and kept it (for seven days) by murder (1 Kgs. 16^{9-15}).

34. This verse illustrates two ancient Hebrew ideas: (*a*) the communal meal established a bond of loyalty; (*b*) the family of a king shared the sanctity of his person.

36, 37. *In the territory of Jezreel*, Jehu murdered Jezebel where she had murdered Naboth. Her fate is represented as fulfilling Elijah's prophecy against the house of Ahab (1 Kgs. 21^{23}).

10. 1. Jehu proceeds to consolidate his position by eliminating Ahab's family and so the possibility of blood-revenge. Although *seventy sons* is a familiar round number (cf. Judg. 12^{14}; Gen. 46^{27}), which might include all Ahab's descendants, it is possible that we should take *sons* in its literal meaning (cf. Judg. 8^{30}; 1 Kgs. 20^2).

4, 5. The leaders of Samaria refuse the challenge to place one of Ahab's sons on the throne, because Jehu has already shown his authority by killing Joram and Ahaziah (2 Kgs. 9^{14-28}).

9. *You are innocent*. An alternative translation of Jehu's assurance to the people is: 'You are impartial.' This would better represent

Jehu as inviting the people to conclude that the bloody massacre was in reality the work of Yahweh, in fulfilment of his prophetic word to Elijah (cf. 1 Kgs. 21²¹, ²²).

12. *Beth-eked of the Shepherds* is thought to be a place about 16 miles north-east of Samaria.

15–17. *Jehonadab* and Jehu were fellow extremists. All we know about Jehonadab comes from Jeremiah 250 years later, when the prophet commended the religious loyalty of a clan of 'Rechabites', who acknowledged Jehonadab as their founder (35¹⁻¹⁹). These Rechabites were worshippers of Yahweh, who zealously maintained a semi-nomadic existence in opposition to the settled life of the farmer, living in tents, refusing to engage in agriculture and abstaining from wine, one of its main products. The Chronicler connects the Rechabites with the Kenites (1 Chron. 2⁵⁵), a clan of travelling tinkers who may have been the original worshippers of Yahweh and the first opponents of the Canaanites (Judg. 4¹⁷⁻²², 5²⁴⁻²⁷).

21. Ahab had built the temple of Baal in Samaria for his wife Jezebel (1 Kgs. 16³²). Jehu's *cunning in order to destroy the worshippers of Baal* (v. 19) is at the same low level as the deceit of the lying spirit which possessed the prophets to entice Ahab to his death (see notes on 1 Kgs. 22¹⁹⁻²³).

26, 27. It is best to suppose that *pillar* in v. 26 means a wooden cult symbol (like the Asherah and in v. 27 a standing stone (see pp. 75 f.).

Judah and Israel (842–783)

Jehu's murder of Ahaziah in 842 B.C. gave his notorious mother Athaliah the opportunity to seize the throne of Judah (842–837). Her promotion of the cult of the Phoenician Baal-Milqart was brought to an end in 837 B.C. by a counter-revolution dimly reflecting Jehu's revolt in the northern kingdom (2 Kgs. 11¹⁻²⁰). Its leader, Jehoiada the priest, who had rescued one of Ahaziah's sons, Joash, from his grandmother's purge of the Judean royal family, contrived to have the young boy crowned and Athaliah killed. Joash (837–800) clearly began his reign under the wing of the priesthood and it may well have been a quarrel with them (as 2 Chron. 24 suggests) which led to his assassination (2 Kgs. 12$^{20, 21}$). Joash had been compelled to give up the accumulated treasure of Jerusalem to save his capital from the Arameans of Damascus (2 Kgs. 12$^{17, 18}$) and, before long, Amaziah, his son and successor (800–783), having foolishly declared war on Israel, was again forced to pay tribute (2 Kgs. 14$^{11-14}$). Jerusalem was badly damaged and Judah reduced to a vassal state of the northern kingdom, a mere thistle to Israel's cedar (2 Kgs. 14^9).

The king of Israel who thus dominated Judah was Jehoash. In a reign of sixteen years (801–786), he initiated the northern kingdom's recovery after its period of desperate weakness under his father Jehoahaz (815–801), and took advantage of the plight of Damascus, devastated by Assyria and under threat from Hamath, to recover the towns on his northern border which his father had lost to Hazael (2 Kgs. 13^{25}). And so the way was prepared for the brilliant reign of his son Jeroboam II.

IV. THE KINGDOMS IN PEACE AND PROSPERITY
(783–742)

14. 23–29 *Jeroboam II of Israel* (786–746)

From a political and economic point of view, the long reign of Jeroboam II was an enormous success; from the point of view of Amos and Hosea, it was an unmitigated disaster; from either point of view, it was of great significance—confident and go-ahead. The perfunctory account in 2 Kings only reveals that Jeroboam rapidly restored the military power of Israel after its unprecedented decline at the turn of the century and was able to push back his frontiers in the north and east to the point of rivalling the achievement of David. The economic prosperity which this expansion implies is suggested also by excavations at Samaria and Megiddo and is made explicit in Amos's denunciations of Israel's self-indulgent upper-classes (see pp. 34–42). Jeroboam's affluent society, with its stately homes of hewn stone (Amos 5¹¹), furnished in the most luxurious Tyrian style (Amos 3¹⁵, 6⁴), supplies evidence of profitable trade relations with Phoenicia and the rapid growth of a plutocracy in Israel. The dark side of this development is the main theme of contemporary prophecy. The new rich were prepared to sell honest folk for money and buy off judges in the courts (Amos 2⁶⁻⁸, 5⁷, ¹⁰⁻¹³); their palaces were piled high with ill-gotten gains (Amos 3¹⁰, 4¹), so insatiable was their greed (Amos 8⁴⁻⁷). Inevitably, this callous indifference to human values was accompanied by an indifference to Israel's austerely moral faith. Both Amos and Hosea inveigh against the people's adoption of the Canaanite cult of Baal and their profligate indulgence in its obscene practices (see pp. 264–306). That Baal-ism was the religion of a large proportion of the population at this time is confirmed by the fact that of the personal names on the Ostraca from Samaria (invoices for wine and oil from the end of this period, see p. 32) only about half are compounded with Yahweh (such as Jedayau—'Yahweh knows') and half with Baal (such as Abibaal—'Baal is Father'). Jeroboam II's prosperity was bought at a price and that it could not last is the verdict of history.

25. *the entrance of Hamath.* Jeroboam established the northern border of Israel somewhere in the valley between the Lebanon and Anti-Lebanon mountains on the southern frontier of the territory of Hamath (cf. Amos 6¹⁴). It has been suggested that the Hebrew translated *the entrance of Hamath* should be rendered as a place-name, Lebo-hamath, and identified with the modern town Lebweh between the rivers Orontes and Leontes. This was the northern border in Solomon's time (1 Kgs. 8⁶⁵) and it later became an ideal limit (cf. Ezek. 47¹⁵; Num. 34⁸). See notes on v. 28. The *Sea of the Arabah* means the Dead Sea. The exact location of Israel's southern border cannot be determined, but the general description probably implies military successes in Transjordan against the Ammonites and Moabites. Amos 6¹³ records Jeroboam's victories in northern Transjordan. *Jonah,*

the Galilean prophet, appears elsewhere only as the central
figure of the post-exilic book which bears his name.

26, 27. These verses show an unexpectedly favourable attitude
towards the northern kingdom (cf. 2 Kgs. 13⁴⁻⁶, ²³).

28. *Damascus and Hamath.* The Hebrew is unintelligible, reading, 'and he restored Damascus and Hamath to Judah in
Israel'. The RSV translation, *he recovered for Israel Damascus and
Hamath, which had belonged to Judah,* makes a defective text into
defective history, since Hamath had never belonged to Judah
and Damascus had been independent since Solomon's time.
One suggestion for alleviating the problem is to read 'in Yaudi'
instead of 'to Judah', Yaudi being a small independent state
in northern Syria (see notes on 2 Kgs. 15¹⁻⁷). The verse at least
implies that Jeroboam extended the boundaries of Israel at the
expense of Damascus and Hamath. Damascus was weakened
by the Assyrians under Adad-nirari (811–783) and Shalmaneser IV (783–773) and by its wars with Hamath.

15. 1–7 *Uzziah (Azariah) of Judah* (783–742)

Uzziah's reign was as brilliant as that of Jeroboam II and
brought Judah to the peak of its prosperity and power. His
achievement is largely ignored in 2 Kings, but the Chronicler
makes good the omission by an account which recent archaeological discoveries have done much to confirm (2 Chron. 26).
Uzziah, having reorganized and re-equipped his army, used
it to gain control of lucrative trade routes along the Philistine
coastal plain, in the Negeb, and as far south as Ezion-geber (cf.
2 Kgs. 14²²). Here, he rebuilt Solomon's copper town, in the
ruins of which an excavator in 1940 discovered a seal probably
owned by Uzziah's son and inscribed, 'Belonging to Jotham'.
It is still held by some scholars that Uzziah's reputation was at
its height after Jeroboam II's death. This view rests on finding
a reference to him in the Assyrian annals for 742 B.C., from
which it appears that one 'Azriau of Yaudi' was then the
leader of an alliance of north Syrian states. It is possible,

however, that this Azariah was the ruler of the state of Yaudi
in north Syria, which is mentioned in a recently discovered
Aramaic inscription. No contemporary prophetic commentary,
like that of Amos and Hosea in the northern kingdom, exists
for the reign of Uzziah, but in the year that he died Isaiah was
called to his ministry (Isa. 6¹) and his view of the state of Judah
was, as we should expect, much less sanguine than that of the
Chronicler (see pp. 315–48).

1, 2. *Azariah*. The king is more frequently called Uzziah (and
always in the prophets). The use of two names may mean that
Uzziah was a throne name, for which the personal name
Azariah was substituted when the king ceased to exercise his
royal functions (see notes on v. 5). A more probable chronology
than the one given here is that Azariah succeeded to the throne
in 783 B.C. (only three years after Jeroboam II) and reigned
about forty-two years.

5. Experts suggest that Azariah's disease (unlike that of
Naaman, cf. 2 Kgs. 5¹) was, in fact, true leprosy (Hansen's
Disease), as a result of which he was ritually unclean (cf. Lev.
13¹⁴) and, therefore, unable to perform his royal duties. It is
improbable, however, that he lived in quarantine *in a separate
house*. The Hebrew thus translated in the RSV is simply 'a
house of freedom' and it may mean that the king was forced
to live 'in his own house, relieved of duties'. In consequence,
Jotham, his son, became regent, *governing the people of the land*,
probably about 750 B.C.

V. THE DECLINE AND FALL OF ISRAEL
(746–721)

15. 8–31 *The decline of Israel* (746–732)

The brilliant period of Jeroboam II and Uzziah was the lull
before the storm and the storm broke with shattering suddenness, when, in 745 B.C., Tiglath-pileser III seized power in
Assyria (fig. p. 57). He was the first of a line of vigorous

military rulers whose ambition it was to create an empire embracing the whole of the ancient Near East and this ambition swept Palestine into the orbit of world history (see pp. 15 f.).

Whatever, in these unprecedented circumstances, Israel, as the most valuable and vulnerable of the two kingdoms, had been able to attempt in the way of counter-measures, would ultimately have made no difference. Her doom was sealed. In fact, Israel was incapable of the least show of resistance and found herself facing the gravest threat in her whole history in a state of unparalleled chaos. The throne of the northern kingdom had always been unstable, but there had never been anything to equal the civil anarchy which broke out on the death of Jeroboam II and threw up six kings (of whom four were certainly murdered) in a mere twenty years.

With Israel thus apparently committed to national suicide, Tiglath-pileser began to execute his purpose. As early as 743 B.C., he was in the field in north Syria, which he began to conquer and absorb into the Assyrian provincial system of government. Within two more years, he exacted tribute from Damascus and Israel, and by 733 B.C. had reached the very south of Palestine and reduced Israel to little more than Samaria, the rest of her territory being annexed as three Assyrian provinces. The following year (732 B.C.), it was the turn of Damascus, which was ravaged and turned into four further provinces. Thus, when Tiglath-pileser died in 727 B.C., the whole of Syria and Palestine was, from his point of view, subject to Assyrian rule. The pathetic residue of Israel and the tiny tributary state of Judah were scarcely worth reckoning as exceptions.

8–12. *Zechariah*, the son and successor of Jeroboam II, reigned in Israel for six months (746–745), before being murdered by Shallum.

10. *Ibleam*: see notes on 2 Kgs. 9²⁷.

12. Zechariah was the last of the five kings of the dynasty of Jehu, who together occupied the throne of Israel for a century (cf. 2 Kgs. 10³⁰).

45944

13, 14. *Shallum* (745), the usurper, survived a mere month. *Tirzah* was the capital of the northern kingdom for forty years before Omri built Samaria (see notes on 1 Kgs. 15²¹). It had become the headquarters of the party of Menahem.

16. *Tappuah* was fourteen miles south-west of Tirzah and apparently the headquarters of Shallum's faction. Menahem's brutality in sacking the place is paralleled by the heathen savagery of the Ammonites condemned by Amos (1¹³; cf. 2 Kgs. 8¹²).

17. *Menahem* (745–738) owed the length of his reign to the help of Assyria, to whom he became a vassal.

19, 20. *Pul* was the name adopted by Tiglath-pileser III, when he took the throne of Babylon in 729 B.C. His invasion of the west in the years 743–740 B.C. and Menahem's payment of tribute are recorded in the Assyrian annals. A *talent of silver* was probably equivalent to 3,000 *shekels* and (as a guide to modern equivalents) this would buy 20 horses (1 Kgs. 10²⁹). The total of the tribute was a thousand talents, which, in contributions of fifty shekels (the price of a slave at current Assyrian rates), implies no less than 60,000 wealthy landowners in Israel!

23–26. *Pekahiah* (738–737) was unique among the last five kings of Israel in actually inheriting the throne. He continued his father's policy of subservience to Assyria and was assassinated for it by Pekah, his anti-Assyrian aide-de-camp.

25. *Pekah* (737–732) usurped Pekahiah's throne and perhaps also his name, which would explain why Isaiah always referred to him sarcastically as 'the son of Remaliah' (7⁴, ⁵). Pekah's fellow assassins came from Transjordan, perhaps with the backing of Damascus.

27. *twenty years* is impossible; the reign probably lasted between four and five years.

29. Tiglath-pileser III's devastation of Israel during his invasion of the west in 734–732 B.C. was provoked by an anti-Assyrian alliance between Pekah of Israel and Rezin of Damascus

(often called the 'Syro-Ephraimitic coalition'), which Ahaz of
Judah refused to join (see pp. 331 ff). *Ijon, Abel-beth-maacah, Jan-
oah, Kedesh,* and *Hazor* are all towns in northern Galilee; at *Hazor,*
a recently discovered three-foot layer of ashes confirms its
destruction at this time. The Assyrian records also confirm the
biblical account. A Nimrud tablet reads: 'Gal'za, Abilakka
which are on the border of Israel [the widespread territory of
Damascus] in its whole extent I restored to the border of
Assyria. My [official] I set [over them] as district-governor . . .
Israel . . . the total of its inhabitants [together with their posses-
sions] I led off to Assyria. Pekah their king they deposed and
Hoshea I set [as king] over them' (D. Winton Thomas, *Documents from Old Testament Times,* p. 55). Israel retained only a
small area of land in the neighbourhood of Samaria, the rest
of its territory being divided into three Assyrian provinces—
Gilead (in Transjordan), Megiddo (including Galilee), and
Dor (on the coastal plain)—and their leading men deported.

30. What little remained of Israel was temporarily saved in
732 B.C. by Pekah's removal at the hands of the usurper *Hoshea,*
a puppet of Tiglath-pileser, to whom (according to the Assyrian
records) he owed his throne.

16. 1–20 *Ahaz of Judah's subjection to Assyria* (735–715)

Within three or four years of his accession to the throne of
Judah, Ahaz meekly travelled to Damascus to await the plea-
sure of the great king of Assyria. He had been driven to seek
the protection of Tiglath-Pileser III principally by his refusal
to join the anti-Assyrian alliance of Damascus and Israel, and
by their consequent threat to take Jerusalem and displace him
on the throne by an Aramean puppet king (Isa. 7[6]). His position
had also been weakened by Edom's revival (involving the
serious loss of the Ezion-geber trade, v. 6) and by Philistine
inroads on the foothills of Judah (2 Chron. 28[18]).

After Ahaz's appeal to Assyria, his subservience seems to
have been complete. It is doubtful however, whether Tiglath-
pileser was as interested in Ahaz's new altar in the Jerusalem

Temple as was the author of the account in 2 Kings. The innovation may possibly represent the imposition of the religion of Assyria on a vassal state, but more probably it betrays the superstitious impetuosity of a king who knew he was cornered and was driven to seek desperate remedies (2 Chron. 28²², ²³). Ahaz is explicitly accused of such pagan abominations as child-sacrifice and divination and only Manasseh is more severely condemned by the deuteronomic historian.

1, 2. *Ahaz* (735–715) succeeded his father Jotham, whose prosperous reign (742–735) was clouded only at its close by the gathering storm of the anti-Assyrian alliance of Israel and Damascus (2 Kgs. 15³⁷).

3. *He even burned his son as an offering.* This is the first reference to human sacrifice in the history of Judah and the practice is said explicitly to have been borrowed from the religion of the Canaanites. Child sacrifice became common during the late period of the monarchy (perhaps because it was a time of exceptional stress, cf. 2 Kgs. 3²⁷), as is made clear by the large number of biblical denunciations (2 Kgs. 17¹⁷, 21⁶, 23¹⁰; Jer. 7³¹, 19⁵, 32³⁵; Ezek. 16²¹, 20²⁶; Deut. 12³¹, 18¹⁰; Lev. 18²¹, 20²⁻⁵; cf. Mic. 6⁷), many of which describe it as an offering to Molech (or Baal) at Topheth in the valley of the sons of Hinnom. Molech is almost certainly the title of a Canaanite god meaning 'the king', for which the Hebrew word (*melekh*) has been deliberately given the vowels of the Hebrew word for 'shame' (*bōsheth*). Molech occurs as the name of the god of the Ammonites (1 Kgs. 11⁷; cf. 'Milcom' of 2 Kgs. 23¹³) and as an element in the names of Adram*melech* and Anam*melech*, the gods introduced to Samaria by the settlers after 721 B.C. and to whom also sacrifices of children were offered (2 Kgs. 17³¹). Topheth (which has also been given the vowels of *bōsheth*) means a burning place (cf. Isa. 30³³, RSV *mg.*) and was adopted as the name of the notorious sanctuary in the valley of the sons of Hinnom just south of Jerusalem. This valley in its turn gave its name to Gehenna, the place of punishment by fire,

translated 'hell' in the gospels (cf. Matthew 5^{22}; Mark 9^{43}), Gehenna being simply the Greek and Latin form of the Hebrew words for the 'valley of Hinnom'.

5. The siege of Jerusalem by the alliance of Damascus and Israel when they failed to win the support of Judah against Assyria is more fully depicted in Isa. 7$^{1-9}$ (see pp. 331 ff.).

6. *the king of Edom recovered Elath.* Elath, as Ezion-geber was later named, was the port for the Arabian trade on the Red Sea, which changed hands between Judah and Edom a number of times. Solomon built and developed it; it was sacked by Egypt in the reign of Rehoboam, but subsequently rebuilt. Edom took it in the reign of Jehoram, but it was recaptured by Uzziah. And now early in the reign of Ahaz, it was lost again to Edom. The reading, *Aram* (Syria), recorded in the RSV *mg.*, is a spelling mistake for Edom, made by a confusion between two similar consonants in the Hebrew names.

7, 8. The bribe with which Ahaz gained the help of Assyria against the Aramean alliance is listed in the records of Tiglath-pileser III.

9. *Damascus* was captured by Assyria in 732 B.C. *Kir*, to which the Arameans were deported (cf. Amos 1^5) and from which (according to Amos 9^7) they originally came, has not been located, although it seems to have been a region in Mesopotamia (cf. Isa. 22^6).

10. The details of Ahaz's installation of a new *altar* in front of the Temple at Jerusalem are obscure and much debated. It seems probable that it was the altar in the temple of Hadad-rimmon at Damascus (cf. 2 Kgs. 5^{18}; 2 Chron. 28^{23}) which Ahaz had copied and put in the place of the old bronze altar at Jerusalem (v. 14). The latter, though pushed aside, was kept for the king's private use when he wanted an oracle (v. 15), presumably by examining the entrails of sacrificial animals (on divination, see pp. 235 f.; fig. p. 117).

12–16. Although on such special occasions as the dedication of a new altar, the king, as a sacred person, offered sacrifice (cf. 1 Kgs. 8^{62-64}), the ordinary conduct of worship was left to the priest (v. 15). Urijah's unquestioning obedience to Ahaz (v. 16) illustrates the authority of the king in Temple affairs and the status of the priests as civil servants of the state sanctuary.

17, 18. *because of the king of Assyria*. In order to satisfy Assyrian demands, Ahaz stripped the Temple of its valuable bronze. The *frames of the stands* were the decorated panels of the ten immense trolleys which held bowls of water—*the laver*, and *the sea* was a large bronze basin fifteen feet in diameter which rested on twelve bronze bulls (1 Kgs. 7^{23-39}). The *sea* survived on its new stone base until the Babylonians carried it off in 587 B.C. (2 Kgs. 25^{13}). For *the covered way for the sabbath*, the Greek has 'a base for the throne' and it seems probable that some valuable part of the king's special stall in the Temple (not the palace) is meant. The removal of the private *entrance for the king* into the Temple is more likely to mean that it was constructed of valuable material, than that, as a vassal to Assyria, Ahaz had forfeited his royal authority over the sanctuary.

17. 1–6 and 17. 24–33 *The fall of Israel* (732–721)

The city of Samaria and the territory around it were all that was left of the northern kingdom when Hoshea came to the throne. His suicidal rebellion against Assyria in 724 B.C. and the consequent capture of Samaria three years later are recorded in a brief and puzzling narrative. The main problem is whether vv. 1–6 are to be understood as a single account, or whether vv. 3 and 4 and vv. 5 and 6 are parallel accounts from different sources. It is probable that the latter view is correct and, therefore, that the Assyrians, provoked by Hoshea's intrigue with Egypt and his refusal of tribute, marched against Samaria about 724 B.C. and after a siege of three years took the city and deported thousands of its inhabitants.

Samaria then became the fourth Assyrian province carved out of Israelite territory. According to the new Assyrian policy for subject peoples, Sargon II deported some 27,000 Israelites to Mesopotamia and repopulated the province with people from Babylon and Syria. The mixed religion which resulted is described in 17²⁴⁻³⁴ᵃ with the clear intention of vilifying the Samaritans and justifying the Jews' later hatred of them.

The disappearance of Israel as an independent kingdom and the deportation of many of its inhabitants have been exploited for centuries by innumerable cranks who wish to glorify their own people by identifying them with 'the ten lost tribes'. Masses of completely bogus interpretation of biblical 'prophecies' are still circulated in an obsessive attempt to prove that some particular group is a master race—that 'Israel' which is destined to share with Judah the blessings of the Messianic Kingdom. In view of such nonsense, it is the more important to be clear that the ten tribes of Israel were never 'lost', because the majority of the Israelites were not deported but remained in their own land under Assyrian provincial government.

1, 2. *Hoshea* (732–724) gained the throne as an Assyrian puppet (see notes on 2 Kgs. 15²⁹, ³⁰). The deuteronomic historian's relatively favourable judgement must mean that he cared little about Israel's loss of her independence.

3. *Shalmaneser* V succeeded Tiglath-pileser III as king of Assyria and reigned for five years (727–722) before being murdered during the siege of Samaria.

4. *So*, with whom Hoshea began negotiations, has been identified with Sib'e, an Egyptian army commander mentioned in Sargon's inscriptions, who may have been one of the many rival rulers in Egypt at this time. However, the name Sib'e is uncertain and *So* may be simply a transcription of the Egyptian for 'vizier', in which case, we could translate, 'the vizier of the king of Egypt'.

6. *the king of Assyria* was now Sargon II (722–705), who was responsible for the final collapse of Samaria in 721 B.C. *Halah*, to which some of its inhabitants were deported, is unknown, but *Habor* is a tributary of the Euphrates on which the city of *Gozan* stood. An inscription of Sargon confirms and

amplifies the biblical account: 'I besieged and conquered Samaria, led away as booty 27,290 inhabitants of it. I formed from among them a contingent of 50 chariots and made remaining [inhabitants] assume their [social] positions. I installed over them an officer of mine and imposed upon them the tribute of the former king' (J. B. Pritchard, *Ancient Near Eastern Texts*, pp. 284–5). The figure 27,290 represents only a proportion of the population, if there were, in fact, as many as 60,000 landowners in the reign of Menahem (see notes on 2 Kgs. 15¹⁹).

24. *Samaria*, not Israel, is now the name of the land. Sargon claimed of its capital: 'The town I rebuilt better than it was before and settled therein people from countries which I myself had conquered.' The foreign settlers were brought from the city of *Babylon*, *Cuthah*, an ancient city fifteen miles north east of Babylon, *Avva* (not identified), *Hamath*, the Aramean kingdom on the river Orontes which was destroyed by Sargon in 720 B.C., and *Sephar-vaim*, an unknown city, identified by some with a place near Hamath, and by others with Sippar, a Babylonian city north-west of Cuthah. Some of this colonization was probably effected by the successors of Sargon II (cf. Ezra 4²).

26. *the law of the god of the land* means the proper procedure ('the done thing') required by the local god. We may compare this pagan way of referring to the worship of Yahweh with the Hebrew idiom of vv. 25 and 28: *how they should fear the Lord*.

27, 28. The author's intention is to trace the origin of the Samaritan community to the priesthood of *Bethel*. Later the Jews contemptuously nicknamed the Samaritans 'lion converts'.

29–31. The foreign settlers in Samaria established their own cults. *Succoth-benoth* may be a corruption of Zir-banitu, the wife of Marduk, the city-god of Babylon. *Nergal* was the city-god of Cuthah (cf. the name 'Nergal-sharezer' in Jer. 39³). *Ashima* is probably the goddess referred to in Amos 8¹⁴ and worshipped by the unorthodox Jews of the military colony at Elephantine, an island on the Nile, during the fifth century B.C. *Nibhaz* and *Tartak* are unknown gods. *Adrammelech* and *Anammelech* stand, perhaps, for Adad-melech ('Adad is king') and Anu-melech ('Anu is king'), Adad (or, Hadad) being the old Semitic storm-god (with whom Baal is identified in the Ras Shamra texts, fig. p. 74), and Anu the Mesopotamian sky-god. On human sacrifice, see notes on 2 Kgs. 16³.

32. *all sorts of people as priests* means not only Levites, as Yahwist orthodoxy demanded.

VI. THE KINGDOM OF JUDAH ALONE
(715–587)

18. 1–8; 18. 13–19. 8; 19. 36, 37 *Hezekiah's reform and rebellion* (715–687)

The biblical record of Hezekiah's reign raises some of the most complicated problems of Old Testament history. Three facts, however, are undisputed. First, Hezekiah reversed the policy of his father Ahaz by standing out against Assyria and so exposed Judah to a fate like that of the northern kingdom. Second, his playing about in power politics cost him a great deal of territory and the payment of a crippling tribute. Third, despite everything, Jerusalem survived.

Hezekiah's religious reform was probably itself an act of rebellion against Assyrian influence. How thoroughgoing it was, the nature of the account in 18¹⁻⁸ makes it impossible to determine, since the deuteronomic historian represents it as anticipating the reform of Josiah a century later and credits Hezekiah with the destruction of the local sanctuaries and the centralization of worship in Jerusalem (cf. 18²²; see pp. 118–25). There is, however, no reason to doubt that his reign witnessed a revival of religious and patriotic enthusiasm. The vigour of the court at this time is also attested in such diverse spheres as hydraulic engineering (cf. 18¹⁷) and literary scholarship (cf. Prov. 25¹ and pp. 195 f.).

Hezekiah's political activities are difficult to determine in detail. The record in 18¹³–19³⁷ of his relations with Assyria seems to derive from three sources: (a) 18¹³⁻¹⁶ is a bare factual summary of Sennacherib's invasion of Judah in 701 B.C., Hezekiah's submission and his payment of tribute. It is probably taken from the annals of Judah and corresponds closely to the Assyrian annals; (b) 18¹⁷–19⁸ is a more elaborate narrative recounting the arrival at the gates of Jerusalem of an Assyrian army and embassy demanding the surrender of the city. Hezekiah appealed to the prophet Isaiah, who was able to assure the king that Yahweh would frighten the Assyrians into withdrawing. The conclusion of this account is to be found in 19³⁶, ³⁷; (c) 19⁹⁻³⁵ repeats the substance of the second account (b), but with a more explicitly *religious* emphasis, culminating in the miraculous slaughter of 185,000 Assyrian troops by the angel of the Lord. Many scholars are agreed that this third account is a later variant of the second. The relationship between the first (a) and second account (b) is the subject of endless debate. The three views which seem most probable are briefly as follows. (1) The order of the biblical narrative (a–b) is substantially correct; that is to say, Sennacherib's demand for the submission of the city and his sudden withdrawal from it did, in fact, follow Hezekiah's payment of tribute. It is true that the Assyrian annals end with Sennacherib's humiliation of Hezekiah, but they are no less likely to be biased than the biblical account. (2) The true course of events is summarized in 18¹³⁻¹⁶ (a) and the Assyrian embassy (b), in so far as it is more than later legend, must be fitted into this outline *before* Hezekiah's payment of tribute. (3) The two accounts, (a) and (b), refer to two quite separate campaigns of Sennacherib to the west. The first campaign, recorded in the Assyrian annals for 701 B.C., is summarized in 18¹³⁻¹⁶ (a); a second campaign, which occurred about 688 B.C., when Sennacherib suffered a crushing defeat just before his death, is recorded in 18¹⁷–19⁸ (b). The disadvantage of this view is that there is not a shred of evidence for any second campaign in the Assyrian annals. Our present knowledge makes it extremely difficult to decide between these three possibilities, but the divergence of (1) and (3) from the Assyrian annals and from the authentic records of Isaiah (see pp. 320 f.) provokes caution in accepting either of them and emphasizes, by contrast, the strength of (2). No doubt Sennacherib's annals are boastful and biased, but they do not claim the capture of Jerusalem, and there was less reason for the great king to misrepresent the fate of a petty Palestinian kingdom than for the religious spokesmen of that kingdom to embroider two undoubted facts—that Jerusalem was spared and its oppressor assassinated (cf. 19[37]).

4. *the pillars . . . and the Asherah*: see notes on 1 Kgs. 14[23, 24]. The *bronze serpent*, to which sacrifice was offered and which Hezekiah destroyed, may have been either part of the cultic paraphernalia taken over from the old Jebusite shrine of pre-Israelite Jerusalem, or a Canaanite fertility symbol associated with the goddess *Asherah*. Its origin was ascribed to Moses (Num. 21[6–9]) to give it respectability. *Nehushtan* may derive from the Hebrew for either serpent or bronze, more probably the former.

8. *Gaza* was the most southerly of the five cities of the *Philistines* and Ekron the northernmost. The annals of Sennacherib, the new king of Assyria (705–681), record that Padi, the pro-Assyrian king of Ekron, was handed over to Hezekiah and imprisoned in Jerusalem, when Judean forces invaded Philistine territory to stir up support for rebellion against Assyria. Hezekiah's intervention on the coastal plain was part of a widespread movement of revolt in the west, to which Sennacherib's campaign of 701 B.C. was the crushing reply. Sennacherib restored Padi to the throne of Ekron and rewarded him for his loyalty with part of Hezekiah's territory.

13. This verse refers to Sennacherib's campaign against the western alliance in 701 B.C., of which we have (on the so-called 'Taylor Prism') the Assyrian king's own record:

> As to Hezekiah, the Jew, he did not submit to my yoke, I laid siege to 46 of his strong cities, walled forts and to the countless small villages in their vicinity . . . I drove out [of them] 200,150 people,

young and old, male and female, horses, mules, donkeys, camels, big and small cattle beyond counting, and considered [them] booty. Himself I made a prisoner in Jerusalem, his royal residence, like a bird in a cage. I surrounded him with earthwork in order to molest those who were leaving his city's gate . . . Hezekiah himself . . . did send me, later, to Nineveh, my lordly city, together with 30 talents of gold, 800 talents of silver, precious stones, antimony, large cuts of red stone, couches [inlaid] with ivory, *nîmedu*-chairs (i.e. arm-chairs) [inlaid] with ivory, elephant-hides, ebony-wood, box-wood [and] all kinds of valuable treasures, his [own] daughters, concubines, male and female musicians. In order to deliver the tribute and to do obeisance as a slave he sent his [personal] messenger (J. B. Pritchard, *Ancient Near Eastern Texts*, p. 288).

14. *Lachish*, a Judean city thirty miles south-west of Jerusalem, which had been captured by Sennacherib, was being used as his headquarters. Although he makes no reference to it in his annals, Sennacherib had the siege of the city depicted in bas-relief (now in the British Museum) with himself triumphantly receiving the submission of its people (fig. p. 340). The Assyrian siege is confirmed by archaeological evidence of the city's destruction about 700 B.C. *thirty talents of gold*. This detail is strikingly confirmed by Sennacherib's account.

17. This verse begins the second account of Sennacherib's campaign (see p. 109). The names of the Assyrian leaders are titles of offices: the *Tartan* was the commander-in-chief, the *Rabsaris* the chief attendant, and the *Rabshakeh* the chief administrator. The *conduit of the upper pool* was part of Jerusalem's waterworks outside the city wall (cf. Isa. 7³). As part of his defence preparations against the Assyrian invader, Hezekiah blocked the external aqueduct from the Spring of Gihon and the Upper Pool and built an underground tunnel to the Pool of Siloam inside the city (2 Kgs. 20²⁰; 2 Chron. 32²⁻⁵, ³⁰; cf. Isa. 22¹¹). This amazing engineering feat was accomplished by two gangs of miners working underground from opposite ends. Between them they covered 1,749 feet, making a large S-bend, and celebrated the triumphant moment of their break-through

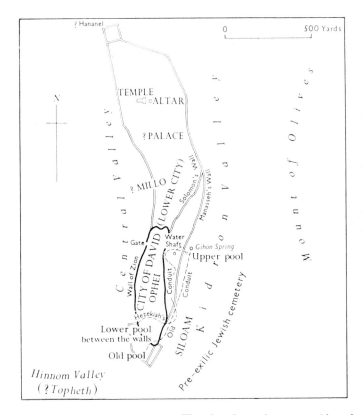

JERUSALEM BEFORE THE EXILE. The plan shows the eastern ridge of
Jerusalem between the Central Valley and the Kidron Valley. The Canaanite city which David took over (but did not extend) lies at the southern end
of the ridge overhanging the Gihon Spring, a vital source of water. Solomon
extended the city northwards, where he built his Palace and Temple.
Hezekiah's Conduit (otherwise known as the Siloam Tunnel), which
replaced the Old Conduit ('the conduit of the upper pool') outside the city,
may be traced in making its S-bend from the Gihon Spring to the Lower
Pool inside the walls. The line of the city walls as shown is largely conjectural
and in one important respect requires correction. Dr. Kathleen Kenyon's
excavations since 1961 have established that the north end of the ancient
city occupied by David extended about 50 yards further east than was formerly supposed and that its wall probably ran along the line marked on the
plan as Manasseh's Wall, so that the old Water Shaft from the Gihon Spring

and meeting with an inscription discovered in 1880 by a boy bathing in the Pool of Siloam:

(? the completing of) the piercing through. And this is the story of the piercing through. While (the stone-cutters were swinging their) axes, each towards his fellow, and while there were yet three cubits to be pierced through, (there was heard) the voice of a man calling to his fellow, for there was a crevice [i.e. a split in the rock] on the right . . . And on the day of the piercing through, the stone-cutters struck through each to meet his fellow, axe against axe. Then ran the water from the Spring to the Pool for twelve hundred cubits, and a hundred cubits was the height of the rock above the heads of the stone-cutters (D. Winton Thomas, *Documents from Old Testament Times*, p. 210).

18. The RSV translation does not adequately suggest that these officers were the first three ministers of the kingdom. *Eliakim* was the master of the palace, that is, the Prime Minister, who acted in the king's absence. *Shebnah* was the king's Private Secretary and Secretary of State, and *Joah* was the Royal Herald, who acted as the king's Public Relations Officer. The three ministers correspond to the first three officials in Egypt, from which (probably through Phoenicia) the government organization of Judah was largely borrowed.

20, 21. The interference of Egypt in the affairs of Palestine with windy promises had always proved fatal for Judah, as the prophet Isaiah was at this time trying to make Hezekiah realize (30$^{1-7}$, 31$^{1-3}$). Sennacherib had already defeated the Egyptian forces in the battle of Eltekeh (see notes on 19^7).

26. The Assyrians' subtle propaganda, suggesting that it was they and not Hezekiah who were serving Yahweh (vv. 22–25),

---

(cf. 2 Sam. 5^8), as one would expect for use in time of war, came up inside the city. Further, in 1965, an excavated portion of this ancient east wall near the Gihon Spring was identified as a tower, which is now thought to be the northern tower of the important water-gate of Jerusalem, through which Solomon entered the city after his anointing at the Spring (see K. M. Kenyon, *Palestine Exploration Quarterly*, 1966, pp. 75–80; the author is indebted to Dr. Kenyon for generously allowing him to see this report before its publication).

was too dangerous for the man-in-the-street to hear. While Hebrew—*the language of Judah*—was the common spoken language, *Aramaic* was already the language of international diplomacy and commerce. Originally the language of the Aramean kingdom of Damascus, known to us from the 'Milqart Stele' (see notes on 1 Kgs. 15¹⁸), Aramaic had spread beyond its borders to the Assyrians. Further evidence of its early use came to light in 1942 by the discovery of the so-called 'Letter from Saqqarah', belonging to the time of Jeremiah and possibly the oldest Aramaic papyrus known (see notes on 2 Kgs. 24¹).

33–35. Yahweh, the Assyrian argues, will no more be able to deliver Jerusalem than were the gods of the Aramean cities which Assyria has already taken. For *Hamath* and *Sephar-vaim*, see notes on 2 Kgs. 17²⁴; *Arpad*, a city in northern Syria, had also been captured by Sargon II in 720 B.C.; *Hena* and *Ivvah* have not been identified. One form of the Greek inserts, 'Where are the gods of Samaria?', before the final question in v. 34.

19. 2. *Isaiah the son of Amoz* is the first canonical prophet to be mentioned in the historical books of the Old Testament; see pp. 315–48.

3. *children have come to the birth* is probably a proverbial expression for extreme weakness and frustration. Judah is like a woman who cannot deliver a child ready to be born.

4. The king's request for Isaiah's prayer and the expression 'the Lord *your* God' illustrate the popular conception of the prophet's authority and function (see pp. 240 f.).

7. *spirit* describes the way in which Yahweh exercises his influence over men. Isaiah is represented as declaring that the Assyrian Rabshakeh will hear a *rumour* of trouble elsewhere and withdraw. As the narrative now stands, it appears that the trouble is the advance of *Tirhakah* in v. 9, but this reference is highly problematical. From texts published recently, it is known that *Tirhakah*, who was king of *Ethiopia* and Egypt, did not succeed to the throne until about 690 B.C., and was probably

too young to march against Sennacherib in 701 B.C. There are, therefore, two main possibilities. (*a*) If the name is a mistake, v. 9 may refer *either* to the Egyptian threat which was crushed by the Assyrians at the battle of Eltekeh, *or* to a rapid Egyptian revival and a new threat to Assyria in 701 B.C. after that battle. In the former case, it was wrongly identified by an editor with the *rumour* which caused the Assyrian withdrawal from Jerusalem and the verse is best understood as an abrupt introduction to the parallel account of 19⁹⁻³⁵. (*b*) If, however, the name *Tirhakah* is historically accurate, there must have been a second Assyrian campaign after 690 B.C. about which the annals of Sennacherib are silent (see pp. 109 f.).

8. *Libnah* was a Judean town ten miles north of Lachish.

36, 37. These verses, which conclude the narrative of 18¹⁷–19⁸, record Sennacherib's withdrawal from Jerusalem to his own capital and his violent death in 681 B.C. at the hands of his sons. The god *Nisroch* is unknown; it may be a corruption of Nusku, the Mesopotamian fire-god mentioned in Assyrian inscriptions. *Ararat* (cf. Gen. 8⁴) is the land of Urartu, roughly equivalent to the later Armenia, north of Assyria. For *Esarhaddon*, see below.

21. 1–26 *The apostasy of Manasseh* (687–642) *and Amon* (642–640)

The long reign of Manasseh was Judah's dark age, when for nearly half a century independent prophecy was silent and pagan cults were actively promoted in the Temple itself. Judah's religious recession was the direct result of her subservience to Assyria, now at the very height of its power. It was during Manasseh's reign that Esar-haddon (681–669) and his son and successor Ashur-banipal (669–633?) decisively crushed Egypt and in the annals of both rulers Manasseh is mentioned among the western kings who performed their bidding. Esar-haddon records: '. . . all these I sent out and made them transport under terrible difficulties, to Nineveh . . . as building material for my palace . . . big logs, long beams [and] thin boards from cedar and pine trees . . . [also] from their quarries in the mountains, statues of protective deities. . . .' And Ashurbanipal, describing Manasseh and his fellow tributaries as 'servants who belong to me', boasts: 'I made these kings accompany my army over the land—as well as [over] the sea-route with their armed forces and their ships' (J. B. Pritchard, *Ancient Near Eastern Texts*, pp. 291, 294). Judah was in chains.

1. *Manasseh* (687–642) reigned longer than any other Hebrew king.

3. Manasseh reversed the religious policy of his father Hezekiah and reverted to his grandfather Ahaz's recognition of Canaanite and Assyrian cults. *Asherah*, here, is an image of the Canaanite mother-goddess (cf. v. 7 and see notes on 1 Kgs. 14^{23}). The worship of *all the host of heaven* (cf. v. 5) was accepted from Assyrian astrological cults, which were based on the belief that the sun, moon, and stars controlled human destiny (cf. Jer. 8^2, 19^{13}; Zeph. 1^5; Deut. 4^{19}).

4. *In Jerusalem will I put my name*: on this deuteronomic expression, see notes on Deut. 12^5.

5. *two courts* are not mentioned in the description of Solomon's Temple in 1 Kgs. 6–7, but occur in Ezek. 40$^{19, 20}$. The second court may mean the area between the Temple and the royal palace.

6. On child sacrifice, see notes on 2 Kgs. 16^3. The four terms used to describe Manasseh's pagan borrowings from Assyria indicate two main types of divination: (*a*) *soothsaying* and *augury* mean the foretelling of the future by observing signs and omens, such as the stars (astrology) and the livers of sacrificial animals (hepatoscopy) (fig. p. 117); (*b*) *mediums* and *wizards* suggest divination by contact with the spirits of the dead (necromancy), such as was practised by the medium of Endor (1 Sam. 28).

7–15. These verses are the work of the deuteronomic historian, who takes the opportunity of accounting for the fall of

DIVINATION: A STUDENT'S TEACHING-AID. This clay model of a sheep's lung, 3½ in. long, was discovered in a temple at Nimrud. It had evidently been brought to Assyria from Babylon for the purpose of teaching students of the ancient 'science' of divination, who were learning how to make predictions on the basis of the markings on the lungs, livers, and kidneys of sacrificial animals. A number of similar teaching-aids for hepatoscopy (cf. Ezek. 21²¹) have been excavated in Mesopotamia. The inscription in the above example gives not only the key to the interpretation of the markings, but also the name and address of the scribe and the exact date of his work—the ninth year of a king of Babylon, probably Merodach-baladan (722–703) (see M. E. L. Mallowan, *Nimrud and its Remains*, vol. i, pp. 275–6).

Jerusalem and the exile of its people as Yahweh's judgement for the wickedness of Manasseh (see pp. 67 ff.).

11. The name *Amorites* is used here to describe the pre-Israelite population of Palestine, who invaded the land about 2300 B.C. and were called Amurru by the Sumerians (cf. Gen. 15¹⁶; Num. 13²⁹, 21¹³; Josh. 10⁵; Amos 2⁹).

13. The *measuring line* and the *plummet* are to be used not for building, but for testing as a preliminary to demolition (cf. Amos 7⁷, ⁸; Lam. 2⁸). Jerusalem will suffer the fate of Samaria

and the house of Ahab, which is described in the vivid metaphor from dish-washing.

16. The tradition that Manasseh slaughtered the prophets (including Isaiah) is late and this verse may refer more generally to his treatment of loyal worshippers of Yahweh. It is, nevertheless, significant that there is no record of prophetic activity during his long reign.

18. Manasseh and Amon (see v. 26) were buried in *the garden of Uzza,* either because the old necropolis of the kings of Judah had ceased to be used after the time of Ahaz (cf. 2 Chron. 32³³), or because this particular garden had pagan associations.

19–26. Amon (642–640) reigned a mere two years before he was murdered in a court conspiracy. The people of the land, however, overthrew the courtiers and made his son, Josiah, king (see notes on 2 Kgs. 22¹).

22. 1–23. 30 *Josiah's rebellion and reformation* (640–609)

Josiah was the chief hero of the deuteronomic historian, but in concentrating so exclusively on his religious reformation he has seriously misrepresented the king's aim and achievement. It is left, therefore, to the modern historian to place these chapters in their proper political context and uncover the overall design with which he was working. Josiah led a movement of national liberation, which was made possible by the break-up of Assyria shortly after his accession to the throne. First Egypt and then Babylon rebelled against the imperial power and established their independence. Finally, the Medes exploited Assyria's weakness and, in alliance with the Babylonians, sacked Nineveh, the capital of Assyria, in 612 B.C. (Nahum 1¹²–3¹⁹). After that, the empire was finished (see p. 17). Now, for the first time for over a century, Judah was free to order her own existence and Josiah dreamed dreams of restoring the dual kingdom of David with its capital at Jerusalem.

It is impossible to be sure how far the resurgent nationalism of Josiah's reign made headway in the old northern kingdom.

The Chronicler affirms enthusiastically that the king was able to carry out his religious reform 'throughout all the land of Israel' (2 Chron. 34[6, 7]), but the references to the north in 2 Kings are little more than marginal (23[4, 15–20]). The fact, however, that Josiah was as far north as Megiddo when he lost his life suggests that he had taken over some of the control in the old northern kingdom, which Assyria in her decline had certainly lost (see notes on 23[29]). As we know directly from slightly later evidence (Jer. 41[4, 5]), there were men in the northern kingdom who still looked to Jerusalem as a place of pilgrimage, and it is intrinsically probable that there was a good deal of traffic across the frontier when the vigilance of the Assyrians slackened.

Josiah's religious reformation, therefore, must be interpreted as an essential part of his bid for Judah's independence by rebellion against Assyria. Equally, his political ambitions were shaped by an authentic quest for a national religious revival; otherwise, it is inconceivable that he would ever have received the unqualified approval of Jeremiah (22[15, 16]). In pursuit of this aim, he abolished all those alien practices with which political bondage and popular paganism had smothered Israel's traditional faith: Assyrian sun and star worship (23[4, 5, 11]; cf. Deut. 17[3]), child-sacrifice (23[10]; cf. Deut. 18[10]), divination and necromancy (23[24]; cf. Deut. 18[11]), and the Canaanite cults of Baal and Asherah (23[4, 6, 7, 14]; cf. Deut. 12[3], 16[21, 22], 23[17]). Positively, Josiah centralized all worship of Yahweh in the Jerusalem Temple as the sole legitimate sanctuary (23[5, 8, 13, 15, 19]; cf. Deut. 12[1–14]) and reaffirmed the nation's true identity as the people of God in a renewal of the covenant (23[1–3]; cf. Deut. 28[3–19]) and an unprecedented celebration of the Passover (23[21–23]; cf. Deut. 16[1–8]).

The close correspondence between Josiah's reformation and the regulations of the book of Deuteronomy reflects, one may assume, both Josiah's actual indebtedness to the deuteronomic school and the enthusiastic exaggeration of the deuteronomic historian. The difficulty of taking literally his account of the discovery of the law book in the Temple and its immediate sequel does not arise from doubts about the king's acceptance of the deuteronomic programme, but, rather, from the improbability that his knowledge of it was gained so late in his reign and in so fortuitous a manner. The Chronicler dates the inauguration of Josiah's reforming policy six years before his discovery of the law book (2 Chron. 34³, ⁸, ¹⁴) and it is likely (as this tradition suggests) that the king was schooled in deuteronomic ideals from the time he succeeded to the throne at the age of eight. If this was the case, the deuteronomic historian, while affirming what was substantially true, has over-dramatized both the way in which the reform began and the speed with which it was concluded. The book of Deuteronomy is imbued with a highly self-conscious and urgent ideal for Israel's revival and it was not by mere chance that Josiah came to share it (see pp. 212 f.).

22. 1. *Josiah* (640–609) was placed on the throne at the age of eight by the people of the land, who put down the court conspiracy in which his father was killed (2 Kgs. 21²³, ²⁴). *The people of the land* was a more or less technical term during the period of the monarchy for a specific social class in the community, consisting of male citizens who owned land and had full rights and responsibilities in the kingdom. In the social hierarchy they seem to follow the priesthood (cf. Jer. 1¹⁸; Ezek. 7²⁷) and are mentioned as playing a significant part in the accession to the throne, not only of Josiah, but also of Joash of Judah (2 Kgs. 11¹², ¹⁸⁻²⁰) and Jehoahaz (2 Kgs. 23³⁰).

3. *eighteenth year*, that is, 621 B.C. In 2 Chron. 34³, Josiah is said to have begun his reform in his twelfth year, that is, 628 B.C. *Shaphan*, Josiah's Secretary of State, was the head of a family with a remarkable record of service to Yahweh in the last days of Judah. We hear of his son Ahikam, who saved the life of Jeremiah (Jer. 26²⁴; cf. 2 Kgs. 22¹², ¹⁴); Elasah, another son, took Jeremiah's famous letter to the exiles (Jer. 29³); Gemariah, a third son, was also associated with the prophet (Jer. 36¹⁰). Micaiah (Jer. 36¹¹) and Gedaliah, who was appointed governor of Judah (Jer. 39¹⁴, 40⁶), were Shaphan's grandsons.

4. *Hilkiah the high priest.* Since it is improbable that the title *high priest* for the head of the priesthood was used before the Exile, this reference (like three others in 2 Kgs. 12¹⁰, 22⁸, 23⁴) appears to be a later gloss.

5. *repairing the house.* Any connexion between the repair of the Temple and the beginning of Josiah's reform by the removal from it of pagan cult objects is highly speculative. Regular repairs were carried out as we know from Joash's arrangements in 2 Kgs. 12⁴⁻¹⁶ and it is from that account that vv. 4–7 of the present chapter were probably borrowed.

8. *the book of the law,* with its definite article, conveys the clear intention of the deuteronomic historian to identify the document with the book of Deuteronomy (see p. 212).

10. Shaphan's casual attitude towards what he describes simply as *a book,* despite the fact that he had read it (v. 8), contrasts strongly with Josiah's violent reaction (v. 11). This may indicate deliberate dramatic skill, or (more probably) the uneven work of an editor.

11. The fact that Josiah *rent his clothes* is no evidence, as is often suggested, that the book must have included the curses of Deut. 28¹⁵⁻¹⁹. Deuteronomy contains much to cause consternation.

12. *Asaiah the king's servant.* The description *servant of the king* may be the title of a special office, but the large number of contemporary seals from Judah and elsewhere with this wording suggests that it was a general description.

13. *inquire of the Lord* is the technical term for seeking an oracle (in this case from a prophetess); see notes on 1 Kgs. 22⁵.

14–20. *Huldah the prophetess.* This whole episode abounds in unsolved problems: (*a*) why should the chief *priest* seek an oracle from a *prophetess,* who was the wife of a minor Temple official employed in looking after its vestments? (*b*) why should a prophecy of unqualified doom on Jerusalem (vv. 17, 20) be interpreted as an encouragement to national reform and renewal? Huldah's assurance that Josiah would die *in peace*

(v. 20) does not necessarily conflict with the account of his violent and tragic end (2 Kgs. 23²⁹). If, as seems probable, the section was written or revised by the deuteronomic historian after
the fall of Jerusalem, v. 20 must mean that Josiah was to be
rewarded for his piety by the postponement of a disaster he
did not live to see (cf. Jer. 22¹⁰; see pp. 67 ff.).

23. 1–3. The *covenant* by which Josiah and his people pledged
themselves to obey the law contained in the book is described
in characteristically deuteronomic language. Joash's covenant
(2 Kgs. 11¹²⁻¹⁸) provides a precedent and, like that of Josiah,
is the prelude to religious reform. The *pillar* by which the king
stood is probably one of the two great bronze pillars in front of
the Temple (fig. p. 140; cf. 1 Kgs. 7¹⁵⁻²²; 2 Kgs. 11¹⁴, 25¹³; 2
Chron. 23¹³). An alternative possibility is a 'platform' (2 Chron.
34³¹).

4. *the high priest*: see notes on 2 Kgs. 22⁴. For *the priests of the
second order*, read 'the second priest' (cf. 2 Kgs. 25¹⁸). The
keepers of the threshold, who appear to have been senior officials,
also connect this narrative with that of Joash (2 Kgs. 12⁹). The
cult objects for Baal, the mother-goddess and star worship (see
notes on 1 Kgs. 14²³, ²⁴ and 2 Kgs. 21³) were burned in the *fields*
(or, ash pits) of the Kidron valley. The scattering of their ashes
at *Bethel* is a ludicrous editorial touch.

5. The intrusion of this verse about the suppression of Canaanite
and Assyrian cults in the provinces into the story of the reform
in Jerusalem illustrates the composite nature of the narrative.

6. The *Asherah* here is a combustible (presumably wooden)
image of the mother-goddess (cf. 2 Kgs. 21⁷).

7. The *cult prostitutes* were men and women who functioned in
the fertility rites which had come to be associated with the
worship of the Temple. The women wove vestments (rather
than *hangings*) either for the image of Asherah or for her
devotees (if not for both).

8. Josiah centralized worship in the Temple by destroying the

provincial sanctuaries from *Geba* on the northern boundary of Judah to *Beer-sheba* in the south and expelling their priests. For the unintelligible *he broke down the high places of the gates*, read 'he broke down the high places of the satyrs [that is, goat-demons]' (cf. Lev. 17⁷; 2 Chron. 11¹⁵).

9. The provincial *priests* either did not come up to Jerusalem at all, or (more probably) when they did they were not allowed to officiate at the Temple sacrifices, but were kept apart in a subordinate role (cf. Ezek. 44¹⁰⁻¹⁴). The eating of *unleavened bread* may refer to the great Passover with which Josiah's reformation ended (23²¹⁻²³). The subordination of the provincial priests reflects the victorious opposition of the Jerusalem priesthood to the equal rights proposed for them in Deut. 18⁶⁻⁸. This note of the exceptional discrepancy between Josiah's reformation and the law of Deuteronomy provides excellent evidence of their connexion.

10. On *Topheth* and child-sacrifice to *Molech*, see notes on 2 Kgs. 16³.

11. The *horses* and *chariots* used in sun-worship within the very precincts of the Temple may be connected with an Assyrian cult of the sun-god, who is described as 'chariot-rider' (cf. 2 Kgs. 21³, ⁵; Jer. 8²; Ezek. 8¹⁶).

12. *the upper chamber of Ahaz* was probably a shrine for worship on the roof of the Temple itself, like the altar used by King Keret in the Ras Shamra texts (see p. 135; cf. Zeph. 1⁵; Jer. 19¹³, 32²⁹). For *the altars which Manasseh had made*, see 2 Kgs. 21⁵.

13. *the mount of corruption* is either a misreading for the Mount of Olives, or a derisive nickname for it, with a play on the similar Hebrew words for 'corruption' and 'ointment'. It was here that Solomon set up the pagan shrines now destroyed (1 Kgs. 11⁵⁻⁷). *Ashtoreth* is the name of the Canaanite fertility goddess, Astarte, vocalized with the vowels of the Hebrew word for 'shame' (*bōsheth*). She is better known in the Ras Shamra texts by her other name, Asherah (see pp. 44 f.), and to the Babylonians and Assyrians as Ishtar (fig. p. 292). Here,

as in 1 Kgs. 11$^{5,\ 33}$, she is associated with the Phoenicians. *Chemosh*, known as the god of the Moabites from the Moabite Stone (see pp. 338 f.), may have a common ancestry with *Milcom*, the national god of the Ammonites (Judg. 11^{24}; 1 Kgs. 11$^{5,\ 7}$), whose name is often deliberately misvocalized as Molech (see notes on 2 Kgs. 16^{3}). Each of these national deities is described as a 'detestable thing' (cf. Deut. 29^{17}).

15–20. This section, describing the extension of Josiah's reformation to *Bethel* (cf. v. 4) and the rest of the cities of *Samaria* (as the Assyrian province is now properly called), looks at first sight like a clumsy addition in the interests of the fulfilment of prophecy (cf. 1 Kgs. 12^{32}–13^{34}). Since, however, the 'prophecy' of 1 Kgs. 13 is itself so obviously a late composition (cf. vv. 2, 32), it may reflect, with this section, an authentic historical tradition of Josiah's activity in the north (see notes on 23^{29}). The slaughter of the northern priests in v. 20 compares unfavourably with the treatment of the idolatrous priests of Judah in v. 5.

21–23. The celebration of the feast of *Passover*, as a great act of national solidarity, was the climax of Josiah's reformation. The novelty of the occasion, which is strongly emphasized in v. 22, arose directly from the fact that the celebration followed the new regulations of Deuteronomy, *as it is written in this book of the covenant*. Deut. 16$^{1–8}$ is consciously innovating when it directs that the feast must be celebrated not 'within any of your towns', but at the central Jerusalem sanctuary (16$^{5,\ 6}$), since (as most scholars agree) the Passover hitherto had been a family festival celebrated at home (cf. Exod. 12$^{21–23}$). It has been recently suggested, however, that before the monarchy, in *the days of the judges* (v. 22; cf. 2 Chron. 35^{18}), the Passover was celebrated at the central shrine of the tribal confederation (cf. Josh. 5$^{10–12}$). It is at least clear that Josiah's centralizing the festival in Jerusalem was a breach with the tradition of many centuries, and probably a step towards the combining of the Passover with the agricultural feast of Unleavened Bread, which was kept during the same month (April) and had always been essentially a public pilgrimage feast (Exod. 23$^{14, 15}$). Passover and Unleavened Bread were, indeed, already associated (albeit awkwardly) in the regulations followed by Josiah (Deut. 16$^{1-8}$), but in the account of his celebration there is no reference to Unleavened Bread. The two feasts are fully combined in the priestly tradition of post-exilic Israel (Lev. 23$^{5-8}$), but it is significant that there Josiah's essential innovation has already been modified and Passover has largely reverted to its age-old character as a feast not of the sanctuary, but of the family and home (Exod. 12$^{3, 4}$; cf. Mark 14$^{12-15}$).

24. *teraphim* were small images (cf. Gen. 31$^{19, 34, 35}$), probably used in divination (Ezek. 21^{21}) and as magical charms (1 Sam. 19$^{13-17}$). On *mediums* and *wizards*, see notes on 2 Kgs. 21^6.

26, 27. The deuteronomic historian explains the fall of Judah and the destruction of Jerusalem by suggesting that Manasseh's wickedness outweighed Josiah's piety, which ought, on his theory, to have received its reward.

29. *Pharaoh Neco king of Egypt* was Necho II (609–593). In 609 B.C. the Egyptian army set off for Haran, north of the *Euphrates*, to *help* the king of Assyria *against* the Babylonians, who had already virtually annihilated Assyria and were simply engaged in mopping up operations (see p. 17). Josiah tried to block Necho at *Megiddo* and lost his life in the battle. The presence of Josiah at Megiddo is the most solid piece of evidence we possess that he had succeeded in extending his control to the Assyrian provinces of the old northern kingdom (cf. vv. 4, 15–20; 2 Chron. 34$^{6, 7}$). It has been suggested that the lists of towns now included in the book of Joshua (15$^{21-62}$, 18$^{21-28}$) reflect the twelve districts of Judah in the reign of Josiah and, therefore, confirm the view that Josiah had been successful in widening his territory to include Bethel (Josh. 18^{22}) and even the Philistine cities of Ekron, Ashdod, and Gaza (Josh. 15$^{45-47}$). Unfortunately, the date of these lists in Joshua is by no means certain and some scholars refer them to the state of Judah under Jehoshaphat in the ninth century B.C.

23. 31–25. 30 *Judah's decline and fall* (609–587)

In less than a quarter of a century, Judah fell from the high hopes of Josiah's reign to the despair of the Exile. The collapse of the Assyrian empire did not mean independence for the southern kingdom, but merely an exchange of foreign master, or, what was more dangerous, an oscillating position between the two powers now contending for the western remains of Assyria's empire—Egypt and Babylon. For some years after the death of Josiah, Judah was vassal to Egypt, who controlled Syria and Palestine, but in 605 B.C. Egypt was routed by the Babylonian army commander, Nebuchadrezzar, who immediately after the battle succeeded his father as king. From now on, the fate of Judah was in his hands. Jehoiakim at first accepted the new situation, but in 601 B.C. reverted to his former reliance on the Egyptians, when they raised false hopes by resisting the Babylonian army. He died before Judah suffered the worst of Nebuchadrezzar's reprisals and it was left to his son, Jehoiachin, to face the Babylonian invasion, surrender Jerusalem, and suffer the first deportation in 597 B.C.

Instead of converting Judah into a Babylonian province, Nebuchadrezzar was content to reduce it to a vassal kingdom under his nominee Zedekiah. For a terrible final decade, Zedekiah vacillated between the clamour of nationalistic prophets, who demanded the restoration of the deported Judeans, and the apparently treacherous counsel of Jeremiah, who urged that submission to Babylon was the will of Yahweh (cf. Jer. 27^1–29^{32}). The nationalists, deceived for the last time by the expectation of help from Egypt, prevailed and Zedekiah rebelled against Babylon. Nebuchadrezzar's forces overran the land and in 587 B.C., after a siege lasting a year and a half, finally captured Jerusalem. The city and Temple were destroyed by fire and Zedekiah was deported to Babylon with the bulk of the nation's leaders.

The kingdom of Judah, deprived of its proud Davidic dynasty and the last shred of political independence, was now absorbed into the provincial administration of the Babylonian empire and after the failure of the short-lived governorship of Gedaliah suffered the final indignity of rule from Samaria.

31–33. *Jehoahaz* (609), called by his personal name, Shallum, in Jer. 22¹⁰⁻¹², reigned for a mere three months after he had been established on the throne of his father, Josiah, by *the people of the land* (23³⁰; see notes on 2 Kgs. 22¹), in preference to his elder brother Eliakim (23³⁴). Evidently, he shared his father's policy, since he was summoned to the Egyptian headquarters at Riblah on the river Orontes and subsequently carried off prisoner to Egypt.

34–37. *Jehoiakim* (609–598), whom Jeremiah dismissed with such scathing contempt (Jer. 22¹³⁻¹⁹), owed his throne and his throne-name to Necho II. He remained subservient to Egypt until the Pharaoh was crushed by Babylon at the battle of Carchemish in 605 B.C. (cf. 24⁷).

24. 1. *Nebuchadnezzar* (605–562), whose name is more correctly given by Jeremiah as Nebuchadrezzar, having succeeded Nabopolassar as king of Babylon, advanced south to secure his position in the Philistine plain, and it was probably during this campaign that Jehoiakim became tributary to him. An Aramaic letter discovered at Saqqarah in Egypt in 1942, containing an appeal by a certain King Adon to the Pharaoh for aid against the advancing Babylonians, may well have been written to Necho II by a Philistine king during Nebuchadrezzar's campaign. In 601 B.C., after three years' vassalage, Jehoiakim was encouraged by an Egyptian victory over Nebuchadrezzar to take the fatal step of rebelling.

2. The guerrilla bands of *Chaldeans* (Babylonians), *Syrians* (probably a spelling mistake for Edomites), Moabites, and Ammonites, sent by Nebuchadrezzar to harass Judah, were the first rumbles of the storm to follow. The deuteronomic historian says they were sent *according to the word of the Lord*, because his central thesis is that Judah deserved her fate (cf. 24³, ⁴ and see pp. 67 ff.).

8–12. *Jehoiachin* (598–597), called Coniah in Jer. 22²⁴ (cf.

BABYLONIAN RECORD OF THE FIRST DEPORTATION FROM JERUSALEM. This clay cuneiform tablet (here reproduced actual size) was first published in 1956 and is one of a series known collectively as the 'Babylonian Chronicle'. The chronicle gives a reliable and probably contemporary account of the history of Babylon for most of the period from 626 to 539 B.C. The (reverse) side of the tablet shown in the photograph records Nebuchadrezzar's capture of Jerusalem and for the first time gives a fixed date for the event—16 March 597 B.C. Lines 11–13 (in the middle of the tablet) read: 'In the seventh year, in the month of Kislev [December 598 B.C.], the Babylonian king mustered his troops, and, having marched to the land of Hatti, besieged the city of Judah [Jerusalem], and on the second day of the month of Adar [16 March 597 B.C.] took the city and captured the king [Jehoiachin]. He appointed therein a king of his own choice [Zedekiah], received its heavy tribute and sent (them) to Babylon' (D. Winton Thomas, *Documents from Old Testament Times*, p. 80).

1 Chron. 3¹⁶), inherited an impossible situation when he succeeded his father on the throne. After three months, on 16 March
597 B.C., he surrendered to the Babylonians.

13, 14. These verses are a late and inaccurate addition,
although the Babylonian Chronicle records Judah's 'heavy
tribute' (fig. p. 128).

15, 16. The royal family (including the young king's *wives*!),
court officials, and leading citizens were deported to Babylon,
with 7,000 soldiers and 1,000 craftsmen of the guilds (cf. Jer.
24¹). Jer. 52²⁸ puts the figure at 3,023 (see p. 131).

17. *Zedekiah* (597–587) was the throne name given by the
Babylonians to Jehoiachin's uncle, *Mattaniah* (a third son of
Josiah; cf. 1 Chron. 3¹⁵), when they established him as their
vassal king for the last desperate decade of Judah's life.

20. *Zedekiah rebelled against the king of Babylon.* The final act of
rebellion in 588 B.C. was (as we learn from Jeremiah) the climax
of a period of hopeless vacillation. Zedekiah was under extreme
pressure from Judean nationalists, who were agitating for
outright revolt against Babylon and the release of the exiles of
the first deportation in 597 B.C. In 594 B.C., Jeremiah denounced
an attempt by the smaller powers—Edom, Moab, Ammon,
Tyre, and Sidon—to plan a concerted action with Judah
against Babylon (Jer. 27) and the false optimism of prophets
like Hananiah, who were encouraging resistance (Jer. 28–29;
see pp. 379 ff.). Zedekiah, who was obviously wavering (cf.
Jer. 37³⁻¹⁰, ¹⁷, 38¹⁴⁻²⁸), took the final and fatal step of rebellion
in collusion with Egypt, whose new king Hophra (588–569)
provoked Babylon by invading Phoenicia. Retribution followed
swiftly. It is to this period that the famous Lachish Letters
belong, 'when the army of the king of Babylon was fighting
against Jerusalem and against all the cities of Judah that were
left, Lachish and Azekah; for these were the only fortified
cities of Judah that remained' (Jer. 34⁷). The letters, written
on broken pieces of pottery, were for the most part addressed to
the military governor of Lachish, a Judean fortress south-west

of Jerusalem, by a subordinate officer in charge of an outpost.
Letter III records an expedition to Egypt by an army officer,
presumably to appeal for help against the Babylonians. Letter
IV reports that 'we are watching for the signals of Lachish,
according to all the signs which my lord hath given, for we cannot
see Azekah'; this reference confirms the use of fire signals at
this period (cf. Jer. 6¹) and suggests the possibility that Azekah
(twelve miles north-east of Lachish) had already fallen. Letter
VI protests against demoralizing communications from the
king and princes in Jerusalem which 'weaken the hands', as
Jeremiah's teaching was also said to have done (Jer. 38⁴). These
letters were found among ashes on the floor of a guard-room
in the city gate of Lachish—ashes which testify to the city's
destruction and the imminent doom of Jerusalem (D. Winton
Thomas, *Documents from Old Testament Times*, pp. 212–17).

25. 1–3. The siege of Jerusalem lasted nineteen months—from
the 10th day of the 10th month of Zedekiah's 9th year (January
588) to the 9th day of the 4th month of the king's 11th year (July
587). The city's long resistance was partly due to the intervention of the Egyptian army in 588 B.C., which forced the Babylonians temporarily to lift the siege (Jer. 37⁵). It is improbable
that Nebuchadrezzar troubled to be present in person (cf. 25⁶).

4–7. When Zedekiah saw that the city was being starved out
(25³; Lam. 4⁴, ⁵, ¹⁰) and its defences breached, he fled with
some of his troops through the southern *gate between the two walls*
(near the pool of Siloam; cf. Isa. 22¹¹) and made for the
Jordan valley. He was overtaken by the Babylonian forces near
Jericho and brought to *Riblah* in the far north, where Nebuchadrezzar had set up his headquarters (cf. 23³³). Having
suffered the torture of watching his sons being put to death, he
was then blinded and taken to Babylon, where, for the rest of
his life, he remained a prisoner (cf. Jer. 52¹¹).

8–12. The Temple, royal palace, and all the other houses in
Jerusalem were burnt down and its walls destroyed. In order
to reduce the city to impotence, the Babylonians deported all

the people who mattered and left only the peasants. Just how literally we should take these statements by the deuteronomic historian it is very difficult to say. Some scholars hold the view that Jerusalem remained important throughout the period of the Exile and suppose that it was the centre of considerable literary activity (including, for example, the composition of works like the Book of Lamentations and the compilation of 1 and 2 Kings). If such speculations are correct, others than the *poorest of the land* (v. 12) must have been allowed to remain. Population figures are even more speculative. It has been estimated that the population of Judah was 250,000 at the end of the eighth century and dropped to about 125,000 before the fall of the kingdom. Jer. 52^{28-30} gives the total number deported at 4,600. Even if one takes the higher figure of 8,000 given in 2 Kgs. 24^{16} for the deportation of 597 B.C. and makes a generous estimate for the second deportation, it is difficult to avoid the conclusion that there is still a great number of people to be accounted for.

13–17. A fuller inventory of Temple treasure carried off as loot to Babylon is given in Jer. 52^{17-23}. In v. 15, the expression *took away as gold . . . as silver* means that the vessels were melted down. The *two pillars* (v. 16) were the great free-standing bronze columns called 'Jachin' and 'Boaz' outside the door of Solomon's Temple (fig. p. 140; cf. 1 Kgs. 7^{15-22}). On the immense bronze basin called *the sea*, see notes on 2 Kgs. $16^{17, 18}$.

18–21. The death penalty was inflicted on selected representatives of three classes of Judean society—the priesthood, officers of state, and *the people of the land* (see notes on 2 Kgs. 22^1). *So Judah was taken into exile out of its land* was probably the concluding sentence of the original book.

22–26. This appendix is a summary account of the ill-fated governorship of Gedaliah drawn from the first-hand description in Jer. 40^7–43^7. *Gedaliah the son of Ahikam* was a member of the distinguished family of Shaphan (see notes on 2 Kgs. 22^3) and, therefore, a supporter of Jeremiah (Jer. 39^{14}, 40^6; cf. 26^{24}). As a conciliatory Jew of moderate views (v. 24; cf. Jer. $40^{9, 10}$),

Nebuchadrezzar diplomatically appointed him governor of Judea and he set up his administrative headquarters at *Mizpah*, some nine miles north of Jerusalem. This promising experiment was shattered by *Ishmael*, a fanatical member of the exiled royal house, who led a nationalist plot and assassinated Gedaliah and some of his immediate associates. The rest, fearing Babylonian reprisals, fled to Egypt. A seal impression from a papyrus document, bearing the inscription '(Belonging) to Gedaliah who is over the household', was unearthed at Lachish in 1935 and is now generally ascribed to the governor of Judea.

27–30. This second appendix records the favoured treatment given to Jehoiachin in 561 B.C. by *Evil-Merodach* (Amel-Marduk), when he succeeded his father Nebuchadrezzar as king of Babylon. It was probably added as a happy ending to the book by one who pinned his hopes on Jehoiachin as the only surviving king of the house of David. The statement that Evil-Merodach *gave him a seat above the seats of the kings who were with him in Babylon* doubtlessly owes less to history than to the conviction that the supremacy of the Jew must, of necessity, be acknowledged even by Gentile kings (cf. Gen. 41[39–43]; Dan. 2[48]; Isa. 60[3]). The nationalistic fervour of which Jehoiachin was the centre is illustrated by Hananiah's prediction of his return from exile (Jer. 28[4]) and by the dating of oracles in the book of Ezekiel from the time of his deportation (Ezek. 1[2]). Three recently excavated copies of a seal impression, bearing the inscription 'Belonging to Eliakim steward of Jehoiachin', may indicate that the king was still regarded as the rightful owner of crown property even in the reign of Zedekiah. There is one further piece of archaeological evidence. A number of tablets unearthed in Babylon in a room connected with the palace and dating from 595 to 570 B.C. record the rations of oil and barley given to prisoners. Among them were Jehoiachin, king of Judah, and his five sons. The tablets thus confirm the king's imprisonment and throw a little light on the restrictions from which this attractive little tailpiece claims the royal family was eventually rescued.

III. WORSHIP

No study of the kingdoms of Israel and Judah would be complete which failed to take into account the most explicit expression of their culture and religious belief, namely, their approach to God in worship. It is easy to overlook this fundamental part of Israel's life in the period of the monarchy for a number of obvious reasons. First, worship was everywhere taken for granted and therefore not deliberately described or recorded by the historians. Second, worship in ancient Israel was primarily an action or drama in which words were of secondary importance. Third, the bulk of the priestly regulations for worship come in their present form from the post-exilic period. Finally, in this as in other periods, we are inevitably ill informed both about the private piety of the people and about their personal understanding of public worship, although these factors obviously played a vital part in preserving the heritage of Israel and in making it the historical phenomenon it was. Within these limitations, however, and with the illumination provided by recent study of the psalms, it is possible to gain some impression of the importance of worship in the life of the divided monarchy.

(i) *Worship at the local sanctuaries*

Until Josiah's reformation in the last days of Judah, most Israelites worshipped at their local sanctuary or 'high place', where their Canaanite predecessors in the land had worshipped before them (1 Sam. 9$^{11-25}$). Recent excavations of these Canaanite sanctuaries have revealed a large number of burial monuments and a greater link with funerary rites than is suggested by the Old Testament evidence and so it is possible that Israelite high places were also cemeteries and centres for the cult of the dead. The feature of worship at the high places

A CANAANITE PROTOTYPE OF SOLOMON'S TEMPLE. This thirteenth-century temple, excavated at Hazor in 1957, is the only prototype of Solomon's Temple so far discovered in Palestine (see Y. Yadin, *Israel Exploration Journal*, vol. 8, no. 1 (1958), pp. 11–14; vol. 9, no. 2 (1959), pp. 81–84). As the photograph illustrates, the plan of the building (some 80 ft. long and 56 ft. wide) is the same as that of Solomon's, with three interconnecting chambers: a porch (top right), a central hall or 'holy place', and a 'holy of holies' (centre). The bases of two round pillars were found in the porch on either side of the doorway leading to the central hall (cf. fig. p. 140). A unique feature of the building is the use of carefully dressed stone slabs 5 ft. long, which were laid on the rubble and (as drilled holes for wooden pegs indicate) used for supporting wooden beams at the base of the wall above. The central hall once had a tower on its west side (right in the photograph) and the discovery of the remains of hinges establishes that there was a door between the central hall and the 'holy of holies'. When the photograph was taken the site had been cleared of the ritual objects which were found at this level; they included a stone incense-altar engraved with the Canaanite emblem of the sun-god, offering tables, bronze figurines of a god, a goddess and a bull, together with a stone statue of a god bearing the sun-disc emblem and (apparently) mounted on a bull (cf. fig. p. 74). Further excavation has disclosed that this Canaanite temple was the last of four erected on the site.

which drew the fire of the prophets and the condemnation of deuteronomists was not, however, necromancy, but its connexion with fertility rituals and the cult of Baal (see pp. 44–48). To these, the sacred stone pillars, representative of the male deity (2 Kgs. 3²), and the Asherim, wooden symbols of the

goddess Asherah, bear unmistakable witness (Jer. 17²; 1 Kgs.
14²³). The larger local sanctuaries, like Shiloh, were also
equipped with buildings (1 Sam. 1⁹; cf. 9²²), but the essential
feature of every sanctuary was its altar (fig. p. 198), which in
Hebrew means simply the 'place of sacrifice' (Exod. 20²⁴⁻²⁶).

All Israelite worship was directly or indirectly sacrificial
and most of the ritual of sacrifice (although not necessarily its
interpretation) was taken over from the 'liturgical use' of the
sanctuaries at the time when they served the indigenous
Canaanite agricultural community (fig. p. 134). To the evidence
of the Old Testament (1 Kgs. 18²⁶⁻²⁹; 2 Kgs. 10¹⁸⁻²⁷) and a
small number of Carthaginian inscriptions for this ancient
Canaanite sacrificial ritual, we may now add that of the Ras
Shamra texts (see pp. 27 f.). These documents use terms comparable to those of the Old Testament for the two principal
types of sacrifice in pre-exilic Israel and include, by chance, an
illuminating description of a burnt offering made by King
Keret. It reads:

> He washed and reddled himself, he washed his hands to the forearms,
> his fingers up to the shoulder; he did enter the shade of the tent (and)
> did take a sacrificial lamb in his hand, a young beast in them both,
> (and) all that was left of his bread-corn, he did take the entrails (?) of
> a sacrificial bird, he did pour wine into a vessel of silver, honey into
> a vessel of gold; and he did go up on to the tower, he did mount the
> shoulder of the wall; he did lift up his hands to heaven, he did sacrifice
> to the bull El his father, did make Baal to come down with his sacri-
> fice, Dagon's son with his (offering of) game. (G. R. Driver, *Canaanite
> Myths and Legends*, p. 33.)

It is in offerings like this that the closest connexion between
Israelite and Canaanite practice is to be found—sacrifices
partially or totally burnt on the altar. They are quite unknown
in Arabia or Mesopotamia but constitute the basis of all Hebrew
sacrificial worship.

These two main types of sacrifice are called the peace offering and the burnt offering (1 Sam. 13⁹). In the *peace offering*,
which is sometimes called simply 'sacrifice' (Amos 4⁴; Jer. 7²¹),
an ox, sheep, or goat was slaughtered by the offerer, its blood

poured over the base of the altar, the fat parts of its intestines burnt on the altar, and the rest of its flesh cut up, boiled, and eaten by the worshippers in a communal meal at the sanctuary (1 Sam. 9^{22-24}, $14^{34, 35}$). No priest was required for the rite, but the evidence suggests that the priest-in-charge of the sanctuary was usually given a payment in kind (cf. 1 Sam. 2^{13-16}; Deut. 18^3). The peace offering was the commonest kind of sacrifice at the local sanctuaries, when the worshippers gathered to celebrate and 'eat before the Lord' (cf. Deut. 12^7). The essence of the rite was not the slaughter of the animal, or the pouring of its blood, but the subsequent communion meal, by which the participants renewed their covenant with God and with each other. In the other main sacrifice, the *burnt offering*, there was no meal and the whole of the victim went up in smoke (cf. Gen. $8^{20, 21}$; Exod. 29^{18}). The fundamental idea embodied here is that of a gift to God and its associations are less carefree than those of the peace offering; it was essentially an act of homage and petition, rather than a renewal of communion and covenant. In the post-exilic period, the burnt offering developed into two further kinds of sacrifice, of which the explicit purpose was the removal of defilement (the sin offering and the guilt offering), but it is highly probable that, even before the Exile, penitence, forgiveness, and restoration to God's favour had their place among the complex and mixed motives of all sacrificial practice (1 Sam. 3^{14}; 2 Sam. 24^{25}; Mic. $6^{6, 7}$).

Since sacrifice had been adopted by the Israelites as *the* way in which they approached God in worship, the intentions underlying their offerings must have been as various as the occasions on which they went to the sanctuary—ranging over the whole gamut of joys, fears, needs, crises, and disasters, to which individuals, families, and communities are subject. Moreover, their understanding of what they were doing in offering sacrifice must have covered the whole scale of religious awareness, from the crudely superstitious to the genuinely spiritual. Since thanksgiving is, perhaps, one of the least ambiguous forms of man's religious activity, it is illuminating to find that the Old Testament has special terms for sacrifices

made as thank-offerings (Amos 4⁵; 2 Sam. 6¹², ¹³) and freewill-
offerings (Deut. 12¹⁷), both of which expressed the worshipper's
spontaneous gratitude for God's goodness. It is also significant
that these spontaneous sacrifices puzzled the priestly systema-
tizers in the post-exilic period (cf. Lev. 22²³). From the information we possess, it seems reasonable to conclude that
although most of Israel's sacrificial ritual was borrowed from
the Canaanites and, therefore, alien to Mosaic Yahwism (Jer.
7²²; see p. 314), it could be and was more or less adapted
for the worship of Yahweh, when the Israelites settled in
Palestine and became agriculturists.

The closest connexion between agriculture and worship is to
be seen in the three great annual festivals which were celebrated
at the local sanctuaries during the period of the monarchy: the
Feast of Unleavened Bread, the Feast of Weeks, and the Feast
of Ingathering (Exod. 23¹⁴⁻¹⁷). *The Feast of Unleavened Bread* was
in origin a Canaanite agricultural festival, held in the spring at
the beginning of the barley harvest. It lasted seven days, during
which the first-fruits of the new crop were presented at the
sanctuary (cf. the later regulations of Lev. 23⁹⁻¹⁴) and (to mark
a new beginning) only bread from the new grain was eaten and
this was baked without the use of any of the old dough as
leaven. *The Feast of Weeks*, also in origin Canaanite, was taken
over as a one-day festival of wheat harvest (Exod. 34²²) and
celebrated seven weeks after the Feast of Unleavened Bread
(Deut. 16⁹, ¹⁰), when the new grain and loaves of ordinary (i.e.
leavened) bread were offered at the sanctuary (cf. Lev. 23¹⁵⁻²¹).
The Feast of Ingathering, which was later called the Feast of
Booths (Deut. 16¹³), was the last and greatest feast of the agricultural year and is sometimes referred to simply as *the* feast
(1 Kgs. 8²; Hos. 9⁵; Ezek. 45²⁵). This was the harvest festival
par excellence, when the Israelite farming community, following
Canaanite precedent, took a week's holiday in the orchards
and vineyards, where they slept in huts made of branches
('booths'), and with the new wine flowing freely had a good
old time (cf. Judg. 9²⁷, 21¹⁹⁻²¹; 1 Sam. 1¹⁴, ¹⁵).

In their basic form, all three of these annual festivals suggest

a great deal of Canaanite fertility religion, little of worship, and
nothing of Mosaic Yahwism. If Israelite feasts were to be
authentically Yahwist, it was essential that they should celebrate not only, or even primarily, the goodness of God in giving
his people the fruits of the earth, but the goodness of God in
delivering their ancestors out of Egypt and in making them a
people bound to himself in a unique covenant relationship.
Yahweh was the God of history, who acted through people and
peoples, and not merely another god of nature who when
activated by religious rites caused the crops to grow. The
strength of this distinctive conviction is nowhere better illustrated than in Israel's historical reinterpretation of the Feast
of Unleavened Bread, which was effected by combining it with
the *Feast of the Passover*. In origin, the Feast of the Passover was
a rite of semi-nomadic shepherd life. It was celebrated in the
spring by the slaughter of a lamb, with the purpose of protecting the flock from malign influences (Exod. 5^1, 10^9). It had no
connexion with sanctuary, altar, or priest and throughout a long
and complex development retained features of its primitive
family character (cf. Deut. 16^3; Exod. $12^{3,\ 4}$; Mark 14^{12-16}).
The roots of the Passover are in Arabian as distinct from Canaanite sacrificial practice and this clearly made it easier for
Yahwism to reinterpret it at an early date as a commemoration
of Israel's deliverance from Egypt (Exod. 12^{21-27}). Since it was
celebrated at the same time of the year as the Feast of Unleavened Bread, the two were eventually combined (Deut.
16^{1-8}; Exod. 12^{1-20}; Ezek. 45^{21-25}; see notes on 2 Kgs. 23^{21-23}).
Although by this means the Passover was brought into the
sphere of the sanctuary and a quite different kind of sacrificial
practice, the Feast of Unleavened Bread was also brought into
the tradition of Israel's distinctive Mosaic faith.

The Feast of Weeks never won the popularity of the other
two major festivals, perhaps because, as its later title, 'Day of
First Fruits' (Num. 28^{26}), suggests, it got lost among the many
individual offerings of first fruits which continued throughout
the summer months. A version of the ceremony for the individual presentation of first fruits is given in Deut. 26^{1-11} and,

characteristically, has at its centre an ancient recital of
Yahweh's great deliverance of his people before he gave them
the land. Once again, we see the history-based faith of Israel
accomplishing a take-over from the old Canaanite sphere of
influence and affirming that it was Yahweh and not Baal 'who
gave her the grain, the wine, and the oil' (Hos. 2⁸).

The Feast of Ingathering, the final celebration at the end of
the agricultural year, was similarly given a basis in the events
of the Exodus. The holiday huts improvised in the vineyards
for the local harvest festival were imitated in Jerusalem after
the Exile (Neh. 8¹³⁻¹⁸) and interpreted in terms far removed
from their original meaning—'that your generations may know
that I made the people of Israel dwell in booths when I brought
them out of the land of Egypt' (Lev. 23⁴³). To judge by the
torchlight dances and the water-libations of the feast in New
Testament times, the attempt to associate it with the Exodus
failed completely. It is now thought, however, that there was
an earlier and more successful attempt to reinterpret this
autumn festival and that throughout the period of the monarchy it dominated the worship of the Temple in Jerusalem
(see pp. 147 f.).

(ii) *Worship at the Temple*

It is fairly obvious on general grounds that the worship of
the Temple in Jerusalem must have been very different from
the worship of the local sanctuaries. Whereas the local sanctuaries went their own way (for better or for worse) with the
very minimum of organization and supervision, the Temple
was under the direct patronage and control of the king. This
meant, as we shall see, that its worship, like its architecture,
had not only to reflect the wealth and pretentious splendour of
the court, but also to serve, in ways which are hard for modern
Western minds to grasp, the religious character of the king's rule.

The Psalms of the Temple

A quite new understanding of the impact of the monarchy on
worship has been gained in recent years from a fresh approach

SOLOMON'S TEMPLE. The photograph reproduces the reconstruction of Solomon's Temple drawn in 1955 by C. F. Stevens from specifications supplied by W. F. Albright and G. E. Wright on the basis of biblical data and archaeological analogies. Solomon's Temple lies engulfed beneath that of Herod and there is no chance that excavation can unearth it. Designed by a Phoenician architect and built of local white limestone and cedar, the structure was much smaller than most people tend to suppose, the inside measurements being about 100 ft. long, 34 ft. wide, and 50 ft. high. Like the Canaanite temple at Hazor (see fig. p. 134), it was divided into three chambers standing one behind the other in a straight line: a porch at the front (east end) 17 ft. long, a 'holy place' (or central hall for worship) 76 ft. long, and a 'holy of holies' at the back (west end), which was a perfect cube of 34 ft., approached by a flight of stairs and reserved exclusively for Yahweh. The two free-standing hollow bronze pillars in front of the building were about 40 ft. high and 20 ft. in circumference and bore the cryptic names 'Jachin' and 'Boaz' (cf. 1 Kgs. 7¹³⁻²²); the Phoenician cressets, however, shown on top of the columns are uncertain. The decorated double doors in the drawing are supposed to be at the entrance of the 'holy place'; the porch was without doors. The side-chambers (used for storage), running round three sides of the building, are shown with a door on the south side near the front. Egyptian slanting light-openings and the same crenellated parapet as decorates the main roof. This architectural style is based on the battlements found in Solomon's Megiddo (see fig. p. 31), but its appropriateness here has been questioned. Doubt has also been expressed about the platform on which the building is represented as standing.

to the Psalter. Half a century ago, students of the psalms expended most of their energies in trying to date the individual poems on internal evidence and (to risk a broad generalization) they concluded that the Psalter was a product of the post-exilic period—the 'Hymn Book of the Second Temple'. It is now believed that this is only half the truth and that the Psalter was the hymn book of the Second Temple only because much of it was derived from the 'Prayer Book' of Solomon's Temple (fig. p. 140). It is thought, that is to say, that many of the psalms as we now have them from the post-exilic period were either modelled on, or directly taken over from, the prayers which accompanied public liturgical worship in the period of the monarchy. This view is based on the conclusion that the psalms fall into a number of distinctive types or forms, which may be directly related to the liturgical setting for which they were originally composed.

The most immediately convincing demonstration of the close connexion of the psalms with the actual action of the liturgy is provided by those pieces which for no apparent reason suddenly change towards the end, most often from a prayer of petition to an outburst of confident thanksgiving (Pss. 6^8, 12^6, 13^5, 22^{22}, 28^6, 94^{17}, 140^{12}; see notes on Ps. 20). The explanation most probably lies in something which the congregation had just seen or heard, such as a reassuring gesture or pronouncement given by a priest or Temple prophet (cf. Ps. 12^5; see p. 234). This feature is most characteristic of the type of psalm called the *Individual Lament*, in which a man who is sick, or suffering from the malice of enemies, appeals to Yahweh for deliverance (e.g. Pss. 3, 6, 7, 13, 22, 28, 51, 102, 109, 120, 130, 140; see notes on Ps. 5). Closely related in type is the *Communal Lament*, in which the congregation, recalling Yahweh's help in ages past, prays to be delivered from some public calamity such as famine or enemy invasion (e.g. Pss. 44, 74, 79; see notes on Ps. 80). There are corresponding types of thanksgiving—the *Individual Thanksgiving*, in which the worshipper invites the assembled congregation to share his gratitude (e.g. Pss. 18, 30, 32, 92), and the *Communal Thanksgiving* (e.g. Pss. 66, 118, 124), although it is uncertain whether the Psalter contains examples of either from the period of the monarchy. There is, in addition, the large, loose category called simply *Hymns*, in which Yahweh is praised for his power and goodness in history and in the order of creation (e.g. Pss. 46, 95–100, 145–50; see notes on Pss. 29, 47, 48, 84).

Among these five types, special interest attaches to the psalms which are focused on the king, as, for example, when he celebrates his enthronement (Pss. 2, 101, 110), or his wedding (Ps. 45), or offers sacrifice before and after battle (Pss. 20, 21; cf. Pss. 18, 89, 118, 144; and see notes on Pss. 2, 20, 72, 132). The preservation and continued use of these royal psalms after the end of the monarchy illustrates the extraordinary conservatism of Israelite (like other) liturgical tradition. The Hebrews, it would seem, never used waste-paper baskets. One important consequence of their reluctance to throw away and start from scratch and their marked preference for retaining, amplifying, and reinterpreting old material is that we cannnot always be certain that the worshippers at any given period were actually engaged in the liturgical actions which the words of their psalms suggest. We know as a matter of fact that the Jews who sang the enthronement psalms in the Second Temple were not then enthroning a king and so, by analogy, we cannot know as a matter of fact that worshippers before the Exile were actually engaged in the various kinds of ritual drama with which the language of their psalms seems to show a connexion. For example, when the psalmist speaks of the faithful singing for joy on their couches with 'two-edged swords in their hands' (Ps. 149$^{5-9}$), it would be unwise to suppose that we have here any reliable evidence for reconstructing their ritual actions. We must certainly take the liturgical language of the psalms seriously, but if we take it too literally, we run the risk of foisting on the people of Jerusalem artificially reconstructed rituals of which they may have known nothing more than a few widely current clichés.

The King and the Temple

From the famous incident when Amos was told by Amaziah to get out and go home, we learn that in Israel, as in Judah, there was an intimate connexion between king and temple: 'Never again prophesy at Bethel, for it is the king's sanctuary, and it is a temple of the kingdom' (Amos 7^{13}). This is one of the few fragments of information we possess about a northern counterpart to the situation in the southern kingdom. After the disruption, Jeroboam I established the sanctuaries of Dan and Bethel to counteract the spell exercised by Jerusalem and inaugurated or revived there the Feast of Ingathering (see notes on 1 Kgs. 12^{28-33}). At this point, Dan virtually disappears from history and Bethel emerges later only occasionally (cf. Amos 4^4, 5^5; 2 Kgs. 17^{28}, 23^{15}). If Ps. 45 was written for the marriage of Ahab and Jezebel (cf. vv. 8, 12) and if, as is more nearly certain, Pss. 80 and 81 are Israelite rather than Judean (see notes on Ps. 80), it is reasonable to suppose that, as in Jerusalem, the principal northern sanctuaries had elaborated their worship (cf. Amos 5^{21-24}; Hos. 4^{15}) and that (perhaps especially in Samaria during the dynasty of Omri) it was closely connected with the king. The general evidence, however, points to the conclusion that worship in Israel was never so centrally controlled as it was in Judah and that, in consequence, it could degenerate to the extremes of Baalism (see notes on 1 Kgs. 16^{32-34}), on the one hand, and retain, on the other hand, its anchorage in a traditional form of Mosaic Yahwism, which was quite uncontaminated by the royal cult (see pp. 49 f.).

In Judah, the position is less in doubt. David and Solomon had adopted the kind of kingship to which the Temple and its cult were an unquestionable necessity. Although the king in Jerusalem was never (like the Pharaohs of Egypt) worshipped as a god (cf. Ps. $89^{26, \; 27}$ and note that Ps. 45^6 should probably be translated, 'Thy throne is eternal *like* that of God'), he is, nevertheless, described in terms which set him in the closest relation to Yahweh and accord him a status which transcends

that of any other human being. He is Yahweh's 'son' by
adoption (see notes on Ps. 2[7]), endowed with superabundant
life (Pss. 21[4, 5], 72[5]), and 'like the angel of God to discern good
and evil' (2 Sam. 14[17, 20]). He is Yahweh's chosen and anointed
servant (Pss. 45[7], 89[19, 20], 132[10]; see notes on Ps. 2[2]), sitting at
Yahweh's right hand and sharing his sovereignty (Ps. 110[1]).
Ruling from 'the throne of the Lord as king' (1 Chron. 29[23]),
he is the very breath of life to his people (Lam. 4[20]) and upon
his success and righteousness they utterly depend (see notes on
Pss. 20, 72).

The king's authority and significance extended far beyond
the political realm. The Temple is the king's sanctuary: he
builds it, dedicates it, refurnishes it, and reforms it (1 Kgs. 5–8;
2 Kgs. 16[10-18], 18[4], 23[4-14]); he appoints its priests as his own
servants and controls their work (2 Sam. 8[17], 20[25]; 1 Kgs. 2[26, 27],
4[2]). Moreover, the king himself exercises a priestly office in the
Temple cult. Saul, David, Solomon, Jeroboam, and Ahaz are
all recorded as having offered sacrifice (1 Sam. 13[9]; 2 Sam.
6[17-19]; 1 Kgs. 3[4], 8[5, 62-64], 9[25], 13[1]; 2 Kgs. 16[12-16]). David,
wearing the priestly ephod, 'danced before the Lord with all
his might' (2 Sam. 6[14]), when the Ark was brought up to Jerusalem, and (as the liturgical character of this account suggests)
it is unlikely that he was the last king to do so (see notes on
Ps. 132). In Ps. 110[4], it is roundly declared that the king is 'a
priest for ever after the order of Melchizedek', Melchizedek
being the ancient priest-king of Jerusalem in the days when it
was still a Canaanite city-state (Gen. 14[18-20]; see p. 156).

The association of the king with 'the order of Melchizedek'

SACRAL KINGSHIP. This white limestone statue of Shalmaneser III (859–
824), standing some 5¾ ft. high, was reconstructed from fragments discovered
in 1956 at Nimrud, where, probably, it originally stood in the temple of
Ninurta. As high priest of this ancient Sumerian god, the Assyrian king wears
the high knobbed and tasselled turban appropriate to his sacral office; his
hands are clasped and his feet bare. A feature of the statue is the inscription
of over 200 lines on the front, back, and sides of the figure. It includes a
record of the king's campaigns which enables the monument to be dated in
836 or 827 B.C.

greatly illuminates the rejection of the priest Abiathar in favour of the priest Zadok, after Jerusalem became the sanctuary of the kingdom (1 Kgs. 2²⁶, ²⁷, ³⁵; cf. 1 Sam. 2²⁷⁻³⁶). It is probable that Zadok, whose origins are unknown and whose name connects him with Melchi*zedek* and Adoni-*zedek*, a later king of pre-Israelite Jerusalem (Josh. 10¹, ³, *Zedek* probably being the name of one of the city's gods), was formerly priest of the Canaanite sanctuary of Jerusalem and simply retained his office when David captured the city. Zadok was certainly one of Solomon's loyal supporters and his descendants kept the priesthood throughout the period of the monarchy. It is possible, therefore, that the worship of the Temple was ordered by a priesthood of Canaanite origin and this would explain much, including Jeremiah's vigorous condemnation of it (see notes on Jer. 7¹⁻²⁶ and Ps. 47).

The Psalter leaves us in no doubt, however, that the Temple and its worship won the deep devotion of the people and this must be remembered alongside its questionable Canaanite character (Pss. 42–43, 46, 47, 87, 122; see notes on Pss. 48, 84). It is, indeed, highly probable that the splendour, the music, and the *mystique* of a Canaanite-type cult satisfied the majority of the people more easily and immediately than the austere, image-less faith of Mosaic Yahwism. Nevertheless, its popularity and its power to inculcate profound religious devotion cannot be taken to mean that it was necessarily an authentic response to Yahweh of Israel, who revealed himself in history not merely to start a new religion, but to inaugurate a wholly new way of knowing and serving God in a world which was already religious enough. The distinctive tradition of Yahweh's self-revelation was not, however, obliterated by the royal theology and cult of Jerusalem. The 'men of Judah' are not simply to be identified with 'the inhabitants of Jerusalem' (Isa. 5³; Jer. 11²; cf. Isa. 1¹). In Judah, outside the capital, Amos and Micah were clearly nurtured on the insights of Mosaic Yahwism and even in Jerusalem itself Isaiah and Jeremiah stood apart from the official theology and vigorously repudiated it. It is clear, therefore, that the psalms and worship of the Temple were by no means fully representative, although what they did represent had by its very nature a popular appeal and staying power which prophecy never possessed.

Festivals in the Temple

The Psalter is singularly uninformative about the use of its contents in relation to the great festivals. The two psalms in which the word 'feast' is actually mentioned refer only to the liturgical use of trumpets and a festal procession (Pss. 81[2, 3], 118[19, 20, 26, 27]). Ps. 68 gives more detail of the proceedings—

> Thy solemn processions are seen, O God,
>   the processions of my God, my King,
>   into the sanctuary—
>   the singers in front, the minstrels last,
>   between them maidens playing timbrels

(vv. 24, 25)—

but there is no explicit indication that it belongs (as many scholars think) to the autumn Feast of Ingathering. It is to this feast, however, that we may ascribe with less hesitation the two straight harvest hymns (Pss. 65, 67) and the two psalms which are most obviously intended to accompany the carrying of the Ark in solemn procession (Pss. 24, 132). These clearly belong to the Temple festival reflected in 2 Sam. 6 and 1 Kgs. 8 and this is described as the Feast of Ingathering (1 Kgs. 8[2]).

The fact that the Feast of Ingathering was held in the autumn at the end of one year (Exod. 34[22]) and the beginning of the next (Exod. 23[16], where 'going out' means 'rising' as in Judg. 5[31]), and the fact that it was connected, as we have seen, with the Ark and the dedication of the Temple, have led to a proliferation of ingenious attempts to give a fuller account of what was undoubtedly the main festival of the year. These theoretical reconstructions draw their material principally from the rites of the Babylonian New Year Festival, the Ras Shamra texts, and *motifs* recurrent in the psalms themselves, as the many and confusing names which scholars have given to this single autumnal celebration—'New Year Festival', 'Covenant

Festival', 'Enthronement Festival'—plainly indicate. For the simple reason that the continued use of liturgical language need not imply the actual performance of the liturgical action to which it originally belonged, reconstructions of the Temple ritual for the Feast of Ingathering are inevitably speculative and, in consequence, diverse and conflicting. Nor is there any good reason for thinking that each of the many dominant *motifs* of the Psalter points either to a separate feast in the Temple, or to a distinct feature of the great seven-day autumnal festival.

In view of the nature of our evidence, it is probably more illuminating, as it is certainly more prudent, to concentrate on the main themes which occupied the thoughts of the worshippers as they sang the psalms in the pre-exilic Temple, and to leave open the questions of what they were doing at the time and when exactly that time was.

The dominant belief of the Temple worshippers and their basic reason for making pilgrimages to it was that Yahweh lived there. The Temple was his house, the home of the Ark, 'a place for thee to dwell in for ever' (1 Kgs. 8¹³; see notes on Pss. 84¹, 132¹). It would be an error to interpret the many references to Yahweh's dwelling in the Temple as mere poetic metaphor. When Hezekiah received a threatening letter from the Assyrians, he 'went up to the house of the Lord, and spread it before the Lord' (2 Kgs. 19¹⁴); the psalmist goes to the Temple 'to behold the beauty of the Lord' (Ps. 27⁴); and it is this well-established piety which the deuteronomist is questioning, when he asks, 'But will God indeed dwell on the earth? Behold, heaven and the highest heaven cannot contain thee; how much less this house which I have built!' (1 Kgs. 8²⁷; see p. 220).

Inevitably and inextricably bound up with Yahweh's dwelling in the Temple are the glory and inviolable security of Zion. The so-called 'doctrine of the inviolability of Jerusalem' is not derived (as is often suggested) from the experience and teaching of Isaiah, but from the old Canaanite tradition of Jerusalem as 'the city of God, the holy habitation of 'El 'Elyôn' (Ps. 46⁴, ⁵; see notes on Pss. 47, 48). The Israelite reinterpretation of this ancient idea is succinctly presented in Ps. 132¹³, ¹⁴:

> For the Lord has chosen Zion;
>> he has desired it for his habitation:
> 'This is my resting place for ever;
>> here I will dwell, for I have desired it.'

As the preceding and following verses of this psalm illustrate, Yahweh's choice of Jerusalem (Pss. 68¹⁶, 76²; see notes on Pss. 48, 132) is inseparably connected with Yahweh's choice of David and his dynasty (Pss. 2⁶, 78⁶⁷⁻⁷²). David, in historical fact, chose Jerusalem; according to the 'royal theology' of the Temple, Yahweh chose both. The emphasis on Yahweh's covenant with David meant that the old covenant tradition of the Exodus was forced into the background (cf. Pss. 80⁸, 81¹⁰, probably from the *northern* kingdom) and either forgotten or represented as being merely the preparation for the Davidic covenant (Pss. 21⁷, 68⁷⁻¹⁰, ¹⁵, ¹⁶, 89²⁴, ²⁸⁻³⁷; cf. 2 Sam. 7⁴⁻¹⁷; Ps. 78). This new 'royal theology', which meant, in effect, that God was primarily thought of in connexion with the king, virtually displaced the old Mosaic Yahwism in Jerusalem, until it was vigorously reaffirmed by Jeremiah, Josiah, and the deuteronomists (see pp. 51–55).

If those who worshipped in the Temple were much occupied with the beneficent rule of the earthly king as Yahweh's Anointed Son (see notes on Pss. 2, 72, 132), it is not surprising that their praises should also have celebrated the kingly rule of Yahweh himself. The idea that Yahweh reigned as King in Zion must have been taken over from the Canaanite tradition of Jerusalem in the very early days of the monarchy (see notes on Ps. 48²), although there is little good evidence for it outside the Psalter before Isaiah, who saw 'the Lord sitting upon a throne, high and lifted up . . . the King, the Lord of hosts' (Isa. 6¹⁻⁵; cf. Num. 23²¹; Deut. 33⁵; 1 Sam. 8⁷; 1 Kgs. 22¹⁹; Jer. 3¹⁶, ¹⁷, 14²¹). The psalms leave us in no doubt, however, that the worshippers of the pre-exilic Temple addressed Yahweh as 'my King and my God' (Pss. 5², 24⁷⁻¹⁰, 84³, 149²) and a group of six psalms (often referred to as the 'Enthronement Psalms') have Yahweh's kingship as their dominant theme (Pss. 47, 93, 96, 97, 98, 99; see notes on Ps. 47).

Since the earthly ruler sits at Yahweh's right hand and shares his sovereignty (Ps. 110¹), it is not surprising that psalms about the Davidic king and psalms about Yahweh as King have many themes in common. In both groups, there is great stress on sovereignty over the nations and sovereignty over the natural order. Just as the rule of the Davidic king was thought of as the people's security against enemies and against famine (see notes on Ps. 72), so Yahweh himself is praised because he 'reigns over the nations' (Ps. 47⁸) and, sitting 'enthroned over the flood', gives his people the fruits of a stable and regular natural order (Ps. 93; see notes on Ps. 29). This means, in effect, that good harvests depend upon the good government of Yahweh— the King who in the beginning created order out of chaos. The surprising association between sovereignty over the nations and sovereignty over nature and the even more surprising ascription of both to the ruling monarch make it plain that the Jerusalem tradition was drawing on widely current ideas of divine kingship, which in Babylon formed the main content of the New Year Festival. In the Exile, the 'royal theology' of the Babylonian Festival entered deeply into Second Isaiah's presentation of Yahweh's sovereignty in the New Creation (Isa. 40⁹⁻¹⁷, 43¹⁵⁻²¹, 51⁹⁻¹¹, 52⁷) and many centuries later these twin New Year concepts of Kingship and Creation were still associated with the worship of Yahweh at the autumnal festival in Jerusalem: 'Then every one that survives of all the nations that have come against Jerusalem shall go up year after year to worship the King, the Lord of hosts, and to keep the feast of booths. And if any of the families of the earth do not go up to Jerusalem to worship the King, the Lord of hosts, there will be no rain upon them' (Zech. 14¹⁶, ¹⁷). Whether or not these associations justify the claim that the pre-exilic Feast of Ingathering was, in fact, an Israelite form of New Year Festival and should be called by that name is an unanswerable and relatively uninteresting question.

2 *A hymn for the king's coronation*

The psalm was composed, like Ps. 110, for the coronation of a Davidic king in Jerusalem. It probably continued to be used on the official anniversary of the king's accession throughout the period of the monarchy and subsequently it was reinterpreted as a prophecy of the Coming Messiah. This later development, in view of the contents of the poem, was altogether lamentable and thoroughly misleading. We know the original setting of the hymn from two accounts of the coronation ceremony in 1 Kgs. 1³²⁻⁴⁸ and 2 Kgs. 11¹²⁻²⁰. It consisted of the investiture with the royal insignia, including the crown and the testimony (cf. 'decree' in v. 7), the anointing (v. 2), the acclamation and homage (vv. 10, 11), and, finally (in the palace), the enthronement. The *motif* of the rebellion of the nations (vv. 1–3) is probably borrowed from foreign coronation rites (see notes on Ps. 72⁸⁻¹¹), but it is impossible to say whether it was actually enacted as a ritual drama in the Temple, like, for example, the sham fight which accompanied the crowning of a king in Egypt.

1–3. *The kings of the nations in rebellion against Yahweh and his anointed king.*

2. *his anointed.* The anointing of kings is mentioned from the beginning of the monarchy (1 Kgs. 1³⁹; 2 Kgs. 11¹²; cf. 1 Sam. 9¹⁶, 10¹; 2 Sam. 2⁴, 5³) and in the early days it was associated with the gift of the Spirit (1 Sam. 16¹³; see pp. 3 f.). As the Anointed of Yahweh (Lam. 4²⁰; Pss. 18⁵⁰, 20⁶, 84⁹, 89³⁸, ⁵¹, 132¹⁰), the person of the king was sacrosanct (1 Sam. 24⁶, ¹⁰, 26⁹, ¹¹, ²³). The word translated 'anointed' is *māshîaḥ*, from which by transliteration the title 'Messiah' is derived.

4–6. *Yahweh laughs the rebels to scorn.*

6. Both the king and *Zion* were chosen by Yahweh (see p. 149 and notes on Ps. 48).

7–9. *Yahweh's decree.* For *the decree of the Lord,* compare 'the testimony' given to Joash (2 Kgs. 11¹²) and the covenant between Yahweh and the house of David (2 Sam. 7⁸⁻¹⁶; cf. Ps. 132¹¹, ¹²). A protocol, affirming the king's divine sonship, was part of the enthronement rite in Egypt. *You are my son, today I have begotten you.* By Yahweh's choice and anointing, the king was admitted to a unique relationship with Yahweh, which is described as being adopted as his *son* (cf. 2 Sam. 7¹⁴; 1 Chron. 17¹³, 22¹⁰, 28⁶; Ps. 89²⁶, ²⁷; see, further, pp. 143 ff.).

8. *the nations your heritage.* The promise to the new king of universal dominion was common form in the ancient Near East. It is reflected in many of the psalms (Pss. 21⁸⁻¹², 46⁶, ⁸⁻¹⁰, 47⁸, ⁹, 48⁴⁻⁸; see notes on Ps. 72⁸⁻¹¹) and was adapted later to describe the coming universal kingdom of Yahweh (Zech. 14⁹; Jer. 10⁶, ⁷; Isa. 49²², ²³; Mic. 4¹¹⁻¹³, 7¹¹⁻¹⁷).

9. *a rod of iron,* perhaps a reference to the king's sceptre (cf. Ps. 110²).

10–12. *The rebellious kings are warned to submit.*

5 *An individual's lament*

In time of trouble, the individual came to the sanctuary, where he believed Yahweh was present, and asked for his help. The situation is illustrated by the story of Hannah at Shiloh, where she poured out her soul before the Lord in 'great anxiety and vexation' (1 Sam. 1⁹⁻¹⁸). It is probable that some of the laments in the Psalter were liturgical compositions provided for general use (as the heading of Ps. 102 suggests); this would explain why it is often difficult to diagnose the nature of the affliction and would to some extent excuse the violence of the psalmists' imprecations. The liturgical form of the individual lament influenced the more personal prayers of Jeremiah (Jer. 11¹⁸⁻²⁰, 12¹⁻⁶, 15¹⁵⁻²¹, 17¹⁴⁻¹⁸, 18¹⁹⁻²³, 20⁷⁻¹³, ¹⁴⁻¹⁸).

1, 2. *Cry for help.* 'My inner musing' is, perhaps, better than *my groaning.*

3–7. *Expression of confidence.* The *sacrifice* was probably the regular morning sacrifice in the Temple (2 Kgs. 16¹⁵), at which the sufferer would *watch* for a divine revelation. The underlying belief is that Yahweh is present in his 'house' (cf. Ps. 18⁶; 1 Sam. 1²²) and through the cult would make his presence known. This idea informs the many references in the psalms to the 'face' of Yahweh (Pss. 24⁶, 42²), which occurs in such expressions as, 'Lift up the light of thy *countenance* upon us, O Lord' (Pss. 4⁶, 80³), and, 'Let us come into his *presence* with thanksgiving' (Ps. 95²).

5. *evildoers* is an ambiguous and much discussed term in the psalms, which in this context means false accusers, who are *boastful, bloodthirsty, deceitful men,* who *speak lies.*

7. The psalmist takes comfort in the fact that, unlike his accusers (v. 5), he may by God's grace come to the Temple. On *thy house,* see notes on Ps. 84¹.

8–12. *Final prayer and imprecation.* God's *straight* path in which the psalmist prays to be kept is contrasted with the devious and deceitful ways of his accusers (v. 9).

10. Their *transgressions,* which means acts of rebellion (see notes on Amos 1³), were against not only the psalmist but God himself.

20 *A prayer for the king before battle*

This psalm was composed to accompany a sacrificial offering in the Temple before the king went out to battle (cf. 1 Kgs. 8⁴⁴, ⁴⁵; 2 Chron. 20¹⁻¹⁹; 1 Sam. 13⁸⁻¹²). It falls into two quite distinct parts, the first interceding for victory (vv. 1–5) and the second expressing assurance of it (vv. 6–9). This sudden change, which is a feature of many psalms of lamentation (see p. 141), points to the psalm's setting in a liturgical 'service' with a priest or cultic prophet to give Yahweh's promise of victory.

1–5. *An intercession for the king addressed to him in the form of a blessing. The name of the God of Jacob.* In the Old Testament, the *name* is synonymous with being (cf. Gen. 2¹⁸⁻²³; Isa. 40²⁶) and itself possesses power (cf. Pss. 54¹, 89²⁴).

2. *help from the sanctuary*. This expression assumes that Yahweh lives in the Temple (see p. 148).

3. The purpose of sacrifice implied here is crude and direct.

6–8. *A proclamation of assurance. Now I know* makes it clear that an oracle or ritual gesture has been given between v. 5 and v. 6 to assure the congregation of the king's victory (cf. 2 Chron. 20¹⁴⁻¹⁷).

7. The same contrast is presented in Isa. 31¹⁻³ (see p. 348).

9. *The final cry of the congregation.*

29 *A hymn to Yahweh as Creator and King*

This psalm is an excellent example of the profound influence of Canaanite religion on the theology of the Temple. Yahweh is depicted as God of the storm, like Baal, who is represented in Canaanite art as hurling thunderbolts (figs. pp. 74, 252) and of whom it is said in one of the Ras Shamra texts: 'Now moreover Baal will abundantly give abundance of rain . . . and he will utter his voice in the clouds, his flashings (and) lightnings on the earth' (G. R. Driver, *Canaanite Myths and Legends*, p. 97). It is not, however, the fertility aspect of the Canaanite mythology which the psalmist develops, but the more fruitful idea that Yahweh, like Baal, has been 'enthroned as king for ever' (v. 10).

1, 2. *Call to worship*. The call is extended to include the *heavenly beings*, which means the gods of the nations now reduced to a subordinate status in Yahweh's heavenly council (v. 10; cf. Ps. 82¹; Job. 1⁶; and notes on 1 Kgs. 22¹⁹).

3–9. *Yahweh's self-manifestation in storm. The voice of the Lord*, which occurs here seven times and is familiar from the descriptions of Baal, means thunder (cf. Ps. 18¹³, ¹⁴). The expression *many waters* reflects the primeval flood over which Yahweh as

Creator and preserver of cosmic order is King (cf. v. 10; and see p. 150).

6. Yahweh's power shakes to their very foundations even the gigantic northern mountains of *Lebanon* and *Sirion* (Hermon) and sets them hopping.

8. *the wilderness of Kadesh*, rocked by cataclysm, may conceivably associate Yahweh's self-manifestation in storm with his appearance at Sinai and the wanderings in the wilderness (Num. 20), but the connexion is at best tenuous.

9. An alternative interpretation of the first two lines is: 'The voice of the Lord makes the hinds calve and causes the premature birth of the kids.'

10, 11. *Yahweh is acclaimed King of Creation and Preserver of his people.* The expression *enthroned over the flood* indicates that Yahweh is King by virtue of his having conquered the primordial chaos of unruly waters in the act of Creation (cf. Gen. 1^2). Yahweh's sovereignty over the hostile waters (Pss. $89^{9,\ 10}$, 93^{1-4}), or the monsters (variously called Leviathan, Rahab, the Dragon), which infest these waters (Ps. 74^{12-17}; Isa. 51^{9-11}), is a recurrent theme in the Old Testament (cf. Job 7^{12}, 9^{13}, $26^{12,\ 13}$; Isa. 27^1; Hab. 3^{4-15}; Nah. 1^{3-5}). This creation mythology has for many years been known in its Babylonian version and the discovery of the Ras Shamra texts now establishes that it was familiar in Canaanite religion. One fragmentary text recounts how Baal is promised an 'everlasting kingdom' (cf. Ps. 145^{13}) and equipped with two magic maces to crush Yam (Sea) and Nahar (River). Baal, who is called 'rider on the clouds' (cf. Ps. 68^4), vanquishes his opponents and assumes the kingship: 'Verily Yam is dead, and Baal shall be king' (G. R. Driver, *Canaanite Myths and Legends*, pp. 82–83).

47 *A hymn for the celebration of Yahweh's Kingship*

This psalm of praise to Yahweh as King of all the earth was clearly composed for a liturgical act of worship, in the course of which the Ark was carried in procession (v. 5). Yahweh was thought of as being *permanently* 'enthroned upon the cherubim' (1 Sam. 4⁴; 2 Sam. 6²; 2 Kgs. 19¹⁵; Ps. 99¹), with which the Ark had come to be associated in the Temple (1 Kgs. 6²³⁻²⁸). The interpretation of this and the other psalms which explicitly celebrate Yahweh's kingship (93, 96, 97, 98, 99) as having been part of a special *annual* ritual in which Yahweh was symbolically enthroned is, therefore, no more than a possibility (v. 8). The adoption of the whole complex of ideas associated with kingship in the ancient Near East for understanding Yahweh, the God of Israel, was for good and ill the most far-reaching consequence of the establishment in Jerusalem of a monarchy on the Canaanite model (see p. 34). Through the concept of the Kingdom of God in the gospels (and sometimes in contradiction of its new and distinctive features), ideas of divine rule have permeated and profoundly influenced Christian thought.

1–4. *Summons to worship Yahweh as King of the world.*

2. *the Most High* is a title taken over from 'El 'Elyôn, the god of the pre-Israelite city of Jerusalem, of whom Melchizedek was priest-king (Gen. 14¹⁸⁻²⁰; cf. Ps. 110⁴; Num. 24¹⁶; Pss. 7¹⁷, 21⁷, 46⁴).

3. *He subdued peoples under us.* Yahweh, the *great king*, like the earthly king, is sovereign over the nations (see notes on Pss. 2⁸, 48⁴, 72⁸⁻¹¹). As Yahweh's Chosen People (v. 4), Israel unfortunately thought that she, too, was 'on top'.

5–7. *Procession of the Ark and the acclamation of Yahweh as King.* The liturgical terms of v. 5 are illuminated by the account of Solomon's dedication of the Temple: 'Then the priests brought the ark of the covenant of the Lord to its place, in the inner sanctuary of the house, in the most holy place, underneath the wings of the cherubim' (1 Kgs. 8⁶). On the Ark, see notes on Ps. 132¹⁻⁵.

7. *with a psalm.* The Hebrew word *maskîl* is of uncertain meaning, suggesting the idea of skill and success.

8, 9. *Yahweh receives the homage of all peoples. God reigns.* Scholars who think that the psalm was intended to accompany a cultic act, in which Yahweh was symbolically enthroned, translate 'God has become King' (and similarly in Pss. 93¹, 96¹⁰, 97¹).

9. This verse probably means that the *princes* of the nations come to do homage along with Israel, described here as *the people of the God of Abraham* (cf. Gen. 12³; see notes on Ps. 72¹⁷). The *shields of the earth* means the rulers of the earth (cf. Ps. 89¹⁸).

48 *A hymn celebrating the beauty and security of Zion*

This beautiful psalm enshrines a dubious doctrine. The idea that the city of God was sacrosanct and secure against all heathen enemies was not, as is sometimes suggested, a prophetic conviction first voiced by Isaiah. Like Micah and Jeremiah, Isaiah, in fact, repudiated the notion (see pp. 346 ff.), for the good reason that it encouraged a completely false complacency. The doctrine was fundamentally alien to the Mosaic Yahwism of the prophets and derived from the sacrosanct character ascribed to the Temple as the house of God (cf. Ps. 46⁴, ⁵) and ultimately from the sacrosanct character of the pre-Israelite Canaanite sanctuary of Jerusalem (called 'Salem' in Ps. 76²; cf. Gen. 14¹⁸). The so-called Songs of Zion (Pss. 46, 48, 76, 87; cf. Pss. 84, 122) in many ways magnificently transcend the Canaanite ideas which lie in the background, but the ancient mythology is still clearly visible (v. 2; cf. Ps. 46⁴; Ezek. 47⁸⁻¹²; Joel 3¹⁸; Zech. 14⁸; Gen. 2¹⁰). The ritual pantomime suggested by vv. 4–8 must have been a great popular success.

1–3. *In praise of Yahweh and Zion.*

2. **Mount Zion,** originally the fortified hill of pre-Israelite Jerusalem (2 Sam. 5⁶⁻¹⁰), came to be used as a name for the Temple, which was built on the same ridge (Ps. 74²), and for the city of Jerusalem (Ps. 51¹⁸; Isa. 10²⁴). *in the far north,* or literally, 'the recesses (or heights) of Zaphon (north)'. In the Ras Shamra texts, Baal's temple was 'in the heights of Zaphon' and the god himself came to be called Zaphon. The psalmist, like the

prophet who spoke of 'the mount of assembly in the far north' (Isa. 14[13]), was undoubtedly drawing on Canaanite mythology to describe Zion, the dwelling place of Yahweh (cf. Job 37[22]; and see p. 148).

4–8. *A dramatic presentation of Yahweh's victory over heathen kings who attack Zion.* Indications that the routing of the kings described in these verses was symbolically enacted in the Temple are found in the expressions *As we have heard, so have we seen* (v. 8) and *We have thought on thy steadfast love, O God, in the midst of thy temple* (v. 9), or, preferably, we have 'portrayed' thy steadfast love.

4, 5. *the kings . . . took to flight.* The panic and defeat of the nations which attempt to storm Mount Zion is a recurrent theme in the psalms (Pss. 46[6, 8–10], 76[3–6]) and the book of Isaiah (Isa. 14[24–27, 32], 17[12–14], 29[7, 8], 31[4, 5], 36, 37). The idea is developed in the onslaught of the heathen nations and their annihilation in post-exilic pictures of the Last Judgement (Ezek. 38, 39; Zech. 14[1–21]; Joel 3[9–21]; cf. Revelation 20[9, 10]); see notes on Ps. 2[8].

7. Translate, 'As the east wind wrecks the ships of Tarshish' (see p. 24).

9–11. *Universal praise for Yahweh's acts of deliverance.*

12–14. A *processional tour of Zion.*

72 A prayer for the king and his people

This psalm splendidly illuminates the Jerusalem conception of kingship and the high hopes which greeted every new king of the Davidic dynasty. So great was the supernatural significance of the king (vv. 5–7, see pp. 143 ff.), that his accession was thought to make everything 'all right'. That is what is meant by the 'righteousness' of his rule. Things were 'all right', when justice was established in the kingdom (vv. 4, 12–14), when the harvests were abundant (vv. 3, 6, 16), and when wealth poured in from subservient nations in the king's universal empire (vv. 8–11, 15). If, as some scholars think, this dream became a 'cultic reality' for worshippers in the Temple, they were being cruelly deceived.

1–4. *Prayer for the king's righteous rule.* These verses convey a lofty ideal of a king, endowed with Yahweh's *justice* and *righteousness*, bringing equity and well-being to his people.

5–7. *Prayer for a long and prosperous reign.* The hyperbole of these verses and their presupposition that the welfare of the people is inextricably bound up with the welfare of the king are found in both Egyptian and Mesopotamian sources.

8–11. *Prayer for the king's world sovereignty.* The idea that the empire of the Anointed is nothing less than the world, *from sea to sea*, is a feature of many royal psalms (Pss. $2^{8, 9}$, 18^{43-45}, 45^5, 89^{20-27}, $110^{5, 6}$). It does not reflect the political aspirations of Israel so much as its indebtedness for its model of kingship to the Canaanites and (through them) to the imperial powers of the ancient Near East. In such terms, for example, an Egyptian hymn of victory represents the god, Amon-Re, as welcoming the empire-builder, Thut-mose III, in the fifteenth century B.C.: 'I establish thee in my dwelling place. I work a wonder for thee: I give thee valour and victory over all foreign countries; I set the glory of thee and the fear of thee in all lands, the terror of thee as far as the four supports of heaven. . . . The great ones of all foreign countries are gathered together in thy grasp' (J. B. Pritchard, *Ancient Near Eastern Texts*, p. 374). This imperialist ideology was borrowed through the Canaanites and adapted to describe the kingship of Yahweh and the universality of his sovereign rule (see notes on Pss. 2^8, 48^4).

9. *his foes* represents a correction of the Hebrew for 'those who dwell in the wilderness' and, in view of v. 10, it is probable that some particular people (like the Ethiopians) is meant.

10. *Tarshish* is an unidentified port on one of the coasts or *isles* of the Mediterranean (see p. 24). *Sheba* is the home of the Sabeans in southern Arabia (cf. v. 15; 1 Kgs. 10^{1-10}; Jer. 6^{20}); and *Seba*, perhaps, a Sabean colony in Africa.

12–14. *The righteousness of the king's rule.* These high expectations are again paralleled in the terms with which the Egyptians expressed their joy at the restoration of divine order with the accession of a new king. Thus, Rameses IV was welcomed in the twelfth century B.C.:

> They who were hungry are sated and gay; they who were thirsty are drunken. They who were naked are clothed in fine linen; they who were dirty are clad in white. They who were in prison are set free; they who were fettered are in joy. The troublemakers in this land have become peaceful. High Niles have come forth from their caverns, that they may refresh the hearts of the common people. . . . 'Thou ruler—life, prosperity, health!—thou art for eternity!' (J. B. Pritchard, *Ancient Near Eastern Texts*, p. 379).

15–17. *The prayer concluded.*

16. Fertility and prosperity are closely associated with kingship in Egyptian, Mesopotamian, and Canaanite thought and these ideas are taken up, like the expectation of universal dominion, into Israel's picture of the coming of the Kingdom of God (cf. Amos 9^{13}; Ezek. 34^{23-27}, 47^{8-12}; Zech. 14^8).

17. *May men bless themselves by him* means may all peoples pray for a blessing like his (cf. Gen. 12^3, 18^{18}, 22^{18}, 26^4).

18–20. These verses are not part of the psalm, but an editorial doxology and a note marking the end of Book II of the Psalter.

80 *A communal lament from the Northern Kingdom*

This communal lament is one of the very few psalms from the northern kingdom (vv. 1, 2) and is distinctive in its appeal to the Exodus rather than the Davidic tradition (see pp. 48–51). The overwhelming disaster which made the kingdom the laughing stock of the nations may well have been the Assyrian invasion of 734–732 B.C. (see notes on 2 Kgs. 15^{8-31}).

1–7. *Appeal for help.* The northern tribes of *Joseph* are *Ephraim* and *Manasseh* and the territory of *Benjamin* lay between the northern and southern kingdoms. The *cherubim*, on which

Yahweh was invisibly enthroned, were by no means exclusive to Solomon's Temple (1 Sam. 4⁴; see notes on Ps. 47 and fig. p. 226).

8–13. Israel, Yahweh's vine, is now ravaged. For the *vine* as a symbol for the people of God, see Hos. 10¹; Isa. 5¹⁻⁷; Jer. 2²¹.

11. Israel stretched from the Mediterranean *Sea* in the west to the *River* Euphrates in the east.

13. *The boar* symbolizes an invading enemy (cf. vv. 6, 16).

14–19. Final appeal for help.

17. *the man of thy right hand* and *the son of man* are probably parallel personifications of Israel, with, perhaps, a reference to Benjamin ('Son of the right hand'). The king, however, was thought of as Yahweh's 'right-hand man' (Ps. 110¹) and an allusion to Hoshea (732–724) has been suggested (see notes on 2 Kgs. 17¹⁻⁶).

84 *A pilgrim's praise for the Temple*

This psalm is one of the finest fruits of the distinctive kind of religious understanding which the Temple enshrined. For the men of Jerusalem, 'the living God' (v. 2) was to be found primarily in the sanctuary and its cultic worship (cf. Ps. 42²). 'As the Lord lives' is clearly an oath used in the cult (Hos. 4¹⁵; Amos 8¹⁴; Jer. 4², 5²) and it is conspicuously absent from the teaching of the prophets. No doubt they avoided the expression because for them Yahweh was to be found primarily in life outside the sanctuary, in the 'secular' encounters of history and human relations (see pp. 55–59). The psalmists' and the prophets' different answers to the fundamental question 'Where does man meet God?' reverberate down the centuries of Christian history, often in uneasy combination, but for the most part the piety of the psalmists has predominated.

1, 2. *Longing for the courts of the Temple.* The transcendent significance of *Lord of hosts* (see notes on 1 Kgs. 18¹⁵, pp. 254 f.) reduces the danger of thinking that Yahweh is entirely localized in the Temple as his *dwelling place* (cf. Pss. 5⁷, 23⁶, 27⁴, 42⁴; see p. 148). The psalmist's whole being (*heart* and *flesh*) sings for joy.

3, 4. *The happiness of those whose home is in the Temple.* The birds and the priests actually live in Yahweh's own *house.*

5–7. *The happiness of the pilgrim to the Temple.* The expression *in whose heart are the highways to Zion* means those whose heart is set upon pilgrimage.

6. *the valley of Baca* has not been identified, but clearly indicates an arid valley on the way to Jerusalem, which (perhaps in imagination) the pilgrims find well supplied with water.

7. *strength to strength* describes the course of their journey until they arrive *in Zion*. On the idea that God is *seen* in the sanctuary, see notes on Ps. 5³.

8, 9. *A prayer for the king.* He is described as *our shield* (cf. Pss. 47⁹, 89¹⁸) and Yahweh's *anointed* (see notes on Ps. 2²).

10–12. *The incomparable joy of being in the Temple.*

11. *sun and shield.* The Hebrew word for *sun* is translated 'pinnacle' in Isa. 54¹² and something comparable (such as 'defence') is needed here.

132 *A processional liturgy of commemoration*

The contents of this psalm clearly suggest that it was part of a liturgy which commemorated the triumphal entry of the Ark to Jerusalem in the reign of David, and with it Yahweh's 'choice' of Zion and the Davidic dynasty. It is also clear that the psalm is related to a liturgy involving a procession with the Ark (v. 8) and many participants—the king (v. 10), priests (v. 9), the first choir (vv. 1–5), a second choir (vv. 6, 7), a speaker who pronounces an oracle of reassurance (vv. 13–18), and the congregation who shout for joy (v. 9). The accounts of David's bringing the Ark to Jerusalem (2 Sam. 6) and of Solomon's dedication of the Temple (1 Kgs. 8) probably reflect the liturgy used in the regular commemoration of which this psalm was a part, but it is now impossible to be precise about its order and movements. Indeed, since the commemoration must have been one of great importance and grandeur (including, of

course, the offering of sacrifice), a psalm which may be sung in
two minutes can reveal little of its total setting.

1–5. *David's quest for a dwelling-place for the Ark. All the hardships
he endured* are recounted in 2 Sam. 6²⁻¹⁵, with which this psalm
is very closely connected. The Ark was a wooden chest (Exod.
25¹⁰⁻²²), in relation to which (perhaps as his 'footstool', cf. v. 7),
Yahweh was believed to be present with his people. It came to
be interpreted as Yahweh's throne, when (probably at Shiloh)
the Canaanite tradition of the cherubim was associated with
it (see notes on Ps. 47 and figs. pp. 19, 79). The tradition of
the Ark goes back to the confederation of the twelve tribes and
it was used as a war palladium before and after the institution of
the monarchy (Num. 10³⁵, ³⁶; Josh. 3–5; 1 Sam. 4¹–7²). David
recovered the Ark from the Philistines and astutely brought it
to Jerusalem (2 Sam. 6), where Solomon established it in the
inner sanctuary of the Temple (1 Kgs. 8). After that, apart
from references in liturgical texts to its cultic use, it totally
disappears from history.

5. *a dwelling place for the Mighty One of Jacob* means a home for
the Ark, with which *the Mighty One of Jacob* (cf. Gen. 49²⁴; Isa.
49²⁶, 60¹⁶) is virtually identified.

6–10. *Liturgical re-enactment of the bringing of the Ark to the sanctuary.*
The references to *Ephrathah* (Bethlehem, the home of David,
cf. 1 Sam. 17¹²) and *the fields of Jaar* (Kiriath-jearim, where the
Ark lodged until it was taken to Jerusalem, 1 Sam. 7¹, ²) suggest that the history of the search for the Ark and its triumphal
entry into Jerusalem were represented in a ritual drama which
ended with the replacement of the Ark under the cherubim in
the holy of holies (cf. 1 Kgs. 6²³⁻²⁸). It is important to notice
that this ritual drama is based not on myth but on historical
fact. In this respect, the Jerusalem tradition rejected the
Canaanite pattern.

7. *footstool*, that is, the Ark (1 Chron. 28²).

8. *the ark of thy might.* This is the only explicit reference to the

Ark in the psalms, although many further allusions are claimed (cf. Pss. 26⁸, 78⁶¹, 95⁶).

9. *saints* (*ḥᵃsîdhîm*) is the adjectival form of the Hebrew word for 'steadfast love' (*ḥesedh*) and here means 'loyal people' or 'devotees' (see pp. 219, 297).

10. *thy anointed one*, that is, the king, who was evidently taking part in the ritual, probably playing the role of David (see notes on Ps. 2²).

11, 12. *Yahweh's choice of David and his dynasty*. The *oath* about David and his house is given in the oracle of Nathan (2 Sam. 7⁸⁻¹⁶), where it is closely associated with the building of a 'house' for Yahweh—the Temple (2 Sam. 7⁵⁻⁷; cf. Ps. 78⁶⁷⁻⁷²).

12. *my covenant*. Yahweh's *covenant* with the house of David is reaffirmed in one of the Psalter's rare explicit references to it. Here (as in 1 and 2 Kings, see pp. 65 f.), the covenant is conditional upon obedience, but in Ps. 89¹⁹⁻³⁷ the covenant stands despite disobedience (cf. 2 Sam. 7¹⁴⁻¹⁶).

13–18. *Yahweh's choice of Zion*.

14. *This is my resting place for ever*. Yahweh's choice of Zion and, therefore, the inviolability of Jerusalem were unconditional and this guarantee of permanence attached itself to the Davidic dynasty (cf. v. 12; see pp. 53 f.).

17. The *horn* symbolizes strength (Ps. 75¹⁰; 1 Kgs. 22¹¹; Deut. 33¹⁷) and the *lamp* life and stability (2 Sam. 21¹⁷; Jer. 25¹⁰; Prov. 24²⁰).

IV. WISDOM

WISDOM is the ability to cope. The things with which people are said to cope in the Old Testament cover, of course, an enormous range. Craftsmen are able to cope with 'gold, silver, bronze and iron' (1 Chron. 22¹⁵; cf. 2 Chron. 2⁷) and sailors with navigating and repairing ships (Ezek. 27⁸, ⁹). To describe these skills (as we should call them), the Hebrew uses the term 'wisdom' (*ḥokhmāh*). The man of wisdom knows what to do, as David said Solomon would know what to do with Shimei. And he meant assassinate him (1 Kgs. 2⁹). Pharaoh told Joseph that because of his wisdom, 'you shall be over my house, and all my people shall order themselves as you command' (Gen. 41³⁹, ⁴⁰). The ability to cope which was a pre-requisite for the statesman was obviously the secret of successful kings. Confessing 'I am but a little child; I do not know how to go out or come in', Solomon prayed for wisdom: 'Give thy servant therefore an understanding mind to govern thy people' (1 Kgs. 3⁵⁻¹⁴). Solomon used his royal wisdom in ways like the king of Tyre, whose undoubted ability is acknowledged in Ezekiel's condemnation:

> by your wisdom and your understanding
>   you have gotten wealth for yourself,
> and have gathered gold and silver
>   into your treasuries;
> by your great wisdom in trade
>   you have increased your wealth. (28⁴, ⁵)

It was inevitable that Yahweh, who made the world like a craftsman and ruled it like a king, should be described as possessing and exercising wisdom:

> There is none like thee, O Lord;
>   thou art great, and thy name is great in might.
> Who would not fear thee, O King of the nations?
>   For this is thy due;

> for among all the wise ones of the nations
>> and in all their kingdoms
>> there is none like thee . . .
> But the Lord is the true God;
>> he is the living God and the everlasting King . . .
> It is he who made the earth by his power,
>> who established the world by his wisdom,
>> and by his understanding stretched out the heavens.
>>>>> (Jer. 10[6, 7, 10, 12])

If it is a long way from the wisdom of the craftsman to the wisdom of the Creator, it is a road without a break; for wisdom at every level is the ability to cope, to design and execute, to plan and put into practice, to succeed by 'know-how', to steer by knowing the ropes (and often by pulling strings). The book of Proverbs is fond of this nautical metaphor (1[5], 12[5], 20[18], 24[6]) and uses it particularly of the 'guidance' provided by counsellors in government service:

> Where there is no guidance, a people falls;
>> but in an abundance of counsellors
>>> there is safety. (11[14])

Many counsellors were needed to steer the ship of state which was launched by Solomon and they provide the vital clue to the meaning and development of wisdom in the period of the monarchy.

(i) *The Counsellor and the Scribe*

Counsellors were the advisers of kings and held high office in the state. The formal title 'Counsellor' was given to Ahithophel by David (2 Sam. 15[12]; 1 Chron. 27[33]) and we are told that his political advice carried much weight: 'Now in those days the counsel which Ahithophel gave was as if one consulted the oracle of God' (2 Sam. 16[23]). There was a comparable office in Egypt, as we learn from Isaiah, who mocked the counsellors' pretension to ancestral wisdom:

> The princes of Zoan are utterly foolish;
>> the wise counsellors of Pharaoh give stupid counsel.

How can you say to Pharaoh,
        'I am a son of the wise,
        a son of ancient kings'? (Isa. 19¹¹; cf. 31¹⁻³)

Further prophetic oracles satirize and denounce the scheming wisdom of the political counsellors of Edom (Jer. 49⁷) and Babylon (Jer. 50³⁵, 51⁵⁷; cf. Isa. 47¹³). The similarity of the situation in Assyria is reflected in the language of political wisdom which Isaiah ascribed to its king (Isa. 10¹³) and directly confirmed by the Aramaic story (discovered in 1906) of the wise Ahikar, in which the hero is described as 'counsellor to all Assyria' and 'father of all Assyria, by whose counsel King Sennacherib and all the host of Assyria were guided'. Ahikar is also called 'a wise and skilled scribe', and this raises a major question for investigation (fig. p. 168).

The office of 'scribe' (*sôphēr*) existed not only in Assyria, but in Babylonia, Egypt, and Judah. Seraiah was 'secretary' in the reign of David (2 Sam. 8¹⁷) and his sons, Elihoreph and Ahijah, held the office in the time of Solomon (1 Kgs. 4³). Shebna was 'secretary' under Hezekiah (2 Kgs. 18¹⁸) and Shaphan in the reign of Josiah (2 Kgs. 22³, ⁸⁻¹⁰; cf. 12¹⁰), until he was succeeded by Elishama (Jer. 36¹²) and Jonathan (Jer. 37¹⁵). The fact that we know the names of so many holders of this office and the influential roles they play in political affairs make it clear beyond all doubt that the 'secretary' was, like the 'Royal Scribe' in Egypt, nothing less than the Secretary of State. As such, of course, he was one of the king's principal 'counsellors'.

It is impossible to say how far the king's Secretary in Jerusalem continued to perform the function which his title suggests. The Foreign Secretary and the Clerk of the House of Commons are not so called because of their unusual ability to write and deal with correspondence; nevertheless, their titles reflect a society in which literacy was the privilege of the few. We may be reasonably certain, therefore, that the officers of State in Judah were distinguished from their contemporaries by being men of education and that the education which equipped them for office included, among other kinds of wisdom, the art of writing (fig. p. 194).

THE OFFICE OF A SCRIBE. The photograph shows a scribal chamber, 31 by 14 ft., excavated in the chancery of the North West Palace at Nimrud, the centre of the imperial administration of Assyria in the last half of the eighth century B.C. The boy is sitting on a burnt-brick bench and to the right are the remains of two rows of brick filing cabinets. The sort of documents which they once contained was made clear by the discovery of some 350 clay tablets in the debris of the chamber, dating from the reigns of Tiglath-pileser III (745–727) and Sargon II (722–705). They deal with a fascinating range of government business—grain supplies, tax evasion, postal delays, the resettlement of deportees; there is even a letter from the king mentioning (for the first time on record) the royal *wagon-lit*, which, it seems, needed overhauling: 'The coach of which the sleeping-compartment is broken goes badly' (see M. E. L. Mallowan, *Nimrud and its Remains*, vol. i, pp. 172–5).

(ii) *Schools of Wisdom*

We know that there were schools attached to temple and court throughout the ancient Near East. School texts copied by pupils and corrected by their teachers from about 2,500 B.C. have been discovered in ancient Sumer (in the lower Tigris–Euphrates valley). They include proverbs, fables, myths, epics, hymns, and word lists, which indicate the kind of liberal education given to the future leaders of Sumerian public life.

In these schools, the teacher was called 'father' and the pupils his 'sons'—a widespread convention which has left its mark on the Old Testament (see p. 186). The terminology is also reflected in a remarkable letter from Canaanite Shechem, dated about 1400 B.C., which an anxious teacher sent to a parent who had stopped paying his son's school fees: 'From three years ago until now thou hast caused me to be paid. Is there no grain nor oil nor wine which thou canst send? What is my offence that thou hast not paid me? The children who are with me continue to learn. I am their father and their mother every day alike...' (J. B. Pritchard, *Ancient Near Eastern Texts*, p. 490). In Babylonia there were two types of school. Primary education in reading and writing was given at 'the tablet-house' and higher education at 'the house of wisdom', where even the students were called 'sages' (cf. Dan. 1¹⁻²¹).

We are most fully informed, however, about education for the professions in Egypt. Much of the Egyptian 'wisdom literature' which has survived consists of copies of texts made (often inaccurately) by schoolboys in class. These texts are 'instructions' given by a teacher to his pupil, often in the form of an address to his son by an experienced state official. Thus, *The Instruction of Ptah-hotep* purports to be the 'wisdom' given by the Vizier of Egypt about 2400 B.C. to his son and successor. *The Instruction for King Meri-Ka-Re*, from about 2100 B.C., is counsel given by a ruler to his son and successor and, among many other things, he urges him to show favour to any old school friend (illuminatingly described as 'one with whom thou once didst *sing* the writings') who gets into trouble. The best known of these texts, *The Instruction of Amen-em-opet*, is proverbial wisdom written for his son by the Egyptian Minister of Agriculture, the content and purpose of which he expounds in a preface:

The beginning of the teaching of life, the testimony for prosperity, all precepts for intercourse with elders, the rules for courtiers, to know how to return an answer to him who said it, and to direct a report to one who has sent him, in order to direct him to the ways of life, to make him prosper upon earth, let his heart go down into its shrine [that is, to allow him to keep his composure], steer him away from evil, and to rescue him from the mouth of the rabble, revered in the mouth of the people (J. B. Pritchard, *Ancient Near Eastern Texts*, p. 421).

This is the work from which a section of the book of Proverbs was borrowed (see pp. 192 ff.) and which, since the recent discovery of a fragment of *The Instruction*, may be securely dated some time before 1100 B.C. Another revealing classroom exercise, *The Instruction of Cheti the son of Duauf*, extant in many messed-up copies, shows how the Egyptian schoolboy was taught to despise the manual worker and revere the learned profession of scribe. It reviews the exhausting and dirty jobs of the metalworker, the woodworker, the engraver of precious stones, the barber, the merchant, the builder, the gardener, the tenant-farmer, the weaver, the arrowmaker, the courier, the embalmer, the cobbler, the laundryman, the birdcatcher, and the fisherman, drawing the expected conclusion: 'Behold, there is no profession free of a boss—except for the scribe: he is the boss. But if thou knowest writing, then it will go better with thee . . .' (J. B. Pritchard, *Ancient Near Eastern Texts*, pp. 432–4). The general pattern of this vilely snobbish exercise with its smug conclusion is still clearly discernible in the work of Ben Sira (Ecclesiasticus 38²⁴–39⁵ in the Apocrypha) as late as 190 B.C. He similarly reviews the jobs of the ploughman, the engraver, the metalworker, and the potter, concluding more generously that although 'they cannot expound discipline or judgement and they are not found using proverbs', nevertheless these workers 'keep stable the fabric of the world and their prayer is in the practice of their trade'. But Ben Sira shows where his real sympathies lie by going on immediately to a eulogy of 'the wisdom of the scribe':

> On the other hand he who devotes himself
>   to the study of the law of the Most High
> will seek out the wisdom of all the ancients,
>   and will be concerned with prophecies;
> he will preserve the discourse of notable men
>   and penetrate the subtleties of parables;
> he will seek out the hidden meanings of proverbs
>   and be at home with the obscurities of parables.

He will serve among great men
   and appear before rulers;
he will travel through the lands of foreign nations,
   for he tests the good and the evil among men.
He will set his heart to rise early
   to seek the Lord who made him,
   and he will make supplication before the Most High;
he will open his mouth in prayer
   and make supplication for his sins. (Ecclus. 39$^{1-5}$)

The astonishing feature of this admirably comprehensive description is that, despite all the developments in post-exilic Judaism towards directing the energies of the 'wise' to the teaching of the Law, Ben Sira's scribe is still basically an educated public figure whose wisdom equips him to 'serve among great men and appear before rulers', like the government scribe in Egypt two thousand years earlier. The book Ecclesiasticus probably represents the teaching which Ben Sira gave in his own 'house of study':

Draw near to me, you who are untaught,
   and lodge in my school. (Ecclus. 51^{23})

In view of the remarkable similarity in outlook between ancient schools of wisdom for the professional classes throughout the ancient Near East and Ben Sira's school in Jerusalem during the second century B.C., we should expect to find evidence of a school of wisdom associated with the Temple during the period of the monarchy. The Ras Shamra texts, which were discovered in a library attached to the Temple of Baal at Ugarit (see pp. 27 f.), suggest that a school for scribes was part of the cultural heritage which Solomon so assiduously imitated in other ways and his creation of a large administrative bureaucracy must have demanded the establishment in Jerusalem of some form of higher education. *There is, however, no direct reference to any such school of wisdom in our sources.* In consequence, the probability of its existence has been generally ignored and with it the activity of an educated class in the pre-exilic period, which had the most profound influence on the character of the Old Testament and the faith to which it bears witness.

Higher education in the period of the monarchy is known only by its fruits, but even a brief review will suggest that these were considerable.

1. While not forgetting the importance of oral tradition before the Exile, we must give due weight to the fact that there were writers in this period capable of producing mature and even sophisticated works like the Court History of David (2 Sam. 9–20; 1 Kgs. 1, 2) and the Yahwist's history of Israel's traditions from the Creation of Mankind to the Conquest of Canaan. Both of these masterpieces reflect the new intellectual quest and literary activity of the early years of the monarchy.

(a) The Court History of David represents an astonishing innovation. The writer presents the background of Solomon's succession to the throne of David (cf. 1 Kgs. 1²⁰) as a realistic political drama, depicting its characters in all their worldliness with complete candour and without a trace of religious or moral comment. It is a work of secular history, in which events are no longer determined by the direct intervention of God, but solely by the decisions of men. The world it describes is the world in which it was written—the new professional, hard-headed world of political counsel which came into being with the establishment of the monarchy. It is admirably character-ized in the debate between Absalom's counsellors, Ahithophel and Hushai, in 2 Sam. 17¹⁻¹⁴; to appreciate the intellectual quality of this exchange is to become convinced that from the early days of the monarchy Jerusalem was governed by men of good education, who were remarkably detached both from traditional Yahwism and from the dominant 'royal theology', which, of course, elevated the king far above the secular realities of political life (see pp. 143 ff.).

(b) The Yahwist's history, which also comes from the early monarchy, shows a comparable detachment and intellectual quality. It needed a man of outstanding ability to take a miscellany of ancient sagas and traditions belonging to differ-ent sanctuaries and exploit them as material for a unified account of Yahweh's dealing with fallen mankind through his choice and guidance of Israel. When we recall that these stories were regarded as being inextricably bound up with the religious life of particular sanctuaries, we can appreciate what a revolution it was to reduce them to the status of literary units in a larger history, a history, moreover, which is connected and governed by the policies and decisions of men. The writer has clearly abandoned the belief that Yahweh acts through the cult of isolated sanctuaries or through direct intervention in isolated episodes of sacred significance. Yahweh is now represented as acting through the human actors in secular history and it is on them that the writer focuses our attention. This revolutionary development is seen most clearly in the Yahwist's story of Joseph (Gen. 37–50), which is told with a deep insight into human nature and human relations. The circles in which this new psychological interest in man was cultivated are revealed unambiguously by the portrayal of Joseph as a 'discreet and wise' counsellor to the Pharaoh and as a model pupil of the school of wisdom (Gen. 41$^{25-45}$).

(c) Similarly, the sources upon which the deuteronomic historian drew, the writing of his history (pp. 60-63), and the skilled presentation of teaching in the book of Deuteronomy (pp. 205 ff.) are quite inexplicable without presupposing an established tradition of higher education in Jerusalem.

2. The pre-exilic psalms, though distinct from the learned psalmography of a later period, are by no means the work of illiterate singing men who simply picked up ideas and expressions from the ancient Canaanite cult of Jerusalem (see pp. 139–42). Their authors were obviously schooled in the psalmography of Babylon and Egypt, which they encountered either directly as one of the cultural imports which were so marked a feature of the monarchy from the time of Solomon, or indirectly through the study of Canaanite literature, which Judah may well have acquired from Phoenicia (see pp. 21–29). It is clear that more than one of the psalmists might have boasted, 'my tongue is like the pen of a ready scribe' (Ps. 45^1),

and that they, too, owed their mastery of the art of writing and of the cultic poetry of the ancient Near East to a school in Jerusalem.

3. The arguments for the existence of a 'school of wisdom', in which professional men were trained for the growing needs of the court, the Temple, and the king's home and foreign affairs, are supported by evidence which suggests that literacy was more widespread in the population than once was supposed. It is not in the least surprising to learn from Isaiah that some people were illiterate (Isa. 29^{12}), but it is, indeed, surprising to come across the prophet's casual comment that 'a child can write them down' (Isa. 10^{19}) and his clear reference to children being taught their ABC (Isa. 28$^{9, 10}$, see pp. 344 f.; cf. 29^{13}). Presumably, Baruch, the scribe of Jeremiah (Jer. 36^4), represents a modest class of professional writers, who would be responsible, among other things, for the preparation of legal documents (Jer. 3^8, 32$^{9-15}$; cf. Ezek. 9$^{2, 3}$). Jeremiah himself drew a distinction between the illiterate and the educated when he spoke of 'the poor', who 'have no sense' and, therefore, cannot be expected to know 'the way of the Lord', and 'the great', who know it but ignore what they know (Jer. 5$^{4, 5}$). The implication of the story of Naboth is that the elders of Jezreel could read (1 Kgs. 21$^{8-12}$) and Deuteronomy at the end of the period takes literacy for granted (6^9, 17$^{18, 19}$; cf. 27$^{2-8}$).

The evidence from the Old Testament is greatly strengthened by archaeological discoveries. A small limestone tablet from the reign of Solomon gives us the writing exercise of a Gezer peasant, who copied out a mnemonic in verse of the calendar of the agricultural year:

> His two months are (olive) harvest,
>   His two months are planting (grain),
>   His two months are late planting;
> His month is hoeing up of flax,
>   His month is harvest of barley,
>   His month is harvest and feasting;

His two months are vine-tending,
His month is summer fruit.
(J. B. Pritchard, *Ancient Near Eastern Texts*, p. 320)

Marks of the alphabet made by masons have been discovered on excavated buildings and it is probable that the inscription describing the triumphant completion of the Siloam tunnel was written by one of the men working on the site (pp. 111 ff.). The ostraca of Samaria were presumably written by ordinary officials (p. 32) and the Lachish Letters by a junior army officer (pp. 129 f.). The fact that the Old Testament never actually mentions schools in the period of the monarchy is clearly not conclusive. However, the most persuasive evidence that Israel became at an early date 'like all the nations' in the sphere of education as in so many other ways is to be found in the influence of its schools of wisdom on the prophets and in the teaching of the Book of Proverbs. These two topics merit special attention.

(iii) *Wisdom and Prophecy*

The influence of the schools of wisdom on the prophets of the eighth and seventh centuries B.C. is revealed in two sharply contrasted ways. On the one hand, they vigorously attacked the leading counsellors of the king and their fellow intellectuals for being calculating in their policies and generally sceptical in their outlook. On the other hand, many of the prophets shared the educational background of their opponents and spoke the same language.

The potential conflict between the counsellors of the king and the prophets of Yahweh is neatly summed up in a passage by the Chronicler: 'Therefore the Lord was angry with Amaziah and sent to him a prophet, who said to him, "Why have you resorted to the gods of a people, which did not deliver their own people from your hand?". But as he was speaking the king said to him, "Have we made you a royal counsellor? Stop! Why should you be put to death?" ' (2 Chron. 25[15, 16]). The conflict came into the open during the second half of the eighth century. Amos clashed with Jeroboam II, was accused of conspiring against him and was expelled from Bethel, 'for it is the king's sanctuary, and it is a temple of the kingdom' (Amos 7^{10-13}). The evidence from Hosea is more explicit. He directly attacked the king and his counsellors (cf. $5^{1, 10}$, 9^{15}, 13^{10}) for their intrigues and foreign alliances:

> Ephraim is like a dove,
>   silly and without sense,
>   calling to Egypt, going to Assyria. (7^{11})

> For they have gone up to Assyria,
>   a wild ass wandering alone;
>   Ephraim has hired lovers. (8^9)

> You have ploughed iniquity,
>   you have reaped injustice,
>   you have eaten the fruit of lies.
> Because you have trusted in your chariots
>   and in the multitude of your warriors. (10^{13}; cf. 8^7)

These references illustrate not only the political activity of the counsellors, but also the kind of proverbial wisdom they learnt at school (cf. Prov. 22^8; Job 4^8; see pp. 181–4). A probable translation of Hos. 8^4 is even more pointed: 'They have taken counsel, but not of me; they have got advice, but I know not (of it).'

Isaiah, as we have seen, exposed the pretensions of 'the wise counsellors of Pharaoh' (19^{11-15}); no less vigorously he attacked the counsellors of Hezekiah, who sought to make an alliance with the Egyptians, instead of consulting Yahweh, who also is 'wise' and able to frustrate their calculations (see notes on Isa. 31^{1-3}). The same clash of 'counsel' is found in Isa. 30^{1-3}, where the Judean leaders are called 'rebellious children, who carry out a plan ['counsel'], but not mine'. The prophet's condemnation of 'the wisdom' of Judah's 'wise men' in Isa. 29^{13-16}, which is associated with the kind of religious instruction 'learned by rote' (vv. 13, 14) and with the superficial scepticism of the half-baked intellectual (vv. 15, 16), may also be aimed at the

professional counsellors of the court (cf. notes on Isa. 5^{18-23}).
Possibly, however, it is a more general attack on the 'school-
men', such as we find in Jer. $8^{8, 9}$:

> How can you say, 'We are wise,
>   and the law of the Lord is with us'?
> But, behold, the false pen of the scribes
>   has made it into a lie.
> The wise men shall be put to shame,
>   they shall be dismayed and taken;
> lo, they have rejected the word of the Lord,
>   and what wisdom is in them?

Since the 'law' (*tôrāh*) often means no more than the 'instruction'
given in the schools of wisdom (see p. 204), it is quite unnecessary to find in this passage any reference either to the book of
Deuteronomy or to teaching of the Law. Jeremiah is simply
including the 'school-men' along with the prophet and the
priest in his despairing judgement that 'every one deals falsely'
(8^{10}). The school-trained professional class, the prophets, and
the priests together constituted the three principal orders in
society (Jer. 18^{18}; Ezek. 7^{26}; cf. Mic. 3^{11}; Job 12^{17-20}) and
Jeremiah's ministry is the story of his struggle with all three
(see pp. 348–54).

When, as is still often the case, the 'wise' are thought of as a
narrow class of religious 'sages', who suddenly emerged in the
time of the prophets as specialists in a new kind of teaching
and a new kind of 'wisdom literature', it is difficult, if not
impossible, to reconcile the prophets' unambiguous attacks on
them with the evidence of their indebtedness to wisdom teaching. The result has been that until recently the degree of this
indebtedness has been underestimated and inadequately ex-
plored. When, however, the 'wise' of Israel are seen as the
products and practitioners of the kind of education which was
well established throughout the ancient Near East, in order to
maintain 'a supply of fit persons' for leadership in the community, it is not in the least surprising that some of the prophets
should have shared the intellectual milieu of those with whom
they came into conflict. The prophets did not live in a cultural

vacuum and, indeed, it is only when they begin to enter the sphere of public policy—the sphere over which professional 'wisdom' had hitherto reigned supreme—that they emerge as distinct figures whose oracles and lives were put on record (see pp. 244–7). Our knowledge of the great antiquity of the wisdom tradition throughout the ancient Near East makes it impossible for us to suppose any longer that the wise in Israel were late arrivals on the scene and made their impertinent challenge to prophecy just before the end of the monarchy. It was exactly the other way round. Prophecy, *as a distinctively Israelite phenomenon*, emerged only when a succession of educated and independent laymen had the impertinence to enter the secular sphere of politics and challenge the wisdom by which it was traditionally governed (see pp. 237–441). The great prophets of the eighth and seventh centuries B.C. had the temerity to claim that all departments of life, no matter what the politicians and civil servants said, were the department of Yahweh and that Israel's only true wisdom was knowledge of his will. As men who believed they had received a disclosure of this knowledge, the independent prophets daringly assumed the roles of counsellors to the king and teachers of the people. In many ways the secularity of the wisdom tradition was congenial to them and it was certainly congruous with their conviction that Yahweh worked primarily in the spheres of history and human relations. That is why they rapidly reinterpreted its idiom and adopted its methods. A brief survey of four major prophets should suffice to make the point.

(i) *Amos.* The prophet's style shows that he adopted many of the didactic methods of the school-men. The most obvious example is the series of rhetorical questions in 3^{3-8} (cf. 5^{25}, $6^{2, 3, 12}$, 9^7), which were characteristically used by the wisdom teachers as an appeal to common sense (cf. Prov. $6^{27, 28}$, 30^4; Job 8^{11}). The voice of the professional teacher can also be heard in the questions of 7^8 and 8^2, in the use of consecutive numbers in pairs (1^3–2^8; cf. Prov. 6^{16-19}, 30^{15-31}; Job 33^{14}, 40^5), and in the distinctive style of 5^3 and 5^{19}. These external features are pointers to a more profound theological and moral encounter with the wisdom of the schools which will be considered later (pp. 265, 274, 280 ff.).

(ii) *Hosea*. Quite apart from its obviously scribal postscript (14⁹), the book of Hosea echoes from beginning to end with proverbial sayings: 'Wine and new wine take away the understanding' (4¹¹; cf. Prov. 20¹); 'a people without understanding shall come to ruin' (4¹⁴; the verb (*lābhaṭ*) occurs elsewhere only in the parallel proverbs of Prov. 10⁸, ¹⁰); 'For they sow the wind, and they shall reap the whirlwind' (8⁷; cf. 10¹³; Prov. 1²⁷, 11²⁹, 22⁸; Job 4⁸); see, in addition, 5¹² (cf. Job 13²⁸), 7⁵ (cf. Prov. 23²⁹⁻³⁵, 31⁴, ⁵), 7¹¹ (cf. 11¹¹; Prov. 9⁴, ¹⁶), 8⁹ (cf. Job 39⁵, ⁶) and 13¹³. Like Isaiah and Jeremiah, Hosea also shows evidence of reflection on the world of nature, which is thought of as being itself corrupted by Israel's forsaking of Yahweh (4¹⁻³; cf. Jer. 4²³⁻²⁶). There are also passing references which assume a familiarity with a number of moral precepts very widely attested in Israelite and foreign wisdom literature: the sanctity of the land mark (5¹⁰; cf. Prov. 22²⁸, 23¹⁰; Job 24²), the prohibition of false balances (12⁷; cf. Prov. 16¹¹, 20²³), and care for the orphan (14³; cf. Prov. 22²², 23¹⁰, 29¹⁴; Job 29¹²). The evidence from Hosea, who had no connexion with Jerusalem, suggests either the existence of a school of wisdom in the northern kingdom at the Court of Samaria, or, possibly, a very thorough editing of his oracles by a scribe of the southern kingdom who shared the prophet's outlook.

(iii) *Isaiah*. The prophet's open conflict with the counsellors and school-men has already been noted (pp. 176 f.). He is, nevertheless, clearly indebted to the culture of his opponents. Once again we find examples of the vivid rhetorical question (10¹⁵, see p. 341; 29¹⁵, ¹⁶); and the book includes a 'wisdom' parable to make the point that, like the farmer, Yahweh works according to a plan (28²³⁻²⁹). Isaiah's reflection on the order of nature (cf. 1³) represents another of his contacts with the wisdom tradition (see pp. 181 ff.).

(iv) *Jeremiah*. The prophet is fond of the teacher's rhetorical question. He employs it to appeal against his contemporaries to man's ordinary common sense (8⁴, ⁵, 13²², ²³), to the universal experience of the nations, and to the order of nature:

> Ask among the nations,
>   who has heard the like of this?
> The virgin Israel
>   has done a very horrible thing.
> Does the snow of Lebanon leave the crags of Sirion?
> Do the mountain waters run dry, the cold flowing
>   streams?
> But my people have forgotten me. . . . (18¹³⁻¹⁵)

It is clear that this contrast between the order of nature and the moral disorder of Israel entered deeply into Jeremiah's awareness and, as the language of his oracles unambiguously reveals, he owed this insight to the wisdom tradition (4^{23-26}, 5^{20-29}, 8^7; cf. 10^{12-16}; and p. 182). Many familiar wisdom words occur in the prophet's teaching: 'fool' ($^{e}w\hat{\imath}l$: 4^{22}; cf. 17^{11}); 'instruction', or 'correction' ($m\hat{u}s\bar{a}r$: 2^{30}, 5^3, 17^{23}, 35^{13}; see pp. 206 f.); 'council' ($s\hat{o}dh$; see notes on $23^{18,\ 22}$ and Prov. 3^{32}); and the term 'wisdom' ($hokhm\bar{a}h$) itself ($9^{23,\ 24}$).

A full statement of the great prophets' indebtedness to the wisdom schools would have to include a study of their theological and moral teaching (see Chap. VI), but it may be claimed that even this brief review establishes three points beyond reasonable doubt: (*a*) the wisdom tradition was taken for granted by the middle of the eighth century B.C.; (*b*) prophecy's engagement with it coincides with and probably accounts for the emergence of 'written' prophecy which was transmitted in the main stream of Israel's literary life; (*c*) the prophets' ambiguous love–hate relationship with the wisdom tradition arises from their profound conviction that it is in the ordinary secular world of political and moral decision that Yahweh is known and served:

> Do you think you are a king
>   because you compete in cedar?
> Did not your father eat and drink
>   and do justice and righteousness?
>   Then it was well with him.

He judged the cause of the poor and needy;
  then it was well.
Is not this to know me? says the Lord. (Jer. 22¹⁵, ¹⁶)

(iv) *The Wisdom of the Schools*

The reputed wisdom of Solomon has two distinguishable aspects. Pre-eminently he is said to possess the ability to cope with the problems of government; he was the oriental king *par excellence* (1 Kgs. 2⁹, 3⁹, ¹², ¹³, 5¹²). Secondly, it is claimed that he was a man of education: 'Solomon's wisdom surpassed the wisdom of all the people of the east, and all the wisdom of Egypt. . . . He also uttered three thousand proverbs; and his songs were a thousand and five. He spoke of trees, from the cedar that is in Lebanon to the hyssop that grows out of the wall; he spoke also of beasts, and of birds, and of reptiles, and of fish' (1 Kgs. 4²⁹⁻³⁴; cf. 10¹). It has been pointed out that the passages dealing with Solomon's literary and 'scientific' wisdom probably come from a source later than those used by the deuteronomic historian and the conclusion has been drawn that the claim they make is without foundation in fact. This scepticism also involves a discounting of evidence from the book of Proverbs: the heading 'The proverbs of Solomon' for the collection in Prov. 10¹–22¹⁶ and 'These also are proverbs of Solomon which the men of Hezekiah king of Judah copied' at the head of the collection in Prov. 25¹–29²⁷. The interpretation of the latter statement to mean that it was really Hezekiah who founded a school of literary wisdom in the eighth century B.C. is unconvincing and is certainly not strengthened by the argument that he did so as part of his desire to imitate the past glories of the age of Solomon!

Although it seems improbable that Solomon himself wrote proverbs and engaged in nature study, it is, as we have seen, highly probable that he established a school of wisdom for the training of his counsellors and administrators. Proverbs and nature study, however, so far from being (as is sometimes supposed) a later and independent development of 'literary wisdom', were almost certainly part of the syllabus in the schools for training professional men. Proverbs are explicitly associated with the education of young men for government service in schools of wisdom throughout the ancient Near East (see pp. 168 ff.) and a whole section of the Old Testament book of Proverbs, which clearly had its origin in the teaching of the schools, is taken over from an Egyptian text-book (see pp. 192–5). While it is true that we have no Hebrew catalogues of the names of trees, plants, beasts, birds, reptiles, and fish like those which have been rediscovered from Egypt and Babylon (fig. p. 194), such compilations are probably reflected in Job 38–39 and Ps. 148 and it is by no means inconceivable that this post-exilic evidence derives from a much earlier tradition. At least when Job says,

> But ask the beasts, and they will teach you;
>> the birds of the air, and they will tell you;
> or the plants of the earth, and they will teach you;
>> and the fish of the sea will declare to you ($12^{7,\ 8}$)

he is commending the kind of reflection on natural phenomena which is found not only in a section of the book of Proverbs going back to a period when kings still ruled ($30^{18,\ 19,\ 24-31}$; cf. 6^{6-11}), but also in the teaching of the pre-exilic prophets:

> The ox knows its owner,
>> and the ass its master's crib;
> but Israel does not know,
>> my people does not understand. (Isa. 1^3)
>
> Even the stork in the heavens
>> knows her times;
> And the turtledove, swallow, and crane
>> keep the time of their coming;
> but my people know not
>> the ordinance of the Lord. (Jer. 8^7)

It is tempting, therefore, to ascribe at least some of the prophets' many references to birds and beasts more to their having been to school than to their having been brought up as countrymen (cf. Amos $3^{4,\ 5}$; Hos. $4^{3,\ 16}$, 7^{11}, 8^9, 11^{11}, $13^{7,\ 8}$; Jer. 13^{23}, 17^{5-11}).

The quest for an order underlying the diversity of raw

experience, which is illustrated by the cataloguing and classification of natural phenomena and by the references to 'nature' in teaching of the prophets (cf. Jer. 18^{13-15}), is also the fundamental purpose of ordinary proverbs. To say that proverbs are often platitudes is not to despise them, but to acknowledge their distinctive achievement. They pin down observed regularities in the confusion of human experience, win an elementary order out of chaos, and so help men to understand and cope with life. What they offer, that is to say, is wisdom:

> For lack of wood the fire goes out;
>> and where there is no whisperer, quarrelling ceases.
>>>   (Prov. 26^{20})

>> He who is sated loathes honey,
>>> but to one who is hungry
>>>> everything bitter is sweet. (Prov. 27^7)

> He who tends a fig tree will eat its fruit,
>> and he who guards his master will be honoured. (Prov. 27^{18})

In a world which was entirely ignorant of abstract 'first principles', knowledge never moved far from its anchorage in experience and the education which imparted this knowledge kept close to a practical goal. Proverbs were used to train men to recognize what actually worked in human affairs and so to act wisely and give sound advice. Without such training, men failed to 'get to the bottom' of things and responded impulsively and superficially to every new situation as though it were unique and without precedent. This failure to penetrate to the order underlying experience, or the deliberate rejection of it, was the mark of the fool:

>> The way of a fool is right in his own eyes,
>>> but a wise man listens to advice. (Prov. 12^{15})

> He who trusts in his own mind is a fool;
>> but he who walks in wisdom will be delivered. (Prov. 28^{26})

The man who listens to advice and walks in wisdom will come through 'all right', because with the help of accumulated human experience he will be able to recognize and do what is 'right' in the complexity of particular circumstances. He will understand the hidden order in the diversity of human experience and will then stand under it. The wise man is a conformist, but in a highly special sense. He is far from simply falling in with what others are saying and doing. That is the uncritical conformity of the fool, who 'believes everything' (Prov. 14^{15}) and whose eyes are 'on the ends of the earth' (Prov. 17^{24}). For the wise man, on the contrary, there is more in life than meets the eye and he disciplines himself to conform to what the eye cannot see. This hidden order is discoverable by discerning men with the help of the advice which other discerning men, drawing on their own experience and the wisdom of the ages, can give. It is not surprising that the followers of this humanist tradition, outside Israel and within it, attained a high order of moral insight and one to which the prophets were profoundly indebted (see p. 310). Nor is it surprising that the order they discerned behind human experience proved too limited a concept to meet the facts of life. The faithful man did not always abound with blessings (cf. Prov. 28^{20}). As the book of Job affirms so superbly, humanist wisdom can provide no resting-place. If a man rigorously pursues that openness to facts which is humanism's characteristic boast, he will find either that his confidence disintegrates and he is thrown into despairing scepticism, or that he is brought to a faith in which his discernment of order in human existence is discovered to have its explanation in the being of a personal God.

It seems, however, that the humanism of the schools of wisdom was not pressed to either of these conclusions until the post-exilic period. During the monarchy, we can only suppose that it lived alongside the religion of the Temple without ever being integrated with it. Certainly, the earliest evidence we possess in the book of Proverbs shows, like the book of Job, a complete detachment from the history, law, worship, and prophecy, in which Israel's distinctive faith found expression. The high regard for kings throughout the book of Proverbs (cf. 14^{28-35}, 16^{10-15}, 19^{12}, $20^{2,\ 8,\ 26,\ 28}$, 21^1, 23^1) firmly anchors its tradition in the pre-exilic period, but it reflects the deference of the royal official rather than the devotion of the Temple worshipper. The relation of the king's school to the king's sanctuary is a problem we lack the information to solve. For the same reason, we can only speculate about the range of learning in which the teachers of wisdom provided instruction. The book of Proverbs clearly derives from the class room (see notes on pp. 186 ff.), but equally clearly its contents are far too general to meet the needs of a professional education. The schools of Sumer, Babylon, and Egypt were the channels through which the whole cultural tradition of the people was transmitted and even their pupils were set to copy works like the Babylonian Epic of Creation. It is improbable, therefore, that candidates for the king's service in Israel were entirely confined to writing out and learning endless proverbs. What other literature they had and where it came from we are left to guess. The best guess is, perhaps, that there once existed a body of Canaanite writings which came to Jerusalem (and, probably, Samaria) from Phoenicia, to which we know that in all cultural matters Israel was heavily indebted (see pp. 23–29). The light which the Ras Shamra texts throw on so much Old Testament literature (without there being evidence of direct dependence) would be more readily explicable if comparable Canaanite literature in larger quantities had found its way to Israel's schools of wisdom. Incomplete though our information is, the little we know suggests that there was a class of educated men in the period of the monarchy who played a highly significant role. It is represented most clearly by those who served the king, but its impact on Israel's life was felt far beyond the spheres of politics and civil administration. This educated *élite* was the principal means by which Yahwism came into contact with the whole cultural tradition of the ancient Near East and the only means by which Israel's own tradition, enriched by its exposure to the wisdom of the nations, was preserved for posterity.

(v) *The Book of Proverbs*

It is generally agreed that the book of Proverbs was compiled after the Exile from several earlier collections. (*a*) The 375 short sayings collected with little regard for order under the heading, 'The proverbs of Solomon' (10^1–22^{16}), are certainly pre-exilic and probably the oldest material in the book. (b) 'The words of the wise' (22^{17}–24^{22}), of which about a third have been directly borrowed from the Egyptian textbook, *The Instruction of Amen-em-opet* (22^{17}–23^{12}; see notes), also come from the period of the monarchy. (c) 'These also are proverbs of Solomon which the men of Hezekiah king of Judah copied' is the heading for 25^1–29^{27} and there is no reason to doubt that the collection was made in Jerusalem from proverbs already traditional at the end of the eighth century B.C. (d) Four smaller sections of the book are impossible to date: 24^{23-34}, 31^{1-9}, 31^{10-31}, and 30^{1-33}, of which the numerical sayings in vv. 15–33 may well be very old. (e) The collection which introduces the book (1^1–9^{18}) is a post-exilic compilation which probably draws on pre-exilic material. It is possible that the nucleus of each of the sections beginning with a formula like 'Hear, my son, your father's instruction' (1^8; see notes on 3^{21-32}) goes back to an early school textbook. The personification of Wisdom in chapter 8 is not conclusive evidence for a post-exilic date (see pp. 188 ff.), although the majority of scholars still incline to that view.

3. 21–32 *A lesson on neighbourliness*

21. *My son.* This was the traditional way of addressing a pupil in the wisdom schools of the ancient Near East and many of their textbooks are in the form of advice given by an official to his son and successor (cf. 1^8, 2^1, 3^1, $4^{1,\ 10,\ 20}$, 5^1, 6^{20}, 7^1). The word translated *sound wisdom* is a technical term meaning something like 'strength', 'capacity', 'ability' (cf. 2^7), and *discretion* means the power to make plans (cf. 12^2, 14^{17}).

22–24. This conventional recital of the advantages of an education in wisdom is echoed in Deut. $6^{7,\ 8}$ (see p. 215).

25, 26. Wisdom is able to cope with all emergencies. The help of *the Lord* belongs to a different way of thinking and it is suspected that both these verses have been added by an editor at a later stage.

27–29. The generous human sympathy of these injunctions is also found in Deuteronomy (cf. 22^1, 24$^{14, 15}$); compare the maxim: 'He gives twice who gives promptly.'

30. The pupil must avoid picking quarrels with people (see notes on 22$^{24, 25}$).

31. The *man of violence* here is lawless rather than impulsive.

32. This verse seems to sum up the section. The *perverse man* is one who is twisted, crooked, devious: not straight or *upright*. On *abomination to the Lord*, see p. 207. The phrase *in his confidence* translates the word *ṣôdh*. It is used in the Old Testament to describe (*a*) an intimate company of friends (Gen. 49^6; Jer. 6^{11}, 15^{17}; Ps. 55^{14}; Job 19^{19}); (*b*) a meeting of men 'in council' (Ezek. 13^9; cf. Ps. 111^1); (*c*) the 'council' of God (Jer. 23$^{18, 22}$; Ps. 89^7; Job 15^8; cf. Amos 3^7); (*d*) the confidential matters ('secrets' or 'counsels') of such groups (Amos 3^7; Pss. 64^2, 83^3; Prov. 11^{13}, 15^{22}, 20^{19}, 25^9); (*e*) God's confidence or friendship (Ps. 25^{14}; Prov. 3^{32}; Job 29^4). It seems probable that the term had its origin in the confidential circles of the 'wise' (cf. Job 15^8).

4. 20–27 *A lesson on vigilance*

20–23. The background of the teacher's emphasis on the pupil's hearing his words in such a way that they enter his heart and so direct the whole of his life may be found in the Egyptian textbooks. The ancient *Instruction of Ptah-hotep* (see p. 169) contains a passage which plays on the word 'hear' and promises the pupil who diligently 'hears' that one day he will become a magistrate who 'hears' cases:

To hear is of advantage for a son who hearkens. If hearing enters into a hearkener, the hearkener becomes a hearer. [When] hearing is good, speaking is good. Every hearkener is an advantage, and hearing is of advantage to the hearkener. . . . How good it is when a son accepts what his father says! Thereby maturity comes to him. He whom god loves is a hearkener, [but] he whom god hates cannot hear. *It is the heart which brings up its lord as one who hears or as one who does not hear. The life, prosperity, and health of a man is his heart* (J. B. Pritchard, *Ancient Near Eastern Texts*, p. 414; cf. 7¹⁻³; see notes on 22¹⁷⁻²¹ and Jer. 31³¹⁻³⁴).

24–27. These verses enjoin the pupil to conform to the established social order. He is to exercise control in what he says (v. 24), in what he gives his attention to (v. 25), and in what he does (26). He must, in other words, watch his step (v. 27).

8. 1–36 *The authority of wisdom*

This chapter admirably illustrates three aspects of the wisdom tradition in Israel: first, the teachers' claim that their wisdom came before everything else and must be acknowledged as authoritative; second, their familiarity with non-Israelite mythology; third, their radical reinterpretation of this foreign material for quite different purposes.

It is often said that the representation of Wisdom as the first-born of all creation (vv. 22–31) was intended to absorb the teaching of the schools into the orthodox tradition of Israelite belief and practice. This view, however, is debatable. It may have been simply an assertion of the antiquity and divine authority of the wisdom tradition in Israel (cf. 3¹⁹, ²⁰). When Ben Sira in the second century B.C. identified Wisdom with the Law of Moses (Ecclus. 24²³, 39¹), he was clearly assimilating the two traditions. The motto of the book of Proverbs, 'The fear of the Lord is the beginning of knowledge' (1⁷), since 'the fear of Yahweh' merely means the practice of Israel's religion (cf. 2 Kgs. 17²⁸ and notes on Deut. 6²), may well have had a similar intention (cf. Prov. 2⁶). It is much more difficult, however, to read this chapter as a take-over bid by orthodoxy, or as a concession to orthodoxy by the wisdom teachers, since the association of Wisdom with Creation (unlike its identification with the Law) does not bring it within the sphere of distinctive Israelite belief. Creation was a concept even more familiar outside Israel. What the chapter does unambiguously is to assert the primacy of wisdom and so the authority of its teachers.

This claim is made both directly (vv. 1-11, 32, 36) and in-directly—through the exploitation of a myth which must have been familiar to the teacher and his pupils (vv. 12-21, 22-31). In the form in which it was then current, the myth has al-most disappeared, leaving mere traces in the text, which have invited scholars to engage in endless speculation. It is virtually certain, however, that the concept of wisdom did not suddenly emerge in the Hebrew Scriptures as 'Lady' Wisdom standing up to praise herself (vv. 12-21) and as a 'darling' little girl playing with God and with his human creatures (for such are the terms of vv. 30, 31), without some provocation from outside Israel. It can hardly be doubted that a pagan goddess of love underlies the surface of the text and that it was she who provoked this astonishing personification (cf. the 'Queen of Heaven' in Jer. 7^18, 44^15-19 and Asherah, pp. 44 f.). To inter-pret these passages as presenting wisdom as a hypostasis, that is, as an actual heavenly being, is to pump back into the descrip-tion precisely those pagan mythological concepts the writer has been at pains to pump out.

If the theologians of the early church, following some New Testament writers, had not used the description of Wisdom as 'the first-born of all creation' (vv. 22-31) in their debates on the person of Christ, it is probable that it would have stood out from its context far less prominently than now it seems to do. Unless, as seems unlikely, the writer is claiming that in receiv-ing wisdom men are responding to God's design in creation and, so to speak, going with the very grain of the universe, his reinterpretation of the myth to boost the wisdom of the schools is neither profound nor particularly successful. The original goddess was probably as shameless as the women of Prov. 7^1-27 and 9^13-18 and it was an impossible task to transform her into Yahweh's first-born child. It is in this section, particu-larly, that evidence is often found of the book of Proverb's post-exilic date. Both the writer's intention and the character of his mythology are, however, far too uncertain to be used as chrono-logical evidence. The chapter may, therefore, be studied as it stands for the possibility that it sheds a little light on the teaching of Jerusalem's school of wisdom during the period of the monarchy.

1–11. *Wisdom appeals to the man-in-the-street.* Wisdom is presented as a woman whose appeal to men is sharply contrasted with the 'seductive speech' of the prostitute in the previous chapter (7^{6-27}; cf. 2^{16-19}, 6^{20-35}).

5. The *simple ones* are the inexperienced, easily led, silly young men of the kind depicted in 7^{6-23} (cf. 14^{15}); the *foolish* are men who are thick in the head and morally insensitive (cf. $17^{10,16,24}$).

12–21. *Wisdom speaks of herself.* There is nothing quite like this passage of self-praise anywhere else in the Old Testament (cf. Job 29), but there are pagan hymns in which Astarte, the goddess of love, similarly glorifies herself.

13. *The fear of the Lord is hatred of evil* is obviously an intrusion.

14. Wisdom is able not only to think things up, but get them done. For *sound wisdom*, see notes on 3^{21}.

15. *By me kings reign.* This claim reflects the widespread notion that kings are the 'sons' of God and share his attributes, which include 'wisdom' (cf. Isa. 9^6, 11^2; and see p. 145). For example, Hammurabi of Babylon represents himself as commissioned by Marduk, 'the Lord of Wisdom', to give laws to his people and describes himself as 'the wise one, the administrator, the one who plumbed the depths of wisdom'.

17. Although wisdom is divine and royal, she is available to all who seek her diligently.

18–21. The combination of righteousness and prosperity in these verses is very similar to the hopes associated with kingship in the 'royal theology' of Jerusalem (see notes on Ps. 72).

22–31. *Wisdom the first-born of all creation.* This passage explains why wisdom possesses the extraordinary qualities just reviewed: she was born of God before he created the world. The currency of a comparable myth and the significance which was attached to it may be illustrated by Eliphaz's rebuke of Job:

> Are you the first man that was born?
>   Or were you brought forth before the hills?
> Have you listened in the council of God?
>   And do you limit wisdom to yourself? (Job 15⁷, ⁸)

This language about the primacy of wisdom was borrowed by New Testament writers to describe the primacy of Christ (Colossians 1¹⁵⁻¹⁷, 2³; 1 Corinthians 1²⁴, ³⁰; cf. Hebrews 1³; John 1¹⁻¹⁴; Revelation 4¹¹, 22¹³).

22. The important point in this verse is not whether *created* is a more accurate translation than 'possessed' or 'acquired' (a question which assumed significance only when the verse was used in theological debate about the person of Christ), but that wisdom came and, therefore, comes, before anything else in the world.

23. *I was set up.* This interpretation and translation of the Hebrew has led to the view that God appointed Wisdom to a royal office (cf. Ps. 2⁶). The parallel verb in v. 24, *I was brought forth*, suggests, however, that a different Hebrew word should be understood and translated 'I was fashioned' (cf. Ps. 139¹³).

24. *When there were no depths.* The word *depths* is the plural of 'the deep' (*tehôm*) in Gen. 1² (see p. 155) and the style is reminiscent of the Babylonian Epic of Creation.

27–29. *I was there.* The purpose of the writer is simply to affirm that Wisdom *was there* when God created the world. His work is described as establishing the heavens in position, drawing the horizon round the ocean, fixing the skies above, stopping up the subterranean springs, setting limits to the sea and marking out the earth's foundations.

30, 31. A decision between the alternatives *master workman* and *little child* (RSV *mg*) is important, because the former asserts that Wisdom was not only with God at the Creation but also took part in it. As the passage now stands, it is probable that

Wisdom is being thought of as a *little child*, playing (*rejoicing*) with God and men. The rendering, *master workman*, however, has strong support and it may well be a residual trace of some myth about the goddess of love, who was instrumental in the creation of the world and equally enjoyed the company of the gods and men. Any such myth, however, has been thoroughly reinterpreted and the writer's purpose is not to speculate about Wisdom's part in Creation but, taking for granted that Yahweh created both Wisdom and the world, to affirm that Wisdom was the primary thing in life. That is why he immediately moves on to represent Wisdom as a teacher (vv. 32–36).

32–36. *The two ways*. The writer's appeal to his pupils to accept the way of Wisdom ends with a sharp challenge. The choice is a matter of life and death (vv. 35, 36; cf. 12^{28}, 15^{24}).

22. 17–23. 5 *The words of the wise in Egypt and Israel*

The obvious indebtedness of the Israelite wisdom schools to the older and more distinguished schools of the ancient Near East has been established beyond reasonable doubt in the case of Prov. 22^{17}–24^{22}. Soon after the publication of the Egyptian text known as *The Instruction of Amen-em-opet* in 1923, it was demonstrated that this work of thirty chapters was the source from which the Hebrew writer borrowed many of the thirty or so sayings of Prov. 22^{17}–24^{22} (see pp. 169 ff. and notes on 22^{20}). This conclusion has been challenged, but never overthrown, and the argument that the Egyptian work was written later than the Hebrew proverbs has been reduced to vanishing point by the discovery of an extract from *The Instruction* made by a pupil no later than 945 B.C. The Hebrew writer is no slavish copyist, but he kept particularly close to his Egyptian original in 22^{17}–23^{12}, as the parallels in the following notes will illustrate.

17–21. *Introduction to 'the words of the wise'*. The corresponding passages in *Amen-em-opet* are as follows (all quotations from J. B. Pritchard, *Ancient Near Eastern Texts*, pp. 421–4):

vv. 17, 18:   Give thy ears, hear what is said,
              Give thy heart to understand them.
              To put them in thy heart is worth while . . .
              They shall be a mooring-stake for thy tongue.

v. 20:   See thou these thirty chapters:
              They entertain; they instruct.

v. 21:   to know how to return an answer to him
              who said it, and to direct a report to one
              who has sent him.

18. *all of them* is unintelligible and may be emended to 'mooring-stake'. The wise constantly counsel restraint in speech (cf. 23⁹, 29²⁰; and see notes on 25⁸⁻¹⁰).

19. The Egyptian has 'to direct him to the ways of life'. If the difficult expression *even to you* is emended (with the support of the Greek), we may read: 'I have made thee know today the way of life' (cf. 2¹⁵, 5⁶).

20. *thirty sayings*. This translation of the Hebrew is derived from the 'thirty chapters' of the Egyptian text. The section (22¹⁷–24²²) can be divided into about thirty admonitions.

21. *those who sent you* were probably the senior officials for whom the pupil hopes one day to work.

22, 23. *The poor*. The Egyptian has:

              Guard thyself against robbing the oppressed
              And against overbearing the disabled.

There is no parallel in *Amen-em-opet* to v. 23 (cf. Exod. 22²¹⁻²⁴; Deut. 24¹⁴), but the idea of a god as 'father of the fatherless' (cf. Ps. 68⁵) is common in Babylonian and Egyptian hymns (cf. Job 29¹⁶). For prophetic teaching on the protection of the poor and justice *at the gate*, see Amos 2⁶, ⁷, 4¹, 5¹⁰; Mic. 3¹¹; Isa. 5²³; Jer. 22¹⁶.

24, 25. *The man who gets hot under the collar*. The Egyptian has:

              Do not associate to thyself the heated man,
              Nor visit him for conversation.

The wisdom teachers trained their pupils to be cool and imperturbable (as befits a good civil servant). The wise man is 'slow to anger' (15^{18}, 16^{32}, 17^{27}, 19^{11}); 'With patience a ruler may be persuaded, and a soft tongue will break a bone' (25^{15}).

A SCHOOL EXERCISE. This wooden writing-board, dated about 1000 B.C., comes from an Egyptian scribal school. When not in use, it was hung on a nail. Making lists of things was a basic part of the scribe's education and this exercise shows a list of names (probably Cretan).

26, 27. *The reckless guarantor.* The pupil is prudently warned against thoughtless generosity in standing guarantor for another person's debts. The caution is often repeated in Proverbs (6^{1-3}, 11^{15}, 17^{18}, 20^{16}, 27^{13}), but is not mentioned in *Amen-em-opet*.

28. *The boundary-stone.* The Egyptian reads:

> Do not carry off the landmarks at the boundaries of the arable land,
> Nor disturb the position of the measuring-cord;
> Be not greedy after a cubit of land,
> Nor encroach upon the boundaries of a widow.

The sacred rights of property, especially for the protection of the poor, are firmly established in Israel's moral teaching (Prov. 23^{10}; Deut. 19^{14}; Hos. 5^{10}; Isa. 5^{8}; Mic. $2^{1, 2}$; Job 24^{2}).

29. *The successful pupil.* The Egyptian original makes it even clearer that it is open to a skilful secretary to become Secretary of State:

> As for the scribe who is experienced in his office,
> He will find himself worthy [to be] a courtier.

23. 1–3. *Table manners.* The Egyptian has:

> Do not eat bread before a noble,
> Nor lay on thy mouth at first.
> If thou art satisfied with false chewings,
> They are a pastime for thy spittle.
> Look at the cup which is before thee,
> And let it serve thy needs.

The version in Proverbs handles the detail differently, but the social awareness is the same. Similar advice goes back in Egypt to *The Instruction of Ptah-hotep* (about 2400 B.C.) and with an astonishing continuity of tradition is still found in the teaching of Ben Sira (Ecclus. 31[12–18]).

4, 5. *Transiency of wealth.* The Hebrew omits the god and goddess, Fate and Fortune, of the Egyptian text and its geese become *an eagle*:

> Cast not thy heart in pursuit of riches,
> [For] there is no ignoring Fate and Fortune . . .
> [Or] they have made themselves wings like geese
> And are flown away to the heavens.

The wisdom teachers acknowledge the transiency of wealth (cf. 11[4, 28]) and repudiate the idea that it is an end in itself (10[2], 11[16], 13[11], 15[27], 20[21], 22[16]), but nevertheless they hold it out as a carrot to their pupils (12[27], 14[23], 21[17], 22[4]).

25. 1–10 *Proverbs from the school of Hezekiah*

1. The heading of the section 25[1]–29[27] may be taken at its face value (see p. 181). It supplies reliable evidence that in the reign of *Hezekiah* (715–687) Solomon's name was associated with proverbs and that some of them were transcribed by the

king's men in Jerusalem. The oracles of Isaiah confirm the influence of the 'wise' at Hezekiah's court (see pp. 176 ff.), but they were school-trained counsellors, taught the kind of wisdom required for the royal service (as illustrated in vv. 1–10), and not the founders of a new literary movement.

2–7. *In praise of kings.* For the high regard for kings in the book of Proverbs, see p. 184.

2, 3. The meaning seems to be that it is the king's duty to bring matters out into the open and that he has the resources of an infinite wisdom for doing so. An *unsearchable* wisdom is generally reserved for God (cf. Isa. 40^{28}; Job 9$^{4-12}$, 11^{7}).

4, 5. *the wicked* presumably refers to crooked counsellors of the king and the *righteousness* in which the throne will be established is the right thinking and straight dealing of wise counsellors (cf. 8^{20}, 10^{2}, 11^{5}).

6, 7. This advice on how to behave at a king's feast is repeated by Ben Sira (Ecclus. 7$^{4, 5}$) and turned into a parable by Jesus (Luke 14$^{7-10}$).

8–10. *do not hastily bring into court.* This translation makes the saying a warning against public litigation (cf. Matthew 5$^{25, 26}$). It may, however, be a warning against indiscretion, particularly against blurting out everything *your eyes have seen* and not being able to keep a secret. Many centuries later, Ben Sira says: 'Have you heard a word? Let it die with you. Be brave! It will not make you burst!' (Ecclus. 19^{10}). The aspirant to office in the close, confidential circles of the court was trained to regard the tongue-wagger with the utmost horror.

V. LAW

THE Law of the Old Testament is the most misunderstood part of the Hebrew heritage. It is widely identified with the scribal legalism which Jesus condemned and the Pharisaic self-righteousness which Paul repudiated when he became a Christian. It is necessary, therefore, to be clear from the outset that Law in pre-exilic Israel was not a perversion of God's self-revelation but a remarkable attempt to interpret its consequences for the whole of human life. It was not the dead letter which stood in opposition to the free spirit of prophecy, but the guardian of a tradition without which prophecy as we know it would have been an impossibility. Nor was it narrowly concerned with such irrelevancies as the distinction between clean and unclean beasts. It was, in fact, the result of a remarkable co-operation between priests and laymen and, with Israelite wisdom teaching, the most conspicuously 'secular' and 'practical' part of Hebrew tradition. It was above all, however, a witness to Israel's understanding of itself as the people with whom Yahweh had entered into a unique covenant-relationship and to all that this relationship involved.

(i) *The Book of the Covenant*

'The Book of the Covenant' is the name given to a collection of laws in Exod. 20^{22}–23^{33}, which are represented as the Law given to Moses at the making of the covenant between Yahweh and Israel at Sinai (cf. Exod. 24^7). The collection presupposes a settled agricultural society and, therefore, its laws must have been formulated after the Conquest. Although it is important to recognize that the Book of the Covenant is not of Mosaic authorship, it is even more important to appreciate that it embodies many of the distinctive characteristics of Mosaic Yahwism (see pp. 48–51). For this reason, it is not misleading

A FORBIDDEN CANAANITE ALTAR. This altar, dated in the thirteenth century B.C., was discovered at Hazor in 1956. It consists of a single block of limestone, measuring 7 ft. 9 in. long, 2 ft. 9 in. wide, and 4 ft. high; it weighs nearly 5 tons. The top of the stone is divided into two sections, one being hollowed out to a depth of about 13 in. to form a basin and the other cut as a shallow tray about 4 in. deep. It is thought that sacrificial animals were slaughtered on the shallow tray, from which their blood flowed into the basin. A large quantity of cattle bones was found near the altar and many objects of a ritual character in buildings near by. This unique discovery illustrates the kind of sophisticated altar of hewn stone disallowed in the earliest Hebrew law (cf. Exod. 20²⁵).

but highly appropriate that it should have been incorporated into the narrative of the Exodus and Sinai.

Although the Book of the Covenant was compiled before the monarchy, it illustrates the character of Israelite law in this period, since the distinctive developments of the book of Deuteronomy occurred only during its closing years. The most immediately striking feature of the laws in the Book of the Covenant is their variety and the way in which social and cultic regulations are jumbled together. Thus, the opening cultic law of the altar, which forbids the sophistication of Canaanite sanctuaries (20^{24-26}), is followed immediately by a law on the release of Hebrew slaves, which sets a limit on their masters' rights (21^{1-11}). The next section is made up of laws for the protection of society and the family (21^{12-32}). The crisp legal declaration of capital offences in vv. 12–17 are noticeably different from the longer and more formal laws dealing with bodily injury in vv. 18–32. Laws dealing with property follow in 21^{33}–22^{17}. It is of interest to notice how they recognize different degrees of seriousness according to the intention of the offender (vv. 3, 4) and how, in cases of doubt, the issue is to be decided by an oath or by a judgement at the sanctuary (vv. 8, 9, 11). A miscellany of religious and social laws comes next (22^{18-31}) and it even includes a direct utterance of Yahweh in defence of the widow and orphan (vv. 23, 24). The conduct of justice in the local courts is dealt with in the regulations which follow (23^{1-9}), their primary aim being to warn the elders against giving partial judgements in favour of the wealthy and powerful. The final sequence gives cultic regulations about the sabbatical year, the sabbath day, and the three annual festivals (23^{10-19}). An epilogue, different in style and date, looking forward to the conquest of Palestine in 'holy war', brings the Book of the Covenant to a close (23^{20-33}).

The rough distinction we have noted between detailed civil laws and laws dealing more directly with moral and religious matters corresponds fairly closely to a more precise distinction which we can make between two different styles of formulation. They may be called 'casuistic' and 'categorical' (or 'apodictic'). The *casuistic* laws envisage definite cases, which are introduced by 'when' or 'supposing that' and end with a statement of the action to be taken: '*When* a man strikes the eye of his slave, male or female, and destroys it, he shall let the slave go free for the eye's sake' (21^{26}). As circumstances alter cases, these are dealt with in subordinate clauses introduced by 'if'. Thus, the slave laws of 21^{2-11} have the following developed structure, dealing first with the male and then (v. 7) the female: '(2) *When* you buy a Hebrew slave, he shall serve six years, and in the seventh he shall go out free, for nothing. (3) *If* he . . ., he shall . . .; if he . . ., then his wife. . .'. (4) *If* his master. . . . (5) *But if.* . . . (7) *When* a man sells his daughter as a slave, she shall not go out as the male slaves do. (8) *If* she does not please her master. . . . (9) *If* he. . . . (10) *If* he. . . . (11) And *if* he. . . .' The *categorical laws*, on the other hand, make unconditional demands, characteristically in the second person: 'You shall not permit a sorceress to live' (22^{18}). Some laws show a mixture of the two forms: 'Whoever strikes a man so that he dies shall be put to death. But if . . .' (21^{12-14}). This law is casuistic in form but categorical in content (cf. 22^{25-27}).

Behind these two styles of law, it is possible to identify two different legal traditions. The *casuistic* laws are often similar to the case law of the ancient Near East, as we now know it from the discovery of ancient Babylonian, Assyrian, and Hittite law codes. Of these, the most celebrated is the Code of Hammurabi of Babylon, which is dated about 1700 B.C. The similarity between the casuistic laws of the Book of the Covenant and the Babylonian law of Hammurabi may be illustrated by the case of lost or stolen property which had been deposited with another person for safe-keeping. The Hebrew law runs: 'If a man delivers to his neighbour money or goods to keep, and it is stolen out of the man's house, then, if the thief is found, he shall pay double. If the thief is not found, the owner of the house shall come near to God, to show whether or not he has put his hand to his neighbour's goods' (Exod. $22^{7, 8}$). Before we find a distinctively Israelite feature in the phrase 'to God', we ought to compare the Babylonian law (§ 120): 'If a seignior deposited his grain in another seignior's house for storage and a loss has then occurred at the granary or the owner of the house opened the storage-room and took grain or he has denied completely [the receipt of] the grain which was stored in his house, the owner of the grain shall set forth the particulars regarding his grain *in the presence of god* and the owner of the house shall give to the owner of the grain double the grain that he took' (J. B. Pritchard, *Ancient Near Eastern Texts*, p. 171). If, as is probable, there is no direct Hebrew borrowing from Hammurabi, the general indebtedness of the Israelites (almost certainly through the Canaanites) to the customary law of the ancient Near East is beyond question. They borrowed, however, with discrimination and so demonstrated the distinctiveness of their faith. Israelite law is different in showing more interest in people than property, in slaves as people rather than as property, in the lot of the oppressed, and in the equality of men before the courts. For all their openness to the civilization which they encountered in Canaan, the Israelites totally repudiated the idea of one law for the rich and another for the poor, which, for example, we find so emphatically elaborated in the Code of Hammurabi (§§ 200–5): 'If a seignior has knocked out a tooth of a seignior of his own rank, they shall knock out his tooth. If he has knocked out a commoner's tooth, he shall pay one-third mina of silver. If a seignior has struck the cheek of a seignior who is superior to him, he shall be beaten sixty [times] with an oxtail whip in the assembly. If a member of the aristocracy has struck the cheek of a [nother] member of the aristocracy who is of the same rank as himself, he shall pay one mina of silver. . . . If a seignior's slave has struck the cheek of a member of the aristocracy, they shall cut off his ear' (J. B. Pritchard, *Ancient Near Eastern Texts*, p. 175). By contrast, what the Israelite said was: 'Consider what you do, for you judge not for man but for the Lord; he is with you in giving judgement. Now then, let the fear of the Lord be upon you; take heed of what you do, for there is no perversion of justice with the Lord our God, or partiality, or taking bribes' (2 Chron. 19[6, 7]; cf. Deut. 10[17]; Exod. 23[1–8]).

Mesopotamian law reflected the class structure of society and was promulgated by the king (albeit with a formal bow to the god in whose name he ruled). Thus, Hammurabi claims in his epilogue: 'I am the king who is pre-eminent among kings; my words are choice; my ability has no equal. By the order of Shamash [the sun-god], the great judge of heaven and earth, may my justice prevail in the land; by the word of Marduk [the state god of Babylon], my lord, may my statutes have no one to rescind them' (J. B. Pritchard, *Ancient Near Eastern Texts*,

p. 178). Israelite law, on the other hand, explicitly opposed the developing class structure of society and ascribed the whole of its authority directly to Yahweh himself. Moreover, *Israelite law was totally independent of the king*. On the one occasion when the Peutateuch acknowledges his existence, the king is firmly put in his place and told to make his own copy of the law 'that he may learn to fear the Lord his God . . . that his heart may not be lifted up above his brethren' (see notes on Deut. 17^{14-20}). While the king probably possessed certain judicial powers (1 Sam. 8^5; 2 Sam. 8^{15}, $12^{5,\,6}$, 14^{4-11}, 15^{2-6}; 1 Kgs. 3^{16-28}, 7^7; 2 Kgs. 8^3), he is never allowed any legislative authority. The fact of the matter is—and it is remarkable and most illuminating—that throughout the period of the monarchy the only law of the state was the 'Law of Moses'. The casuistic forms of this law, which deal with the immediate problems of daily life, are, as we have seen, interspersed with and reinterpreted by *categorical* laws for which the State Codes of Mcsopotamia provide no significant parallel. Of these categorical laws, the Ten Commandments are the most familiar and their prologue, which instead of the wise rule of the king proclaims the redemptive action of God, suggests that for the origin of this second type of law we must look to a distinctively Israelite tradition: 'I am the Lord your God, who brought you out of the land of Egypt, out of the house of bondage' (Exod. 20^2). It is clear that Mosaic Yahwism was never smothered by the pretensions and power of the Canaanite courts in Jerusalem and Samaria and that, outside the capitals and away from their temple cults, many men now forgotten were, through teaching and the administration of justice, maintaining Israel's continuity with the historical roots of her existence as the people of God.

(ii) *Law in the courts and in the sanctuaries*

The gap between the Book of the Covenant and the book of Deuteronomy is three or four centuries and our information for bridging it is scanty. The emphatic moral concern of Mosaic Yahwism, which affirmed that right human relations

were of prime importance in Israel's response to the righteousness of Yahweh (see p. 222), was maintained by the elders and
principal men of each community who administered justice 'at
the gate' of the city (fig. p. 7; Amos 5$^{10, 12, 15}$; Ruth 4$^{1-12}$;
Deut. 21$^{3, 4, 18-21}$). This was the local magistrates' court which,
for example, Jezebel had to suborn when she wanted to secure
the death penalty against Naboth (see notes on 1 Kgs. 21$^{8-14}$).
It was presumably for such Justices of the Peace that the 'casuistic' laws, which we find already in the Book of the Covenant,
were collected and (in a rough and ready way) codified. This
was probably the work of the priests at the local sanctuary.
The Book of the Covenant indicates that the local sanctuary
was from the earliest days a court of appeal (Exod. 22$^{7-9}$) and
Deuteronomy, in abolishing the local sanctuaries, simply trans-
fers this 'higher court' to Jerusalem (Deut. 17$^{8-13}$; cf. 2 Chron.
19$^{8-11}$). If we may assume that the procedure in Deuteronomy
was based on traditional local practice, it gives us confirmatory
evidence that the priest at the sanctuary gave legally binding
decisions in disputed civil cases as well as on specifically religious
issues (Deut. 16$^{18-20}$, 19$^{16-19}$, 21^5; cf. Ezek. 44^{24}).

Such evidence should warn us against taking too narrow a
view of the work of a priest in pre-exilic Israel. It is, for
example, quite mistaken to suppose that the priest at the local
sanctuary was primarily concerned with the offering of sacrifice.
The sacrificial victim was slaughtered by the layman making
the offering (1 Sam. 1$^{3-5}$, 14^{34}; cf. Lev. 1^5, 3^2, 4^{24}) and the priest
had a quite subsidiary part in the proceedings. His primary
function is made clear in the so-called 'Blessing of Moses',
which was probably written no later than the eighth century
B.C.:

> They shall teach Jacob thy ordinances,
>   and Israel thy law;
> they shall put incense before thee,
> and whole burnt offering upon thy altar (Deut. 33^{10})

It is for their failure as *teachers* that the priests come under the
condemnation of the prophets. Thus, of eighth-century Jerusalem Micah laments:

> Its heads give judgment for a bribe,
>> its priests teach for hire,
>> its prophets divine for money;

and Jeremiah repeats the stricture a century later:

> The priests did not say, 'Where is the Lord?'
> Thou who handle the law did not know me.
>> (Mic. 3¹¹; Jer. 2⁸; cf. Jer. 18¹⁸; Ezek. 7²⁶)

The Hebrew word, *tôrāh*, which describes what it is the priests teach and 'handle', is much wider in meaning than the translation 'law' suggests. No doubt *tôrāh* included decisions given to the laity on ritual questions concerning the clean and the unclean (cf. Hag. 2¹¹⁻¹³; Ezek. 22²⁶, 44²³; Lev. 10¹⁰, ¹¹) and in the early days of the monarchy such decisions may have been obtained by various cultic devices like the sacred lots, *Urim* and *Thummim* (cf. 1 Sam. 14³⁶⁻⁴²; Deut. 33⁸; Num. 27²¹; Neh. 7⁶⁵), but from the beginning the teaching of the priests must have been much greater in scope. There is nothing in the term *tôrāh* itself to suggest a restriction to narrowly legalistic matters, since it simply means 'teaching' and is used to describe both the instruction given by the scribal teachers (Jer. 8⁸, ⁹; Prov. 1⁸, 3¹, 6²⁰⁻²³, 7², 13¹⁴, 31²⁶) and the preaching of the prophets (Isa. 1¹⁰, 5²⁴, 8¹⁶, ²⁰, 30⁹, 42⁴, 51⁴, ⁷; Jer. 6¹⁹). Both Hosea (4⁶) and Malachi expect the *tôrāh* of the priest to be the instruction of the people in *the knowledge of Yahweh*: 'For the lips of a priest should guard knowledge, and men should seek instruction (*tôrāh*) from his mouth, for he is the messenger of the Lord of hosts' (Mal. 2⁷).

Knowledge of Yahweh, according to Israel's distinctive faith, was inseparable from knowledge of Yahweh's action in history, when he delivered his people from Egypt and brought them into 'a plentiful land to enjoy its fruits and its good things' (Jer. 2⁵⁻⁷). We may, then, safely take it for granted that the *tôrāh* of the priest included instruction of the laity in the historical basis of their faith. The ancient confession preserved in Deut. 26⁵⁻⁹ is now associated with the offering of first fruits at the Temple, but it suggests both the occasion and the content of the

instruction given by the priest-in-charge at the local sanctuaries. At great sanctuaries, like Shechem, it is probable that
regular festivals were held, at which the making of the Covenant
was celebrated and the Law proclaimed in a public recital of
the deliverance from Egypt, similar to that in which it is now
set in the book of Exodus (cf. Deut. 27$^{1-26}$, 31$^{9-13}$; Josh. 8$^{30-35}$,
24$^{1-28}$). But such great occasions still left much teaching for the
local priests to do. Hosea and Jeremiah leave us in no doubt
that these men often neglected their duties, but unless some
had been faithful, it would be impossible to account for the
religious education of Hosea and Jeremiah themselves.

(iii) *Teaching and Law in Deuteronomy*

The book of Deuteronomy is more obviously a book of
teaching than a code of law (cf. 1^5). The other Old Testament
codes of law are addressed by Yahweh to Moses (cf. Exod.
20^{22}, 25$^{1,\,2}$; Lev. 24$^{1,\,2}$); Deuteronomy is explicitly an address
by Moses to the people, in which a selection of laws are expounded both by detailed commentary and by means of
introductory and concluding discourses. The introduction in
chapters 5–11 is represented as Moses' farewell address to Israel
'beyond Jordan' (in the land of Moab), when the people were
about to enter Canaan. It begins (5$^{1-21}$) by recalling the Covenant, which Yahweh had made with Israel at Horeb (the name
which the deuteronomist always uses for Sinai), and the Ten
Commandments, which Yahweh had then given to the people
as a summary of their covenant obligations. There was,
however, more for the people to learn of Yahweh's will and so
Moses is given further commandments to teach them (5$^{22-33}$).
Before these commandments are stated and expounded, there
is a series of exhortations occupying six chapters, which
emphasize with immense passion Israel's unique privilege as
the elect people of God and their obligation to remain loyal to
him by resisting all the temptations of the Promised Land they
are about to enter (6–11). A selection of laws is then presented
with a distinctively deuteronomic commentary (12–26; see below,
pp. 207–12). The conclusion of Moses' address is to be found

in chapter 28, which consists of a series of six blessings and curses with homiletic exposition. This main address (chapters 5–11,12–26, 28) has been supplemented by additional material. Chapters 1–4 consist of a further address by Moses, which was probably placed in its present position as an introduction to the great deuteronomic edition of the history of Israel from the Conquest to the Exile (see pp. 68 f.). Chapter 27, which obviously breaks the connexion between chapters 26 and 28, provided for a Covenant festival at Shechem with a public reading of the Law. Chapters 29–34 are divided between a third address of Moses (29, 30), which also reflects a festival when the Covenant was renewed, and a miscellany of material, some of which is ancient (33^{2-29}), even though it was almost certainly added as an appendix during the exilic period. Most of the material in which the main core of the book is now enclosed comes from the deuteronomic successors of the principal teacher and illuminates the tradition in which he stood.

There is no direct evidence that the law was expounded by professional teachers until after the Exile, when, in the time of Ezra, we are told that the Levites 'helped the people to understand the law . . . and read from the book, from the law of God, clearly; and they gave the sense, so that the people understood the reading' (Neh. $8^{7,\ 8}$). However, the *indirect* evidence that the author of Deuteronomy was primarily a teacher, who used Israel's legal tradition as the basis for his instruction, is very considerable. It is even possible that *tôrāh*, the ordinary word for teaching (see p. 204), eventually became the regular term for the Law as a whole, including 'the ten words' (Exod. 34^{28}), the 'statutes' and the 'ordinances' (see notes on Deut. 6^1), because these had formed the core of the 'teaching' of Deuteronomy.

The author of the book constantly uses the ordinary vocabulary of those concerned with education—'teach', 'commandment', and the 'fear of the Lord' (see notes on Deut. 6^{1-9}). He also shares some of the more technical terms which were used by the pre-exilic *scribal* teachers of Israel. For example, he speaks of the 'moral instruction', or 'discipline' (*mûsār*) given by Yahweh

to Israel as his 'son' (11², cf. 8⁵, 4³⁶; Prov. 1², 3¹¹, 4¹, 19¹⁸, 29¹⁷;
see p. 186); and his frequent use of the term 'abomination'
(7²⁵, 17¹, 18¹², 20¹⁸, 22⁵, 25¹⁶) also connects him with the scribal
teachers (Prov. 20¹⁰, 21²⁷, 24⁹), who had themselves borrowed
it from the wisdom literature of Egypt. As confirmatory
evidence of this connexion, we may notice that the deuteronomic editor who added chapters 1–4 explicitly uses the
'wisdom' language of the teachers: 'Behold, I have *taught* you
statutes and ordinances, as the Lord my God commanded me,
that you should do them in the land which you are entering to
take possession of it. Keep them and do them; for that will be
your *wisdom* and your *understanding* in the sight of the peoples,
who, when they hear all these statutes, will say, "Surely this
great nation is a *wise* and *understanding* people" ' (4⁵, ⁶).

Deuteronomy reflects not only the language of Israel's
wisdom teachers, but also their methods (see pp. 178 ff.). The
author, for example, is always very much aware of the audience
he wishes to instruct. He addresses himself to their questions
and problems (6²⁰, 13¹, ⁶, ¹², ¹³, 18²¹), anticipates their unspoken thoughts (7¹⁷, 9², ⁴, 12²⁰, ³⁰, 15⁹, 17¹⁴), and tries to keep
their attention by using questions and dialogue (5²⁵⁻²⁷, 10¹², ¹³,
20⁵⁻⁸; cf. 4⁷, ⁸, ³²⁻³⁴). The whole style of the work, with its fullness of description (6⁶⁻⁹, 7¹³, 8⁷⁻⁹, 11¹¹, ¹²), deliberate rhetoric
(12¹², ¹⁸, 15⁶, 28¹², ¹³), and even a touch of proverbial wisdom
(20¹⁹), bears witness to a teacher who was determined to get
through to the mind and conscience of his hearers (cf. 6⁵, 10¹²,
13⁴). Deuteronomy is poles apart from a cold-blooded code of
law; it is an earnest appeal for a total response to Yahweh from
'all of us here alive *today*' (5³, 11²⁶⁻²⁸, 28¹; cf. 30¹¹⁻²⁰).

(iv) *Deuteronomy's interpretation of Law*

It is a common error to suppose that the author of Deuteronomy was responsible for introducing legalism into the
religion of Israel by adopting a compromise position in which
he reinterpreted the faith of the prophets in terms of obedience
to the Law. It would be much more nearly true to say that the
whole purpose of his teaching was to reinterpret the Law in

prophetic terms. His disciples, as is only too plain, reduced the concept of Yahweh's covenant-relationship with Israel to the level of keeping 'all the words of this law which are written in this book' (Deut. 28⁵⁸, 29²⁵⁻²⁸; 1 Kgs. 11¹¹), but the author of Deuteronomy is not to be blamed for the distortions of his followers and editors.

The form of Deuteronomy, as a great address by Moses beginning with the Ten Commandments, suggests at first glance that the contents of the book are to be understood as the obligations imposed upon Israel by the Covenant which Yahweh made with the people at Sinai, like the laws of the Book of the Covenant in their present position in the Exodus narrative (Exod. 24⁷). Formally, it is true, the laws of Deuteronomy are represented at the outset as teaching given by Yahweh to Moses at Horeb (5¹⁻³³). The writer, however, makes comparatively little use of the term 'covenant' and, when he does so, it refers either to the giving of the Ten Commandments (5², ³, 9⁹, ¹¹, ¹⁵; cf. 4¹³, ²³), or to the promise which Yahweh made to the patriarchs (7⁸, ⁹, ¹², 8¹⁸; cf. 4³¹). In so far as he retains the association of the Law with the Covenant at Horeb, it is presented not as a code of stipulations to be observed, but, rather, as the means by which Israel may continue to enjoy her unique privilege of hearing 'the voice of the living God' (5²⁶). At Horeb, Yahweh spoke to his people 'face to face' (5⁴) and this means that the Law is to be understood as sharing the immediacy of prophetic revelation (cf. 34¹⁰⁻¹²; Exod. 33¹¹). The writer explicitly identifies himself and his 'Mosaic' teaching with Israelite prophecy, which, he declares, was itself instituted with Moses at Horeb and continues to disclose Yahweh's will to his people (18¹⁵⁻¹⁹). Throughout Deuteronomy what Israel is asked to do is not merely to observe the Law but to obey 'the voice' of Yahweh (8²⁰, 13⁴, 15⁵, 26¹⁴, 28¹⁵). There are many synonymous expressions which reveal the author's conviction that much more than formal obedience is involved in 'doing all the statutes and the ordinances'. It means *walking in Yahweh's ways* (8⁶, 10¹², 11²², 19⁹, 26¹⁷), *doing what is right and good* in his eyes (6¹⁸, 12²⁸), *cleaving* to him as a husband cleaves to his wife (10^{20}, 11^{22}, 13^4; cf. Gen. 2^{24}), behaving as his *sons* (14^1; cf. 8^5; Hos. 11^{1-4}) and, above all, *loving* him: 'provided you are careful to keep all this command-ment, which I command you this day, by *loving* the Lord your God' (19^9); 'you shall *love* the Lord your God with all your heart, and with all your soul, and with all your might' (see notes on 6^5 and 7^9).

The ground for this far-reaching reinterpretation of Law as love appealing for love in return is given most explicitly in the deuteronomist's model answer to a child's question:

When your son asks you in time to come, 'What is the meaning of the testimonies and the statutes and the ordinances which the Lord your God has commanded you?' then you shall say to your son, 'We were Pharaoh's slaves in Egypt; and the Lord brought us out of Egypt with a mighty hand . . . and he brought us out from there, that he might bring us in and give us the land which he swore to give to our fathers. And the Lord commanded us to do all these statutes, to fear the Lord our God, for our good always, that he might preserve us alive, as at this day' (6^{20-24}).

This means that the Law is to be understood as the generous gift of Yahweh, which accompanied his gift of the land of Canaan, in order that Israel should enjoy it, without falling from the unique privilege of being his very own people.

The writer was addressing himself to two closely related and pressing contemporary problems. First, there was the question of Israel's proper attitude to all the new opportunities for development which Palestine and its Canaanite culture afforded. On the one hand, groups like the Rechabites had totally rejected them and insisted on living the semi-nomadic life of the 'good old days' (see p. 95). On the other hand, the kings and the majority of the people had welcomed the new world and its wealth with open arms and in religion and morality had often virtually become Canaanites. The writer of Deuteronomy rejects both these solutions to Israel's problem. In opposition to the Rechabites, his attitude to the material opportunities of Palestine is extraordinarily positive and appreciative:

> For the Lord your God is bringing you into a good land, a land of brooks of water, of fountains and springs, flowing forth in valleys and hills, a land of wheat and barley, of vines and fig trees and pomegranates, a land of olive trees and honey, a land in which you will eat bread without scarcity, in which you will lack nothing, a land whose stones are iron, and out of whose hills you can dig copper. And you shall eat and be full, and you shall bless the Lord your God for the good land he has given you (8^{7-10}; cf. 6^{10-12}, 7^{13}, 8^{18}, 11^{10-12}).

According to Deuteronomy, the only proper attitude to Palestine is to accept it gratefully as Yahweh's gift and 'serve the Lord your God with joyfulness and gladness of heart, by reason of the abundance of all things' (28^{47}). The word 'rejoice' echoes through the book from beginning to end—'the Lord your God will bless you in all your produce and in all the work of your hands, so that you will be altogether joyful' (16^{15}; cf. $12^{7, 12}$, $16^{11, 14}$, 26^{11}); and the writer always shows an extraordinary sympathy towards people's legitimate desires ($12^{15, 20}$, 14^{26}, 18^6). To appreciate the immense significance of the writer's outlook, we must remember that the whole sphere of nature was by tradition as foreign to Mosaic Yahwism as it was native to the gods and cults of Canaanite fertility religion (see pp. 42–51). If Yahwism were to embrace the agricultural life of Israel, it was imperative that Canaanite influence should be totally wiped out. This is the motive underlying both the abolition of the local sanctuaries (see notes on 12^{1-14}) and the revival of the ancient notion of 'holy war', according to which the heathen were to be totally destroyed (see notes on 7^{1-11}). The writer finds the basis for this two-fold policy of accepting the land and rejecting the influence of its previous occupants in 'the word which the Lord swore to your fathers, to Abraham, to Isaac, and to Jacob' (9^5). This oath to the patriarchs is interpreted as including the promise of the land of Canaan (Gen. 12^7, $15^{17, 18}$; Deut. 11^9, 19^8, $26^{3, 15}$; see notes on 12^{8-14}) and the 'election' of Israel to be Yahweh's chosen people (14^2; see notes on 7^{1-11}). In the perspective of Deuteronomy, therefore, the deliverance from Egypt, the gift of the Land, and the gift of the Law were all part of the fulfilment of Yahweh's promise to the fathers of his chosen people (6^{21-24}, 10^{10-15}, $11^{8, 9}$).

The writer is clear, however, that it was with the Exodus that Israel's distinctive life as the people of Yahweh really began (see notes on $7^{7, 8}$). This fact provoked his second major problem. How was it possible for Israel in his own time to be related to the God who disclosed himself in history—in events which were of crucial significance, but were now past and in danger of being forgotten? The writer could not suppose that Yahweh was to be encountered as a real presence in the Temple and its cult, because they were part of the Canaanite outlook he had repudiated (see notes on 12^{1-14} and pp. 146 f.). The independent prophets, who were no less aware of the prob-lem, were proclaiming that Yahweh of the Exodus was to be met in contemporary history (see pp. 55–59), but our writer was a 'law teacher' and so radical a reinterpretation of Mosaic Yahwism was beyond him. Within his tradition, he did the next best thing and declared that *the Law was the means by which Yahweh of the Exodus was 'remembered' and through loyal response was known to be present with his people* (see notes on 15^{15}). Thus, for example, the ancient law of the sabbath is reinterpreted in terms of historical 'remembering' and moral response. The day was not to be kept holy for the cultic reason that it just was so, or for the legalistic reason that it was commanded to be kept so, but in order that the humanity of slaves should be recognized and that the whole community should *remember* their deliverance from Egypt and so *become* what they properly were—the people of God (5^{12-15}).

For Deuteronomy, obedience to the Law involved a spiritual and moral response in the depths of a man's being (cf. 26^{16}) and in every aspect of his life (cf. 6^{7}), for which, as we have seen, the only adequate word was love. By this means, Israel was to be dynamically related to those past events by which it became a distinctive people and so enabled to encounter *in the present* the God of the Exodus. Deuteronomy's reinterpretation of the Law as a gracious means of access to the present reality of Yahweh is a highly significant attempt to deal with a problem which confronts any faith founded in history and to which even Christianity has not yet discovered a completely satisfactory answer.

(v) *The origin of Deuteronomy*

The origin of Deuteronomy is unknown. The principal considerations which any speculation must take into account are briefly the following:

(i) Deuteronomy is a book of teaching based on ancient laws. Since its purpose is not to promulgate priestly legislation, its origin was not necessarily in priestly circles.

(ii) The distinctive style of the book is also found in the 'deuteronomic' editing of Israel's history from the Conquest to the Exile and in the book of Jeremiah. This suggests a date at the end of the monarchy and a close connexion with literary and learned activity.

(iii) The deuteronomic historian of 1 and 2 Kings clearly intends his readers to conclude that Deuteronomy was the inspiration of Josiah's reform in 621 B.C. (see pp. 118–25). On the evidence he provides (and there is no other), it is difficult to disagree.

(iv) Deuteronomy makes a very deliberate effort to explain, simplify, and exhort. Its passionate appeal for Israel's wholehearted response suggests that it comes from a period of religious revival and this again points to Josiah's reformation after the long and faithless reign of Manasseh.

(v) Deuteronomy's emphatic proclamation of Mosaic Yahwism and its detachment from the sphere of the cult make it improbable that the writer's intention is deliberately to exalt the status of the Temple (see pp. 219–22).

(vi) The complete absence from the book of the 'royal theology' which dominated Jerusalem (see pp. 51–55) suggests that it originated either outside the capital, or in Jerusalem circles critical of the pretensions of the monarchy. The latter is more probable, since the book was fundamental for the deuteronomic historian and he almost certainly wrote in Jerusalem.

(vii) Deuteronomy is familiar with prophecy and deeply influenced by it. The writer is often said to be particularly indebted to Hosea, but so also is Jeremiah and this suggests that it was in Jerusalem that he encountered the work of the northern prophet.

(viii) A further connexion with the north has been found in the Shechem covenant ceremony described in 27¹⁻²⁶ (see pp. 49 f.). It should be noted, however, that this passage is considered by most scholars to be a later addition to the body of the book.

(ix) The references in the book to the Levites, that is, the Yahwist priests of the local sanctuaries (see notes on 12⁸⁻¹⁴), have led to the widely accepted view that it had its origin in their preaching. It is further suggested that the Levites were the spokesmen of country folk still interested (even after a lapse of four centuries or so) in the possibility of waging 'holy war'. An alternative explanation of the 'military' passages of the book is that they have a clear theological purpose and were never intended to be interpreted literally (see notes on 7¹⁻¹¹).

(x) It may be more accurate to describe the author of Deuteronomy as a teacher rather than a preacher, in which case the possibility of his having been a well-informed lay scribe in the time of Josiah and Jeremiah cannot be ignored. The family of Shaphan, for example, included many such learned and loyal Yahwists (see p. 120).

6. 1-9 *The Great Commandment*

Deuteronomy had a profound influence on the writers of the New Testament and Jesus himself quoted vv. 4, 5 of this passage in answer to the question 'Which commandment is the first of all?' (Mark 12²⁸⁻³⁴).

1. *the commandment . . . God commanded me to teach you*. Vocabulary concerned with teaching and learning dominates Deuteronomy more than any other book of the Old Testament (5³¹, 6¹, 11¹⁹, 17¹⁹; cf. 31¹², ¹³, 4¹, ⁵, ¹⁰, ¹⁴), with the possible exception of Proverbs (cf. 4⁴, ¹¹, 5¹³, 6²³). It is interesting, therefore, to observe that *commandment*, one of Deuteronomy's favourite

words (7^9, 11^{13}, 13^{18}, 26^{18}), often means instruction given by a wisdom teacher (Prov. 2^1, 3^1, 4^4, $6^{20, 23}$, $7^{1, 2}$, 10^8, 13^{13}, 19^{16}). The *statutes* had their origin in decisions given by a judge, or by Yahweh as judge, and the *ordinances* originally meant things inscribed and, therefore, fixed, prescribed decrees. On *the land*, see pp. 209 ff. and notes on 12^{8-14}.

2. *that you may fear the Lord your God.* To inculcate the *fear* of Yahweh, meaning an obedient and grateful response to his goodness (cf. $10^{12, 13}$), is the goal of the deuteronomist's work as a teacher (cf. 2 Kgs. 17^{28}; Isa. 29^{13}). He did not differ from other teachers in holding out the promise *that your days may be prolonged* (11^9, 17^{20}, 22^7; cf. Prov. $3^{1, 2}$, 4^{10}, $7^{1, 2}$, 28^{16}). We may also compare the opening chapter of the Egyptian wisdom book, *The Instruction of Amen-em-opet* (see pp. 169 f.):

> Give thy ears, hear what is said . . .
> If thou spendest thy time while this is in thy heart,
> Thou wilt find it a success,
> Thou wilt find my words a treasury of life,
> And thy body will prosper upon earth.
>   (J. B. Pritchard, *Ancient Near Eastern Texts*, pp. 421-2)

3. *a land flowing with milk and honey.* Deuteronomy's positive appreciation of Canaan as the *promised* land reflects an important stage in the development of Israel's thinking about the relationship between Yahweh and the natural order. The bounty of nature takes its place in Yahweh's providential care for his people in history, but the matter is not pursued further. The writer never suggests that nature is as much Yahweh's realm as history and he is quite independent of the theology of Jerusalem, in which Yahweh's sovereignty in history had been subordinated to his creativity in nature. It was the achievement of Second Isaiah to appreciate the best in both worlds and weld them together (cf. 42^{5-17}).

4. *The Lord our God is one Lord.* The Hebrew has four words: 'Yahweh / our God / Yahweh / one.' The difficulty of translating them is suggested by the four possibilities proposed in the RSV.

It is probable that the declaration meant not only that Yahweh, the God of Israel, demanded his people's exclusive allegiance, but also that he alone was God (cf. 4³⁵, ³⁹, 7⁹). Verses 4–9 (with 11¹³⁻²¹ and Num. 15³⁷⁻⁴¹) are recited twice daily by Jews and called the 'Shema', the Hebrew for the first word, 'Hear'.

5. The author of Deuteronomy is the first Old Testament writer to make *love* towards God Israel's primary obligation (10¹², 11¹, ¹³, ²², 13³, 19⁹), corresponding to and in response to God's love for his people (7⁷⁻¹³, 23⁵; cf. 10¹⁵, ¹⁸; Hos. 3¹, 11¹). The word for love here, it is important to note, is the ordinary one, which elsewhere is used to describe a man's love for his wife and a slave's love for his master (21¹⁵, 15¹⁶). The word *heart* in Hebrew roughly means mind and will (cf. Mark 12³⁰) and *soul* a man's vitality; together they mean a man's whole being (see p. 251).

7–9. Teaching of the kind represented by Deuteronomy is reflected, perhaps, in Jeremiah's prophecy that when the new covenant is made, 'no longer shall each man teach his neighbour and each his brother, saying, "Know the Lord" ' (Jer. 31³⁴). The hyperbole of vv. 7, 8 is paralleled by the language of other teachers (Prov. 1⁹, 3³, 6²¹, ²², 7³), but it was eventually interpreted literally and led to the phylacteries which Jesus condemned (Matthew 23⁵).

7. 1–11 *The Holy War of the People of God*

Deuteronomy's wholehearted acceptance of the blessings of Canaan as the Promised Land contrasts sharply with his wholesale rejection of the Canaanites and their religion (see pp. 209 ff.). The writer declares his total opposition to Canaanite civilization by reviving and developing the ancient concept of 'holy war', in which, it was believed, Yahweh used to lead the tribes of Israel to victory against their enemies. An authentic sample of the fanatical devotion which inspired this sacred warfare may be found in the Song of Deborah (Judg. 5). In Deuteronomy, a comparable fanaticism finds expression in a number

of laws directly concerned with the waging of 'holy war' (20^{1-20}, 21^{10-14}, 23^{9-14}, 24^5), teaching discourses on the subject ($7^{1-5,17-26}$, 9^{1-5}), and interspersed comment (6^{19}, 11^{22-25}, 12^{29-31}, 19^1, 25^{17-19}). It is inconceivable that the author of Deuteronomy envisaged any military exploits along these lines during the last years of the monarchy and so it is doubtful whether the revival of the concept has any connexion at all with the reintroduction of a citizens' army in Judah after 700 B.C. (see pp. 5 f.). If one is looking for an historical explanation of this curious phenomenon, the resurgent nationalism in Judah after it shook itself free from Assyrian domination in the reign of Josiah affords the most probable background (see pp. 118–25). It is difficult, however, to escape the conclusion that the language of 'holy war' in Deuteronomy is the language of a theologian describing what Yahweh has done for his people and demanding in an environment still dangerously Canaanite their unqualified allegiance. This is resurgent Mosaic Yahwism rather than resurgent Judean nationalism and it no more stands in need of a political explanation than 'Onward, Christian Soldiers'. 'Holy war' provided imagery for prophetic oracles on the 'Day of the Lord' (Zeph. 1^{14-18}; Joel 2^{1-11}; see pp. 274–7) and for the Chronicler's ecclesiastical history, in which the enemies of the true faith are routed by nothing more forbidding than the Temple choir (2 Chron. 20^{1-23}). However,

---

THE ALIEN CULTURE OF THE NATIONS. This beautiful hollow carving, fashioned from a longitudinal section of an elephant's tusk, is the largest ivory head excavated in the ancient Near East ($6\frac{5}{16}$ in. high and $5\frac{3}{16}$ in. wide) and was found in 1952 at the bottom of a well in the North West palace of Nimrud, after lying in mud for 2,600 years. The hair, eyebrows, and pupils are stained black and must originally have made an even more effective contrast with the ivory cheeks. The fact that the head rests on a base and that both ears are drilled with a hole for a peg makes it probable that the carving was intended to stand as a decoration on a pedestal or in a niche. The lady's enigmatic smile has earned her the name 'Mona Lisa of Nimrud', but her identity is still unknown. She may be an Assyrian queen, or even the Phoenician goddess Astarte. Considered by some scholars to be of Phoenician workmanship, the carving is dated in the reign of Sargon II (722–705), more than a century before comparable sculpture was executed for the Acropolis of Athens (see M. E. L. Mallowan, *Nimrud and its Remains*, vol. i, pp. 128–32).

it re-emerges most fully (and with direct reference to Deuteronomy) in a document (? of the first century A.D.) from the Qumran community, which depicts the final struggle between the 'Sons of Light' and the 'Sons of Darkness'. Although the writer of Deuteronomy was not thinking of any apocalyptic encounter, he was convinced, nevertheless, that the choice which confronted Israel was a matter of life and death (cf. 30^{15}; see notes on 20$^{1-9}$).

1. The *seven nations* are simply quoted from a traditional list of the peoples expelled by Israel at the conquest of Palestine (cf. Josh. 3^{10}, 24^{11}; Gen. 10$^{15-18}$). Their primary purpose is to sound impressive.

2. *utterly destroy them.* This is the technical term for 'devoting' the conquered to Yahweh in 'holy war'. It is used to describe the destruction of idolatrous Canaanites (7$^{23-26}$, 20$^{16-18}$) and an idolatrous Israelite city (13$^{12-18}$).

5. For the paraphernalia of a Canaanite sanctuary, see p. 296.

6. The people of Israel differs from the nations of Canaan, because it is (*a*) *holy* that is, set apart for Yahweh; (*b*) *chosen* from all the nations of the world; (*c*) Yahweh's *own possession* (a word which is used elsewhere of private property, 1 Chron. 29^3; Eccles. 2^8). The formulation of Exod. 19$^{5, 6}$ was probably derived from this verse. Israel's election was part of the Yahwistic faith of the prophets (see pp. 269 f.), but in Deuteronomy it is given extra emphasis and a technical term (cf. 10^{15}, 14^2, 4^{37}).

7, 8. Israel's special status derives not from the people's merit but from the *love* of God (cf. 7^{13}, 10$^{15, 18}$, 23^5). The primacy of God's love is the fundamental teaching which unites the Bible (cf. 1 John 4^{19}). The word translated *redeemed* means ransomed (cf. Exod. 21^8), but it is often (as here) used metaphorically without any thought of payment (9^{26}, 13^5, 15^{15}, 21^8, 24^{18}; Hos. 13^{14}). The deliverance of Israel from *Egypt* is regarded as a fulfilment of Yahweh's promise to the patriarchs (see pp. 210 f.)

and is constantly referred to both in the introductory discourses (6^{21}, $7^{8, \, 18}$, $8^{\, 14}$, $9^{7, \, 26}$, 11^{1-7}) and in the laws ($5^{6, \, 15}$, 15^{15}, $16^{3, \, 12}$, $24^{9, \, 18, \, 22}$, 25^{17}, 26^{5-10}). The formula in 10^{19} and 23^7 suggests a different motive for Israel's grateful response.

9. The verse is rich in theological terms. Yahweh is (a) *God*, that is to say, 'God in heaven above and on the earth beneath; there is no other' (4^{39}); (b) *faithful*, that is to say, trustworthy and not capricious, especially in personal relationships; (c) one who *keeps covenant and steadfast love*. The term translated *steadfast love* (*ḥesedh*) means basically the loyalty which a *covenant* between two people involves (1 Sam. 20^8; 2 Sam. $9^{1, \, 3}$, 10^2; Gen. 21^{22-24}); *steadfast love*, therefore, is the content of *covenant* (cf. 1 Kgs. 8^{23}; Isa. 54^{10}). It is interpreted as demanding from Israel a *love* which finds expression in obedience (see notes on 6^5). On the use of the term *covenant* in Deuteronomy, see p. 208.

12. 1–19 *The abolition of the local sanctuaries*

The injunctions of this chapter are often referred to as 'the law of the single sanctuary', by which the *one* people of the *one* God was given *one* place of worship. It is also often suggested that the idea of a single sanctuary did not originate with Deuteronomy, but was deeply rooted in the tradition of Shechem as the central shrine of the tribal confederation before the institution of the monarchy (see pp. 49 f.). Support for this hypothesis is found in the fact that 12^{13-28}, which insists on worship at a *chosen* sanctuary (v. 14) without explicitly enjoining the destruction of the local sanctuaries (v. 13), is expressed in the *singular*, while 12^{1-12}, which makes the chosen sanctuary the *sole* sanctuary, is expressed in the *plural*. The influence of the old Shechem tradition is seen in 12^{13-28} and it is suggested that the writer of Deuteronomy embodied in his work this and other northern material, which was brought to the southern kingdom after the fall of Samaria in 721 B.C.

We are on firmer ground, however, in observing that the emphasis of this chapter as it now stands is more negative than positive and falls rather on abolishing the local sanctuaries than on uniting the people of God at the Jerusalem Temple. In contrast to the rich terminology of the Psalter, the only thing Deuteronomy has to say about the Temple is that it is the place in which Yahweh has chosen 'to put his name' (v. 5) and this is more a critical modification of its distinctive theology than an affirmation of it (see pp. 148 f.). It is difficult to suppose that a writer who secularized the eating of meat (vv. 15–19) and rationalized the offering of tithes (14^{22-29}) was passionately concerned to unite Israel at a single cultic centre. His root-and-branch opposition to the Canaanite worship of the local sanctuaries is much better attested.

2, 3. The high places are to be destroyed because they had been and were Canaanite sanctuaries (cf. 7^{1-5}). For their *pillars* and *Asherim*, see pp. 75 f.

4. This cryptic command, differentiating the worship of Yahweh from that of the Canaanites, is expounded in the verses which follow.

5. The ambiguity of the Hebrew of this verse reflects the sophistication of the writer's thought. He wishes to limit the worship of Yahweh to a single sanctuary without localizing his presence. The theological device he adopts is to say that Yahweh did not *dwell* in the Temple (cf. 1 Kgs. 8^{27-30}), but, rather, he chose to put *his name* there. In ancient thought, the *name* was part of its bearer's personality, almost a double of his being, and in revealing his name (Exod. $3^{13, 14}$), Yahweh had entrusted himself to Israel. Deuteronomy makes a further qualification when he says that Yahweh caused his name to 'tent' or 'tabernacle' in the central sanctuary (a nuance which is concealed in the RSV's *habitation* and *dwell*), since this term is intended to suggest a relationship to the Temple of a less settled and permanent kind than Yahweh's having established his home there (12^{11}, 14^{23}, $16^{2, 6, 11}$, 26^2).

6. On *burnt offerings* and *sacrifices*, see pp. 135 f.; *tithes*, cf. 14^{22-29}; Amos 4^4; *the offering that you present* was the portion 'lifted off'

and given to the priests (cf. Exod. 29²⁷, ²⁸); *votive offerings* were made in fulfilment of the worshipper's vow that he would offer sacrifice if his prayers were answered (cf. 23²¹⁻²³); on *freewill offerings*, see p. 137; *firstlings*, cf. 15¹⁹⁻²³.

7. *eat before the Lord*, in the communal meal (see pp. 135 f), *and ... rejoice*: joy is one of the most splendid and distinctive features of Deuteronomy's religion (see p. 210).

8–14. The writer, assuming Moses' time and place in Moab (*here this day*), emphasizes that the centralization of worship is an innovation. It belongs to the coming new order—the *rest* and the *inheritance*, which the writer's contemporaries now, in fact, enjoy in the good land of Canaan (cf. 8⁷⁻¹⁰, 11¹⁰⁻¹², 25¹⁹, 26⁵⁻⁹; cf. Josh. 21⁴³⁻⁴⁵). Yahweh's gift of the land to Israel is presented in Deuteronomy as the consummation of his dealings with his people; it takes its place, therefore, with the deliverance from Egypt as a summons to present obedience (19¹⁰, ¹⁴, 21²³, 24⁴, 26¹). *the Levite that is within your towns* (v. 12) probably refers to the priests of the local sanctuaries which were now being abolished. The tribe of Levi owned no land (18¹; Josh. 13¹⁴) and so the priests depended on the offerings of the people. The abolition of the local sanctuaries deprived the country priests of their livelihood, which is the reason for their being mentioned along with the poor as standing in need of assistance (12¹⁹, 14²⁷, ²⁹, 16¹¹, ¹⁴, 26¹², ¹³). The men referred to by the term 'Levitical priests' (literally, 'the priests, the Levites') are probably the priests of the Jerusalem Temple (17⁹, ¹⁸, 18¹, 24⁸; cf. 18⁷), who are also called simply 'priests' (17¹², 18³, 19¹⁷, 20², 26³, ⁴; cf. 21⁵). The provision of 18⁶⁻⁸ that the country Levites should be permitted to come and minister in the Temple was rejected by the Zadokite priesthood of Jerusalem (2 Kgs. 23⁹; see p. 123).

15–19. The deuteronomist fearlessly accepts the consequence of the abolition of sacrifice at the high-places and secularizes the eating of meat (cf. 14²²⁻²⁶). Hitherto, all meat, except game —the *gazelle* and the *hart*—had been eaten sacrificially; from now on, all animals could be killed and eaten at home (cf. vv. 20, 21) in what we regard as the ordinary way (except for the *blood*, v. 16; cf. Lev. 17¹¹). This meant that animal sacrifice was to disappear from the religious practice of the ordinary Israelite except on special occasions (vv. 17, 18). It would be impossible to conceive of a more radical break with Canaanite religion and the cultic practice which the Israelites had borrowed from them (see pp. 135 ff.).

15. 1–18 *Two sabbatical laws for the protection of the poor*

The character of the deuteronomist as a person is to be found in the good sense and generosity of his laws affecting people, rather than in his adoption of the fanatical terminology of 'holy war'. As we have seen (pp. 215 ff.), he used the concept of 'holy war', not because he was a zealous nationalist, but as part of his exposition of Israel's privilege and responsibility as the people of God. It was entirely congruous that Yahweh who disclosed his purpose by creating a people in the human sphere of history should be encountered and revered in the human sphere of social and personal relationships. These two related convictions constitute the core of Israel's historical and moral faith as it finds its fullest expression in the preaching of the prophets and the teaching of this book. The preaching and teaching differ in their manner of presentation and their underlying modes of experience, but both of them derive fundamentally from Mosaic Yahwism and they are more closely related to each other than is either to the cultic interpretation of Israel's faith which flourished at the local sanctuaries and in the royal sanctuary of Jerusalem. Whereas the cult borrowed largely from the cosmological myths and rituals of the Canaanites, the Mosaic tradition of Deuteronomy and the prophets drew on human experience as it found expression in international law and wisdom. The Jerusalem and Mosaic traditions both extended their range in the period of the monarchy, but they moved in different directions; the first towards nature and the second towards man.

(a) 15. 1–11 *Sabbatical release from debt*

Every seventh year will be a Year of Release in honour of Yahweh: those who have lent money to fellow Israelites must then drop their claim to repayment. This is a good example of a law which is not so much a law as an appeal to the moral awareness of Israel as the people of God. Its aim is to mitigate the evil effects of the economic and social developments which took place during the monarchy and to prevent the poor from sinking into permanent pauperism or slavery (see pp. 34–42).

1. The sabbatical year, or year of *release* (literally, 'letting drop'), in the Book of the Covenant (Exod. 23[10, 11]) and the Holiness Code (Lev. 25[1-7]) has nothing to do with debts, but is the year when cultivation must be dropped and the land allowed to lie fallow. It is this ancient cultic law which the deuteronomist rationalizes and reinterprets for his own day.

2. *And this is the manner of the release* introduces the new application of the old law to the problem of poor debtors.

3. The *foreigner* was not to be released from his debts, because he was in the land only temporarily for trade purposes. This law was not designed for business relations, but for the social well-being of the Israelite community. Deuteronomy reveals a deep conviction that Israel is the family of God by its distinctive use of the word *brother* in the singular (17[15], 19[18, 19], 22[1-4], 23[19, 20], 25[3]).

4–6. The law of release, as we have seen, is not for good business but for good community. In these verses the writer goes further. The moral response which underlies obedience to the law is a response to God and God can be thought of by the writer only in terms which would make the law unnecessary. He is not trying to bribe people into obedience by making bogus promises; he is, rather, affirming in his own characteristic terms that generosity to the poor is a part of the Israelite's religious allegiance. On *inheritance,* see notes on 12[8-14].

7–11. The writer is aware that the people of God live among the hard realities of this world, where *the poor will never cease* (v. 11) and calculating men refuse to lend to them when *the year of release is near* (v. 9), since any loan will then be tantamount to a gift. It is precisely for such generous giving that the writer is making an urgent appeal.

(b) 15. 12–18 *Sabbatical release from slavery*

Enslavement to an Israelite master was the extremity to which debtors were driven (see pp. 41 f.). The distinctive character of Deuteronomy may be seen in this case by comparison with the earlier casuistic law in the Book of the Covenant (Exod. 21²⁻¹¹). Deuteronomy extends its provisions to include women on an equal footing with men (v. 12), makes entry into voluntary service a secular rather than a cultic ceremony (v. 17), and appeals both to the Israelite's moral awareness (v. 18) and to his awareness of Yahweh who redeemed him from slavery in Egypt (v. 15; see notes on 7⁷, ⁸). The Book of the Covenant promulgates a detailed and precise piece of case law, while the deuteronomic teacher makes an appeal. The evidence suggests that both were largely ignored (Jer. 34⁸⁻¹⁶; Neh. 5¹⁻⁵).

12. The inclusion of the *Hebrew woman* shows that she is now regarded as a person and not merely as a possession (contrast Exod. 21⁷⁻¹¹). Similarly, in the deuteronomic version of the tenth commandment, the wife is differentiated from a man's domestic property and placed first (5²¹; contrast Exod. 20¹⁷). For further evidence of Deuteronomy's awareness of woman's proper status, see 21¹⁰⁻¹⁴, 22¹³⁻¹⁹, 24¹⁻⁵.

13, 14. *you shall furnish him liberally*. These verses are without parallel in the Book of the Covenant and speak the language not of law but of a warm and practical generosity.

15. *You shall remember*. The word *remember* is one of Deuteronomy's distinctive theological terms. Memory establishes the continuity between Yahweh's dealing with Israel in the past

and in the present (7^{18}, 8^2, 9^7, 24^9, 25^{17}) and makes actual for the present generation the ground of its faith and obedience (5^{15}, 15^{15}, 16^{12}, $24^{18, \ 22}$; cf. 8^{18}); see further, pp. 211 f.

16. *because he loves you* is an illuminating comment on the treatment of domestic slaves in Israelite society.

17. The ceremony of piercing the *ear* of the man or woman who voluntarily chooses to remain in perpetual slavery has not been satisfactorily explained. In Exod. 21^6, it is a cultic rite; in Deuteronomy it is no more than a domestic ceremony. Elsewhere in the ancient Near East, slaves were branded or marked with a tag like animals; it is probable, however, that the ear was pierced not for this purpose, but because it was the organ associated with hearing and obedience.

18. The deuteronomist's characteristically down-to-earth persuasiveness may reflect a knowledge that in Babylonia the debtor slave was supposed to be released after *three* years' service (Code of Hammurabi, § 117). There is little evidence that he was.

17. 14–20 *A king like all the nations*

There is no trace of the 'royal theology' of Jerusalem in Deuteronomy and this isolated passage on kingship is no exception. It regards the king as an unavoidable liability to be kept in check by subordination to the Law. This is poles apart from the piety of the Temple (see pp. 143 ff.). Even this grudging recognition of the existence of the monarchy may reflect the outlook of the deuteronomic historian rather than that of the original teacher. Deuteronomy is referred to as 'this law' (v. 18) in other passages which have been added to the book (1^5, 4^8, 27^3, 29^{21}, 30^{10}, 31^{26}) and the idea of its being kept by a priest in the Temple also points to the work of an editor.

14. *a king . . . like all the nations.* The writer shares the view of the later narrative of 1 Samuel which regards the monarchy as an alien innovation (1 Sam. 8^{1-22}, 10^{17-27}).

A KING LIKE ALL THE NATIONS. This line-drawing clarifies the detail of an ivory plaque discovered in the palace treasury of the Canaanite city of Megiddo and dated 1350–1150 B.C. It is 10 in. long and, as the holes in it indicate, was made to be fixed as decoration to some object like a sheath. The central figure is a king celebrating victory in war from an elaborate throne flanked by two sphinxes—winged lions with human heads (cf. fig. p. 79). It was to such Canaanite thrones that Solomon was indebted both for his own throne (1 Kgs. 10¹⁸⁻²⁰) and for the two cherubim of olivewood over which Yahweh was said to be enthroned in the 'holy of holies' of the Temple in Jerusalem (1 Kgs. 6²³⁻²⁸). The king is drinking from a bowl and is being offered by one of the royal ladies a lotus blossom (and the end of her shawl for use as a napkin!). Behind her stands another woman playing a nine-stringed lyre. She is followed by a soldier, armed with spear and shield, who is leading two naked prisoners, their hands bound behind them and attached by a rope to the harness of the two horses drawing the war chariot. It has been plausibly suggested that the figure in the chariot is another representation of the king himself. A soldier carrying a sickle-sword follows the chariot. At the opposite end of the ivory, behind the throne, two servants are shown preparing the king's refreshment and apparently using for the purpose a large jar with a lid decorated with the heads of a gazelle and a lion. The winged solar disc (on the right) is Asian and the long garments Syrian in type, although the basic artistic convention is Egyptian. The ivory vividly illustrates the diverse blend of cultural traditions upon which Solomon drew when he developed the Israelite monarchy after Canaanite models.

15. The monarchy is tolerated on conditions, as it is in the work of the deuteronomic historian (see pp. 65 f.). The possibility that a *foreigner* might be chosen as king has been taken to mean that the writer was thinking of the northern kingdom, but a crisis in Jerusalem may be indicated (cf. 2 Kgs. 11¹⁻²⁰, 21²³, ²⁴, 23³¹⁻³⁷).

16, 17. The king's horse trading with Egypt, his wives, and his wealth indicate that Solomon is the awful warning in the writer's mind (1 Kgs. 10¹⁴–11⁸; cf. 1 Sam. 8¹¹⁻¹⁸).

18. *a copy of this law* was misunderstood by the Septuagint translators as meaning 'this repetition of the law', from which

the name 'Deuteronomy' ('the second law') is derived. That the king should be governed by *this law* is the presupposition of the deuteronomic historian (see pp. 65 f.). For *the Levitical priests*, see notes on 12$^{8-14}$.

20. *that his heart may not be lifted up above his brethren*. This indicates a radical rejection of the Canaanite pretensions of Israel's monarchy.

20. 1–9 *Israel's good fight of faith*

As they now stand, these laws for the waging of 'holy war' are demands for the total commitment of faith (see notes on 7$^{1-11}$). At the Exodus, according to the Yahwist, Moses said to the people: 'Fear not, stand firm, and see the salvation of the Lord, which he will work for you today. . . . The Lord will fight for you, and you have only to be still' (Exod. 14$^{13, 14}$). In addressing Ahaz, Isaiah spoke the same language: 'Take heed, be quiet, do not fear, and do not let your heart be faint. . . . If you will not believe, surely you shall not be established' (see notes on Isa. 7$^{1-9}$); and similarly in another oracle: 'In returning and rest you shall be saved; in quietness and in trust shall be your strength' (Isa. 30^{15}). Three times in these laws fear is mentioned as a disqualification for 'holy war' (vv. 1, 3, 8); like the man with a new house, a new vineyard, or a new wife (vv. 5–7), the man who fears lacks the total commitment which God's warfare demands. No doubt ancient ritual regulations lie in the background of vv. 5–7, but as now interpreted they are nearer in meaning to Jesus' parable of those who excused themselves from attending the feast (Luke 14$^{15-26}$) and his sayings on discipleship (cf. Luke 18$^{29, 30}$). The uncommitted are not fit for the work of the Lord.

1. The faith that *the Lord your God is with you* is grounded in the conviction that it was he who acted in history and *brought you up out of the land of Egypt* (see notes on 7$^{7, 8}$). This is the way in which Mosaic Yahwism interpreted the primitive concept of 'holy war' (cf. 7$^{17-26}$; Judg. 4^{14}; 2 Sam. 5^{24}). It differs

significantly from the interpretation of war in the 'royal theology' of Jerusalem (see pp. 157 f.) and is radically transformed in the independent prophets' interpretation of Yahweh's action in contemporary history (see pp. 55–59).

2–4. It has been suggested that the address of the priest reflects the kind of preaching undertaken by the country Levites, in which (according to some scholars) Deuteronomy originated. But *the priest* thought of here is probably a priest of the Jerusalem Temple (see notes on 12⁸⁻¹⁴) and, in any case, he says nothing which was not generally current (cf. Isa. 7¹⁻⁹).

5–8. The first speech of the officers, in contrast with v. 8, looks like a rationalized version of regulations which ensured that the combatants in 'holy war', like the camp itself (23⁹⁻¹⁴), should be in a state of ritual purity (cf. Josh. 3⁵; 1 Sam. 21⁵; 2 Sam. 11¹¹). Things which are *new* often have a supernatural significance in primitive societies (cf. 1 Sam. 6⁷; 1 Kgs. 11²⁹; 2 Kgs. 2²⁰; Jer. 13¹; Deut. 21³). In v. 6, the expression *has not enjoyed its fruit* uses the ritual term meaning 'profaned', that is, put to common use, the new fruit being regarded as sacred (cf. Lev. 19²³⁻²⁵). The man in the parable who said 'I have married a wife, and therefore I cannot come' (Luke 14²⁰) was sheltering behind a very ancient tradition (v. 7; cf. 24⁵). The rationalizing reinterpretation already evident in vv. 5–7 becomes explicit in the psychological explanation of v. 8, which is clumsily appended with the phrase, *And the officers shall speak further*, and reveals how far the writer is removed from the ancient understanding of 'holy war' and the whole ritual outlook to which it belongs.

22. 1–25. 3 *Laws of humanity*

These characteristically humane laws of Deuteronomy are not peripheral to the writer's faith. They reveal, rather, that Yahwism was vitally concerned with what it means to be a human person.

22. 1–4. *A neighbour's lost property.* The briefer laws of the Book of the Covenant (Exod. 23⁴, ⁵) require help to be given to one's

enemy. In making the law refer to *your brother's* property, the deuteronomist is less likely to be weakening the earlier version than to be revealing his ignorance of it. Verses 2 and 3 are a good example of his style, his moral earnestness, and his determination to be fully understood.

8. *A safety precaution*. The roof of an Israelite house was a meeting-place (cf. Isa. 22¹). The Code of Hammurabi (§§ 229–33) makes builders responsible only for accidents caused by bad workmanship.

23. 15, 16. *Asylum for the runaway slave*. If this provision referred to an Israelite slave who simply sought asylum with another household round the corner, it would have meant the abolition of slavery. It is therefore more likely to mean that an Israelite slave who has fled to Palestine from a foreign master must neither be returned nor exploited as a slave. It is probable that the Canaanites practised the extradition of their own countrymen who escaped from foreign masters. Deuteronomy with more feeling for his own people and a greater humanity forbids it and declares that the freedom of the fugitive must be respected.

24. 10–13. *Pledges and human rights*. Although Hebrew law differentiated Israel from the commercial world of the ancient Near East by forbidding loans on interest within the community (Exod. 22²⁵; Deut. 23¹⁹, ²⁰), it recognized the need of the poor in permitting loans on the security of a pledge. Deuteronomy and the Book of the Covenant equally forbid the lender to keep as a pledge anything essential to life (vv. 12, 13 Exod. 22²⁶, ²⁷; cf. Amos 2⁸). Deuteronomy further protects the debtor by excluding from use as a pledge the mill needed for making bread (24⁶; cf. Job 24³) and by forbidding the lender to march into the house of the debtor as though he owned the place. He must wait at the door and (probably, before witnesses) receive the pledge which the debtor had chosen. This sensitive enlargement of the ancient law is distinguished by the deuteronomist's 'categorical' style.

24. 14, 15. *Hired labourers to be paid promptly.* There was urgent need for this law against exploitation and oppression in the later days of the monarchy (Lev. 19¹³; Ezek. 22²⁹; cf. Mal. 3⁵). The *sojourner* was a person who did not belong to the community but enjoyed its hospitality and protection. His status as a guest was midway between that of the native and the foreigner. Like the native Israelite, he kept the festivals (5¹⁴, ¹⁵, 16¹⁰⁻¹⁴, 26¹¹, 29¹⁰⁻¹³), but he was thought of as being inferior (14²¹, 28⁴³, ⁴⁴) and, therefore, like the poor, in need of special protection (14²⁹, 24¹⁴, 26¹², 27¹⁹).

25. 1–3. *Flogging of criminals controlled.* This piece of casuistic law is peculiar to Deuteronomy and lays it down that a man must be (*a*) *guilty*, (*b*) deserve *to be beaten*, (*c*) punished in the *presence* of the judge, and (*d*) *in proportion to his offence.* The deuteronomist's distinctive contribution is made in fixing the maximum number of stripes at *forty* (cf. 'the forty lashes less one'—to be on the safe side—of 2 Corinthians 11²⁴) and in recalling that the criminal is a fellow human being—*lest . . . your brother be degraded in your sight.* This humanism pervades the deuteronomist's outlook and is akin to that found in the wisdom literature of the ancient Near East (cf. Job 31¹³⁻¹⁵).

VI. PROPHECY

WHEN we speak of Old Testament prophecy, we most naturally think of that extraordinary succession of radical teachers whose names we know from the books ascribed to them—Amos, Hosea, Micah, Isaiah, Jeremiah, and Ezekiel, together with the anonymous exilic author of Isaiah 40–55. There can be no doubt that the message of these men sprang from a more profound and intense experience of God than is to be found anywhere else in Israel's tradition and remains unequalled in its power to communicate the distinctive character of Old Testament revelation.

It would be convenient if we could simply rest content with a definition of Hebrew prophecy in terms of these outstanding individuals, but the Old Testament evidence clearly shows that the phenomenon of prophecy in Israel was more extensive in time and diverse in character. Anonymous men called prophets appear in the record from the earliest days of the monarchy and continue, apparently in considerable numbers, until its final collapse in 587 B.C. It is impossible, therefore, to avoid asking how the few great prophets of the later period (760–538 B.C.) were related to the many anonymous prophets who seem to have played a recognized role in Israelite society for over four centuries.

Until comparatively recently, the most generally accepted answer to this question represented Israelite prophecy as a developing movement, from primitive beginnings early in the monarchy, through more independent figures like Elijah in the ninth century, to its full maturity in Amos and his sucessors. Indeed, this movement was often taken to represent not only the development of prophecy in Israel, but the evolution of Israel's central and distinctive religious tradition. Recent Old Testament scholarship has in many important respects cast doubt upon this evolutionary reconstruction, although it can hardly be said to have established any generally agreed alternative.

As we have already seen (pp. 48–51), Israel's central and distinctive religious tradition is now traced back not to primitive prophecy but to Moses and the Exodus; and its continuity is found to depend less on a succession of inspired prophets (although, like Elijah, they could and did speak out for it) than on more regular teachers, such as the loyal Yahwist priests (see pp. 203 ff.). There is a sense, therefore, in which the 'Yahwistic tradition', including, as it did, history and law, has displaced 'the development of the prophetic movement' as the key to Israel's distinctive faith. In consequence, we must now ask not only how the great independent prophets were related to the anonymous prophets of Israel, but also how they were related to the central tradition of Yahwism.

A second change in perspective has arisen from the explicit recognition that, apart from the prophets whose teaching has survived, the anonymous prophets were members of an established institution in the Hebrew kingdoms and that this institutional prophecy closely resembled the kind of prophecy we find in the neighbouring religions of the ancient Near East. It has become possible, therefore, to give a coherent account of Old Testament prophecy which, so far from leading up to Amos and his successors as the climax of a continuous development, demonstrates that they were really the odd-men-out— 'prophets' for want of a better name, rather than characteristic representatives of the institution.

These two changes mean that both the great independent prophets and the anonymous institutional prophets are now seen in a new context—the former in the context of Yahwism and the latter in the context of a widespread religious phenomenon. Inevitably, therefore, the relationship between the two has become problematical and the whole concept of 'Hebrew prophecy' infinitely more complex.

(i) *The institutional prophets*

The institution of prophecy first emerges in Israel at the very beginning of the reign of Saul, who, it is recorded, was instructed by Samuel to go to Gibeah: '. . . and there, as you come to the city, you will meet a band of prophets coming down from the high place with harp, tambourine, flute, and lyre before them, prophesying. Then the spirit of the Lord will come mightily upon you, and you shall prophesy with them and be turned into another man' (1 Sam. 10⁵, ⁶). Later, we are told: 'When they came to Gibeah, behold, a band of prophets met him; and the spirit of God came mightily upon him, and he prophesied among them. And when all who knew him before saw how he prophesied with the prophets, the people said to one another, "What has come over the son of Kish? Is Saul also among the prophets?"' (1 Sam. 10¹⁰, ¹¹). A comparable incident is recorded in connexion with Saul's search for David after his flight to Ramah:

> Then Saul sent messengers to take David; and when they saw the company of the prophets prophesying, and Samuel standing as head over them, the spirit of God came upon the messengers of Saul, and they also prophesied. . . . Then he [Saul] himself went to Ramah . . . and the spirit of God came upon him also, and as he went he prophesied, until he came to Naioth in Ramah. And he too stripped off his clothes, and he too prophesied before Samuel, and lay naked all that day and all that night. Hence it is said, 'Is Saul also among the prophets?' (1 Sam. 19²⁰⁻²⁴).

This evidence suggests that early Israelite prophecy was (a) a group phenomenon organized under a leader, (b) associated with sanctuaries, (c) violently frenzied in character, and (d) deliberately stimulated—for example by music. A similar picture emerges from the record of guilds of 'the sons of the prophets' in the ninth century B.C. (see notes on 2 Kgs. 2³, pp. 261 f.). They appear to have been drawn from the more impoverished section of Israelite society (cf. 2 Kgs. 4¹⁻⁷) and to have lived in communities under the charge of masters like Elisha (2 Kgs. 4³⁸, 6¹) at such ancient cult centres as Bethel and Jericho. Their predilection for the abnormal and irrational is evident from the fact that Elisha is depicted as a miracle-worker (see p. 248), clairvoyant (2 Kgs. 5²⁶, 6⁹, ¹², ³²) and, like the prophets encountered by Saul, as using music to stimulate prophetic trance (2 Kgs. 3^{13-20}). It comes as no surprise to discover that the 'sons of the prophets' were regarded with contempt as madmen (2 Kgs. 9^{11}; cf. 1 Sam. 19^{24}) and that the very word 'prophesy' became synonymous with 'raving' (see notes on 1 Kgs. 18^{29}, p. 256).

Although the early prophets were despised, they were also feared and held in superstitious awe (cf. 1 Kgs. 17^{18}, 18^7; 2 Kgs. 1^{13}). Because they were believed to be in direct contact with God, they were consulted both by individuals on private matters (cf. 1 Kgs. 14^{1-6}; 2 Kgs. $8^{7, 8}$) and by the king on matters of public policy, as when Ahab 'gathered the prophets together, about four hundred men, and said to them, "Shall I go to battle against Ramoth-gilead, or shall I forbear?" ' (see notes on 1 Kgs. 22^{1-40}). The prophets' established institutional role is confirmed by the pagan parallel of 'the four hundred and fifty prophets of Baal and the four hundred prophets of Asherah, who eat at Jezebel's table' (1 Kgs. 18^{19}; cf. 2 Kgs. 10^{19}).

Although there is little *direct* evidence that the Jerusalem prophets were also organized in guilds in the pre-exilic Temple (cf. Jer. 35^4), it is probable that the post-exilic Chronicler assumed their existence during the period of the monarchy and regarded the guilds of the Temple-singers of his own day as their direct successors (1 Chron. 25^{1-8}; 2 Chron. 20^{14-23}). Whether or not the Chronicler was correct in his belief, the way in which Micah, Isaiah, Jeremiah, and other contemporary sources explicitly associate prophets with the priesthood of Jerusalem leaves us in little doubt that the prophets had an official part in the worship of the Temple (Lam. 2^{20}; see notes on Jer. 23^{11}). This view has been strengthened by the recognition in recent years that some of the psalms may contain prophetic oracles (Pss. 12^5, 85^{8-13}, 91^{14-16}), or imply the utterance of them during the performance of the cultic ritual (see p. 141).

Most of our evidence for institutional prophecy in the later years of the monarchy comes, however, from the great independent prophets' condemnations of it (see notes on Jer.

23^{9-32}). Their indictment is, indeed, formidable. The prophets of Jerusalem 'commit adultery and walk in lies' (Jer. 23^{14}), sell and steal oracles like so much merchandise (Mic. 3^5; Jer. 23^{30}) and are a source of ungodliness for the whole land. Their utterances are either simply inventions (Jer. 14^{14}, $23^{16, 26}$; Ezek. $13^{2, 3}$), or the product of mere dreams (Jer. 23^{25-32}), so that they cruelly deceive the people by promising them ' "Peace, peace", when there is no peace' (Jer. $6^{13, 14}$, 14^{13-16}, $23^{16, 17}$; Ezek. 13^{10}; cf. Mic. 3^5). Although they claim to prophesy in the name of Yahweh, they were not sent or commanded to speak by him (Jer. $14^{13, 14}$, 23^{21}; Ezek. $13^{6, 7}$). The view that men like Jeremiah had no doubts about the institution of prophecy and were simply condemning the abuse of it (cf. Mic. 3^{11}) is severely challenged by the terms in which they criticize its contemporary representatives. At least, it is impossible to believe that they thought of themselves as their colleagues.

If, then, there are good grounds for thinking that guilds of professional prophets existed in both kingdoms throughout the monarchical period, what, we may inquire, was their function in Israelite society? The evidence makes it clear that, like the 'holy men' of many different religions in many different ages (such as the shamans of North Asia and the dancing dervishes of the Arab world), the institutional prophets of Israel exercised a two-fold role as specially endowed intermediaries between God and the people. As *representatives of the people in relation to God*, they played a leading part in the worship of the sanctuaries (cf. 1 Kgs. 18^{30}, 19^{10}; 2 Kgs. $4^{23, 27}$; see notes on 2 Kgs. 2^3 and Jer. 23^{11}) and, in particular, were specialists in prayer (1 Kgs. 13^6, 17^{20}, $18^{36, 37}$; 2 Kgs. 6^{17}; Jer. 27^{18}; cf. Gen. 20^7). As *representatives of God in relation to the people*, their principal function was to foretell future events (1 Sam. 2^{34} (cf. 4^{11}), 3^{19}, 9^6; 2 Sam. 12^{14}; Deut. $18^{21, 22}$; Jer. 28^9; see p. 66) and, like their colleagues the priests, give oracular guidance to those who consulted them: 'And when Saul inquired of the Lord, the Lord did not answer him, either by dreams, or by Urim, or by prophets' (1 Sam. 28^6). Since the institutional prophets were professional consultants, it is obvious that they must have had at their command recognized and regular techniques for obtaining guidance in answer to their clients' inquiries. The general term for these techniques was 'divination' (Mic. 3^{11}), whether the oracle was obtained by frenzied dancing (1 Kgs. 22^{10-12}), the stimulation of trance (2 Kgs. 3^{15}), visions (Mic. 3^{5-7}), dreams (Jer. 23^{25-32}; cf. Num. 12^6), the interpretation of omens, (cf. 2 Sam. $5^{23, 24}$), or other familiar methods (cf. Ezek. 21^{21}). The professional prophets' service to the community was by no means limited to divination. Popular credulity credited them with the power to work extraordinary miracles (see p. 248) and to determine the course of events by acts of imitative magic (1 Kgs. 22^{5-12}; 2 Kgs. 13^{14-19}).

The conclusion is clear. Institutional prophecy in Israel was simply a particular version of a widespread religious phenomenon. It was known in Phoenicia (2 Kgs. 10^{19}; see notes on 1 Kgs. 18^{19}, p. 255) and (as the Mari texts now reveal) in Mesopotamia. It exists even today among the Rwala Bedouin in northern Arabia and in a form which shows a remarkable correspondence to prophecy in ancient Israel, as may be seen from the following description:

War expeditions on a large scale are always accompanied by a sorcerer who instructs the commander in anything he may undertake. The latter asks the sorcerer's advice only on occasions when he is at a loss what to do. Then the seer stimulates himself with music and works himself into an ecstasy, which helps him hear the angel speak and proclaim the will of Allâh [cf. 2 Kgs. 3^{4-20}, especially vv. 11, 15]. Very often a sorcerer is summoned to the bedside of a person who is seriously ill. He comes either with all or a few of his disciples and settles down in the tent as a regular guest. During the day, but especially in the evening, he orders his disciples to play, while he squats by the fire with his head wrapped up and his face in his hands, listening to the music [cf. 1 Kgs. 18^{42}, 19^{13}]. After a while he begins to contort the upper part of his body, jumps up, seizes a small drum, beats it wildly, circles around the fire, and, dancing around the patient, raps him with the drum on the head and legs; then, throwing the drum aside, he lies above the patient, supporting himself by the feet and hands, breathes into his mouth and nostrils, kneels down, rubs the patient on the breast, stomach, and back, jumps up, dances around,

and then, lying on him again, mumbles unintelligible words [cf.
1 Kgs. 17¹⁷⁻²⁴; 2 Kgs. 4³²⁻³⁷] (quoted by A. R. Johnson, *The Cultic
Prophet in Ancient Israel*, from A. Musil, *The Manners and Customs of the
Rwala Bedouins*, pp. 402 f.).

Like the sacrificial cult with which it was so closely associated,
institutional prophecy was not a distinctively Israelite phenomenon. Although during the period of the monarchy it became
deeply embedded in the religious life of Israel and at times
emerged as an influential nationalistic force to fight with
fanatical zeal against the heathen (see pp. 89–95), it did not
originate in Mosaic Yahwism and by its very nature was ill
fitted either to represent or transmit a faith which found God's
self-disclosure in history and knowledge of the divine in moral
obedience.

(ii) *The independent prophets*

The recent recognition of the importance of institutional
prophecy throughout the period of the monarchy has made the
relationship to it of prophets like Amos, Hosea, Micah, Isaiah,
and Jeremiah a much-debated question. Two main views are
possible. We may concentrate on the fact that these radical
teachers of the eighth and seventh centuries B.C. were called
prophets like their anonymous contemporaries and are represented as sharing in some degree their experience, their role,
and their methods. From these considerations, we may be led
to conclude that it is wrong to make a sharp distinction between
the two types of prophet, as though one were 'true' and the
other 'false', and necessary to suppose that they were engaged
in a common task, even to the extent of collaborating in the
cult of the sanctuaries. An alternative and very different view
is possible. We may insist that it is misleading to give too much
weight to the title 'prophet' and to concentrate on the common
external features with which the title is associated, since these do
not go to the heart of the matter and, in any case, were almost
certainly exaggerated in the tradition which preserved and
shaped the prophetic books (see pp. 242 f.). The conclusion to
which we may be led is that Amos and his successors were even

more distinctive than they are now represented as being and
that they cannot be adequately understood as a variety, even
a rare variety, of prophecy as an institutional phenomenon.

We may approach the current debate by setting down a
number of considerations which are not generally disputed.
(1) The independent prophets are nowhere depicted as being
members of prophetic guilds; they are figures who stand alone.
(2) The independent prophets were remembered for what they
said rather than for what they did; only from them has a body
of teaching been preserved. (3) The independent prophets
were not specialist consultants, who were paid for their services
(see notes on 2 Kgs. 5^{16}, p. 264); characteristically, they take
the initiative in proclaiming their message, without waiting to
be asked. (4) The independent prophets were not workers of
miracles; the healing of Hezekiah and the miraculous reversing
of the sun ascribed to Isaiah (2 Kgs. 20^{1-11}) come from a highly
legendary source, which, in providing the exception, prove
the rule. (5) The independent prophets did not practise clair-
voyance; their oracles concerning the future were not detailed
predictions arising out of any special faculty of foresight, but,
rather, proclamations of what was morally certain on the basis
of their spiritual insight. (6) The independent prophets did not
employ artificial stimuli (like music) or techniques of divination
(like dreams) to achieve their oracular utterances; they spoke
because they could not remain silent (see notes on Jer. 15^{10-21},
20^{7-18}). (7) The independent prophets did not ascribe their
experience or activity to the violent power of the spirit (see notes
on Mic. 3^{8}); the variety of the literary forms they employ, the
individuality of their style and the coherence of their message
exclude the possibility that they proclaimed their oracles in a
state of irrational frenzy. (8) The independent prophets were
fully aware of the activities of the institutional prophets and
were vehemently opposed to them (see notes on Jer. 23^{9-32},
29^{24-32}; Mic. 3^{5-12}). (9) At least two, and probably three, of the
pre-exilic independent prophets proclaimed the destruction
of Jerusalem and its Temple (see notes on Mic. 3^{9-12}; Jer.
7^{1-15}, 26^{1-16}; Isa. 29^{1-8}) and all five of them were vehemently

critical of the sacrificial worship of the sanctuaries (see notes on Mic. 6⁶⁻⁸). The institutional prophets, on the other hand, played an official part in the cult. (10) The independent prophets were characteristically prophets of judgement, whereas the institutional prophets were exclusively prophets of salvation (cf. Jer. 6¹⁴, ₍ 8⁸, ⁹; see notes on Jer. 4⁹, ¹⁰ and 1 Kgs. 22¹⁻⁴⁰). It is probably among the latter that Nahum and Habakkuk should be reckoned. Nahum's triumphal celebration of the fall of Nineveh, the capital of the Assyrian empire, in 612 B.C. is widely held to be a liturgy composed by a cultic prophet and the core of the book of Habakkuk (2⁶⁻²⁰) may well represent another cultic prophet's savage warning to the Assyrians in approximately the same period.

These ten points of difference strongly suggest that there was a deep gulf between the two types of 'prophet', but a number of counter-arguments are regularly advanced and these must be considered before any final conclusion is reached.

(1) One of the most obvious features in common between the institutional and independent prophet is the use of so-called *symbolic actions*. Just as the institutional prophet Zedekiah 'made for himself horns of iron, and said, "Thus says the Lord, 'With these you shall push the Syrians until they are destroyed' " ' (1 Kgs. 22¹¹) and Elisha on his death-bed 'laid his hands upon the king's hands' before he shot the arrows and struck the ground with them (2 Kgs. 13¹⁴⁻¹⁹), so also the independent prophets are recorded as having performed strange and significant acts. Isaiah, it is said, went about Jerusalem for three years stripped like a prisoner of war, as a warning that Egypt would be conquered by the Assyrians and was, therefore, useless as Judah's ally (see notes on Isa. 20¹⁻⁶). Jeremiah was commanded to go to one of the gates of Jerusalem and deliberately smash a bottle, as a sign that the idolatrous city would be irreparably smashed (Jer. 19¹⁻¹⁵), and, on another occasion, to wear an ox-yoke, as a sign that Judah must accept the yoke of Babylon (Jer. 27¹–28¹⁷; cf. 13¹⁻¹¹, 43⁸⁻¹³, 51⁵⁹⁻⁶⁴; see notes on 32¹⁻¹⁵). It is clear that all these symbolic actions are similar in form and that they are related to primitive acts of imitative

magic, which in the ancient Near East (as elsewhere) were held actually to bring about the situation they depicted. Technically, the prophetic examples are not magical, because Yahweh is not coerced by the acts but, rather, is their originator; he commands the prophets to undertake them and, like his words, they are the expression of his purpose. Nevertheless, the symbolic actions of the institutional prophets were not far removed from the realm of magic, since they were evidently expected to effect a change in the situation (cf. 2 Kgs. 13^{19}). It is often asserted that the similar acts of the independent prophets were performed with a similar intention. While it is impossible to prove the contrary, it is probable that the similarity is superficial and has been greatly exaggerated. The acts of the independent prophets have the appearance of being genuinely symbolic, rather than in any sense magical; they are always public demonstrations which declare Yahweh's purpose to his people, on the principle that actions speak louder than words, and are always intended to provoke a responsible response (see notes on Jer. 5^{12-14}, 32^{1-15}). They are, moreover, relatively rare in the records of the independent prophets and some of them look like legends which originated in later popular tradition (Jer. 13^{1-11}, 43^{8-13}, 51^{59-64}). The book of Ezekiel, which in so many ways is a good witness to later popular tradition, abounds in examples of prophetic symbolism (Ezek. 4^{1-17}, 5^{1-17}, 12^{1-20}, 24^{15-27}, 37^{15-23}), but it explicitly presents them as being simply a method of teaching (cf. 24^{19}, 37^{18}). We may conclude, therefore, that the evidence of symbolic actions does nothing to narrow the gap between institutional and independent prophecy.

(2) More attention has recently been drawn to the fact that the independent prophets, no less than the institutional prophets, were representatives of the people before Yahweh in prayer; they were *intercessors* as well as spokesmen. There can be no doubt that the independent prophets felt a deep compassion and responsibility for Yahweh's people as they stood under the threat of divine judgement and that this naturally led them to intercede on their behalf (cf. Amos $7^{2, 5}$; Jer. 7^{16}, 11^{14}, 14^{11}, 18^{20}). There is no evidence, however, that they

regarded themselves as powerful specialists in prayer like the institutional prophets (cf. Jer. 27^{18}) and it is significant that Jeremiah replies to three requests that he should intercede for the people with a word of rebuke (Jer. 21$^{1-10}$, 37$^{1-10}$, 42$^{2, 20}$). Isaiah's reassuring reply to Hezekiah's request for the prophet's prayer (2 Kgs. 19$^{1-7}$) is without parallel and merely illustrates the tendency in popular tradition to approximate the independent prophets to the more familiar institutional prophets.

(3) The independent prophets, it is claimed, resembled the institutional prophets in the *abnormality of their experience*; they, too, lost control of their faculties and received their divine revelations in a state of frenzy. For lack of any decisive evidence of the independent prophets' inner experience, opinion on this subject is likely to remain divided. The account we have of their 'calls' to become Yahweh's spokesmen are all characterized by a sense of responsibility which totally excludes the idea that they were beside themselves in any kind of abnormal frenzy (see notes on Amos 7$^{14, 15}$; Isa. 6$^{1-13}$; Jer. 1$^{4-10}$). Their visions, too, are sober and restrained (see notes on Amos 7^{1}–8^{3} and Jer. 1$^{11, 12}$) and presuppose a continuous, personal, and intelligent knowledge of God, which is well described as being present in his divine 'council' (see notes on Jer. 23^{18}). This is not to deny, however, that the religious experience of the great independent prophets was quite out of the ordinary, as the agonized 'confessions' of Jeremiah make perfectly plain (see notes on Jer. 15$^{10-21}$, 20$^{7-18}$; cf. 4^{19}, 5^{14}, 6^{11}, 23^{29}). Extraordinary religious experience, as a remarkable passage in the book of Numbers recognizes, may, however, be of very different kinds: 'If there is a prophet among you, I the Lord make myself known to him in a vision, I speak with him in a dream. Not so with my servant Moses; he is entrusted with all my house. With him I speak mouth to mouth, clearly, and not in dark speech; and he beholds the form of the Lord' (12$^{6-8}$). To this we may add a comparable description: 'Thus the Lord used to speak to Moses face to face, as a man speaks to his friend' (Exod. 33^{11}). Amos, Hosea, Micah, Isaiah, and Jeremiah were

not frenzied recipients of visions and dreams like the institutional prophets (see notes on Mic. 3^{5-8}); they shared the privilege of Moses and knew God in direct and personal encounter.

(4) The strongest argument for affirming a close relationship between the independent and institutional prophets is that they are called by the same name; both are said to *prophesy*. Thus we read: 'Then the *prophet* Jeremiah spoke to Hananiah the *prophet*. . . . "The prophets who preceded you *and me* from ancient times prophesied war, famine, and pestilence against many countries and great kingdoms" ' (Jer. 28^{5-8}). Since Hananiah is clearly an institutional prophet, the association of the two types, it seems, could hardly be closer. Against this, however, must be set a number of significant facts: (*a*) the overwhelming majority of the references to 'prophets' and 'prophesying' in the Old Testament describe institutional prophets; (*b*) the description of the independent figures as 'prophets' appears to be confined to material which shows the influence of the work of editors after 587 B.C. (cf. Isa. 37^2, 38^1, 39^3; Jer. 1^5, 19^{14}, 20^2, 25^{13}, 29^1, 45^1, 46^1, 47^1) and more particularly the deuteronomists (cf. Jer. 26^{4-6}, 29^{19}, 35^{15}, 44^4; Amos 3^7); (*c*) the independent prophets are never recorded as describing themselves as 'prophets', except, by implication, Isaiah, who refers to his wife as 'the prophetess' (Isa. 8^3). Amos quite explicitly denies that he was a prophet or one of 'the sons of the prophets', although he is compelled to use the verb 'prophesy' to describe his work as Yahweh's spokesman to the people (see notes on Amos $7^{14, 15}$; cf. 3^8). In the light of this evidence, it is difficult to avoid the conclusion that the use in our sources of the words 'prophets' and 'prophesy' for both institutional and independent prophets is far less significant in determining their relationship than at first appears. Indeed, it may mainly indicate that the writers of the deuteronomic school had approximated the two types in the interest of their comprehensive theory that Yahweh was sovereign and active throughout Israel's history by sending 'his servants the prophets' (2 Kgs. 9^7, $17^{13, 23}$, 21^{10}, 24^2; cf. Jer. $7^{25, 26}$, 26^5, 35^{15}). The prophets who play so large a part in 1 and 2 Kings (see

pp. 66 f.) are certainly a curious conflation of the institutional
and independent types and it is possible that we are primarily
indebted to the deuteronomic historian for the once popular
and still prevalent notion that all Israel's prophets belonged to
a single and developing tradition. The conflation (not to say
confusion) of the two types in later tradition was made easier
by the fact that both claimed to be Yahweh's *spokesmen*, which
appears to be the basic meaning of the term 'prophet' (*nābhî*).
It is derived by most scholars from the Accadian verb *nabû*, to
'call', either in the passive sense of one who has been 'called',
or, more frequently, in the active sense of one who 'calls' or
'speaks'. The latter interpretation is supported by two alternative descriptions of the relationship between Moses and
Aaron in the late (post-exilic) sections of the book of Exodus.
In the first, Aaron is represented as Moses' *spokesman*: 'And you
[Moses] shall speak to him and put the words in his mouth; and
I will be with your mouth and with his mouth, and will
teach you what you shall do. He shall speak for you to the
people; and he shall be a mouth for you, and you shall be to
him as God' (4[15, 16]). In the second description, Aaron is called
Moses' *prophet*: 'And the Lord said to Moses, "See, I make
you as God to Pharaoh; and Aaron your brother shall be your
prophet. You shall speak all that I command you; and Aaron
your brother shall tell Pharaoh to let the people of Israel go
out of his land" ' (7[1, 2]). A prophet was God's spokesman and
by the time of the Exile (as the marginal note of 1 Sam. 9[9]
suggests) the term had acquired so wide a meaning that
the distinction between the various different types was easily
blurred.

If, as appears necessary, we conclude that the independent
prophets were in a class apart and are to be differentiated
sharply from the institutional prophets, it by no means follows
that we must represent them as isolated individuals detached
from the mainstream of Israel's religious tradition. This view,
which used to dominate the interpretation of 'canonical'
prophecy, has now rightly been abandoned. The content of
their message proves beyond any doubt that they were heirs to

and representatives of the continuing tradition of Mosaic Yahwism, as it found expression in the ministry of the priests at loyal sanctuaries and in the teaching given both in the schools of wisdom and in the domestic circle of the family (see pp. 49 ff.). There is equally no doubt, however, that their reinterpretation of Mosaic Yahwism was radical in the extreme —so radical, that the preservation of their preaching will never cease to be a source of wonder.

(iii) *From prophetic oracle to prophetic book*

As they now stand, the four great collections of prophetic literature—the 'Major Prophets' (Isaiah, Jeremiah, and Ezekiel) and the so-called 'Minor Prophets' (including Amos, Hosea, and Micah)—bear witness to the convictions and concerns of the post-exilic Jewish community, for it was only after the return from Babylon that these great literary documents were brought into their final shape. The aim of critical scholarship is to select from this mass of material those parts of it which bear reliable witness to the convictions and concerns of the prophets themselves.

The independent prophets were primarily public speakers, who characteristically communicated their teaching in brief poetic oracles, introduced for the most part by a formula of the kind used by messengers throughout the ancient Near East— 'Thus says Yahweh' (cf. Gen. 32^{3-5}; Ezra 1^2; 1 Kgs. 2^{30}). The style of these oracles is full of variety and violence (cf. Hos. 5^{12}; Isa. 7^{20}; see pp. 285 f.). The unexpected and shocking content of the prophets' message was evidently matched by their unexpected and shocking exploitation of all sorts of familiar forms, whether sacred or secular. Thus, we find prophetic versions of the priestly direction (Isa. 1^{10-17}), the funeral dirge (Amos 5^2), the liturgical lament (Hos. 6^{1-3}), the legal indictment (Isa. 3^{13-15}), the lesson of the wisdom teacher (Amos 3^{3-8}), and the popular song (Isa. 5^{1-7}, 22^{13}). The very daring of the prophets' stylistic forms illustrates their freedom and confirms their independent status. The fact that it is a *finished* style raises, however, a number of complicated questions, many of which cannot, unfortunately, be answered with any degree of confidence. Did Amos, the first known practitioner of this finished style, create it himself, or did he inherit it? If he inherited it, from whom and through what channels did it reach him? Although, according to our records, Amos is the first prophet of his particular kind, it is always possible that there were comparable prophets earlier, who either disappeared without leaving any trace, or now appear in the record in a form which misrepresents their true character. Elijah is the obvious example of a prophetic figure who may well have resembled Amos much more closely than is suggested by the popular biographical narratives in which the memory of him has been preserved (see pp. 248 f.). This possibility further suggests that what we know as 'written' prophecy may have emerged in the eighth century B.C. simply because it was only then that the independent kind of prophet made contact with a scribal tradition capable of preserving and transmitting his teaching (see p. 178). The opportunity for speculation is endless. However, whether or not Amos was the first of the independent prophets and whether or not he himself created the prophetic style, his skilled use of it and the faithful preservation of his polished oracles both point to an intellectual tradition which is too easily overlooked.

The difficult problem as to how the prophets' oracles came to be preserved gains in significance when we see that it has a direct bearing on the kind of people they themselves were. A man, that is to say, is known by the company he keeps. At the present time, the most-discussed view of the matter is that for the preservation of the prophets' oracles we are primarily indebted to their own intimate circle of disciples. It is held that the disciples learnt by heart the content of their master's teaching and transmitted it to their successors by word of mouth, until, finally, perhaps as late as the period of the Exile, it was recorded in writing. Most scholars hold a modified version of this theory and assert that the oracles were handed down partly in written and partly in oral tradition, with mutual interaction between the two. Such a reconstruction is plausible, but serious problems remain.

If the independent prophets were laymen and if, as seems probable, their so-called 'ministries' were not life-long commissions but occasional and brief interventions, it is very difficult to believe that they surrounded themselves with circles of disciples. There is, moreover, no clear evidence that this was the case (since Isa. 8^{16} is, at best, highly ambiguous). The ministry of Jeremiah is exceptional in that it seems to have been permanent, but, although he had a secretary and an influential group of friends, he is never seen in the company of any circle of disciples. In the one case of a prophet who is known to have cultivated disciples, namely Elisha (see notes on 2 Kgs. 2$^{1-18}$, pp. 261 f.), the kind of pious tradition they transmitted about their master does not suggest itself as a very promising precedent for understanding the practice of the later prophets (see pp. 248 f.). Even if it were conceivable that Amos and Micah attracted disciples in their lifetime, is it really possible to imagine that small circles of devotees remained in being, generation after generation, solely to treasure and transmit orally a small amount of the master's teaching, until, over a century later, they relinquished their task to a sympathetic scribe? However retentive the oriental memory and however reliable oral tradition may have been in the transmission of the Koran (to which appeal is often made), the faithful preservation of the teaching of men like the independent prophets, who were of small significance in their own time, demands a transmitting tradition of greater stability than anything they themselves could possibly have created.

What that tradition may have been is suggested by the only detailed evidence we possess about the recording of spoken oracles and this occurs in the book of Jeremiah. Two features of Jeremiah's situation are significant. First, he had a secretary to whom he dictated his oracles (see notes on Jer. 36$^{1-32}$); secondly, he was in close touch with a family of educated and influential citizens, who showed their sympathy with his teaching by protecting him on more than one occasion when he fell foul of the authorities (see notes on 2 Kgs. 22³). It is at least possible that this group of men demonstrated their sympathy with the prophet in a more permanent way by helping to preserve his collected oracles (see p. 351). Although, no doubt, Jeremiah's circumstances were in some ways unrepresentative, there is no reason why the independent prophets of the eighth century should not equally have enjoyed the support of a section of the loyal Yahwists among whom they were brought up and whose faith they shared and, again, no reason why these sympathizers should not have been sufficiently educated to preserve the prophets' oracles in writing. Literacy at this time was more widespread than is often supposed (see pp. 174 f.); the eighth-century prophets were certainly acquainted with the teaching of the wisdom school (see pp. 175–81); and there are explicit references to the prophets' writing down their oracles (Isa. 8¹⁻⁴, ¹⁶, 30⁸; Hab. 2²; Jer. 30²; cf. Ezek. 2⁸–3³). Since in the ancient world all written documents were intended for reading aloud, the suggestion that the prophets' oracles were written down from the outset (and, perhaps, by the prophet himself) in no way excludes the possibility of a dependent and lively oral tradition, which would in its turn have influenced the written tradition, as and when it was recopied by the scribes. The advantages of this literary hypothesis over the oral theory are, it may be claimed, quite considerable: (1) it accounts for the crispness with which the prophets' oracles have been preserved; (2) it points to an established and stable transmitting tradition, which no private circles of disciples could possibly have provided; (3) it helps explain the common features and continuity between the individual prophets; and, finally, (4) it anchors the prophets firmly in the Yahwist tradition and suggests how their radical reinterpretation of it came to have permanent consequences.

ELIJAH AND ELISHA

Elijah and Elisha are figures of fundamental importance. Elijah, in particular, illuminates the vitality of Mosaic

Yahwism in its life-and-death struggle with resurgent Canaanite religion and culture in the ninth century B.C. and anticipates the emergence of the new kind of prophecy we find in Amos and his successors, through whom Mosaic Yahwism found its fullest and finest expression.

Unfortunately, the only surviving records of Elijah and Elisha are biographical narratives and these often tell us more about the writers than about their venerated master. While it is possible, for example, to correct the picture of Isaiah which emerges from the narratives of 2 Kgs. 19–20 by the independent and less garbled tradition in the book of Isaiah, in the case of Elijah and Elisha there is no such counter-check. We are compelled, therefore, to evaluate the material by general criteria and take a great deal of it with a pinch of salt. With the exception of Elijah's intervention in the scandal over Naboth's vineyard (see notes on 1 Kgs. 21$^{1-23}$), all the activities of the two prophets are recounted in a context of miracle. In much of the material about Elisha (2 Kgs. 2$^{14-25}$, 4$^{1-44}$, 6$^{1-23}$, 13$^{14-21}$), it is evident that the writer's sole purpose is to demonstrate the prophet's supernatural stature and miraculous powers. We are regaled with stories about the dividing of the Jordan, the disinfecting of the spring at Jericho, the massacre of the mocking children, the production of oil in the widow's cruse, the reviving of the widow's dead son, the neutralizing of deadly poison in the pot, the feeding of a hundred prophets, the floating of an iron axehead, the blinding and restoring of Aramean raiders, and, finally, the raising of the dead by the deceased prophet's bones. It may fairly be taken for granted that these pious legends come from the uncritical veneration of Elisha's disciples in the prophetic guilds (see notes on 2 Kgs. 2^3). The incidental records of Elisha's intervention in political affairs in the years 850–800 B.C. (2 Kgs. 3$^{4-27}$, 8$^{7-15}$, 9$^{1-6}$, 13$^{14-19}$) and the delicately sophisticated story of his healing of Naaman (see notes on 2 Kgs. 5$^{1-19}$) seem to have originated in less crude and credulous circles.

The best testimony we possess to Elisha's personal stature, however, is his connexion with Elijah and the comparatively

sober records of Elijah's ministry. Elisha was Elijah's disciple
and successor and it is probable that he was originally responsible for collecting most of the material about his master, which
subsequently was preserved and amplified (cf. 1 Kgs. 17; 2 Kgs.
1, 2) in the prophetic guilds of the northern kingdom. We have
no means of knowing just how far Elisha was, in fact, detached
from the prophetic guilds with which he is now identified, but
in the case of his master there is no doubt. Elijah stands alone.

The sudden emergence of Elijah in the reign of Ahab (869–
850) discloses the desperate conflict which then existed between
Yahwism and Baalism. Although Jezebel's active promotion of
the cult of her Phoenician gods and goddesses exacerbated the
struggle, it is improbable that her importations introduced to
Israel anything that was really new. The paganism of Tyre
simply reinforced the Canaanite pressure on Yahwism which
had existed from the time of the Conquest and which, through
the activities of the monarchy, had become almost a strangle-
hold (see pp. 81 ff.). It was in this critical situation that Israel's
Mosaic faith found in a new kind of prophecy its appropriate
mode of expression.

The five main episodes recorded of Elijah's ministry illustrate the character of this momentous development. In the
opening scene, set against the background of a great drought
and famine (1 Kgs. 17$^{1-24}$), Elijah, though independent both of
the king and the prophetic guilds, is still presented merely as the
wonder-working holy man. Through such, the distinctive faith
of Israel could never find expression. In the second scene on
Mount Carmel (1 Kgs. 18$^{20-40}$), Elijah in splendid isolation
forces the incompatibility of Yahwism and Baalism into open
conflict and exposes the fraudulence of the Canaanite gods and
their raving prophets. At Carmel, however, there is little real
advance beyond the conviction that Yahweh can beat Baal at
his own game. The third scene on Mount Horeb goes further.
Elijah had confronted Baal; now he is confronted by Yahweh
(1 Kgs. 19$^{1-18}$). Through a profound spiritual experience,
Elijah learns that prophecy is not a matter of using word
and action to call down Yahweh's power, but, rather, a

matter of responding in word and action to Yahweh's own self-disclosure. In the fourth scene at Jezreel, Elijah demonstrates prophecy's new maturity (1 Kgs. 21[1–20]). The prophet's obedient response must now be made not on the top of a sacred mountain but in human society and human history. Here, too, the outlook of the Canaanites threatened the insights of Israel's distinctive tradition. Elijah's zeal in upholding the moral order of society and in condemning the king for his treatment of Naboth reflects the Mosaic Yahwism which is so powerfully expressed in the message of Amos and Micah (see notes). The fifth scene with Elisha and the 'sons of the prophets' purports to show how Elijah maintained the prophetic succession (2 Kgs. 2[1–18]). In effect, it serves as a reminder that independent prophecy cannot be regularized and maintained in institutional forms. The 'double portion' of Elijah's spirit which Elisha received was but two-thirds of his master's inheritance and even that was dissipated among his dim disciples (see p. 262).

1 KINGS 17. 1–24 *Elijah the Man of God*

The Elijah saga makes a sudden and undistinguished start with three miracle stories (vv. 1–7, 8–16, 17–24), which tell us more about their composer's credulity than about the prophet himself. This abrupt beginning suggests that there was once a fuller introduction to Elijah's ministry which was not available to the compiler.

1. The historical significance of *Elijah* is summed up in the meaning of his name—'My God is Yahweh'. He intended to prove that it was Yahweh, *the God of Israel*, who gave *rain* and not Jezebel's Canaanite god, Baal.

3. *Depart from here*, in order to escape Ahab. The *brook Cherith* is in north Gilead, very near the traditional site of Elijah's home, *Tishbe* (v. 1).

4. The Hebrew word for *ravens* is sometimes repointed to mean Arabs, but if we start trying to evade the miraculous in the stories of Elijah and Elisha we shall totally miss the writers'

intention. We may, of course, recognize their intention without sharing their credulity.

9. *Zarephath* is a village on the Phoenician coast midway between Tyre and Sidon.

14, 15. This miracle, which is repeated in the Elisha saga (2 Kgs. 4[1-7]), uses a familiar folk-lore theme to demonstrate the power of Yahweh.

17. *there was no breath left in him.* The boy was not 'breathless', but had stopped breathing. It is pointless to speculate that he may merely have been *revived* (v. 22) from a severe illness. The bringing back to life of the widow's son is also paralleled in the Elisha stories (2 Kgs. 4[32-37]).

18. *What have you against me, O man of God?* The title *man of God* is more frequently used of Elisha (2 Kgs. 4[7, 9, 21], 8[2, 11], 13[19]) and implies the possession of divine powers (cf. Mark 1[24]). In this passage, they include the ability to recognize and punish secret sins (v. 18; cf. John 4[16-19]) and the power to bring the dead to life (v. 24).

21. *he stretched himself upon the child three times.* This magical procedure, described in greater detail in Elisha's miracle (2 Kgs. 4[34]), was probably thought to transfer life by contact or breathing (cf. Acts 20[9-12]; for a non-Israelite parallel, see pp. 236 f.).

22. *the soul of the child came into him again.* We should say that 'the child came to life' again, when the Old Testament says 'life came to the child' again. The Hebrews (in contrast with the Greeks) did not think that man *has* a body and a soul, but rather that he *is* a body-animated-by-soul. The word translated *soul* would be better paraphrased here as 'breath of life', since it means the life principle which animates the flesh of a living person. It has no existence apart from the body, and, therefore (unlike the soul in Greek thought), is not immortal.

I KINGS 18. 1-46 *Elijah's contest on Mount Carmel*

In this celebrated chapter, two distinct narrative strands are clearly distinguishable. The first deals with Ahab's searching

for Elijah in order to secure the end of the drought (vv. 1–16) and the prophet's miraculous production of rain (vv. 41–46). The second strand presents the contest on Carmel, in which Baal, the god of storm (figs. pp. 74, 252), fails to produce lightning to ignite the altar fire and is exposed as a fraud by Yahweh, who succeeds in doing so (vv. 17–40). Differing views about the extent to which the two strands have been unified in tradition depend very largely on the interpretation of the contest on Carmel. If it is essentially a competition between Baal and Yahweh in the production of lightning (cf. v. 24), then the two strands are artificially associated by the common theme of Yahweh's supremacy over natural phenomena (lightning and rain). If, however, the contest on Carmel is interpreted as being essentially a rain-making ritual, to which the burning of the sacrifice is incidental, the two strands may be said to contribute towards a unified narrative with a single climax. Some scholars, indeed, regard the two strands as being no more than episodes in a story which was a unity from the outset. It seems more probable, however, that two distinct stories have been artificially combined.

What emerges from this farrago of miracle and magic is a devastating exposure of Baal religion and the ritual antics of its prophets and an insight into the isolation, confidence, and courage of Elijah, who in the ninth century fought a hard battle to keep the faith of Yahweh alive.

BAAL OF THE LIGHTNING. This limestone stele, 56 in. high, 18½ in. wide, and 11 in. thick, was found in a sanctuary at Ras Shamra and is dated between 1900 and 1500 B.C. It depicts in relief Baal as god of storm and admirably illustrates Elijah's contest on Mount Carmel. Baal stands on a platform above what appear to be mountains, holding a club in his right hand and in his left hand a spear of which the top end is forked to represent lightning. The influence of Egypt is seen in the striped loin cloth and the conventional posture of the figure, showing the left shoulder facing the front with the head and legs in profile. Otherwise, the detail reflects the Syrian tradition. Baal wears a pointed helmet (from which protrude two horns, recalling the fertility symbolism of the bull), two pigtails, and a curved dagger. The little figure in front, probably representing the donor of the stele, is dressed in the long fringed robes typical of Syria.

1. *I will send rain upon the earth.* Yahweh had caused three years' drought in Samaria (I Kgs. 17[1, 14]) and now he is about to end it (vv. 41–46). First, however, it is established that the drought was *caused* by Yahweh, who alone was Lord, and *occasioned* by Ahab's having forsaken him in favour of the gods of the Canaanites (vv. 17–19). This is the present context of the great contest on Mount Carmel (vv. 20–40).

2–16. Before Elijah goes to show himself to Ahab (v. 17; cf. v. 41), there is a preliminary scene which serves the two-fold purpose of establishing the severity of the drought (vv. 5, 6) and the status of Elijah as a prophet (vv. 7–16).

3. *Obadiah* was Ahab's prime minister and his loyalty to Yahweh illuminates the tolerant indifference of the king. Their joint search for fodder admirably reduces to scale the grandeur of the court in Samaria (see p. 24).

7. *my lord Elijah.* The prophets were feared and revered even by kings and their ministers (cf. 2 Kgs. 1[13], 8[9, 12]; Jer. 38[14–28]).

10. *your God* suggests the authority of Elijah and the rest of the verse his tremendous reputation.

12. *the Spirit of the Lord will carry you whither I know not.* The behaviour of the prophet is unpredictable because he acts in obedience to the direct prompting of Yahweh. This is more obvious in the inexplicable comings and goings of the early institutional prophets, whose extraordinary behaviour was attributed to the compelling power of Yahweh's spirit (cf. 2 Kgs. 3[15]; see notes on Mic. 3[8]).

13. *a hundred men of the Lord's prophets.* The prophets whose names we know were a tiny and unrepresentative minority among the hundreds of prophets who swarm anonymously through the pages of the Old Testament (see note on 2 Kgs. 2[3] and pp. 232–7). On *Jezebel*, see p. 83.

15. *the Lord of hosts.* This title of Yahweh is characteristic of the teaching of the prophets (who claim 247 out of its 278 occurrences). In its original use, it probably referred to Yahweh as

the leader of the military hosts of Israel (1 Sam. 17⁴⁵), who, with the Ark of God, engaged in 'holy war' (2 Sam. 6², ¹⁸). In the teaching of the prophets, however, the title stands for Yahweh as the one transcendent God (Isa. 44⁶), sovereign over the nations of the earth (Amos 5¹⁴, ¹⁵; Isa. 1²⁴, 2¹², 29⁶, 47⁴), as he was sovereign over all the host of heaven (Deut. 4¹⁹; 1 Kgs. 22¹⁹; cf. Isa. 1², 42⁵, 45¹⁸, 51⁶).

17. *you troubler of Israel*. Unlike the institutional prophet (see notes on Jer. 4⁹, ¹⁰), the independent prophet was inevitably a disturber of the peace and condemned even kings (cf. 1 Kgs. 21²⁰).

18. The *Baals* were not, as once was thought, little independent gods, but local manifestations of the cosmic deity of the Canaanite pantheon.

19. The 450 *prophets of Baal* and 400 *prophets of Asherah* belonged to Jezebel's royal establishment and had, presumably, been imported from Tyre. We learn a little of the ecstatic prophecy of Phoenicia about the year 1100 B.C. from the account of the travels of Wen-Amon, an Egyptian temple official. He was sent to the Phoenician city of Byblos, where he was ill received by the king, until one day one of his young courtiers was seized with a prophetic frenzy in which the god instructed him to welcome the visitor. The character in Egyptian writing for the youth's prophetic 'possession' shows a man in violent motion or epileptic convulsions (cf. vv. 26, 28).

20–40. The contest on *Mount Carmel*, the head of a range which juts into the Mediterranean to the north-west of Samaria, now the centre of this chapter, was probably at one stage in tradition independent of it. Ahab, the 400 prophets of Asherah and the 100 prophets of Yahweh (cf. vv. 13, 22) disappear from the scene and the drought is no longer explicitly in view.

23. *let them choose*, to avoid any suggestion of trickery, as the challenger in a duel invites his opponent to choose his weapon.

24. *the God who answers by fire, he is God*. The contest between

Yahweh and Baal was in producing lightning, rather than rain. As Baal was the god of the storm and frequently depicted hurling a thunderbolt (fig. p. 252), Elijah intends to demonstrate that Yahweh could beat Baal at his own game.

26. *And they limped about the altar* does not adequately convey a picture of the prophets of Baal in a frenzied ritual dance (cf. v. 29).

27. *Elijah mocked them.* This scathing satire on Baal's being 'otherwise engaged' is comparable to Second Isaiah's mockery of pagan idols ('If one cries to it, it does not answer'; Isa. 46⁷; cf. 44⁹⁻²⁰).

28. *cut themselves after their custom.* Self-laceration as part of the ecstatic ritual of the cult is attested in Canaanite sources (see p. 46) and was not unknown in Israel (Zech. 13⁶; cf. Hos. 7¹⁴).

29. *they raved on.* The same verb, which means literally 'to play the prophet', is used to describe Saul's prophetic frenzy (1 Sam. 10⁶, 18¹⁰, 19²³, ²⁴), the wild behaviour of groups of prophets (1 Sam. 10⁵; 1 Kgs. 22¹⁰) and 'every madman who prophesies' (Jer. 29²⁶; cf. 2 Kgs. 9¹¹; Hos. 9⁷).

31, 32*a. he built an altar* is difficult to reconcile with *he repaired the altar* in v. 30. It is generally supposed that vv. 31, 32*a* are an insertion based on Gen. 35¹⁰.

32*b*–35. The *two measures of seed* indicate the capacity of the trench and it is unlikely that they reflect any fertility rite. The pouring of *water*, however, is commonly regarded as a ritual to produce rain by sympathetic magic. If, however, the contest was in producing lightning rather than rain (cf. v. 24), the water may have been intended simply to heighten the miracle of Yahweh's scorching flame (cf. v. 38).

36. *God of Abraham, Isaac, and Israel* is unusual both in its reference to the patriarchs, whom the prophets before Second Isaiah virtually ignore, and in speaking of *Israel*, instead of the more usual Jacob (cf. Exod. 3⁶), as in the post-exilic work of the

Chronicler (1 Chron. 29¹⁸; 2 Chron. 30⁶). Elijah's serene confidence is a further exposure of the frenzy of the Canaanite prophets.

38. *the fire of the Lord* means a miraculous flash of lightning (cf. v. 24; 2 Kgs. 1¹⁰; Gen. 19²⁴), which even *licked up the water that was in the trench.*

42. *he bowed himself . . . and put his face between his knees.* It is probable that Elijah was either imitating a cloud in an act of sympathetic magic to produce rain, or assuming the posture favoured by clairvoyants (see p. 236).

46. A cross-country run of seventeen miles from Carmel to *Jezreel* in *a great rain* was considered sufficiently abnormal to be ascribed to ecstatic energy from *the hand of the Lord.*

1 KINGS 19. 1–18 *Elijah's confrontation on Mount Horeb*

On Mount Carmel we saw Elijah in a public contest with Baal. On Mount Horeb we find him in a private confrontation with Yahweh. The fire which proved Yahweh's supremacy on Carmel says nothing to Elijah now on Horeb, when despair has driven him to ask wherein really his assurance lies. The answer is given in an experience of which the record is clearly intended to recall the experience of Moses. It is that assurance may be found only in response to Yahweh's self-disclosure and this is given not in the external manifestations of wind and earthquake and lightning, but in the inner recesses of man's spiritual and moral awareness. It was this which distinctively characterized Israel's Mosaic faith. It was, moreover, a faith to be expressed in the shaping of history and renewed in the understanding of history. Elijah's ferocious zeal in discharging his political role does not, perhaps, wholly cancel the validity of his vision.

3. Elijah left Jezreel because he was afraid of Jezebel and went 130 miles south to Beer-sheba. The note that this city *belongs to Judah* suggests that the story originated in the northern kingdom before its fall.

5. *an angel touched him*, evidently in a dream. An angelic inter-
mediary occurs relatively frequently in the Elijah stories (2
Kgs. 1³, ¹⁵; cf. 1 Kgs. 13¹⁸).

8. *Horeb the mount of God*, the name given in the northern tradition (Exod. 3¹, 17⁶; Deut. 1², ⁶, ¹⁹, 4¹⁰, 18¹⁶) to the mountain
called Sinai in the southern tradition, where Yahweh revealed
himself to Moses (Exod. 33¹⁷⁻²³). The parallel with Moses is
strengthened by Elijah's *forty days and forty nights* without food
(cf. Exod. 34²⁸).

10. *I have been very jealous for the Lord*. Elijah was very 'zealous'
for Yahweh (cf. vv. 15–17), like Jehu (2 Kgs. 10¹⁶).

12. The *still small voice*, superbly contrasted with the *wind, earthquake*, and *fire* (lightning), affirms that Yahweh reveals himself
not in spectacular and violent natural phenomena, but in a
form which is addressed to man's inner awareness and is
morally demanding. This conviction underlies all mature
Hebrew prophecy.

15–17. *And the Lord said to him*. The best that can be said for the
demands arising out of Yahweh's self-revelation to Elijah is
that they are authentically prophetic in being concerned with
action in history. Otherwise, they are lamentably fanatical in
their ferocity. Elijah is told to *anoint* three men to slaughter the
unfaithful in Israel: *Hazael*, the usurper of the throne of
Damascus (see p. 12), *Jehu*, the usurper of the throne of Israel
(see pp. 89 ff.), and *Elisha*, his own successor (see pp. 261 ff.).
None of these commands was obeyed to the letter. Although
Elijah commissioned Elisha, he did not anoint him (see notes on
1 Kgs. 19¹⁹⁻²¹); it was Elisha who 'nominated' Hazael (2 Kgs.
8⁷⁻¹⁵); and a member of Elisha's prophetic guild who anointed
Jehu (see notes on 2 Kgs. 9¹⁻⁶). These verses reflect the support
which Jehu actually received from the prophetic guilds in his
purge of paganism and they interpret Hazael and his brutal
excesses as the instrument by which Yahweh punished Israel for
its apostasy (cf. 2 Kgs. 8¹², ¹³). Faced with catastrophe from
Assyria and Babylon, the independent prophets of the eighth

and seventh centuries B.C. proclaimed a comparable interpretation of history (cf. Isa. 10⁵ and pp. 55 f., 338 f.).

18. *Yet I will leave seven thousand in Israel*: a righteous remnant
will be preserved (see p. 332).

I KINGS 21. 1–20 *Elijah at Naboth's vineyard*

Elijah's impassioned defence of the right of a private citizen
to withstand the rapacity of a despotic king is universal in its
appeal. In its own time and situation, however, it illustrates the
head-on clash between Israel's traditional social order and the
new society introduced by the monarchy, which was only
another side of the religious conflict dramatized on Mount
Carmel. Elijah's denunciation of Ahab for acquiescing in
Naboth's murder in order to confiscate his family property is
an authentic response to the 'still small voice' of prophetic
revelation and is echoed by more than one prophet in the
following centuries (see notes on Mic. 2¹⁻⁵ and Isa. 5⁸⁻¹⁰).

1. *Naboth* was a prominent citizen of Jezreel and the owner of
a vineyard adjacent to Ahab's country palace.

2. *its value in money* illustrates the new language of a new social
order (cf. v. 15).

3. *the inheritance of my fathers*. Israelite law and custom made
careful provision to ensure that ancestral property remained
in the family (see pp. 40 f.).

7. *Do you now govern Israel?* The Canaanite queen does not share
Ahab's scruples (cf. v. 2) about exploiting the king's absolute
rights over his subjects (see p. 34).

8. *the elders and the nobles* formed the city council, of which
Naboth was apparently chairman. Jezebel clearly had the
council under her control.

9. *Proclaim a fast*. A public fast was to be held as an expression
of the community's penitence (cf. Judg. 20²⁶; I Sam. 7⁶, 14²⁴),
presumably for a trumped-up reason which would not arouse

Naboth's suspicions, since he was to be *set on high among the people* and preside at the subsequent communal tribunal.

10. The *two base fellows*, who were suborned to make the false denunciation, satisfy the legal requirement of two witnesses in a capital case (Deut. 17[6]; Num. 35[30]; cf. Matthew 26[59, 60]). The charge of blasphemy is a perversion of the law in Exod. 22[28], which couples not *God and the king*, but God and the 'ruler', that is to say, the religious representative of the twelve tribes before the institution of the monarchy. The penalty for blasphemy was death by stoning—with everybody joining in (Lev. 24[14-16]).

17–20. Elijah comes thundering down on Ahab as the avenger of Naboth's blood and prophesies that the king will die where his victim was murdered. The introduction in v. 18 of *Samaria* as the scene of the crime allows Ahab's death there to be represented as the fulfilment of Elijah's prophecy (1 Kgs. 22[38]), in addition to the death of his son and his wife at Jezreel (2 Kgs. 9[26, 36, 37]).

1 KINGS 19. 19–21 *Elijah calls Elisha*

This primitive little story tells how Elijah called Elisha to share his prophetic ministry by investing him with his cloak. Elisha's entry on his new vocation is celebrated in a sacrificial meal.

19. *Elisha*, to judge by his twelve yoke of oxen, was a man of substance. Moses and Amos, similarly, were at work in the fields when the 'call' came (Exod. 3[1-6]; Amos 7[15]), but by contrast claim that it was Yahweh himself who called them. Elijah suddenly appeared and invested Elisha with his *mantle*, a cloak of haircloth (2 Kgs. 1[8]; cf. Zech. 13[4]), which was believed to be imbued with miraculous power (2 Kgs. 2[8, 14]).

20. Elisha's call meant leaving home. Elijah's reply to Elisha's request is not altogether clear, but it suggests that he had done nothing to stop him going home, with the further implication

that he would later realize his vocation and return (cf. Luke 9⁶¹).

21. Elisha's sacrifice of two oxen and his cooking a communal meal over a fire made from the wood of their yokes (cf. 1 Sam. 6¹⁴; 2 Sam. 24²²) marks the end of his old life and the beginning of his new discipleship.

2 KINGS 2. 1–18 *Elisha succeeds Elijah*

The picture of Elijah in this narrative is markedly different from that presented in the earlier chapters. Here Elijah is a wonder-worker rushing hither and thither between various prophetic guilds, in whose circles, probably, the account originated. The main purpose of the episode is to claim that Elijah had well and truly been translated to heaven (vv. 16–18) and that Elisha, the master and hero of the prophetic guilds, was his rightful successor with a 'double share' of his spirit. The condition of Elisha's being granted a vision (v. 10), which in the event he saw (v. 12), reflects, perhaps, an awareness that true prophets are called directly by Yahweh himself and do not receive their office simply by succession and investiture. The writer was sufficiently prophetic to wish to claim that Elisha was mysteriously called and at the same time sufficiently institutionalized to insist that he was invested by Elijah as his successor. The problem of the relationship between prophetic faith and historical continuity in the life of the people of God is recurrent and continuing.

1, 2. *Gilgal*, here, is not the important city near Jericho, but a place in Ephraim some eight miles north of *Bethel*. The rapid movements in this chapter (Gilgal, Bethel, Jericho, Jordan) amply justify the comment in 1 Kgs. 18¹².

3. The *sons of the prophets* are mentioned in this period as living at *Bethel* (v. 3), *Jericho* (vv. 5, 15) and *Gilgal* (2 Kgs. 4³⁸). Similar groups are found earlier at *Gibeah* (1 Sam. 10⁵, ¹⁰) and *Ramah* (1 Sam. 19¹⁹, ²⁰). The expression *sons* does not imply physical descent, but means members of communities or guilds

of prophets, who lived together (2 Kgs. 6$^{1, 2}$) with their families (2 Kgs. 4^1) in a loose organization under a master like Elisha (2 Kgs. 4^{38}). Their number was probably considerable; 100 are mentioned in 2 Kgs. 4^{43} (see 1 Kgs. 18^{13}, 22^6; 2 Kgs. 2$^{7, 16}$; cf. 1 Kgs. 18^{19}).

8. *and the water was parted* is a legendary detail to associate Elijah with Joshua at Jordan (Josh. 3$^{1–17}$) and Moses at the Exodus (Exod. 14$^{16, 21, 22}$).

9. *a double share of your spirit* means not twice as much but the legacy of two-thirds due to the eldest son (Deut. 21^{17}). For the primitive idea of transferring *spirit* from one person to another, see Num. 11$^{16, 17, 24, 25}$.

10. Elijah seems to mean that the gift is not his to give, but if Elisha is granted a vision of his ascent, he will also be allowed to receive his spirit. The sequel claims that this vision was granted: *Elisha saw it* (v. 12; cf. v. 15).

11. *a chariot of fire and horses of fire.* The imagery of this vision (cf. 2 Kgs. 6^{17}) is probably drawn from sun worship, in which model chariots and horses were used (cf. 2 Kgs. 23^{11}; Ezek. 8^{16}). *And Elijah went up by a whirlwind into heaven.* The mysterious and privileged translation of Elijah to heaven led to the expectation that he would return as the herald of the 'Last Days' (Mal. 4^5; Ecclus. 48^{10}; Matthew 11^{14}, 16^{14}, 17$^{3, 4, 10–13}$; Luke 1^{17}, 9^8; Mark 9$^{4, 5}$; John 1^{21}).

12. *My father, my father! the chariots of Israel and its horsemen.* This cry of despair is also used to describe the political importance of Elisha in 2 Kgs. 13^{14}. It is probable that it was transferred from Elisha to Elijah by the attraction of the similar imagery in v. 11.

13. *the mantle of Elijah.* Elisha's rending of his own clothes and his taking up the mantle of Elijah repeats the break with his old life and his entry into the prophetic office which have already been described (see notes on 1 Kgs. 19$^{19–21}$).

14. The crude expression *God of Elijah* is used to invoke a crude repetition of Elijah's miracle (v. 8).

15–18. The failure of the fifty able-bodied men to find Elijah after a three days' search is intended to confirm that *the Spirit of the Lord*, which was thought of literally as a whirlwind, had indeed taken him up into heaven.

2 KINGS 5. 1–19 *Elisha converts Naaman*

This gentle little success story has no specific chronological setting and offers a much less primitive portrait of Elisha than the rest of his miracle stories. The distinguished army commander from Damascus, the aloof prophet in his house in Samaria, the Israelite slave girl who works for the army commander's wife, and the suspicious king, are all delicately sketched. Naaman is presented as a noble pagan. His cure converts him to the true faith and he offers his sincere apologies (since he is confident that Elisha is a gentleman and will understand) for having to continue to attend heathen services in his official capacity when he gets back home.

1. *by him the Lord had given victory to Syria*. Unless this is simply a conventional phrase, it is remarkable for implying that the victory won by Naaman (which almost certainly included victory over Israel) was the work of Yahweh. Naaman *was a leper*, or, more probably, was suffering from a skin disease.

5. The present was a handsome one (? £30,000).

8. It is assumed that the business of *a prophet* was to perform miracles of healing (see p. 236).

11, 12. *Naaman was angry* because of Elisha's off-hand manner and because the muddy Jordan, in which he was instructed to wash, was vastly inferior to the rivers at home. The River *Abana*, which is not mentioned anywhere else, is identified with the River Barada, flowing down from Anti-Lebanon through *Damascus*. The River *Pharpar* rises in Hermon and flows south-east of Damascus.

15. *I know that there is no God in all the earth but in Israel.* The story-tellers of Israel took great pride in the confessions of distinguished gentile converts (cf. Dan. 2⁴⁷, 3²⁸⁻³⁰, 4¹⁻³, ³⁴⁻³⁷, 6²⁵⁻²⁸).

16. *I will receive none.* The writer heavily underlines this refusal of a reward in the story about Gehazi which follows (vv. 20–27) and is evidently determined to distinguish his hero from paid prophets (1 Sam. 9⁵⁻¹⁰; 1 Kgs. 14¹⁻³; 2 Kgs. 8⁷, ⁸) and profes-sional money-grubbers (Mic. 3⁵, ¹¹; Ezek. 13¹⁹; cf. Amos 7¹², ¹³; Num. 22¹⁸).

17. *two mules' burden of earth.* Naaman's request illustrates the notion that Yahweh was localized like the gods of the nations and could not be worshipped outside his own 'holy land' (cf. Zech. 2¹²; 1 Sam. 26¹⁹; 1 Kgs. 20²³).

18. *the house of Rimmon*: see notes on 1 Kgs. 15¹⁸.

AMOS

The essential point to grasp about the first of the 'writing prophets' is that he was an educated and morally sensitive layman, who came to see absolutely everything in the light of the reality and activity of Yahweh. Amos ascribed this over-whelming awareness to a direct and dramatic summons by Yahweh himself (7¹⁵) and there is no better way of accounting for it. As a result, he exposed the religion and social conduct of Israel to a scrutiny of unprecedented rigour and came to the con-clusion that it was impossible that they could be allowed to continue. What precisely Amos meant by Yahweh's destruction of Israel, we do not know. It is as difficult to suppose that he expected the literal physical annihilation of the whole people, as it is unwise to interpret his message merely as a demand for certain reforms expressed in urgent and somewhat exaggerated language. At the very least, Amos taught that Israel had with-drawn from its special relationship to Yahweh and, therefore, that its distinctive existence as the people of God was coming to an end. Yahweh, the sovereign Lord of all the families of the earth, had freely chosen Israel at the beginning of its history

(3^2); its election was now cancelled $(9^{7,\ 8b})$. This cancellation was the very reverse of capricious. No prophet expounds more clearly than Amos the reason for Yahweh's judgement, but since it is so startlingly simple, it is hard to accept. *Israel was doomed because it was spiritually and morally dead.*

All the oracles of Amos convey this single stark conviction. Yahweh will not continue to tolerate corruption in the courts $(5^{12}, 6^{12})$, corruption in the markets $(8^{5,\ 6})$, corruption in high society $(3^{10,\ 12,\ 15}, 4^{1-3}, 6^{4-7})$, with all the cruel suffering they cause $(2^{7,\ 8}, 5^{11,\ 12})$. Israel's religious practice is not so much corrupt as a contemptible sideshow $(4^{4,\ 5}, 5^{21-24})$; its religious tradition is merely a cloak for pride and complacency $(2^{9-11}, 3^2, 5^{18}, 9^7)$. The people's refusal to turn to Yahweh extinguishes the last gleam of hope $(5^{15}, 7^{3,\ 6,\ 8,\ 9}, 8^{1-3})$.

This was not a new faith, but an extraordinarily radical interpretation of Mosaic Yahwism. Nor was it a kind of prophecy wholly without precedent; Elijah had blazed the trail (pp. 249 f.). But it was prophecy mediated by the most independent mind in the whole of its history. Amos cared for nothing except the living God and righteousness of life and he said exactly what he thought. The mature style of his oracles has been interpreted as indicating his indebtedness to an established tradition of prophetic preaching of which we are otherwise ignorant, but it may as readily be accounted for by his own education. Shepherd though he was $(1^1, 7^{14,\ 15})$, his considerable knowledge of history, geography, and the wisdom of the schools (p. 178) makes it absurd to regard him as an illiterate rustic who spent his time brooding over the Judean desert from the rugged heights of Tekoa. His detachment from the popular religion of the sanctuaries may well reflect an intellectual background of some sophistication, which, in any case, is demanded by the probable suggestion that he wrote down many of the oracles himself (cf. $1^3-2^{16}, 5^1$).

The references to Jeroboam II (786–746), both in the title (1^1) and in the body of the book $(7^{9,\ 10})$, agree with the general picture of Israel's confidence and prosperity which emerges from his oracles. We may safely conclude, therefore, that Amos did his preaching (probably during a fairly short period) in the northern kingdom about 760–750 B.C.

I. 1–2. 16 *Yahweh's judgement of crimes against common humanity*

The first two chapters of the book make a tremendous sweep round Israel's neighbours—Damascus, the Philistines, Tyre, Edom, Ammon, and Moab—pronouncing doom on each for its inhuman crimes and finally coming home with the accumulated momentum of judgement to condemn Israel itself. This discourse certainly reveals an effective preaching technique; but, more important, it discloses the prophet's fundamental conviction that the moral obligation of which all men are aware (and which in later centuries was called natural law) is identical with the personal will of Israel's God, who exercises universal sovereignty and holds all peoples accountable for their conduct. It is probable that some of the oracles have been touched up in the process of transmission, but even the edited oracles retain the distinctive style of Amos (the one on Judah being the glaring exception which proves the point) and so we may be confident that the discourse as a whole gives us access to the amazingly radical mind of the prophet himself.

I. I. *General Title.* The unusual word used here for *shepherd* (*nôqēdh*) is found elsewhere in the Old Testament only in 2 Kgs. 3⁴, when it describes the king of Moab as a 'sheep breeder' (cf. Amos 7¹⁴). Assertions that the term is here the title of a cultic official (as, according to the Ras Shamra texts, it was at Ugarit) may be safely ignored. *Tekoa* was a village 12 miles south of Jerusalem overlooking the Dead Sea. For *Uzziah* (783–742), see notes on 2 Kgs. 15¹⁻⁷; and for *Jeroboam* II (786–746), see notes on 2 Kgs. 14²³⁻²⁹. The *earthquake* is mentioned again in Zech. 14⁵, but it cannot be dated with precision.

2. *Motto.* This verse has been interpreted (with 9¹¹⁻¹⁵) as evidence that Amos was closely associated with the Jerusalem Temple. A more probable view is that it is a liturgical fragment

added (not inappropriately) as a motto to the book by a Judean editor (cf. Jer. 25³⁰; Joel 3¹⁶).

3–5. *Damascus*. The Aramean kingdom, of which Damascus was the capital, had reduced Israel and Judah to complete subjection in the reign of *Hazael* (843–796), whose barbarity was notorious. *Ben-hadad* was the name of the two kings who came before and after Hazael (see pp. 11 ff.). *For three transgressions ... and for four*, which introduces each of the oracles against the nations, is an idiom which describes a repeated occurrence and reflects the didactic style of the wisdom teachers (cf. Prov. 30¹⁵⁻³¹; Job 33¹⁴; Ecclus. 26⁵; see p. 178); *transgressions* means acts of rebellion against Yahweh rather than breaches of a code (cf. 1 Kgs. 12¹⁹; 2 Kgs. 3⁵; Isa. 1²; Mic. 3⁸). *I will not revoke the punishment* is an interpretation of the Hebrew, 'I will not cause it to return'; Yahweh's judgement of the nation stands. The *Valley of Aven* probably means the valley between the Lebanon and Anti-Lebanon mountains, represented here as 'wickedness' (Hebrew, 'āwen; cf. 'Beth-aven' for Bethel in Hos. 4¹⁵, 5⁸, 10⁵, ⁸). *Beth-eden* (in the Assyrian records, Bit-adini) was a city-state between the Euphrates and Balikh rivers (cf. 2 Kgs. 19¹²; Ezek. 27²³), and *Kir* was a region in Mesopotamia from which the Arameans came and to which in 732 B.C. they were exiled (cf. 9⁷; Isa. 22⁶; 2 Kgs. 16⁹). The *people of Syria* is properly 'the people of Aram', namely the Arameans of Damascus (see p. 10).

6–8. *The Philistine cities*. Amos proclaims doom on four of the Philistine cities—*Gaza, Ashdod, Ashkelon*, and *Ekron*. The fifth city of the confederation, Gath, was destroyed by Assyria in 711 B.C. and its omission here has led some scholars to conclude that the whole oracle was written by another prophet after that date. The offence of the Philistines was slave-trading with Edom (v. 6; cf. 2 Chron. 21¹⁶, ¹⁷; Joel 3⁴⁻⁸), for which, Amos says, they will be totally wiped out; no *remnant* of them will be left (v. 8).

9, 10. *Tyre*. This short oracle against the principal city-state of Phoenicia (see pp. 23 ff.) repeats ideas and language found in

vv. 4, 6 and is judged by many commentators to be an editorial insertion. The *covenant of brotherhood* is best explained as the bond of kinship (cf. v. 11); Tyre's slave-trading was not only inhuman, but unnatural (cf. Ezek. 27¹³).

11, 12. *Edom.* The indictment is that Edom ravaged its own kinsmen. The reference is almost certainly to Edom's exploitation of Judah's weakness after the fall of Jerusalem in 587 B.C., which Obadiah also has in view: 'But you should not have gloated over the day of your brother in the day of his misfortune', v. 12 (cf. Lam. 4²¹, ²²; Mal. 1²⁻⁵; Ps. 137⁷; Isa. 34⁵⁻⁷, 63¹⁻⁶; Ezek. 25¹²⁻¹⁴; also see Deut. 2⁴, 23⁷). If this oracle is by Amos, Israel must have suffered comparably at the hands of Edom in an earlier century. *Teman* was a district and *Bozrah* a city of Edom.

13–15. *Ammon.* The Ammonites of Transjordan had raided *Gilead*, Israelite territory on their northern border. What they are accused of, however, is hideous cruelty in pursuit of their selfish ambitions. Amos is incensed by a crime against humanity (cf. 2 Kgs. 8¹², 15¹⁶). *Rabbah*, the capital of Ammon, is now Amman the capital of the Kingdom of Jordan.

2. 1–3. *Moab.* Israel is in no way involved in Moab's offence against Edom, but Yahweh, the God of Israel, is. Any crime against human decency is an affront to Yahweh's universal moral sovereignty and will be punished. To deny a body decent burial was an act of desecration reserved for criminals (cf. Lev. 20¹⁴). *Kerioth* was presumably the capital of Moab.

4, 5. *Judah.* Compared with the concrete detail of the other oracles against the nations, these verses are flat and conventional. It is extremely probable that they were inserted by a conscientious Judean editor of the deuteronomic school, who failed to see that he was wrecking the climax of Amos' indictment of Israel which follows.

6–16. *Israel.* If the prophet's Israelite audience had applauded his sermon so far, they had committed themselves to consequences beyond their expectations. Amos had been saying not simply that Yahweh would not tolerate the heathen, but that he would not tolerate their inhumanity. He now draws the inevitable conclusion that Yahweh will not be tolerant towards the abominable behaviour of his own people. The chosen people stands under the same condemnation.

6–8. *The present rebellion of the people against Yahweh.* Rapacious creditors sell ordinary decent folk into slavery for trivial debts (like the price of a pair of sandals); see pp. 41 f. The first half of v. 7 means that poor and modest people get pushed around. Father and son resort to the same sanctuary prostitute and, to make matters worse, use for their debaucheries garments and wine acquired from defenceless debtors. For *garments taken in pledge*, cf. Exod. 22²⁵, ²⁶ and see notes on Deut. 24¹⁰⁻¹³; for cultic prostitution at Israelite sanctuaries, cf. Hos. 4¹⁴; Deut. 23¹⁷.

9–12. *Yahweh's past guidance of the people.* Such, says Amos, is the behaviour of the elect people of God! The unique relationship into which Yahweh had admitted Israel began with the Exodus (v. 10) and was shown in the conquest of Canaan (v. 9) and the gift of men of God to guide them (v. 11). *Amorite* is the term used to describe the Canaanites' country cousins (cf. Num. 13²⁹; see notes on 2 Kgs. 21¹¹). According to later law, the *Nazirites* were men who took a vow to abstain from the products of the vine, from cutting their hair, and from the ritual uncleanness acquired by contact with the dead (Num. 6¹⁻²¹). In the earlier period, they were men specifically dedicated to God, like Samson and Samuel, and, therefore, cut off from the normal life of society (Judg. 16¹⁷; 1 Sam. 1¹¹). Like the Rechabites, therefore, the Nazirites symbolized the opposition of Yahwism to the corruption of Canaanite civilization (see p. 95). It has been suggested that vv. 10–12 are the work of a later compiler. They are certainly prosaic and v. 10 is rather awkward after v. 9; it would, therefore, certainly be unsafe on their evidence alone to identify the outlook of Amos with the sectarian conservatism of the Nazirites.

13–16. *Yahweh's coming judgement of the people.* In vigorously metaphorical language, Amos announces the theme which dominates his message. Yahweh is dynamically alive and is about to inaugurate new dealings with Israel, which will result in the people's utter destruction. *I will press you down in your place* is one of many attempts to elucidate this image for overwhelming disaster, which (as the succeeding lines assert) is quite inescapable. The only course open even to the stoutest of warriors is to throw away his weapons and bolt (v. 16).

3. 1–8 *Israel's election and the prophet's authority*

It was completely unprecedented for a prophet to get up and proclaim that Yahweh would destroy his own people. Amos does not deny Israel's special relationship to Yahweh, but accepts it as the premiss for his own startling conclusion. That conclusion came from Yahweh himself—as sure as eggs are eggs.

1, 2. *Israel's special position.* Israel was Yahweh's chosen people by virtue of its creation at the Exodus and the people could still be addressed as though they had themselves been *brought up out of the land of Egypt.* Yahweh's choice of Israel was a genuine and significant choice, because he was the God *of all the families of the earth,* and out of all the nations he had selected this one as his special care: *you only have I known* (see notes on Deut. 7$^{1-11}$). In the Old Testament to 'know' means to care for in an intimate and personal way (cf. Gen. 4$^{1, 17}$, 39^8; Prov. 12^{10}, 29^7); it was the word used by Jeremiah to describe his own prophetic calling (Jer. 1^5, 12^3). But this intimate relationship gave Israel no licence to sin. On the contrary, Israel's privilege exposed the people more directly to Yahweh's righteous rule: *therefore I will punish you for all your iniquities.*

3–8. Nothing happens without a cause and the cause of Amos' strange prophesying is what Yahweh himself has spoken. In the manner of the wisdom teachers (see p. 178), Amos points for his credentials to the compelling utterance of God (cf. 1 Kgs. 22$^{13, 14}$; Isa. 8^{11}; Jer. 5^{14}, 6^{11}, 20^9; Ezek. 3^{14}). The prose note of v. 7 is an apposite deuteronomic comment added later; for the term *secret* (Hebrew, *sôdh*), see notes on Prov. 3^{32}.

3. 9–4. 3 *Samaria doomed to destruction*

With relentless consistency, Amos invites two heathen nations to come to Samaria and confirm that its behaviour is repugnant to common humanity.

9, 10. *The nations are called to bear witness.* If the RSV is correct in following the Greek and reading *Assyria* for the Hebrew Ashdod (one of the Philistine cities), this is the only direct reference to Assyria in Amos' oracles. It is preferable to retain Ashdod. The meaning of v. 10 is that those who hoard ill-gotten gains in their palaces obviously care nothing about honesty.

11, 12. *Samaria's annihilation.* Yahweh will use an unnamed enemy to sack Samaria (v. 11) and leave only a few scraps as evidence of its total destruction (cf. Exod. 22¹³). The RSV translation represents *the corner of a couch and part of a bed* as the bits left over. An alternative would be: '. . . so shall the people of Israel be rescued, who sit in Samaria on the corner of a bed and a Damascus couch.' On this interpretation, Amos is condemning their idle luxury (fig. p. 278).

13–15. *The destruction of Bethel.* The royal sanctuary of Bethel will share Israel's fate. For the *God of hosts*, see notes on 1 Kgs. 18¹⁵. The *horns of the altar*, which projected at the four corners and provided sanctuary to a man in danger of his life (1 Kgs. 1⁵⁰, 2²⁸), will not themselves be safe from destruction. The luxurious houses of the wealthy, furnished with *ivory* and ebony (reading this word instead of *great* in the last line; cf. Ezek. 27¹⁵), will be reduced to rubble (cf. 6⁴; 1 Kgs. 22³⁹; Ps. 45⁸; see p. 24).

4. 1–3. *Women thrown on the dung-heap.* With utter contempt Amos calls the fat, pampered women of Samaria prize *cows* (cf. Ps. 22¹²; Deut. 32¹⁴). Their callous indifference to human values epitomizes Israel's corruption (cf. Isa. 3¹⁶, ¹⁷). In v. 2, instead of *they shall take you away with hooks*, translate, 'they shall carry you away in large shields'; *the last of you* probably means 'your children' (cf. 'your posterity' in the Authorized Version),

who will be carried off in fish-pots (rather than *with fishhooks*). The women will be taken straight through *the breaches* in the city walls and thrown on to a dung-heap. *Harmon* has not been identified and dung-heap translates a plausible emendation.

4. 4–5. 15 *Rites and righteousness*

The question which underlies this series of oracles is 'Where is God to be found and what does he want?' Popular religious practice got no further than the sanctuaries and their festivals. The prophet proclaimed that God was to be found and served in everyday experience and human relationships.

4. 4, 5. *Futile festivals.* With biting sarcasm, Amos invites the people to carry on with their festivals and come to the sanctuaries of *Bethel* (cf. 7¹³) and *Gilgal* (cf. Hos. 4¹⁵)—to rebel against Yahweh! The RSV translation, *sacrifices every morning . . . tithes every three days*, suggests a rather crude caricature of the normal practice; 'sacrifices in the morning . . . tithes on the third day' describes the regular custom; without any guying of the people's ritual punctiliousness, Amos' satire finds its mark. The *freewill offerings*, as optional extras to the regular programme, were something to boast about! These men revelled in their religion, but God was not well pleased (cf. Matthew 6²⁻⁴). On the sacrificial terminology, see pp. 135 ff.

6–12. *Israel's failure to learn its many lessons.* The people who met the kind of God they wanted to meet at the sanctuaries had failed to recognize the warnings of Yahweh in the calamities they had suffered: famine (v. 6), drought (vv. 7, 8), bad crops (v. 9), disease and loss in war (v. 10), and (perhaps) earthquake (v. 11). Since they had not come back to Yahweh, Yahweh was about to come to them: *prepare to meet your God, O Israel!* The precedent of *Sodom and Gomorrah* (v. 11), cities of the plain which were utterly destroyed (Gen. 19¹⁻²⁸), is also used by other prophets (Isa. 1⁹; Hos. 11⁸; Jer. 23¹⁴, 49¹⁸; Ezek. 16⁴⁶⁻⁵⁸; cf. Lam. 4⁶). Amos assumes without argument that it is Yahweh (and not, as was popularly supposed, the Canaanite

Baal) who is sovereign in the order of nature (see notes on Hos. 2⁸ and 1 Kgs. 18¹⁻⁴⁶, pp. 251–63).

13. This is the first of three so-called 'doxologies' (4¹³, 5⁸, ⁹, 9⁵, ⁶), which proclaim Yahweh's transcendent power as Creator. Although they may be fragments of a hymn quite as old as the oracles of Amos, it is generally agreed that they owe their present position to the compiler of the book.

5. 1–3. *A dirge over Israel.* Amos is convinced that Israel is as good as dead and with astonishing courage he offers in v. 2 a regular dirge. Here, the people is personified for the first time as a *virgin* (cf. Jer. 18¹³, 31⁴, ²¹). The more prosaic v. 3 means not that a remnant will be spared but that the whole people will be decimated (cf. 3¹²).

4–15. *Seeking God.* Amos affirms unambiguously that Yahweh is not to be found in the sanctuaries, but, rather, in right human relations.

4–6. *Seek* was a technical term for going to the sanctuary to 'inquire of the Lord' on some question or other (cf. 1 Sam. 9⁹; 2 Kgs. 3¹¹; Deut. 12⁵). Israel should seek Yahweh and he is not to be met at the sanctuaries of Bethel, Gilgal, or Beer-sheba. The mention of *Beer-sheba*, in the far south of Judah, may mean that Amos was addressing the whole nation (cf. 3¹, 6¹); but in v. 6 *the house of Joseph* stands for the northern kingdom.

8, 9. This second 'doxology' (see notes on 4¹³) obviously breaks the connexion between vv. 7 and 10.

7, 10–13. Justice is perverted to a poison in society (vv. 7, 10, 12) and the poor are oppressed and exploited (v. 11). In v. 12, *the righteous* are the innocent who are persecuted; *turn aside the needy in the gate* means push the poor out of court. On city courts held *in the gate*, cf. Ruth 4¹, ²; Job 31²¹; and see p. 203. However, the fine stone houses and vineyards obtained by twisting and bullying will never be enjoyed (cf. Luke 12¹⁶⁻²¹).

14, 15. *Seek good . . . that you may live* is identical in the prophet's thought with *Seek me and live* (5⁴), for to do good is to turn to

Yahweh. The content of the prophets' moral teaching is derived from the common stock of ethical thinking to be found throughout the ancient Near East, but the use they make of it is distinctively their own (cf. 8⁴⁻⁷; see pp. 179, 374). Morality in Amos' teaching is an index to the character of God and the pursuit of goodness the primary way of knowing and serving him. *It may be* (v. 15) is the brightest gleam of hope in the whole of Amos' oracles; it depends entirely on the moral reformation of *the remnant of Joseph*, an expression which means no more than Israel as it now is. Since, in the teaching of Amos, Israel's future is wholly determined by its moral response to Yahweh, the avoidance of destruction by the people's reformation must always have remained at least a theoretical possibility. This is explicit in the prophet's appeals to the people (5⁴⁻⁶, ¹⁴, ¹⁵); it also underlies his announcements of doom, which, we may suppose, are not simply to give information, but, rather, to provoke reformation. It is unnecessary, therefore, to regard these verses as an editorial intrusion, simply because they contain a glimmer of hope.

5. 16–27 *The Day of the Lord*

This central section of the book contains the most powerful negative presentation of the prophet's message. It assumes throughout the positive affirmation of v. 24.

16, 17. The day of Yahweh's visitation will be a day of lamentation for the whole people. Modern radicalism asserts that God is dead; prophetic radicalism asserts that everybody is dead except God. The theme is developed in the following verses.

18–20. The origin and meaning of *the day of the Lord* are still vigorously debated. These verses show (*a*) that the people of Israel looked forward to such a day, and (*b*) that the prophet radically reinterpreted its character: *it is darkness, and not light.* For Amos, the popular expression became a way of speaking about Yahweh's coming to judge Israel; it became part, that is to say, of the main theme of all his preaching. Later prophecy

continued to speak of the Day of the Lord and it always retained its association with Yahweh's coming in judgement.
The judgement, however, came to include the Gentile nations,
sometimes *in addition* to Israel (Isa. 2^{6-22}; Zeph. 1^2–2^{15}) and
sometimes *instead* of Israel (Isa. 13^{2-22}, 34^{1-17}; Ezek. 30^{1-19},
38^1–39^{29}). This later development reflects more the original,
popular conception of the Day of the Lord than Amos' reinterpretation of it. In the popular religion of the eighth century
B.C., it was the day on which Yahweh came in order to assert
his sovereignty over the Gentile nations (who were regarded
as his enemies) and Israel rejoiced to share his universal
dominion. Amos retained the idea of Yahweh's coming to
assert his sovereignty in the world, but he made a radical break
with all popular expectations when he declared that it was
Israel (and not the Gentiles) who was Yahweh's enemy and,
therefore, that it was his own people who would be brought to
judgement. It is not surprising that the mainstream of Israel's
religious tradition was unable to accept this revolutionary
teaching and that after the preaching of the great pre-exilic
prophets, the Day of the Lord was toned down to something
very much like what it had been originally in popular religion
—a day of judgement for the nations and a day of salvation for
Yahweh's people. Opinions differ about the way in which the
Day of the Lord was understood and expected to come in
popular pre-exilic religion. It was clearly thought of as a day
of battle (Joel 2^{1-11}; see notes on Isa. 9^4), but it is debated
whether this feature derived from Israel's ancient conception
of 'holy war' (pp. 215–19), or from the foreign imperialist
ideology, which came into Israel with the institution of the
monarchy and was asserted at the accession of every new king
in the ancient Near East (see p. 159). The latter seems the
more probable source of the battle terminology and it immediately suggests an explanation of the way in which the notion
of Yahweh's day was maintained and propagated in popular
religious thinking. As the Psalms show so clearly, the complex
of ideas associated with oriental kingship had come to be used
of Yahweh and to play a significant role in Israel's worship.

Although it cannot be proved that there was any one particular festival at which Yahweh's kingship was celebrated and 'realized' in some form of ritual drama (see pp. 155 ff.), it is probable that in both the northern and southern kingdoms Yahweh's universal sovereignty and his triumph over his enemies were reaffirmed in pilgrim-feasts held at the sanctuaries. Whether Yahweh's 'day' meant the actual day of such feasts (cf. Hos. 2^{13}, 9^5,) or the day of victory celebrated *at* the feasts, must remain uncertain. It is, however, safe to conclude that Amos wrenched a term from cultic usage, pinned it down to the grim moral and historical realities of his own time, and turned it against the very people who had been bandying it about so complacently with song and harp (cf. v. 23).

21–27. The case for finding the origin of the popular conception of the Day of the Lord in the cult is strengthened if these verses of invective against the pilgrim-feasts were originally a continuation of the previous oracle. The verbs resound with impassioned repudiation: *I hate . . . despise . . . take no delight in . . . will not accept . . . will not look upon . . . will not listen.* The pilgrim-feasts and sacred assemblies at the sanctuaries, with their burnt offerings, cereal offerings, peace offerings, psalms and music (cf. 2$^{7, 8}$, 4$^{4, 5}$, 8^{10}), are rejected without qualification and without any suggestion that they can be made acceptable to Yahweh by being reformed and reinterpreted. It is often suggested that Amos could not have totally repudiated the worship of the sanctuaries and must have had in mind a purified cult for the future. But according to the prophet, *Israel had no future.* That is the whole burden of his message, *unless* the people stopped seeking the sanctuaries and started to seek God and goodness (5$^{4–15}$): *let justice roll down like waters, and righteousness like an ever-flowing stream* (v. 24). This moral alternative to the cult of the sanctuaries had been clear, Amos asserts, from the very beginning of Israel's Mosaic faith. The answer to the question of v. 25 is emphatically 'No' (cf. Jer. 7$^{21–23}$). Whether or not Amos was historically accurate in this claim is neither here nor there; that was his conviction (see pp. 314f.). The difficulties of v. 26 do not obscure its main point: Israel will be driven with its idols into exile. *Sakkuth* and *Kaiwan* are Assyrian star-gods (deliberately written in Hebrew with the vowels of the word *shiqqûç*, meaning 'abomination'). An alternative interpretation finds a corruption of the word for 'shrine' in *Sakkuth* and for 'pedestal' in *Kaiwan*, giving: 'You shall take up the shrine of your king and the pedestal of your images, the star-gods which you made for yourselves.'

6. 1–14 *A corrupt people on the brink of disaster*

These oracles are addressed primarily to the leaders of the people, with whom all the pre-exilic independent prophets came into conflict (see pp. 175 ff.).

1–7. *Self-indulgent and self-satisfied leaders led into exile. Woe* (v. 1; cf. v. 4) is an interjection of disgust. If *Zion* is authentic, Amos had Judah as well as Israel in mind. *the notable men of the first of the nations* ironically describes the 'top people' of the 'top nation' in their own terms.

2. *Calneh*, a city in northern Syria (the Calno of Isa. 10⁹), was destroyed by Assyria in 738 B.C.; *Hamath*, a Syrian city on the river Orontes, and *Gath*, one of the five Philistine cities in the south-west of Palestine, fell to the Assyrians respectively in 720 and 711 B.C. Since these three cities were connected only by their common fate at Assyria's hands, it is probable that this is the point of the reference. Why should Judah expect to escape? This interpretation involves reading the text as: 'Are *you* better than these kingdoms [i.e. Calneh, Hamath, and Gath]? Or is *your* territory greater than *their* territory?' It also means accepting the verse as an editorial interpolation made after 711 B.C. If the text is read as it stands and ascribed to Amos, it may be understood to mean that *these kingdoms* of Israel and Judah are superior to the three cities—either a boast repeated in irony, or a warning that much, therefore, is expected of them. But the latter view is forced and the former preferable.

3. *bring near the seat of violence* is an obscure expression which

seems to mean 'giving way' to violence and endowing it with authority.

4. The leaders, who lounge and sprawl on *beds of ivory* (cf. 3¹⁵), demand specially fattened calves (fig. p. 278).

6. *in bowls*, that is, by the bowlful ('by the bucket').

7. The so-called leaders of the people will lead them *into exile* and that will be the end of these lounge-lizards.

8. A brief oracle on the fate of Samaria and its proud fortresses.

9–11. Two fragments describe the horrors of a plague (vv. 9, 10) and the shock of an earthquake (v. 11).

12–14. By using a wisdom saying (v. 12), Amos represents the Israelites' corruption of the courts as an unnatural perversion (cf. 5⁷; see p. 180). Their confidence in their own capacity is ridiculed by the prophet's selecting two of the towns they had captured and of which the names allow him to prick the bubble of their pride. *Lo-debar*, a town in Transjordan just south of the Sea of Galilee, means a *thing of nought*; *Karnaim*, another town to the north-east in the same region, means *horns*, symbolic of power (see notes on Ps. 132¹⁷). The thought of these verses and their echo of the methods of the wisdom teachers are found again in Isa. 10¹³⁻¹⁹. *I will raise up against you a nation.* Assyria as Yahweh's agent of judgement will harry Israel from the far north to the far south (see notes on 2 Kgs. 14²⁵).

BEDS OF IVORY. This elaborate and brilliant ivory carving, about 32½ in. long and 25 in. deep, was discovered at Fort Shalmaneser in Nimrud (cf. fig. p. 19), where it once decorated the back of a royal bed (cf. Amos 6⁴). The side panels and the two right-centre panels depict bearded soldiers grasping the sacred tree; the figure in the centre is a four-winged goddess or guardian spirit. The top panel shows the winged disc and the bottom panel a bull hunt with horse and chariot. Just as a modern photograph may be dated by the model of any motor-car it happens to include, so an ancient Assyrian carving may be dated by the model of the king's chariot it depicts. This chariot is a four-seater with six-spoked wheels and reinforced hubs, which (with other considerations) makes the year about 730 B.C. (see M. E. L. Mallowan, *Nimrud and its Remains*, vol. ii, pp. 488–94).

7. 1–8. 3 *Divine patience and prophetic insight*

The four so-called 'visions' of this section more closely resemble the 'object-lessons' of the wisdom teachers than the irrational experiences of the ecstatic prophets. Amos' insight into his people's peril and his awareness of Yahweh's patience reveal a degree of sensitivity comparable to that of Hosea and find an entirely appropriate mode of expression in these snatches of quiet and intimate dialogue. Since this kind of reflection probably lies behind the call of Amos, it is illuminating to read in the same context his denial that he was a professional prophet.

7. 1–3. *Devouring locusts.* The RSV's clumsy translation of v. 1 is intended to present a picture of locusts hatching out when the late growth of corn was beginning to shoot. The early crop was known as *the king's mowings.* The king of Ugarit had certain rights of pasturage and so, apparently, had the king of Israel. The locusts' relentless devouring of the vegetation symbolized for Amos the threat to Israel's existence and provoked him to intercede for the people. He received an assurance that the worst would not happen.

4–6. *Devouring fire.* The object lesson here appears to be a summer fire of so devastating a kind as to have seemed to dry up even the subterranean waters of *the great deep* (cf. Gen. 7[11]). Instead of *the Lord God was calling for a judgement by fire,* we should probably read, 'the Lord God was summoning a flaming fire'. Amos again intercedes and receives assurance.

7–9. *Demolition.* Amos saw (as the Greek suggests) 'a *man* standing beside a wall with a plumb line in his hand'. Like the wall, Israel was out of true and fit only for demolition (cf. Isa. 28[17]). Doom was certain. The time for interceding with Yahweh had passed; Amos must now become Yahweh's spokesman to the people.

10–17. *The divine authority of Amos' treasonable preaching.* This biographical narrative has become attached to the previous autobiographical narrative, because it begins with a threat to Jeroboam (vv. 10, 11; cf. v. 9).

12, 13. The language of Amaziah is more abusive than the RSV translation suggests. The priest of the royal sanctuary contemptuously tells Amos to get back where he belongs and earn his living as a prophet in Judah (cf. Mic. 3⁵, ¹¹; Ezek. 13¹⁹; 2 Kgs. 5¹⁹⁻²⁷).

14, 15. Amos indignantly denies that he is a professional prophet and insists that he preaches as he does because Yahweh took him and told him to do so. The detail of these verses has been the subject of much debate. The statement of v. 14 has no verbs in the Hebrew, with the result that some scholars supply the present tense, *I am no prophet . . . but I am a herdsman*, thus representing Amos as repudiating any suggestion that he is a prophet, and other scholars supply the past tense, *I was no prophet . . . but I was a herdsman*, representing Amos as claiming to have become a prophet by virtue of Yahweh's unsought summons. There is a danger that the discussion may become a mere dispute about words. As Jeremiah makes abundantly clear (see notes on Jer. 23⁹⁻³²; cf. Ezek. 13¹⁻²³) and as the antics of *the sons of the prophets* amply confirm (see notes on 2 Kgs. 2³), the title 'prophet' was not necessarily one which a responsible man convinced of a divine vocation would wish to claim (cf. Zech. 13⁴, ⁵). It is certain: (a) that Amos denied being the kind of prophet Amaziah supposed him to be; (b) that he based his authority to preach not on a professional training in the prophetic guilds but on a totally unexpected 'call' by Yahweh; (c) that as a spokesman for Yahweh he believed that he was sent to *prophesy to my people Israel*. In addition to being a *herdsman* (or shepherd, cf. 1¹), Amos is described as *a dresser of sycamore trees*, which suggests the humble, seasonal job of puncturing the unripe fruit. It would, however, be easier to think of a man of the prophet's general status as a grower of sycamore trees.

16, 17. This fearsome oracle is not a new threat made by the prophet to get his own back on the priest, but a pointed reminder to Amaziah that he and his family will not be spared the horrors of the enemy invasion which Israel is about to suffer.

8. 1–3. *The time is ripe.* The association in sound between *qayiç*, the Hebrew for *summer*, and *qēç*, the Hebrew for *end*, was enough for a familiar sight to bring to explicit expression the prophet's deep-rooted conviction that Israel was ripe for enemy invasion. The fall of the year means the fall of the people. This meditative origin of Amos' oracles (cf. Jer. 1¹¹⁻¹⁴) is wholly different from the visions of mystics or the ravings of ecstatics (see pp. 241 f.).

8. 4–14 *Destroyers destroyed*

Those who (v. 4) *bring the poor of the land to an end* (vv. 4–7) will themselves find (v. 10) *the end of it like a bitter day* (vv. 8–14).

4–7 Commercial swindlers. The *new moon* and the *sabbath* were closing days in the markets. The two, although independent in origin, are often mentioned together as days of rest and festival in pre-exilic Israel (2 Kgs. 4²³; Isa. 1¹³; Hos. 2¹¹; cf. Isa. 66²³) and both are of great antiquity. The *sabbath* has its place in all the law codes (Exod. 34²¹, 23¹²; Deut. 5¹²⁻¹⁴; Exod. 20⁸⁻¹¹, 31¹²⁻¹⁷), and the *new moon* is mentioned as a religious feast in the reign of Saul (1 Sam. 20⁵, ¹⁸, ¹⁹, ²⁴⁻²⁶). The rapacious merchants are impatient for these rest days to be over, so that they may return to their swindling—making *the ephah small* (giving short measure of grain) and *the shekel great* (taking over-weight of silver) and, even then, for rubbish—*the refuse of the wheat.* The condemnation of commercial dishonesty appears in many traditions of the Old Testament: *prophecy* (Hos. 12⁷; Mic. 6¹⁰, ¹¹; Ezek. 45¹⁰⁻¹²), *law* (Deut. 25¹³⁻¹⁶; Lev. 19³⁵, ³⁶), and *wisdom* (Prov. 11¹, 16¹¹, 20²³), as it also does outside Israel. In the Babylonian wisdom hymn to the sun-god Shamash (dated between 1000 and 650 B.C.), for example, we find:

The merchant who practises tr[ickery] as he holds the corn measure,
Who weighs out loans [of corn] by the minimum standard,
  but requires a large quantity in repayment,
The curse of the people will overtake him before his time . . .

    (D. Winton Thomas, *Documents from Old Testament Times*, p. 109)

In v. 7, *the pride of Jacob*, by which Yahweh swears, may either be taken literally (cf. 6⁸), or understood as a name given to Yahweh himself (cf. 4²; Hos. 5⁵, 7¹⁰); on either interpretation, the prophet is using the expression ironically.

8–14. *The bitter end.* The comparison (v. 8) of an earthquake, which makes the whole earth (rather than merely *the land*) tremble, to the rising and falling waters of the Nile, is reproduced in 9⁵, ⁶.

9, 10. A complex of imagery depicting convulsions in nature, with trembling earth, quaking mountains, darkness, cloud, and thunder, was already well established in Hebrew tradition to convey the presence and power of Yahweh (Judg. 5⁴, ⁵, ²⁰, ²¹; Josh. 10¹¹⁻¹⁴; Pss. 18⁷⁻¹⁵, 29⁴⁻⁹; Exod. 19¹⁶⁻¹⁹). Amos (or, as some think, his editor) drew on this tradition to describe Yahweh's coming to fight against his people on the Day of the Lord. Shaving the head to produce *baldness* (v. 10) was a common but forbidden mourning custom (Deut. 14¹; cf. Jer. 48³⁷).

11–14. The *famine* in vv. 11, 12 is universal (cf. Zech. 9¹⁰; Ps. 72⁸) and figurative (cf. Deut. 8³; Prov. 9⁵). It is less likely to represent the authentic teaching of Amos than is the localized and literal *thirst* (v. 13) of the young and foolish devotees of the goddess *Ashimah* (see notes on 2 Kgs. 17³⁰). For '*As the way of Beer-sheba lives*' (v. 14), read 'As thy beloved lives, O Beer-sheba', the 'beloved' being the local deity.

9. 1–8a *The conclusion*

1–4. *A vision of the end.* This nightmare vision is totally different from the 'object lessons' of the previous chapters (7¹⁻⁹, 8¹⁻³). Instead of the Lord's 'showing' Amos details of the familiar world, he himself appears standing over an unidentified altar and giving horrifying instructions to an unidentified agent of his wrath. The destruction of the sanctuary (cf. 3¹⁴, 7⁹) and the inescapability of judgement (cf. 2¹⁴⁻¹⁶, 5¹⁹) are certainly themes in Amos' oracles, but they are developed here in a manner without parallel in the rest of the book. Like Yahweh's gracious

presence in Ps. 139⁷⁻¹², here the power of his wrath knows no
bounds and will hunt out fugitives from the underworld of
Sheol (cf. Job 10²¹, ²²; Isa. 14⁹⁻²⁰) or from the heights of heaven,
from the top of Mount Carmel (cf. 1²) or from the bottom of the
sea (on *the serpent*, see notes on Ps. 29¹⁰, ¹¹); even in enemy
captivity, they will not be safe from his judgement. The language and mythological colouring of this vision in many ways
resemble the teaching of Ezekiel more than that of Amos (cf.
Ezek. 5¹², 6¹⁻⁷, 11⁹, 12¹⁴, 15⁷) and it would be unwise to take its
authenticity for granted.

5, 6. The last of the three fragmentary 'doxologies' (cf. 4¹³,
5⁸, ⁹).

7, 8*a*. *Israel and the nations*. The intention of this oracle, which
ends with the words *I will destroy it from the surface of the ground*
(that is, from 'the face of the earth'), is to affirm yet again that
Israel will be judged. The peculiar interest of the verses lies in
their comparison between Israel and the other nations. The
Israelites had become as alien to Yahweh as the far-off
Ethiopians, even though he chose them to be his own people in
bringing them up from the land of Egypt. Israel's origin did
not in itself give the people any immunity from judgement.
Yahweh had also brought up *the Philistines* into Canaan *from
Caphtor* (Crete) and *the Syrians from Kir* (cf. 1⁵) and yet he was
about to punish both these peoples for their rebellion against
his righteous will (cf. 1³⁻⁵, ⁶⁻⁸). Amos was clearly convinced
that Yahweh was sovereign over 'all the families of the earth'
(3²) and that he had entered into a special relation with Israel,
but this unique bond was conditional upon his people's moral
response and, therefore, not (as they thought) indissoluble. It
is highly speculative to find any elaborate 'doctrine of univer-
salism' in the prophet's words.

9. 8*b*–15 *A later appendix*

Beginning with *except that I will not utterly destroy the house of
Jacob*, which flatly contradicts the previous oracle and Amos'

whole message, to the end of the book, the material (with the possible exception of vv. 9, 10) presupposes the fall of the house of David in 587 B.C. (v. 11) and the exile of the people (vv. 14, 15). Attempts to defend the authenticity of this appendix must be reckoned among the curiosities of recent Old Testament scholarship.

HOSEA

The book of Hosea yields a powerful impression of a prophetic personality, rather than a clear picture of his life and ministry. Although it is nowhere stated explicitly, it is safe to conclude that Hosea was a native of the northern kingdom and taught there from about 750 B.C. to about 730 B.C. On the basis of the mockery referred to in 9⁷, it has been suggested that Hosea was an institutional prophet, but the vigorous independence and deep insight of his message make it virtually certain that he belonged to the chosen few who were called from other occupations to be Yahweh's spokesmen. The book contains no explicit reference to his call, although some interpreters have found the reality of it in his tragic experience of marriage. Even if it is improbable that his ministry actually originated in his marriage, there can be no doubt that his whole message was profoundly influenced by it.

The theme of all his teaching is what St. Paul was later to call 'the kindness and the severity of God' (Romans 11²²). The popular view of Hosea, which, in contrast to Amos, represents him as a prophet of the kindness *as opposed to* the severity of God, is clearly mistaken. No less emphatically than Amos, Hosea proclaims Yahweh's judgement on his apostate people and the language he uses for doing so is, if anything, even more violent. Yahweh's wrath is kindled against Israel (5¹⁰, 13¹¹); he has withdrawn from his people in hate and detestation (5⁶, 9¹⁰, ¹⁵). Like a wild beast, or a bird of prey (5¹⁴, 8¹, 13⁷, ⁸), he will rend and devour them (6¹, 8¹⁴, 11⁶), so that they will be utterly destroyed (4⁵, 5⁹, 13⁹, ¹⁶). The prophet's characterization of Israel's failure is more monotonous but equally impassioned. The people's ungrateful forsaking of Yahweh for Baal and his licentious worship at the sanctuaries is again and again denounced as nothing less than harlotry or whoredom, a term which (apart from the allegories of Ezek. 16 and 23) Hosea almost monopolizes in its metaphorical usage in the literature of the Old Testament (1^2, $2^{2, 4}$, $4^{10, 12-14}$, 5^4, 6^{10}, 9^1).

The prophet's horror at Israel's wholesale desertion of Mosaic Yahwism for the religion of Canaan (cf. $2^{14, 15}$, 12^{13}, 13^4) completely dominates his oracles and the only other main indictment in the book is closely associated with it. In political no less than religious life, Israel had abandoned Yahwism in favour of the Canaanite way. Although it is impossible to extract from Hosea's teaching anything so abstract as his attitude to kingship *as such*, the faithless attempts of Israel to find security in foreign alliances in the chaotic years after the death of Jeroboam II in 746 B.C. (5^{13}, 7^{11}, $8^{9, 10}$, 10^{13}, 12^1; cf. 14^3) represented for the prophet the characteristic policy of a monarchy, which for centuries had promoted Canaanite practices ($8^{4-6, 14}$, $10^{5, 6}$) and was now not only alienated from Yahwism, but decadent even by its own criteria of success (8^7, 10^3, $13^{10, 11}$).

It is with these two aspects of Israel's infidelity that (according to our evidence) Hosea was almost exclusively concerned: alike in religion and politics, 'Ephraim mixes himself with the peoples. . . . Ephraim has hired lovers' (7^8, 8^9; cf. 2^5). In contrast with Amos, it is noteworthy that Hosea shows very little awareness of the moral corruption of Israelite society (the most explicit reference, 4^2, being of doubtful authenticity; cf. $7^{1, 2}$, $12^{7, 8}$) and that, correspondingly, his positive demands are less directly moral than spiritual—loyalty and knowledge of God (see notes on 4^1, 6^{4-6}). If the range of Hosea's concern is severely restricted in breadth, he more than makes up for this limitation by his penetration and depth. No prophet, except, perhaps, Jeremiah, discloses a more profound awareness of the nature of God as personal and loving. Any suspicion that his presentation of Yahweh's love for Israel under the figure of marriage was merely a conventional borrowing from Canaanite myth and ritual is decisively scotched by two considerations. First, the conviction is expressed quite independently in the prophet's parallel analogy of a father's personal and loving care for his child (see notes on 11^{1-9}) and, secondly, it is inextricably associated with his own direct experience of what it means to be a person in a relationship of love with another person (see notes on 1^{2-9} and 2^{2-15}).

Hosea's insight into the character of God as personal and loving provides the context in which his proclamation of judgement must be understood. Without in the least mitigating its terror, Yahweh's personal commitment to his people in love transforms what at first appears to be retributive punishment into reformatory discipline and holds out the invincible hope of Israel's ultimate restoration. Although this hope of salvation beyond judgement has clearly been amplified by the prophet's editors ($1^{10}-2^{1}$, 2^{16-23}, (?) $11^{10, 11}$, 14^{1-9}), there are good grounds for believing that it came in the first place from Hosea himself. So far from being an easy assurance like the institutional prophets' vapid preaching of peace (Jer. 6^{14}, 14^{13}, 23^{17}; Mic. 3^{5}; Ezek. 12^{24}, 13^{10-12}), the invincibility of Yahweh's love was for Hosea a daring and hard-won conviction, anchored in nothing except his personal experience of Gomer and of God *as persons*. As he found he could not abandon his adulterous wife, so Yahweh, he discerned, could not abandon his adulterous people ($2^{14, 15}$, $11^{8, 9}$).

The pattern of Hosea's personal relationship with Gomer is the pattern of Yahweh's personal relationship with Israel, as it emerges from the teaching of the book as a whole. For the prophet, these two relationships are inseparable, the one illuminating and deepening the commitment of the other, as may be seen from an analysis of the five features which they have in common: (1) the initial relationship of openness and spontaneity; (2) the rejection of the relationship; (3) the invincible love which cannot accept rejection as final; (4) the training for the renewal of the relationship by the acceptance of responsibility for its breach; (5) the final restoration.

The book of Hosea gains immensely in coherence when its

elusive and scattered oracles are gathered under these five themes. (1) *The initial relationship of openness and spontaneity* which, we may suppose, characterized the beginning of Hosea's marriage ('Go, take to yourself a wife', 1^2), is comparable to Yahweh's relationship with Israel, 'in the days of her youth . . . when she came out of the land of Egypt' ($2^{14, \ 15}$, 11^{1-4}, $13^{4, \ 5}$; cf. 12^9). (2) *The rejection of the relationship* in Gomer's infidelity is paralleled by Israel's adulterous desertion of Yahweh for Baal (1^{2-9}, 2^{2-5}, $4^{1-3, \ 4-19}$, 5^{1-7}, 6^7-7^{16}, 8^{1-14}, 9^{10-17}). (3) *The invincible love which cannot accept rejection as final* is enjoined on Hosea and affirmed of Yahweh in $3^{1, \ 2}$: '. . . even as the Lord loves the people of Israel, though they turn to other gods.' It is also clearly reflected in other oracles ($5^{15}-6^6$, 7^1, 11^8). (4) *The training for the renewal of the relationship by the acceptance of responsibility for its breach* is the feature with which, not surprisingly, Hosea is most immediately concerned. Judgement of a severity congruous with the magnitude of the offence against love is proclaimed with passionate emphasis, but its purpose, so far from being destructive, is wholly creative ($3^{3, \ 4}$, 2^{6-13}, 5^{8-15}, 8^{7-14}, 9^{1-9}, $10^{1-8, \ 9-15}$, 11^{5-7}, 13^{7-16}). (5) *The final restoration* is not a happy ending arbitrarily appended to a message of judgement, but an invincible hope grounded in the prophet's experience of invincible love: 'Afterward the children of Israel shall return and seek the Lord their God' (3^5, $2^{14, \ 15}$, 11^9; cf. $1^{10}-2^1$, 2^{16-23}, $11^{10, \ 11}$, 14^{1-9}).

In the transmitted record of Hosea's teaching, his oracles have lost the sharpness of outline which we find in other prophets of the eighth century B.C. and are now fused into larger discourses which defy detailed literary analysis. It is, therefore, more than usually difficult to be confident in distinguishing between the prophet's original teaching and the interpretation of it by his editor. The editor was clearly a Judean (see notes on $1^{6, \ 7}$) and one may surmise that he received Hosea's oracles from the northern kingdom in a fragmentary (but probably written) form. If, as appears to be the case, the successful transmission of prophetic teaching was confined to literate Yahwistic circles in the southern kingdom (see pp. 244–7 o), it is not surprising that Hosea is the only northern prophet whose oracles have survived and that what has survived is evidently in great disorder. Nevertheless, the collection as it now stands still bears the impress of a single and highly sensitive personality.

I. I *Hosea and his ministry*

Apart from the mere name of his father and a little information about his wife and children (see below), all we know about Hosea is derived from his sensitive and passionate proclamation of *the word of the Lord* (cf. Mic. 1¹; contrast Amos 1¹; Jer. 1¹). The later Judean compiler of this superscription represents the prophet's ministry as extending from the reign of *Uzziah* (783–742) to the reign of *Hezekiah* (715–687), but Samaria fell in 721 B.C. and there is no evidence that Hosea had any knowledge of it. The second dating of the ministry *in the days of Jeroboam the son of Joash* (786–746) inspires more confidence and is confirmed by the reference in 1⁴ to the dynasty of Jehu (842–745), of which Jeroboam II was the last significant member. It is probable, however, that Hosea was active after the death of Jeroboam and lived to condemn both the Aramean-Israelite alliance of 734 B.C. (see notes on 5⁸⁻¹⁵) and the political chaos of the following decade (see notes on 6¹¹ᵇ–7¹²).

I. 2–9 *The marriage of Hosea*

It is important to be clear that the disputed question of Hosea's marriage is worth discussing only in so far as it illuminates his message. Domestic details, even in the case of a prophet, are in themselves of small significance. Of the many theories which scholars have proposed, five deserve serious consideration: (*a*) the narratives of 1²⁻⁹ and 3¹⁻⁵, like the material of 2²⁻¹⁵, are not factual but *allegorical*; they present the relationship between Yahweh and Israel under the daring figure of a marriage; (*b*) the two narratives are accounts of real events, but refer to Hosea's relationship with *two different women*; (*c*) the two narratives are *parallel accounts*, in the sense that they describe two different aspects of a single relationship; (*d*) the two narratives are in *true chronological order* and describe two stages of Hosea's marriage to a woman *known from the outset to be an adulteress*, which he undertook as an act of prophetic symbolism in obedience to Yahweh's command; (*e*) the two narratives are in *true chronological order* and describe a marriage relationship *which began normally*, but was broken by the adultery of the prophet's wife. The final breach occurred between the events recorded in the two narratives and was then projected back to colour the description of Hosea's entry on the marriage.

None of these reconstructions is without its merits or its difficulties. The allegorical theory (*a*) is severely challenged by circumstantial detail in the narratives (e.g. the name Gomer in 1³), but has the great advantage of emphasizing that it is their *meaning* which matters. It is its failure to illuminate Yahweh's relationship with Israel which tells against theory (*b*) and against the distinctive feature (union with an acknowledged adulteress) of theory (*d*). The development of Israel's relationship with Yahweh (loyalty–apostasy–discipline–repentance–restoration), which seems to constitute the basic pattern of Hosea's teaching (see pp. 287 ff.), is most clearly reflected in theory (*e*), but the closeness of the correspondence points to its weakness as an independent reconstruction of the actual events. The advantage of the remaining view (*c*) is its modesty in not claiming to reconstruct the whole story of the prophet's marriage, but in pointing simply to the evidence which the two narratives preserve. Since the narratives preserve only such evidence as illuminates the prophet's message and in a form which the message has profoundly affected, it is now impossible to disentangle what *happened* from what he understood it to *mean*. Hosea was wedded to Gomer and his marriage was no less inextricably wedded to his message. On balance, then, (*e*) is to be preferred.

The first narrative (1²⁻⁹) relates in the third person the fact of the prophet's marriage and the birth of three children to his wife. Whatever the original circumstances, the whole purpose of the present account lies in its exposure of Israel's harlotry

in forsaking Yahweh for Baal and Yahweh's consequent cancellation of the covenant with his people.

2, 3. *When the Lord first spoke through Hosea* misrepresents the
Hebrew and gives the false impression that Yahweh's command to marry was the way in which Hosea received his call
to the prophetic ministry. The words, however, are simply a
heading, as the rendering of the Authorized Version makes
clear: 'The beginning of the word of the Lord by Hosea.'
Yahweh's command that Hosea should marry *a wife of harlotry*
has been taken literally by many scholars and interpreted as a
command to perform an act of prophetic symbolism. But what
precisely so loathsome an act was meant to *symbolize* is obscure.
Union with profligacy is hardly an obvious way of exposing it
and, in any case, the symbolic acts of other prophets (like Hosea's
symbolic naming of his son in v. 4) always represent the action of
Yahweh himself (see pp. 239 f.). It is preferable, therefore, to suppose that Hosea's wife committed adultery and produced *children
of harlotry* some time after their marriage and that this unhappy
outcome was read back into Yahweh's inscrutable intention
(see notes on Isa. 6⁹⁻¹³), just as its meaning for Hosea was read
back into the initial significance of the relationship: *for the land
commits great harlotry by forsaking the Lord*. The name *Gomer* has no
symbolic significance, although *daughter of Diblaim* (literally,
'daughter of two fig-cakes') has been interpreted as meaning
that she was a worthless prostitute, or a worshipper of Baal (cf.
3¹), or (combining the two) a Canaanite cult prostitute (cf. 4¹⁴;
2 Kgs. 23⁷; Deut. 23¹⁷; Amos 2⁷; Jer. 3²; Ezek. 8¹⁴). *Diblaim*,
however, may be simply the name of Gomer's father, or (possibly) birthplace (cf. Num. 33⁴⁶; Jer. 48²²).

4, 5. *Jezreel*, the symbolic name of Gomer's first child, pronounces Yahweh's judgement on Jeroboam II (786–746), the
last great king of the *house of Jehu*, which began a century earlier
with a bloody *coup d'état* at Jezreel. What Elijah and Elisha
then approved, Hosea condemns (see pp. 91–95).

6, 7. *Not pitied*, the name of Gomer's second child (perhaps by
another man), expresses the finality of Yahweh's judgement

on Israel (cf. Amos 8²). The statement about *Judah* in v. 7 is one of a number of Judean editorial insertions in the book (cf. 4¹⁵, 6¹¹, 10¹¹, 11¹², 12²); for the contrast between deliverance by Yahweh and by military power, see 2 Chron. 13¹³⁻¹⁸, 14⁹⁻¹⁵, 20¹⁻³⁰.

8, 9. *Not my people*, the name of the third child (again, perhaps, by another man), combined with the direct declaration, *I am not your God*, announces that the covenant is cancelled (cf. Exod. 6⁷) and brings Yahweh's judgement to its terrifying climax.

2. 2–15 *Yahweh's dealing with his unfaithful wife*

The loosely connected oracles of this section make fully explicit, both by their content and by their present position, Hosea's theological extension of his experience of marriage to the 'marriage' between Yahweh and Israel. Just as this interpretation is indicated in the two accounts of the prophet's relations with Gomer, so his personal tragedy is recalled in these oracles on Yahweh's relations with Israel (vv. 2, 4, 5*a*); indeed, some scholars find in these verses additional fragments of Hosea's own story. The section as a whole is notable for two reasons. First, it looks beyond the judgement of 1²⁻⁹ to discipline and final restoration and so prepares the way for 3¹⁻⁵. Secondly, it demonstrates Hosea's daring annexation of the concept of the 'sacred marriage', which was central to the fertility cult of Canaan (fig. p. 292). Like other loyal Yahwists, the prophet was clear that the 'natural order', whether between men and

FERTILITY CULT SYMBOLS. The identity of these nude females is unknown, but the artist's sensuous representation illustrates the emphasis on sexuality and fertility associated with the goddess variously called Asherah, Astarte, and Ishtar in the cults of Palestine, Phoenicia, Assyria, and Babylonia. The figures, 6½ in. high, were carved in ivory about the end of the eighth century B.C., probably for use as the handle of a luxurious fan; they were found in the throne room of the palace at Nimrud. The ladies' crowns, decorated with gold, resemble that represented on the Canaanite ivory from Megiddo (see fig. p. 226) and support a capital (see M. E. L. Mallowan, *Nimrud and its Remains*, vol. i, p. 211).

women or between men and the earth (vv. 5, 8), came under the providence of Yahweh and should, therefore, be appropriated and properly interpreted by the faith of Yahweh. So far from being a piece of superficial apologetic, this significant extension of Mosaic Yahwism arose from an experience as profound and personal as Hosea's marriage is shown to have been.

2–5. *Appeal and warning to Israel*. Yahweh summons the children of Israel to *plead* his cause with their mother, so that she will abandon her soliciting appearance and adulterous embraces (v. 2; cf. Prov. 7[10–23]). If the clause *for she is not my wife, and I am not her husband* is really a formula of divorce, it is misplaced; it would fit its present context better if it were read as a question: '. . . or is she not my wife . . . ?' If Israel refuses to repent, Yahweh, her husband, will punish her as an adulteress and *strip her naked*, according to the ancient divorce procedure (cf. Ezek. 16[38–40]), now illustrated in the Nuzi tablets (dated about 1400 B.C.). The figure of the *parched land* in v. 3 gains added point from the description of Israel's adultery in v. 5; instead of trusting in Yahweh as the giver of food and drink (cf. v. 8), she had forsaken him for the Canaanite gods of fertility (see pp. 44–48).

6, 7. *Restraint and return*. Because he cares for his faithless wife, Yahweh will discipline her by separation and solitary confinement, until she recognizes that it would be better to return to him (cf. 3[3–5]).

8–13. *Exposure and punishment*. Hosea's bold claim that the fertility credited to the Canaanite cult (v. 5) was really the gracious operation of Yahweh is made explicit in v. 8, with the further thought that he, too, was responsible for his people's commercial prosperity—the *silver and gold*, which ironically they used for making idols of Baal. This gross infidelity will be punished by Israel's deprivation and exposure (vv. 9, 10; cf. Lam. 1[8]; Nah. 3[5–7]). Yahweh will put a stop to the licentious pleasures of the sanctuaries (v. 11) and destroy the vines and fig trees, which Israel regards as payment for her prostitution; her cultivated land will be reduced to a dangerous jungle (v.12;

for the meaning of *forest*, cf. 2 Sam. 18⁸; Isa. 5⁶). Hosea's judgement of Israel's cult is made quite unambiguous in v. 13: it is
the adulterous worship (under various local names) of the
Canaanite Baal.

14, 15. *Invitation and Response.* Judgement is Yahweh's first
word, but not his last. Here, he is represented as wooing Israel
back into the wilderness and making love to her as in the early
days. And from there, he will lead her a second time into 'the
land of the Lord' (cf. 9³), when the *Valley of Achor*, on the first
occasion the valley of trouble (Josh. 7²⁰⁻²⁶), will be turned into
a *door of hope* (cf. Isa. 65¹⁰). To this invitation, Israel will respond. It is important to notice that the prophet finds hope
for his people not in any nostalgic dream of getting away from
Canaanite culture by a return to the semi-nomadic conditions
of the wilderness, but in the continuing fidelity of Yahweh and
the continuing validity in Israel's new circumstances of her
ancient Mosaic faith—*as at the time when she came out of the land
of Egypt* (cf. 9¹⁰, 11¹⁻⁴, 12⁹, ¹³, 13⁴; see pp. 218 f.).

3. 1–5 *The discipline of redeeming love*

Whereas the form of 1²⁻⁹ is biographical, this account of
Hosea's relations with his wife, as befits its more intimate
character, has evidently come from the prophet himself. The
oracles of 2²⁻¹⁵ fully support the view that it was Hosea's in-
extinguishable love for Gomer, which, despite her desertion
and adultery, led to her repentance and return and that it was
this decisive experience which enabled him to see that Yahweh
would discipline and ultimately redeem his people.

1. *Go again, love a woman.* The word, *again*, here, has played a
large part in the discussion of the problem of Hosea's marriage
(see pp. 289–93). Those who take the view that the woman in
this chapter is a woman other than Gomer generally attach it
to the previous words and read: 'And the Lord said to me again:
Go, love a woman. . . .' The introduction of a second woman,
however, destroys the analogy between Hosea's continuing

love for his wife, even though she has forsaken him and become *an adulteress*, and Yahweh's continuing love for Israel, *though they turn to other gods*. The *cakes of raisins*, eaten at the autumn vintage festival, were a feature of Canaanite celebrations (cf. Jer. 7[18]; 2 Sam. 6[19]). If, as seems probable, Hosea gained insight into Yahweh's love for his people from his own experience of loving his unfaithful wife, it is interesting to note that, in the prophet's thought, it is Yahweh's love which has now assumed the priority and is appealed to as a model for his personal behaviour (cf. 'Husbands, love your wives, as Christ loved the church and gave himself up for her', Ephesians 5[25]).

2. *So I bought her*. To whom the payment was made is unknown; speculations include the *paramour* (v. 1), the authorities of the sanctuary at which she had become a cult prostitute, and the master whom she was serving as a slave. The price paid (including the estimated value of the barley) has been calculated at thirty shekels, which, according to Exod. 21[32], was the price of a slave. The term *lethech* is otherwise unknown; for *a lethech of barley*, the Greek has 'a measure of wine'.

3. On her return, Hosea subjects his wife to a prolonged period of discipline, during which she is denied all sexual intercourse, whether illegitimate or legitimate (cf. 2[6, 7]).

4. As Hosea disciplines Gomer, so Yahweh will discipline Israel. The interpretation of this verse is extremely difficult. Are the things of which Israel is to be deprived regarded here as illegitimate or legitimate, or (as a strict analogy with v. 3 would require) a combination of both? Hosea, like other loyal Yahwists, shows hostility to *king* and *prince* (see notes on 6[11b]-7[12]), *sacrifice* (cf. 2[11, 13]; see notes on 6[6] and p. 314), and ritual paraphernalia such as the *pillar*, which represented Baal at Israel's Canaanite sanctuaries (cf. 10[1, 2]; Mic. 5[13]; 1 Kgs. 14[23]; see pp. 134 f.), the *ephod*, an image, or vestment, or vested image (Judg. 8[27]; 2 Sam. 6[14]; Isa. 30[22]), and the small household images called *teraphim* (Gen. 31[19, 34]; Ezek. 21[21]; 2 Kgs. 23[24]). The inevitable conclusion seems to be that these are the

things which Israel must learn to do without for ever—by the discipline of exile (cf. 12⁹).

5. The purpose of Israel's discipline is positive—to inculcate that penitence which begins in *fear* and ends with restoration to Yahweh's *goodness* (cf. 2¹⁴, ¹⁵). The phrase *and David their king* is an obvious interpolation by the Judean editor, but *in the latter days* may be retained as meaning simply 'in the days to come'.

4. 1–3 *Yahweh's charge against his people*

This compendious statement of Israel's failure provides a general introduction to the oracles which make up the rest of the book and may well represent the compiler's attempt to summarize Hosea's message.

1. The term *faithfulness* (*'ᵉmeth* from the Hebrew root *'āman*) means reliability in personal relationships—'good faith' (see notes on Jer. 5³) and the term weakly rendered 'kindness' is the untranslatable *ḥeṣedh*, for which 'loyalty' is a better approximation than most (see notes on Deut. 7⁹). Although *ḥeṣedh* is especially characteristic of Hosea among the prophets (4¹, 6⁴, ⁶, 10¹², 12⁶; cf. 2¹⁹), it is found frequently throughout the Old Testament and over thirty times in close association (as here) with *'ᵉmeth* (cf. Prov. 3³, 14²², 16⁶, 20²⁸). The people's lack of faithfulness and loyalty is virtually equivalent to their lack of *knowledge of God*, since in this context, *da'ath 'ᵉlōhim* ('knowledge of God') means knowledge of what God requires (cf. 4⁶, 6⁶; Prov. 2⁵).

2. It is probable that this list of charges reflects a familiarity with the Ten Commandments (Exod. 20¹⁻¹⁷), but uncertain whether it comes from Hosea or his editor. The terms *swearing* and *lying* should be read together as meaning that solemn oaths are being broken.

3. The section ends with the threat of Yahweh's judgement; it should, therefore, be expressed in the future tense. The inclusion of *the fish of the sea*, of which few Israelites had any direct

knowledge, suggests that the prophet (or, more probably, his editor) is borrowing conventional terminology (cf. Gen. 9²; Zeph. 1², ³; Ezek. 38¹⁹, ²⁰; Job 12⁷, ⁸).

4. 4–19 *Yahweh's charge against the priests*

This series of oracles presents a vivid picture of the degradation of Canaanite religion at the local sanctuaries and of the syncretism which threatened the very life of Yahwism in the northern kingdom. Yahweh was being worshipped in licentious rites appropriate to Baal but utterly alien to the character of Israel's God. Like the later deuteronomist, Hosea positively accepted the land of Canaan as Yahweh's gift to his people (cf. 2⁸, ¹⁴, ¹⁵; see pp. 209 ff.), while totally repudiating the fertility cults with which its agricultural life was still so closely associated. The blame for failing to make this distinction and equating Yahweh with Baal fell on the corrupt and apostate priesthood.

4. The Hebrew of this verse is obscure. It may be read to mean that accusation is not man's business but God's and that his contention is with the *priest*.

5. The kind of *prophet* meant here was no doubt the cultic functionary associated with the priest in the canonical prophets' condemnations (see notes on Jer. 23¹¹ and pp. 232–7). Priest and prophet alike go on stumbling day after day (rather than *shall stumble*), when it is their duty to lead Yahweh's people. For *I will destroy your mother*, read, 'Your mother [that is, Israel] is destroyed'.

6. Yahweh's people is ruined for lack of *knowledge*, because the priests have neglected their primary function of teaching, the *law* (*tôrāh*) being instruction in faith and morals (see pp. 204 f.). The priest and his *children* are therefore rejected.

7, 8. The more the priests *increased* in number, the greater their offence; their *glory* probably means the dignity of their office. In receiving their share of the people's sacrifices (cf. 1 Sam.

2^{12-17}), the priests are simply feeding on *the sin* which they encourage (cf. v. 10).

9, 10. The phrase, *like people, like priest*, is one of many proverbial sayings in the book (see p. 179) and means simply that the priests will be punished like the people. They will cease to find satisfaction in the gluttony of the sanctuaries and their sexual orgies will be sterile.

11–14. The effect on the people of the priests' failure is now introduced by another proverbial saying (v. 11). They seek oracles from the idolatrous symbols of the Canaanite sanctuaries (see pp. 75 f.), even though they are merely bits of wood (cf. Isa. 44^{9-20}), because *a spirit of harlotry* has possessed them. Hosea, unlike Amos, ascribes Israel's sin to an inner alienation (cf. 5^4). The men sacrifice at pagan 'high-places' (cf. 2 Kgs. 17^{9-12}) in the shade of the oak, poplar, and *terebinth* (that is, the huge turpentine tree) and the women indulge in sexual rites. Some scholars read the first two lines of v. 14 as a question, but many take the view (represented by the RSV) that the women are excused on the grounds that they have been led astray by the men.

15, 16. The first sentence of v. 15 is difficult. The Greek attaches the word *harlot* to the previous verse and the reference to *Judah* is probably an editorial gloss. Read, perhaps, 'You, O Israel, do not incur guilt'. *Gilgal* and Bethel were famous northern sanctuaries, the latter being referred to here by the contemptuous name, *Beth-aven*, that is, 'house of wickedness' (cf. 5^8, 10^5; see notes on Amos 1^{3-5}). For the cultic cry, *'As the Lord lives'*, see notes on Ps. 84. The question in v. 16 is reminiscent of the wisdom teacher's characteristic appeal to common sense (see pp. 178 ff.); a stubborn heifer cannot expect to be treated like a lamb.

17–19. The text of these verses is corrupt, although their general drift is fairly clear. Israel (*Ephraim*) has become tied up with idolatry, drunken debauchery, and sexual licence, preferring Baal (*shame*) to Yahweh (*glory*). The people, therefore, will be carried away by a wind in the day of judgement (read, 'A wind *will* wrap them') and they will be ashamed of their debased religion.

5. 8–15 *Yahweh's judgement on Israel and Judah*

This section is principally significant for the severity with which Hosea presents Yahweh's 'day of punishment'. Even if, as seems probable, Judah was now the agent of Yahweh's judgement on Israel (vv. 10–12), Judah would not escape the same condemnation. Both kingdoms were guilty of seeking their security in Assyria's military power (v. 13) and for the people of God such behaviour was intolerable apostasy. The exact historical setting of this material is debatable. The northern kingdom was subservient to Assyria from the accession of Menahem in 745 B.C. to 734 B.C., when Pekah joined Damascus in an anti-Assyrian alliance, and again from Hoshea's accession in 732 B.C. to his rebellion in 724 B.C. (see notes on 2 Kgs. 15$^{8-31}$, 17$^{1-6,\ 24-33}$). The southern kingdom was subject to Assyria throughout the reign of Ahaz (735–715); see notes on 2 Kgs. 16$^{1-20}$.

8, 9. The sounding of an alarm in the three cities of Benjamin is to give warning of a military invasion of Israel. *Beth-aven* is the prophet's contemptuous name for Bethel (see notes on 4^{15}). The probability that the advance was expected from the south suggests that in the last line of v. 8 the Hebrew *after you, O Benjamin* (RSV *mg.*) should be retained and understood as a battle-cry, warning that the enemy is at the rear. This is Yahweh's *punishment*, irrevocably declared against (rather than *among*) *the tribes of Israel* (v. 9).

10–12. In an authentic reference to *Judah*, Hosea accuses its rulers of land-grabbing (see p. 310) and pronounces Yahweh's judgement. The reference may mean that Judah was the enemy invading the northern kingdom, perhaps in the period when Ahaz enjoyed Assyrian help after he had refused to join the Aramean–Israelite alliance in 734 B.C. (see pp. 102–5). The concluding declaration of v. 12 makes it probable that v. 11 should be read with active verbs as a description of Ephraim's wickedness: 'Ephraim oppresses, perverting justice. . . .' The figurative language of v. 12 is even more startling than *moth* and *dry rot* suggest: Yahweh is a septic sore on Ephraim's body and a cancerous growth in Judah's vitals.

13–15. Both kingdoms are now represented as having appealed to Assyria, if (as the parallelism suggests) Judah should be read in the fourth line of v. 13: 'and Judah sent to the great king.' The *great king* was a title used by the kings of Assyria (cf. 10⁶). Like the other independent prophets, Hosea condemns this reliance on foreign aid as useless (cf. 7¹¹, 8⁹, ¹⁰, 10¹³, 12¹, 14³; and see pp. 321 f.). The real enemy could not be stayed by the Assyrian army, since it was none other than Yahweh himself (cf. v. 12). The popular conception of Hosea as a gentle prophet who taught a hopeful message of Yahweh's mercy is again shattered by the savage image of v. 14 (see p. 285). It is probable that v. 15 should be regarded as the conclusion of the section and interpreted as describing Yahweh's withdrawal from his people *until . . . in their distress they seek me*. For *they acknowledge their guilt*, it has been proposed that we should read, 'they are made desolate'.

6. 1–6 *Israel's confession and Yahweh's reply*

The two units juxtaposed in this section—Israel's confession (vv. 1–3) and Yahweh's reply (vv. 4–6)—are probably modelled on conventional liturgical forms. Yahweh's reply, however, is not an oracle of assurance of the kind which so often follows a prayer of lamentation and petition in the psalms (see p. 141), but an almost despairing restatement of the priorities of true Yahwism (cf. Mic. 6⁶⁻⁸).

1–3. Israel's confession takes up in v. 1 the terms of Yahweh's judgement in 5¹³⁻¹⁵ and interprets it as disciplinary rather than final. The expression, *after two days . . . on the third day* (v. 2), indicates an indefinite number, as in the Ras Shamra texts and the wisdom tradition (cf. Amos 1³–2⁸; see p. 178). It has been suggested that v. 2 reflects the kind of resurrection rites which were practised at the Canaanite sanctuaries (see pp. 45–48), but the terms *revive* and *raise* do not necessarily imply more than national restoration from adversity to greater vitality, which in its fullness is life in God's presence (cf. Pss. 80¹⁸, 85⁴⁻⁷, 143¹¹). In v. 3 *his going forth* must mean his coming to help, unless (as some scholars propose) the phrase *my judgement goes forth as the light* in v. 5 is misplaced and belongs here to give something like 'whose judgement goes forth as the light, and is as sure as the dawn'. Hosea's use of the simile of *showers* and *spring rains* is especially daring against the background of Israel's apostasy, which approximated Yahweh to Baal, as the giver of rain (see p. 47).

4–6. Yahweh's reply to Israel's confession is a warning and a demand. Their loyalty to him (*hesedh*, see notes on 4¹) is as unstable as the morning mist, though they have been battered by his words of judgement through the prophets. Yahweh, however, continues to demand loyalty (*ḥesedh*), that true response which is equivalent to *the knowledge of God*, and not *sacrifice* and *burnt offerings*. In earlier oracles, Hosea had dismissed sacrifice as 'sin' (4⁷, ⁸) and declared that it was not by offering 'flocks and herds' that Yahweh was to be found (5⁶). To exploit the phrase, *rather than*, of this verse in order to reduce the prophet's meaning to the expression of a mere preference ('loyalty is more desirable than sacrifice'), is totally to miss his radical re-affirmation of Mosaic Yahwism. Baal likes sacrifice; Yahweh does not (8¹³, 9⁴). Yahweh is totally different from Baal and what he desires of his people is that loyalty which is the ground of faith and goodness (see notes on Mic. 6⁶⁻⁸).

6. 11b–7. 12 *Israel's political failure*

The political anarchy of the northern kingdom which followed the death of Jeroboam II in 746 B.C. was so disastrous that Hosea's wholesale condemnation of Israel's kings and politicians was virtually inevitable (see pp. 99–102). It is impossible to say with confidence whether or not the prophet's attitude to the monarchy would have been more favourable in different circumstances, but the probability remains that he regarded it as an alien institution largely responsible for seducing Israel from her God (see p. 286).

6. 11b–7. 2. Characteristically, Hosea presents Yahweh as engaged in an agonizing conflict between the desire to forgive and the impossibility of ignoring the terrible reality of sin (cf. 6⁴, 11⁸, ⁹). Indeed, it is Yahweh's redemptive purpose which exposes his people's falsehood, as when light shines in dark places (cf. John 3¹⁹⁻²¹, 12⁴⁶⁻⁵⁰). In these introductory verses, the only social corruption specified is robbery and violence.

3. The king and the court, so far from trying to cure the disorder, are themselves in league with those responsible for it. A slight emendation would give, 'In their wickedness they *anoint* kings', but the *princes* (that is, the leading courtiers) were not anointed and the change is unnecessary.

4. The corrupt leaders of Israel burn in their passionate intrigues *like a heated oven*. The figures drawn from baking in vv. 4–8 defy detailed explanation, but the emphasis falls on the heat of the fire under the oven, which, even after being left unattended (v. 4) and merely smouldering (v. 6), quickly bursts into flame again. So the underhand plotting of the courtiers is never far from open revolt.

5–7. These verses seem to describe a recurrent pattern of political intrigue which rocked the throne in the last twenty years of the northern kingdom. On his accession (a probable interpretation of *the day of our king*), the courtiers would welcome the king and gain his confidence, even to the extent of encouraging him to join their drunken orgies (v. 5). Such cordiality, however, was merely a cloak for their scheming and they would get rid of him as soon as it suited their convenience (vv. 6, 7). In this period of chronic instability, the kings of Israel fell in rapid succession and the throne, instead of being an instrument for the government of Yahweh's people, was regarded simply as a pawn in the political game: *none of them calls upon me.*

8–12. The major factor in Israel's political instability was its faithless reliance on foreign support (see notes on 5^{13-15}). The two cooking metaphors in v. 8 suggest that the people's life is contaminated by alien ingredients and even then only half-baked; it is, therefore, fit for nothing. Foreign powers, so far from being a source of strength, are the cause of the country's weakness; like an old man, it is unaware that its vitality has been gradually sapped (v. 9). But even though pride has brought it to so feeble a condition, Israel remains impenitent (v. 10). Yahweh, therefore, will chastise his people, netting them like birds, as they fly off in senseless panic, first one way and then the other, to seek alliances with Egypt and Assyria (vv. 11, 12; cf. 8^{8-10}; see notes on 2 Kgs. 15^{8-31}, $17^{1-6,\ 24-33}$).

II. I–II *The kindness and severity of God*

This section of the book is unsurpassed in the whole of prophetic literature for the intimacy and tenderness with which it portrays Yahweh's relationship to Israel. In disclosing Yahweh's affection, disappointment, severity, and mercy as the father of his people, it closely parallels Hosea's development of the figure of Yahweh as Israel's husband. In both versions of the prophet's basic message, each successive stage in the relationship is directly motivated by Yahweh's loving care for his people—his disciplinary punishment no less than his final restoration. Hosea was a man of sentiment, but he was no sentimentalist. The divine love of which he speaks made Israel's restoration inevitable, but it did not make it easy. The cost of forgiveness is depicted here in the prophet's daring picture of God's agony (v. 8), and this reveals more clearly than anything else the depth of his spiritual insight.

1. *I called my son.* Israel's unique relationship to Yahweh is grounded in Yahweh's love (see notes on Deut. 6^5) and began with the Exodus from *Egypt* (see notes on $2^{14,\ 15}$). Hosea was by no means tied to his favourite figure of Israel as Yahweh's bride

(for it was no more than a figure) and adopts in vv. 1–4 the alternative model of a father's love for his son.

2. *The more I called them.* The text, restored (as in the RSV) on the basis of the Greek, makes it clear that Yahweh's election of Israel was not merely a once-for-all act, but a continuing caring (cf. Amos 2⁹⁻¹¹). The people, however, spurned this care and adopted the religion of Canaan.

3, 4. In a vividly observed picture, Hosea ascribes to Yahweh the deep disappointment of a father who recalls his rebellious son's childhood, when parental care was spontaneously and gratefully accepted. Yahweh had taught Israel to walk and carried him in his arms. Unfortunately, textual difficulties obscure the detail in v. 4. If the suggestion is correct that *cords of compassion* and *bands of love* mean the leather straps of a child's harness, the picture of Yahweh's teaching his people to walk still occupies the prophet's mind. This proposal fits the further suggestion that the second half of the verse should be translated: 'and I became to them as one who lifts a child to his cheek, and I bent down to them and fed them.'

5–7. With a sudden switch from Israel as a child dependent on his father to Israel in the present, now mature in apostasy (cf. v. 2), Yahweh is represented as pronouncing judgement. The inclusion of *Egypt* with Assyria as an agent of punishment is noteworthy (cf. 7¹⁶, 8¹³, 9³, ⁶) and confirms the view that Hosea did not entertain the idea of a single and decisive judgement on 'the day of the Lord', such as is found in Amos (see notes on Amos 5¹⁶⁻²⁷). The character of the punishment, rather, was closely related to the character of the people's sin (cf. 7¹¹, 8⁹), since it was reformatory in purpose. For all that, it was terrible in its severity. In v. 6, instead of *consume the bars of their gates*, it is possible to translate, 'consume their babblers', and retain the Hebrew 'counsels' (that is, political plotting), emended in the RSV (see *mg.*) to *fortresses*. The confused text of v. 7 may originally have made a reference to Baal; for *so they are appointed to the yoke, and none shall remove it*, we may read, 'though they call to Baal, he will not raise them up'.

8, 9. Baal cannot save, but Yahweh cannot do otherwise. To abandon his people, sinful though they were, would be to act contrary to his nature. With unparalleled daring, Hosea represents Yahweh as suffering a tumultuous inner conflict between the demands of righteousness and the demands of love, such as he himself had experienced in his marriage (cf. 6^{4-6}, 6^{11b}–7^2). How can Yahweh utterly destroy his people, as *Admah* and *Zeboiim* were destroyed with Sodom and Gomorrah (cf. Deut. 29^{23}; see notes on Amos 4^{11})? The very heart of God is torn by an agony of indecision, as his compassion kindles. Yahweh's love prevails; he can forgive his people, because he is *God and not man*. God transcends man by possessing and exercising in infinite degree the highest capacity which belongs to man in his finitude.

10, 11. The authenticity of these verses is open to doubt. Although they describe the restoration of Israel from exile, it should be noticed that they do so in Hosea's own characteristic terminology. The welcome roaring of Yahweh *like a lion* contrasts with 5^{14} and $13^{7, 8}$; similarly, the homecoming of Israel *like birds from Egypt, and like doves from the land of Assyria* contrasts directly with 7^{11} (cf. 8^9; and see notes on 11^5). It is clear, therefore, that this expression of hope has come from a writer attentive to the teaching of Hosea, if not from the prophet himself.

MICAH

All we know about Micah, apart from what may be deduced from his message, is that he came from Moresheth-gath in Judah ($1^{1, 14}$) and prophesied in Jerusalem on a number of occasions during the last quarter of the eighth century B.C. On the evidence of his message, it is generally held that he was a simple and forthright countryman of farming stock, who loathed the corruption of city life and deeply resented the way in which the *nouveaux riches* were oppressing the members of his own social class. Himself a poor man, Micah, it is said, became the prophet of the poor.

This widely accepted view is open to serious objections. It implies, most obviously, that the preaching of the prophets was so conditioned by class consciousness (not to say self-interest) that we can deduce from the content of their moral conviction their own particular status in society. Weighty general criticisms could be made of the adequacy of this kind of sociological interpretation of prophecy, but it is enough to point out that the whole of Micah's moral teaching, so far from deriving either its content or its emphasis from his own peculiar circumstances, is part of a common Yahwistic tradition upon which other prophets similarly drew. Whether he is denouncing the wealthy property-grabbers ($2^{1, 2}$; cf. 1 Kgs. 21^{1-20}; Isa. 5^{8-10}), the callous oppression of the weak (2^{8-10}, 3^{1-4}; cf. Amos 4^{1-3}; Isa. 3^{15}), the money-grubbing of the professional prophets (3^{5-8}; cf. Ezek. 13^{19}), the corruption of the judges (3^{11}; cf. Amos 5^{10-13}; Isa. 5^{23}), or the sacrosanct status of the Temple (3^{12}; cf. Jer. 7^{12-14}), his convictions are, without exception, paralleled elsewhere. On the evidence of their moral concern, it would be possible to reach the improbable conclusion that Amos, Isaiah, and Micah all came from the same class of the community. The view that Micah taught in Jerusalem as a simple peasant up from the country is questionable for other reasons. It fails to explain both his skill in the use of language—shown especially clearly in the series of puns on the names of the places threatened with devastation in 1^{10-16} (cf. Isa. 10^{27-32})—and also the means by which the prophet's oracles came to be recorded and preserved (see pp. 244–7).

If, for lack of evidence, we cannot determine Micah's social position, for the same reason we cannot satisfactorily describe his theological position. Although his repudiation of the royal theology of Jerusalem (3^{12}) would suggest that he stood in the tradition of Mosaic Yahwism (see pp. 48–51), his recorded oracles contain no reference to Moses, the Exodus, the Law, or the Election of Israel. While he clearly expected a day of judgement for Samaria (1^6) and Jerusalem (1^9, $2^{3, 4}$, 3^{12}) and warned his countrymen of the coming exile (1^{16}, 2^{10}), there is no evidence that he ever mentioned the Assyrians or developed any theological interpretation of contemporary history. There are no references to Yahweh's past dealings with his people or to his purpose for them beyond the coming judgement. Micah appears to have been concerned exclusively with the demands of Yahweh's righteousness in the present social order.

Such conclusions about the character of Micah's message (within, of course, the limitations of our knowledge of it) rest, inevitably, upon critical decisions about the authenticity of the oracles now ascribed to him. It is generally agreed: (*a*) that chapters 1–3 are the work of Micah himself (with the exception of $1^{1, 7}$, $2^{12, 13}$; and, possibly, $1^{2–4}$) ; (*b*) that chapters 4–5, which look forward to the people's restoration, had their origin in the period after 587 B.C.; (*c*) that, of the remaining chapters 6–7, the four oracles $6^{1–5}$, $6^{6–8}$, $6^{9–16}$, and $7^{1–4}$ may be pre-exilic in date and that, of these, the last three may possibly have come from Micah himself.

1. 1 *Micah and his ministry*

Moresheth, or more fully, Moresheth-gath (1^{14}), the home of Micah, lay in the hill country of Judah, near the Philistine border, some twenty-two miles south-west of Jerusalem. According to this later editorial superscription, the period of Micah's activity extended over the reigns of three Judean kings: *Jotham* (742–735), *Ahaz* (735–715), and *Hezekiah* (715–687). This dating is confirmed for the reign of Hezekiah by Jer. $26^{18, 19}$ and also for the reign of Ahaz, if, as is probable, 1^6 means that Samaria, which was captured by the Assyrians in 721 B.C., remains as yet untouched. Micah, therefore, was a younger contemporary of Isaiah, whose public teaching belongs roughly to the period 725–701 B.C.

1. 2–9 *Yahweh's judgement on Samaria and Jerusalem*

It cannot be claimed that this oracle is one of Micah's most characteristic utterances, since the only explanation of the coming judgement is the idolatry of Samaria (v. 7) and many scholars have doubted the authenticity even of this reference.

Although the Assyrians are never mentioned, it is clear that the prophet regarded them as the agent of Yahweh's punishment. Since Samaria was not actually destroyed by Sargon II in 721 B.C. (see notes on 2 Kgs. 17²⁴), it is probable that this oracle was an unfulfilled threat made before the capture of the city.

2–4. *The coming of the Lord.* This eloquent description of Yahweh's coming down from his dwelling in heaven, melting the mountains as though they were wax and carving out valleys like a torrent, is strangely addressed as a warning to all the peoples of the earth. The language used is the conventional language of theophany: *his holy temple* in heaven (cf. Hab. 2²⁰); *tread upon the high places of the earth* (cf. Hab. 3⁶; Ps. 18⁶, ⁷; Isa. 40⁴; see notes on Amos 4¹³). These two considerations, together with the fact that the verses are *about* God and not spoken by God (contrast v. 6), suggest the hand of an editor rather than the prophet himself.

5–7. *The doom of Samaria.* The sin of the two rebellious kingdoms will be visited upon their capital cities. In v. 5, *the house of Israel* must mean Judah, as the parallel in the second half of the verse suggests. Attention is focused first upon Samaria, which will be reduced to rubble (v. 6), and all its idolatrous images (so we may interpret *her hires*) destroyed, or (presumably) carried off by the enemy and reconverted into money for paying temple prostitutes. It was with temple prostitutes' fees in Samaria that the idols were paid for in the first place (v. 7). The authenticity of v. 7 has, however, been questioned.

8, 9. *The doom of Jerusalem.* These verses, which may either conclude the previous oracle or introduce the one which follows (vv. 10–16), represent the prophet as going about dressed like a mourner (cf. 2 Sam. 15³⁰; Isa. 20²) and making lamentation for Jerusalem's fate. The phrase *my people* affords us a glimpse of Micah's fellow-feeling for his doomed countrymen (cf. 3², ³).

2. 1–11 *The prophet denounces the exploiters of the poor*

Economic expansion during the period of the monarchy and the patronage of the king gave rise to a new and unscrupulous upper class in the Hebrew kingdoms (see pp. 34–42). In the first oracle of this section (vv. 1–5), Micah denounces their oppression of the poor and proclaims that they are bringing ruin upon the whole nation. In the second oracle (vv. 6–11), they dismiss the prophet's warning with complacent contempt (vv. 6, 7) and provoke an emphatic rejoinder (vv. 8–11).

The emphasis of Micah and the other great independent prophets on right human relations and social justice is distinctive of their Yahwist tradition and central to their understanding of the character of God. It is, however, inaccurate to claim, as is often done, that the moral teaching of the prophets is distinctive in actual content. For example, the misappropriation of the small man's property by the rich and powerful, which is one of Micah's particular concerns (vv. 1, 2, 9), is forbidden as early as 2100 B.C. in the Egyptian wisdom text known as *The Instruction for King Meri-Ka-Re*: 'Do justice whilst thou endurest upon earth. Quiet the weeper; do not oppress the widow; supplant no man in the property of his father.' In view of the familiar prophetic contrast between social righteousness and sacrificial rites (see notes on Mic. 6⁶⁻⁸), it is interesting to discover that the same Egyptian document includes the following saying: 'More acceptable is the character of one upright of heart than the ox of the evildoer' (J. B. Pritchard, *Ancient Near Eastern Texts*, pp. 415, 417). A much later Egyptian wisdom text, *The Instruction of Amen-em-opet* (see pp. 169 f.), shows how firmly this teaching on respect for property was established in general ethical tradition (see notes on Prov. 22²⁸) and it is more than probable that the prophets were indebted to it.

1, 2. *Shame on the property-grabbers!* Like Isaiah, his contemporary, Micah was incensed by the inhumanity of the new wealthy class in Israel, who even lay awake at night plotting their next ruthless take-over of property from the defenceless poor (cf. Amos 4¹; see notes on Isa. 5⁸⁻¹⁰).

3–5. *The ruin of the rich.* The figure for Yahweh's punishment of the people (*family*) of Judah in v. 3 is a heavy yoke which makes it impossible for the wearer to walk 'upright' (so read for *haughtily*). An uncertain text underlies the unintelligible RSV translation of v. 4. The sense may be restored by reading '*and* [you will] *wail with bitter lamentation, and say* . . .'. The substance of the people's lamentation is that the land which they schemed to possess is now being parcelled out to their enemies, the Assyrians. The meaning of v. 5 is obscure, but it seems to be that those who have deprived the poor will themselves remain deprived of the land they once were able to measure out by *the line*.

6, 7. *The prophet's complacent opponents*. The extortioners whom Micah attacked in vv. 1–5 now tell him to shut up (cf. Amos 2^{12}, 5^{10}, 7^{16}; Isa. 30^{10}). Among Yahweh's people (transferring *in the assembly of the Lord* from v. 5 to v. 6), such talk, they said, was wholly out of place (v. 6). Micah retorts: how dare you ask with such smug self-satisfaction whether Yahweh's patience is really exhausted and whether he will really bring such calamities upon you! If, with the Greek, we read 'his words' for *my words*, the end of v. 7 is a further claim made by Micah's self-righteous opponents; if *my words* is retained, the final question must be read as a warning either from Yahweh or the prophet.

8–10. *Rapacious victimization*. So far from being 'upright', the rich and powerful are enemies of Yahweh's people. Like gangsters, they commit outrages against men, women, and children—stripping the clothes from men off their guard like those returning from war, evicting the women from their homes, and wrecking their children's chances. The expression *my glory*, of which the children are deprived, must mean something regarded as Yahweh's gift, but precisely what gift cannot be determined. Because these extortioners have polluted the very land with their iniquitous behaviour (cf. Lev. 18^{25}), they will be driven into exile (v. 10).

11. This verse, which in its present position is inconsequential and is associated in theme with v. 6, depicts the kind of drunken driveller who would get a ready hearing from Micah's degraded opponents.

3. 1–12 *The fate of Jerusalem's ruling classes*

The most remarkable feature of this series of oracles is Micah's assertion that Jerusalem, and with it the Temple, would be utterly destroyed (v. 12). The basic dogma of the royal theology, which dominated the capital, was thus flatly denied (see pp. 52 f.); and it was denied because it conflicted with the prophets' fundamental conviction that in the sight of God nothing was more sacred than justice and equity (v. 9).

1–4. *Rulers become butchers.* The very people charged with the maintenance of justice in Judah were hell-bent on the deliberate pursuit of evil (cf. Amos 5¹⁴). In an extended figure which discloses the prophet's sense of complete outrage, Micah describes the ruling classes as butchering and devouring the poor (cf. Isa. 3¹⁵). The time is coming, however, when Yahweh will utterly forsake these inhuman monsters and leave them to their well-deserved fate (cf. Isa. 1¹⁵; Deut. 31¹⁷).

5–8. *Professional prophets in eclipse.* Jerusalem's institutional prophets were part of its corruption. They promised prosperity to those who were prepared to feed them (cf. Ezek. 13¹⁰, ¹⁹) and stirred up trouble for those who refused their demands (literally, they declared 'holy war' against them). Professional prophets were paid to give comforting assurance to their clients and there is much evidence that they did what was expected of them (see notes on Jer. 4⁹, ¹⁰). Without questioning the validity of their visions and divination, Micah proclaims that the prophets' abuse of their position will bring them under judgement on the Day of the Lord (v. 6; see notes on Amos 5¹⁸). Then they will *cover their lips* in shame (cf. Lev. 13⁴⁵) and mourning (cf. Ezek. 24¹⁷). The terms *seers* and *diviners* are simply alternative descriptions of the prophets (cf. v. 11; 1 Sam. 9⁹; Amos 7¹²; Isa. 30¹⁰; Jer. 29⁸).

In contrast to the institutional prophets who promise prosperity, Micah claims that he is empowered to declare to Judah its sins. The phrase *with the Spirit of the Lord* (v. 8) should be disregarded as a prosaic gloss. It is of interest to note that none of the pre-exilic independent prophets ascribes his prophetic activity to the Spirit. Early institutional prophecy of the frenzied kind is explained in terms of the violent action of the Spirit (1 Sam. 10$^{5-13}$, 19$^{20-24}$; Num. 11$^{24-30}$; cf. Judg. 13^{25}, 14$^{6, 19}$, 15^{14}; 1 Sam. 11$^{6, 7}$) and prophetic proclamation continues to be regarded as 'inspired' (although in a less dynamic way) from the period of the Exile onwards (Ezek. 2^2, 3$^{12, 14, 24}$, 11^1; Isa. 42^1, 59^{21}, 61$^{1-3}$; Zech. 7^{12}; Neh. 9^{30}; Joel 2$^{28, 29}$; 2 Chron. 15^1, 20^{14}, 24^{20}). It is probable that institutional prophets claimed to be possessed by the Spirit throughout the period of the monarchy and that the silence of the independent prophets on the subject indicates their quite different status (see pp. 232–44).

9–12. *The corruption and destruction of Jerusalem.* In his most trenchant oracle, Micah exposes the insatiable greed which so dominates the actions of Jerusalem's leaders that the city itself may be said to be built with bloodshed and violence (vv. 9, 10; see notes on Isa. 1$^{21-26}$ and Jer. 22$^{13-17}$). The civil rulers accept bribes in the law courts (cf. Isa. 5^{23}); the priests give their direction on legal questions with an eye to the money (cf. Ezek. 22^{26}; see pp. 203 f.); and the prophets practise divination for gain (cf. vv. 5, 6; see notes on 2 Kgs. 5^{16}, p. 264). And yet these very men, whose behaviour so blatantly flouts the will of God, dare to *lean upon the Lord* and claim smugly that he is with them in his Temple to protect them from any disaster which may befall (cf. Amos 5^{14}; Jer. 7$^{10, 14}$). Such were the pernicious effects of belief in the inviolability of Zion (see notes on Ps. 48). With astonishing courage, Micah roundly denies that Zion gives these evil men the security they suppose; on the contrary, they will be the cause of its total destruction. Nothing will be left of this proud stronghold but ruins in a field, with the Temple mount reduced to the insignificance of a deserted hill. A century later, when Jeremiah repeated this seeming combination of treason and blasphemy, Micah's words, it is said, were remembered (see notes on Jer. 26$^{17-19}$).

6. 6–8 *The old religion and the new faith*

Opinions differ about the origin of this detached fragment of teaching, for the good reason that it affords no decisive evidence of its date or authorship. Opinion can hardly be divided, however, about the content of the teaching, which presents with crystal clarity one of the fundamental distinctions between Yahwistic faith and the religion of the ancient Near East. Although Yahwism adopted the sacrificial cultus it encountered in Canaan and adapted it to serve its own historical faith, it could never adequately represent Israel's characteristic response to Yahweh's distinctive self-disclosure. This insight became explicit in the radical teaching of the great independent prophets, who consistently repudiated the sacrificial worship of the sanctuaries and with equal consistency pointed to the basically human and moral alternative, which alone was congruous with faith in Yahweh (Amos $5^{21\ 25}$; cf. $2^{7,\ 8}$, $4^{4,\ 5}$, $5^{4,\ 5}$; Hos. 5^6, 6^6, 8^{11-13}; cf. $2^{10,\ 11}$, 4^{4-14}; Mic. 3^{12}, 6^6; Isa. 1^{10-17}; Jer. 6^{19-21}, 7^{21-28}, 11^{15}; cf. 1 Sam. 15^{22}).

The conviction of the pre-exilic prophets was shared by psalmists (Pss. 40^{6-8}, $50^{7-15,\ 23}$, 51^{15-17}), prophets of the Exile (Isa. 43^{22-24}; cf. 58^{3-9}, 66^{1-4}), and teachers of the wisdom schools (Prov. 15^8, $21^{3,\ 27}$). It is probably with these less vehement and more didactic criticisms of the sacrificial cult that the present fragment of teaching has the greatest affinity. Its five rhetorical questions may well reflect a catechetical lesson in the wisdom schools (see pp. 178–80).

6. The contrast between *bow myself* and *God on high* is intended to caricature the popular conception of Yahweh as an oriental potentate for whom his subjects must bring gifts when they approach his presence (cf. Isa. 58^{5-7}).

7. The caricature becomes more savage with the absurdly exaggerated quantities of rams and oil (cf. Exod. 29^{40}; Lev. 14^{12}) and reaches its climax with the revolting conception that Yahweh accepts the sacrifice of children in atonement for sin. On the prevalence of the pagan practice of human sacrifice

during the later period of the monarchy, see notes on 2 Kgs. 16³. It should be noted that this verse does not imply the Greek distinction between body and soul. The Hebrew word translated *body* here means that part of the body involved in procreation and the phrase *the fruit of my body* is frequently used in the Old Testament for 'children' (cf. Deut. 7¹³). The *soul* simply means one's 'person' or 'self' (cf. Job 30²⁵), so that the last line of v. 7 could be translated, 'my children for my sin' (see notes on 1 Kgs. 17²²).

8. After the mounting series of questions which were asked only to invite a negative reply, comes a final question intended to provoke a positive response, which is stated with supreme and profound simplicity (cf. Mark 12²⁸⁻³⁴). As the RSV *mg.* indicates, *kindness* is a translation of *ḥesedh*, meaning 'steadfast love' or 'loyalty' (see notes on Deut. 7⁹ and Hos. 4¹). The kind of humility envisaged in the incomparable expression, *to walk humbly with your God*, is suggested by the literal meaning of the Hebrew word translated *humbly*, that is, 'wisely' or 'carefully'.

ISAIAH

The prophetic ministry of Isaiah of Jerusalem began in 742 B.C., 'in the year that King Uzziah died' (Isa. 6¹), and continued intermittently through the reigns of Ahaz and Hezekiah until some time after 701 B.C., the year Assyria besieged Jerusalem. The period was completely dominated by the resurgence of the Assyrian Empire on the accession of Tiglath-pileser III in 745 B.C., and by the consequent intensification of political intrigue between the smaller nations of Palestine and Syria, whose very existence was now threatened (see pp. 15 ff.). Isaiah's prophetic activity was focused, to judge by the surviving records, on four major crises which erupted in Judah from this turbulent international situation.

The *first* crisis occurred in 734 B.C., when the combined forces of Damascus and Israel (the 'Syro-Ephraimitic Coalition') marched on Jerusalem and the unfortunate Ahaz was confronted with a choice between three courses of action: (*a*) yielding to military pressure and joining the Damascus–Israelite alliance against Assyria; (*b*) yielding to his own political counsellors and seeking the protection of Assyria; and (*c*) yielding to Isaiah and, in exclusive reliance on Yahweh, taking no action at all (see notes on 7^{1-9}, 7^{10-17}, 8^{5-8a}). Ahaz opted for the second course and remained subservient to Assyria throughout the whole of his reign (see notes on 2 Kgs. 16^{1-20}). After the king's decision, Isaiah seems to have retired from public life and for twenty years (734–715) nothing is heard of him (see notes on 8^{16-18}).

The *second* crisis was provoked in 711 B.C., when a further attempt was made to involve Judah in rebellion against Assyria, on this occasion plotted by the Philistine city Ashdod with (as was mistakenly supposed) the support of Egypt. Isaiah vigorously opposed this move like all other political entanglements and, for the moment, Hezekiah held his hand and remained uncommitted (see notes on 20^{1-6}). However, the death in 705 B.C. of the Assyrian king, Sargon II, encouraged a general movement of rebellion among the subject Palestinian states and Hezekiah was one of the rulers who took the opportunity of asserting his independence (see notes on 2 Kgs. 18–19). This momentous decision led to the *third* major crisis of Isaiah's ministry. With unwavering consistency, he roundly condemned the negotiations which Hezekiah then began with Egypt as being nothing less than apostasy from Yahweh and he flagellated the statesmen of Judah for their self-confident scheming (see notes on 28^{1-13}, 28^{14-22}, 31^{1-3}; cf. 18^{1-6}, 30^{1-7}, 30^{15-17}). The *fourth* and final crisis was Assyria's crushing reply to Judah's rebellion, when in 701 B.C. Sennacherib advanced and besieged Jerusalem (fig. p. 340). Isaiah accepted the terrible devastation of Judah's territory as Yahweh's judgement of his people's faithlessness (see notes on 1^{2-9}, 22^{1-14}), but he affirmed that Assyria, too, was subject to Yahweh's sovereign rule and would be punished for her arrogant pride (see notes on 10^{5-15}; cf. 14^{24-27}).

Superficially, it appears that Isaiah was a prophet-statesman and such he has often been called. There have been many attempts to explain his total opposition to political involvement and his advocacy of unwavering isolationism as being, in the circumstances, the most realistic *policy*, if Judah were ever to survive under the dark shadow of Assyrian imperialism. It is possible, indeed, to make out a persuasive case for the political wisdom of Isaiah's preaching, especially in view of the fate which befell Damascus, Israel, and the other small states which foolishly made a bid for their independence. Nevertheless, such an interpretation of the prophet's teaching overlooks its most striking and fundamental feature. What Isaiah did was to substitute the sovereignty of Yahweh for the rule of earthly kings and the transcendent purpose of Yahweh for the political calculations of their royal counsellors:

> The Lord of hosts has sworn:
>   'As I have planned,
>   so shall it be,
>   and as I have purposed,
>   so shall it stand . . .'
> This is the purpose that is purposed
>   concerning the whole earth;
> and this is the hand that is stretched out
>   over all the nations.
> For the Lord of hosts has purposed,
>   and who will annul it?
> His hand is stretched out,
>   and who will turn it back? (14[24–27])

Isaiah was not content to make a contribution to state policy from a 'religious point of view'; rather, from a single, uncompromising conviction that it was Yahweh alone who determined the course of history, he flatly denied the legitimacy of all human political activity:

> 'Woe to the rebellious children,' says the Lord,
> 'who carry out a plan, but not mine;
> and who make a league, but not of my spirit,
>   that they may add sin to sin;
> who set out to go down to Egypt,
>   without asking for my counsel, . . .' (30[1, 2])

All Isaiah's titles for Yahweh are proclamations of his majestic sovereignty: *Lord of hosts* ($1^{9,\ 24}$, $6^{3,\ 5}$; see note on 1 Kgs. 18^{15}, pp. 254 f.); *Mighty one of Israel* (1^{24}); *Holy One of Israel* ($5^{19,\ 24}$); *Lord* (1^{24}, 3^{1}); *King* (6^{5}). In his inaugural vision, Isaiah with his own eyes saw Yahweh enthroned on high as King of the world (see notes on 6^{1-13}) and all his subsequent teaching was an affirmation of 'the glory of his majesty' ($2^{10,\ 19,\ 21}$). Yahweh, the lord of all nations, simply whistles and the proud Assyrians come running to do his bidding (5^{26}), since they are tools (7^{20}), and merely tools (see notes on 10^{5-15}), in his hands.

For Isaiah, Yahweh, first and last, is the God to whom belongs 'the kingdom, the power and the glory' and this conviction dominates his preaching to the exclusion of almost everything else. Unlike his prophetic contemporaries and successors, Isaiah shows virtually no awareness of the belief that Yahweh, who governs the present course of history, especially disclosed himself in the past to Israel as the people of his choice. He never so much as mentions the Exodus from Egypt (unless, as seems improbable, 10^{24-27} is an authentic oracle) and the evidence hardly justifies the claim that, as an alternative, his faith was rooted in the conviction that Yahweh had made a covenant with the house of David (cf. $7^{2,\ 13}$, 22^{22}, 28^{21} [see notes], 29^{1}; the following verses are judged to be non-Isaianic: 9^{7} [see notes], 37^{35}, $38^{5,\ 6}$). Past history provides little more than a peripheral reference to Sodom and Gomorrah ($1^{9,\ 10}$).

If, in Isaiah's teaching, the purpose of Yahweh is without explicit anchorage in any event in Israel's past, it may equally be said that it is never given firm motivation by any clear goal in Israel's future. It is true, of course, that we have no right to expect in a prophet of the eighth century those developed pictures of Israel's supremacy and bliss in the Coming Kingdom which illuminate the purpose of God in the work of Second Isaiah and his successors. They do not appear in Amos or Hosea. Nevertheless, both these early prophets expound Yahweh's purpose in terms of his special historical relationship with Israel in the past, the present, and the imminent future. We may discover what in their belief Yahweh *is getting at* from these three distinct points of reference. The fact that the God of Isaiah has (so to speak) no past history makes it all the more noticeable that equally he has no clear future goal.

There is no doubt, of course, that Isaiah accepts and expects Yahweh's imminent judgement. Jerusalem is estranged from God and deserves the fate it has suffered at the hands of the Assyrian invader (see notes on 1^{2-9}); its leaders are 'rulers of Sodom' and its festivals futile (see notes on 1^{10-17}); the people face a choice between obedience and destruction (see notes on 1^{18-20}); at present, this so-called 'faithful city' is a den of iniquity (see notes on 1^{21-26}). The Day of the Lord is coming, not, however, as a day of Yahweh's special dealing with Israel (see notes on Amos 5^{18-20}), but as a day on which the whole of mankind will be made to regret its pride and self-sufficiency (see notes on 2^{6-22}). Judah and its capital will be reduced to impotent anarchy, because of the defiant behaviour of its upper classes ($3^{1}-4^{1}$); the Lord's vineyard will become a waste land (see notes on 5^{1-7}). Retribution will overtake the callous *nouveaux riches*, the pub-crawlers, the mocking sceptics, and the clever, self-satisfied intellectuals (see notes on 5^{8-24}). The destruction of 'this people' will be the inevitable consequence of their failure to respond to Isaiah's ministry (see notes on 6^{1-13}, 22^{1-14}, 28^{1-13}, 28^{14-22}, 29^{1-8}). Because Yahweh is sovereign over *all* the nations, the prophet is also able to proclaim that Damascus and Israel (see notes on 7^{1-9}; cf. 17^{1-6}), the Philistines (14^{28-32}), Egypt (see notes on 20^{1-6}; cf. 18^{1-7}, 19^{1-15}), and Assyria (see notes on 10^{5-15}) will all meet their doom.

Yahweh's judgement dominates Isaiah's preaching almost to the degree it dominates the preaching of Amos. However, notwithstanding the fact that the early oracles of Isaiah have much in common with those of Amos (cf. $3^{1}-4^{1}$, 5^{1-24}, 6^{1-13}, $9^{8}-10^{4}$), there is a significant difference between them. Isaiah thinks much more of judgement as punishment meted out to particular classes of people for particular kinds of offence and much less of the cancellation of Yahweh's covenant with his people as a whole. Isaiah could never have said to Jerusalem, as Amos said to Israel: 'You only have I known of all the families of the earth; therefore I will punish you for all your iniquities' (Amos 3^2). Whereas Amos, for all his conviction that Yahweh was sovereign over all the nations (see notes on Amos 1^3–2^{16}, 9^7), never loses his awareness of Yahweh's special relation to Israel and, therefore, of the inexpressible pathos and terror of his people's fate (see notes on Amos 7^{1-9}), Isaiah is infinitely more detached and so is Yahweh as he presents him. Although Isaiah does occasionally speak of Israel as Yahweh's 'sons' (1^{2-4}) and as the Lord's 'vineyard' (5^{1-7}), of Judah (in Yahweh's name) as 'my people' (1^3, 3^{12}, 5^{13}), and of Yahweh's punishment of Jerusalem as an alien, paradoxical work (28^{21}; cf. 22^4), the prophet stands for the most part above and apart from those whom he calls 'this people' (6^{10}, $8^{6, 11, 12}$, 9^{16}, $28^{11, 14}$, $29^{13, 14}$) and all the great terms used in the Old Testament to expound Yahweh's special relationship with Israel ('love', 'choose', 'know', 'name') are missing from his oracles.

Many scholars would not accept this interpretation of Isaiah's teaching. They hold that Yahweh is represented as directing history to a future goal in which his chosen people will be restored and that the oracles about Jerusalem's deliverance contain the evidence. The whole subject is highly debatable, but two points can hardly be disputed: (i) oracles of judgement on Jerusalem are, as has been seen, numerous and of unchallenged authenticity; (ii) oracles which the general consensus of scholarly opinion ascribes to a *later* tradition are those predominantly concerned with Jerusalem's deliverance (1^{27-31}, 4^{2-6}, 11^{10-16}, 12^{1-6}, 28^{5-6}, 29^{17-24}, 30^{18-26}, $32^{1-8, 15-20}$, 33^{17-24}). There remains (iii) a further series of oracles which also express the conviction that Yahweh will deliver Jerusalem, but about the authenticity of which there is considerable disagreement (2^{2-4}, 9^{2-7}, 10^{24-27}, 11^{1-9}, 14^{32}, 17^{12-14}, 29^{5-8}, $31^{5, 8, 9}$, 37^{33-35}). The question is whether these passages (iii) should be accepted as authentic and therefore interpreted as reversing the oracles of doom under (i), or whether they should be regarded as coming from later tradition and reckoned with the oracles listed under (ii). In view of the fact that an editor is more likely to reverse the meaning of a prophet's oracles than the prophet himself (see notes on 29⁵⁻⁸; cf. 31⁴, ⁵), the fact that the evidence for Isaiah's having promised the preservation of a remnant is at best weak (see notes on 7³), and the fact that the evidence for the non-Isaianic origin and character of the idea of Zion's inviolability is overwhelmingly strong, it is probable that Isaiah did *not* speak clearly of Yahweh's purpose as directed towards a future goal or of any special future role for his people as such. The most that may be said with confidence is that Isaiah looked for Yahweh to build a true 'house of faith' (as distinct from the Temple) in Jerusalem and for the city's renewal after the purging fires of judgement (see notes on 28¹⁴⁻²² and 1²¹⁻²⁶).

If, in Isaiah's teaching, Yahweh's sovereignty is unrelated to any historical event in the past and only tenuously related to any goal beyond judgement in the future, *it is absolute in the present*. Yahweh's actual direction of history demands of all men a calm, trusting, and complete acceptance of what he gives, for which 'faith' becomes for the first time in Isaiah the technical term (see notes on Deut. 20¹⁻⁹). This attitude of faith utterly excludes fear. It also excludes all the calculations and defences which derive from fear and from man's delusion that he is independent of God and able to shape his own destiny. That is why Isaiah's counsel to Ahaz to be content to do nothing when Jerusalem was threatened by the combined forces of Damascus and Israel ran clean counter to the counsel of the politicians: 'Take heed, be quiet, do not fear, and do not let your heart be faint because of these two smouldering stumps of firebrands. . . . It shall not stand, and it shall not come to pass. . . . If you will not believe, surely you shall not be established' (see notes on 7¹⁻⁹, 20¹⁻⁶, 22¹⁻¹⁴, 31¹⁻³). 'He who believes will not be in haste' (28¹⁶) does not mean a withdrawal from the real world, but an acceptance of the world as it really is, that is to say, as ruled by God. Isaiah's theological realism was totally incompatible with the political realism of Judah and its statesmen:

> For thus said the Lord God, the Holy One of Israel,
> 'In returning and rest you shall be saved;

in quietness and in trust shall be your strength.'
And you would not, but you said,
'No! We will speed upon horses,'
    therefore you shall speed away;
and, 'We will ride upon swift steeds,'
    therefore your pursuers shall be swift. ($30^{15, 16}$)

To 'trust in chariots because they are many and in horsemen because they are very strong' (31^1) is not simply to ignore Yahweh, but to act against him, *defying his glorious presence* (3^8). This splendid phrase sums up Isaiah's conception of sin as the *proud* refusal of faith (cf. 2^{7-11}, 3^{16}, 5^{19-21}, 10^{5-15}, $28^{14, 15}$).

We know virtually nothing about the background or the inner life of this quite extraordinary prophet with his one great doctrine of Yahweh's absolute sovereignty and its absolute acceptance by man in faith. He is so remarkably detached from all the familiar religious traditions, from the Mosaic Yahwism of Amos, Hosea, and Jeremiah, the David-Zion theology of Jerusalem, and the cult of the Temple, that if his inaugural vision had not been preserved it would have been necessary to invent it (see notes on 6^{1-13}). For Isaiah, who always sees matters in black and white, is the outstanding *convert* of the Old Testament, although from exactly what he was converted it is impossible to say. The most attractive speculation (and there is interesting evidence to support it, see p. 179) is that he was educated for the king's service and before his conversion was one of those royal politicians, 'wise in their own eyes, and shrewd in their own sight' (5^{21}), whom subsequently he spent his life in opposing. This would account for his remarkable eloquence and many otherwise inexplicable features of his thought.

The teaching of Isaiah has been preserved with much later material in chapters 1–39 of the book which bears his name. The following list (with passages of debated authenticity marked [?]) will serve as a *general* guide to what may be regarded as being basically oracles from Isaiah himself: 1^{2-9}, 1^{10-17}, 1^{18-20}, 1^{21-26}, 2^{2-4}[?], 2^{6-22}, 3^{1-15}, $3^{16}-4^1$, 5^{1-7}, 5^{8-24}, 6^{1-13}, 7^{1-17}, 8^{1-4}, 8^{5-8}, 8^{16-18}[?], 9^{2-7}[?], 9^8-10^4 (with 5^{25-30}), 10^{5-15},

10^{24-27}[?], 11^{1-9}[?], 14^{24-27}, 14^{28-32}[?], 17^{1-11}, 17^{12-14}[?], 18^{1-6}, 19^{1-15}, 20^{1-6}, 22^{1-14}, 22^{15-22}, 28^{1-22}, 28^{23-29}, 29^{1-4}, 29^{5-8}[?], 29^{9-12}, $29^{13, 14}$, $29^{15, 16}$, 30^{1-5}, 30^{8-14}, 30^{15-17}, 31^{1-3}, $31^{4, 5}$[?], 32^{9-14}, $36^{1}-39^{8}$[?] (from 2 Kgs. $18^{13}-20^{19}$ except for 38^{9-20}).

1. 1 *Isaiah and his ministry*

Information about the historical background of Isaiah's ministry will be found as follows: *Uzziah* (783–742), see notes on 2 Kgs. 15^{1-7}; *Ahaz* (735–715), see notes on 2 Kgs. 16^{1-20}; *Hezekiah* (715–687), see notes on 2 Kgs. 18–19.

1. 2–9 *Judah's rebellion and terrible plight*

The historical background of this oracle is the devastation of Judah by Assyria in 701 B.C. (vv. 7, 8; see pp. 108 ff.). The disaster was provoked by Hezekiah's rebellion against Sennacherib, to which Isaiah had been consistently opposed (see notes on 31^{1-3}).

2, 3. Yahweh's having brought up the people as his *sons* makes their stupid rebellion against his teaching (cf. 1^{10}) all the more culpable (see pp. 206 f.). This language may, but does not necessarily, imply a father–son relationship (cf. Hos. 11^{1-4}; Jer. 3^{19-22}), since teachers also addressed their pupils as *sons* (cf. Prov. 1^8; and see p. 186). On the use of the verbs *know* and *understand* in the schools of wisdom, see Prov. 1^2, 4^1, 17^{27}, 28^2, $30^{2, 3}$.

4. *the Holy One of Israel* occurs for the first time in Isaiah's oracles as a title for Yahweh ($5^{19, 24}$, $10^{17, 20}$, $30^{11, 15}$, 31^1).

7. For the unintelligible *as overthrown by aliens*, read 'as the overthrow of Sodom' (cf. v. 9).

8. Jerusalem is personified as *the daughter of Zion*, now left in complete and miserable isolation (see notes on 2 Kgs. 18^{13}).

9. For the *Lord of hosts*, see notes on 1 Kgs. 18^{15}, pp. 254 f. The fact hat *a few survivors* were left is not elaborated into any doctrine about the preservation of a remnant (the Hebrew word is not that used for the name of Isaiah's son in 7^3), but is mentioned

to indicate Judah's narrow escape from a destruction as total as that of *Sodom* and *Gomorrah* (see notes on Amos 4[11]).

1. 10–17 *Rites and righteousness*

This invective against the religion of the Temple, with its assertion that righteousness in human relations is the alternative which Yahweh requires, springs from an insight shared by all the great independent prophets (see notes on Mic. 6[6–8]). Isaiah is quite explicit in declaring that sacrifice is a ludicrous way of worshipping the transcendent King whose glory fills the whole earth: 'I am surfeited . . . with the grease of specially-fattened beasts. . . . I don't enjoy the blood of bulls. . . . Who has asked for this when you come to worship me?' It is strange that so many commentators are able to interpret such vituperative language as being no more than a demand that sacrifice should be offered only by moral persons with the right intention.

12, 13. The text presents difficulties. Read: 'Trample my courts no more! To bring offerings is futile; the stench of sacrifice [not *incense*] is an abomination to me. New moon and sabbath, the calling of festival assemblies, I cannot endure.'

14. *My soul* simply means 'I' (cf. Lev. 26[11]).

15. Yahweh will not listen to the people's *prayers*. This verse is often taken to prove that the prophet did not wish to abolish sacrifice, because he could not have wished to abolish prayer. The argument is based on the groundless assumption that Isaiah's attitude to sacrifice in this passage is identical with his attitude to prayer. He condemns the people's prayer because it had sunk to the level of sacrifice (cf. Matthew 6[7]).

16, 17. Yahweh's alternative to the futility of sacrificial worship is given in a series of short, sharp imperatives. For *correct oppression*, read 'restrain the ruthless'.

1. 18–20 *The choice which faces the accused*

Judah stands accused before Yahweh; *reason together* means 'argue the case', as before a judge (cf. Job 23[7]). The RSV represents v. 18 as an unconditional promise of forgiveness and renewal, which is almost certainly wrong. To prepare for the choice between obedience and destruction in vv. 19, 20, v. 18 may be read either as the judge's summing up of Judah's defence, or as two sarcastic questions or exclamations: '. . . they shall be as white as snow [?] [!] . . . they shall become like wool [?] [!]' The status of Judah as Yahweh's people is strictly conditional (cf. Exod. 19⁵, ⁶; Deut. 30¹⁵).

1. 21–26 *Yahweh's purge of Jerusalem*

This lament (vv. 21–23) and oracle of judgement (vv. 24–26) on Jerusalem offer a striking contrast with the psalmists' uncritical devotion to the city of David. Although Isaiah looks forward to Jerusalem's becoming 'the city of righteousness' (v. 26) after the purging fires of judgement, he was obviously not deceived by the dominant 'royal theology' of the capital (see pp. 51–55).

23. The *princes* were the rulers and officials of Jerusalem, now utterly corrupt.

24. The solemn titles of Yahweh as Judge are recited before he pronounces sentence. The Authorized Version's 'I will ease me of mine adversaries' is better than the RSV's *I will vent my wrath on my enemies*; the verb means 'to take a rest from'. Yahweh's *enemies* are Judah's leaders.

25. *as with lye*. Lye is usually associated with washing rather than smelting (Jer. 2²²; Mal. 3²). We may either understand it as a chemical used in metallurgy, or accept a speculative emendation, 'in the furnace'.

26. After this purging, and only then, Jerusalem will deserve the names by which it is popularly known: *the city of righteousness* ('the city of Zedek'; cf. Gen. 14¹⁸; Ps. 110⁴; see p. 146) and *the faithful city* (cf. v. 21). This second name in current use meant 'The Enduring City' (cf. Ps. 48⁸); Isaiah says its status will be confirmed only when it has reformed.

2. 6–22 *The Day of the Lord*

Unfortunately, the editor's attempt to combine two oracles of Isaiah has left the text of this passage mutilated and disturbed, although Amos' interpretation of the Day of the Lord as a dark day of judgement is reflected clearly enough (vv. 12–17; see notes on Amos 5^{18-20}).

6–11. Yahweh has abandoned his people, because they have become corrupt since the monarchy involved them in the commercial and military activities of the ancient Near East (see pp. 29–42). Foreign idolatry has come in with foreign trade. From the muddle of vv. 10, 11, two tremendous phrases emerge. The first, *the glory of his majesty* (v. 10; cf. vv. 19, 21), illuminates Isaiah's distinctive understanding of Yahweh as 'high and lifted up' (6^1). The second, *the Lord alone will be exalted in that day* (v. 11; cf. v. 17), admirably describes the Day of the Lord and illustrates the transcendent, God-centred character of the prophet's teaching.

12–17. In the Day of the Lord, nothing in nature (vv. 13, 14) or in man-made civilization (vv. 15, 16) will escape the abasement of divine judgement. On *the ships of Tarshish*, see p. 24; *the beautiful craft* is a possible emendation of the Hebrew, but some more specific kind of ship would fit the context better.

18–22. These verses take up the earlier condemnation of idols (vv. 6–11), which was interrupted by the oracle on the Day of the Lord (vv. 12–17). The strange concluding v. 22 is omitted by the Greek version and is grammatically corrupt.

5. 1–7 *The parable of the vineyard*

This sad little ballad interpreted as an allegorical parable certainly illustrates the prophets' startling use of popular forms in order to get across their message (see p. 244), but commentators' descriptions of how Isaiah came forward to contribute his piece at the autumn vintage festival and at first gained a hearing for what turned out to be a proclamation of doom owe, perhaps, more to the imagination than to the evidence. Even revellers cannot have been so easily deceived. Like the parables of Jesus, this story challenges the hearers to make a judgement (vv. 3, 4) and, as often in the gospels, moves from realism to allegory (vv. 5, 6).

1. This verse is hopelessly obscure. The expression *my beloved* was used by the devotees of heathen gods (see notes on Amos 8¹⁴), but it is highly improbable that Isaiah used it of Yahweh. Further, this ballad about a vineyard is in no sense a *love song*. To read, 'Let me sing for my friend my friend's song about his vineyard', makes sense, but sense of a kind which is hardly worth having.

2. To build a *watchtower* and a *wine vat* was to complete an expensive project intended to produce profit. All it produced, however, was *wild grapes*—literally, 'stinking fruit'.

3, 4. With this question to the listeners, the parable slips into the prophetic first person and the allegorizing conclusion of v. 7 is clearly foreshadowed. Judah is asked to judge herself (cf. 2 Sam. 12¹⁻¹⁵).

5, 6. The language (now fully allegorical) describes punishment rather than neglect, and the end of v. 6 reveals that the owner of the vineyard is none other than Yahweh himself.

7. The contrast between the righteousness which Yahweh expected of the people he had cherished and the rebellion he suffered from them is stated in a powerful play on words which, unfortunately, is lost in translation:

> and he looked for justice (*mishpāṭ*),
>   but behold, bloodshed (*mispāḥ*);
>   for righteousness (*ṣᵉdhāqāh*),
>   but behold, a cry (*ṣᵉˁāqāh*)!

Yahweh expected morality and found murder, riotousness instead of righteousness.

5. 8–24a *Cry havoc!*

This series of six (originally, perhaps, seven) 'Woes' comes from the early years of Isaiah's ministry and reflects the moral disintegration of Judah's affluent society.

8–10. *Shame on the land-grabbers!* Covetous developers use their commercial profits to crowd out the peasant proprietors (cf. 3¹⁴; see notes on Mic. 2¹⁻⁵ and 1 Kgs. 21¹⁻²⁰, pp. 259 f.). They have sought isolation from the common herd and they shall have it (v. 8). Yahweh's judgement is that their houses and farms will go to rack and ruin. A yield of *one bath* (5½ gallons) of wine from ten acres of land spells disaster, as does a crop of *an ephah* (a bushel) of grain from ten times that quantity (*a homer*) of seed.

11–13. *Shame on the pub-crawlers!* Such feckless characters are condemned by more than one prophet (cf. Amos 6⁴⁻⁶; Hos. 7⁵). It is illuminating to find their befuddled wits described in terms of their failure to recognize Yahweh's *deeds* and *work* (v. 12). According to the faith of the Old Testament, God is encountered in his activity within history and human experience (cf. 28²¹). The saying of v. 13, in which *exile* is mentioned for the only time in Isaiah, is loosely attached (cf. Hos. 4⁶), but there is a fine ironical touch in the implication that, as some men drink themselves silly, the common people are *parched with thirst*.

14–17. These fragments are out of place here and little is lost by disregarding them (cf. 2⁶⁻²²).

18, 19. *Shame on defiant sceptics!* The figure is that of a man dragging wickedness after him like a bullock by its harness and cart ropes. It has been suggested that v. 19 is a separate denunciation, which once began with 'Woe to . . .'; as the text now stands, the sin to which the men of v. 18 are so attached is mocking disbelief in Yahweh's ability to do anything (cf. Jer. 17¹⁵; Zeph. 1¹²).

20. *Shame on the clever!* The reproach seems to be directed to 'advanced' intellectuals, who assert their 'new morality' in (of course) witty, paradoxical form (cf. Prov. 27⁷; Isa. 32⁵).

21. *Shame on the self-satisfied!* As in the previous verse, conceited graduates of the wisdom schools seem to be the prophet's target (cf. Prov. 3⁷, 26⁵, ¹², ¹⁶, 28¹¹; see pp. 177 f.).

22, 23. *Shame on the big men of the bars!* The well-known characters who cut an heroic figure in their own drinking-clubs are moral cowards when it comes to dispensing justice.

24a. These shameful elements in Judean society will be like a plant rotten to the root whose blossom blows away as dust.

6. 1–13 *The prophet's inaugural vision*

This celebrated account of the circumstances in which Isaiah became a prophet of Yahweh has three distinguishable movements: (*a*) Isaiah's vision of Yahweh as King and his realization of its meaning (vv. 1–5); (*b*) Isaiah's experience of being accepted and commissioned by Yahweh (vv. 6–8); (*c*) Isaiah's task as Yahweh's spokesman (vv. 9–13).

The scene of the prophet's call is the Temple in Jerusalem, where, we may suppose, an act of worship was in progress. The imagery of the vision is clearly derived from the things Isaiah saw and heard, but it transcends their limitations and combines with them new perceptions, as in the world of dreams. In the middle of the singing and movement of the liturgy, no doubt confidently proclaiming that 'the Lord is King' (see pp. 149 f.), Isaiah experienced a vision of Yahweh enthroned in universal glory and for the first time it dawned on him what divine sovereignty really meant. The confidence engendered by the cult was instantly shattered. He and the people around him were not fit to enter 'his glorious presence' (cf. 3⁸): 'Woe is me! For I am lost; for I am a man of unclean lips, and I dwell in the midst of a people of unclean lips; for my eyes have seen the King, the Lord of Hosts!' (v. 5).

Isaiah was called out of the religion of the Temple by the reality of God (see notes on 1¹⁰⁻¹⁷). From this moment, he knew that, like Amos, his task was to destroy the illusion of light and proclaim darkness (see notes on Amos 5¹⁸⁻²⁰); he was commissioned to be the spokesman of Yahweh's judgement on his people.

1–5. *Isaiah's vision.* The account, which is autobiographical, was presumably written by the prophet to introduce a collection of his oracles a short time after 742 B.C., *the year that King Uzziah died* (see notes on 2 Kgs. 15¹⁻⁷). *I saw the Lord sitting upon a throne* suggests a vision of Yahweh enthroned in his heavenly council, like that seen by the prophet Micaiah (see notes on 1 Kgs. 22¹⁹⁻²³). But this imagery is fused with pictures drawn from the Temple. The *train* of Yahweh's royal robes fills the building (v. 1); the song of the *seraphim*, which shook the Temple to its foundations (v. 4), is probably that of the Temple choir (v. 3; cf. Ps. 47⁶⁻⁸); the cloud of Yahweh's *glory* which fills the whole earth begins with the *smoke* of the incense (v. 4; cf. Lev. 16¹³; 1 Kgs. 8¹⁰, ¹¹; Ezek. 10⁴; Exod. 40³⁴). The *seraphim* (vv. 2, 6), literally, 'burning ones', are creatures of fire and light attendant upon the heavenly throne and belong to the same class of mythical creatures, half human and half animal, as the cherubim attendant upon the Ark in the Temple (figs. pp. 15, 19, 79; see pp. 160 f.). Everything, however, is transformed and transcendentalized—*the whole earth is full of his glory* (v. 3). With his own eyes and with unprecedented consequences, Isaiah had seen the King in his majesty. The contrast presented here between belief through tradition and faith through prophetic vision is given classical expression in the book of Job:

> I had heard of thee by the hearing of the ear,
>   but now my eye sees thee;
> therefore I despise myself,
>   and repent in dust and ashes. (42⁵, ⁶)

6–8. *Yahweh accepts and commissions Isaiah.* The prophet's experience of being forgiven and of being accepted by Yahweh for his work is conveyed in curious cultic terms. In accordance with ritual usage familiar throughout the ancient Near East, the prophet's lips are purified by a glowing *coal* (or, perhaps, stone) taken from the altar. Isaiah is now admitted to the heavenly council (see notes on Jer. 23¹⁸) and responds without hesitation to Yahweh's request for a spokesman whom he may send to his disobedient people.

9–13. *The terms of Isaiah's prophetic task.* The first question to be asked is whether the 'hardening' of Israel in vv. 9, 10 expresses the initial purpose of Isaiah's preaching or its actual result. The latter is more likely, although it must be acknowledged that the result was probably foreseen as a moral certainty from the beginning. This alone might account for the imperative form of the commission in v. 10, *shut their eyes*, but there is a further consideration: the Old Testament constantly represents man's response as Yahweh's action and, therefore, as his own will and purpose. We may conclude, therefore, that Isaiah was never in any doubt that the final outcome of his mission was the people's rejection of Yahweh and Yahweh's rejection of the people (vv. 11, 12), but in line with his initial word of protest (v. 11)—*How long, O Lord?*—even if illogically, he continued to preach and hope against hope (cf. 8¹⁷). It is held by some scholars that this hope is explicit in v. 13, but the whole verse looks like a later explanation of the fact that the destruction of Judah in 587 B.C. had not been complete and its only hopeful statement, *The holy seed is its stump*, is not in the Greek version and has all the marks of a gloss. It is certainly a flimsy foundation for any doctrine of the 'remnant' (see notes on 7³).

7. 1–9 *Isaiah counsels Ahaz*

This passage records the first and most explicit collision between Isaiah and Judah's politicians, when Jerusalem was besieged by Damascus and Israel (see pp. 315 f.). For the prophet the issue was whether Ahaz would accept Yahweh's direction of historical events, or make a futile attempt to change it by following the view of his political counsellors that he should seek the protection of Assyria. Isaiah's counsel was that the king should take no active steps at all, but, in faith, wait and see what Yahweh had determined. Although the prophet be-lieved that Yahweh used human agents like Assyria to *punish* Judah (see notes on 10⁵⁻¹⁵), he does not appear to have believed

that Yahweh used political experts as agents for the welfare of
his people.

1. In 734 B.C., Jerusalem was besieged by an alliance of
Damascus and Israel. Their purpose was either to gain the
support of Ahaz against Assyria, or replace him by a ruler (cf.
v. 6) who was willing to fall in with their policy (see notes on
2 Kgs. 15²⁹ and 16¹⁻²⁰). For *Syria*, understand Damascus (see
p. 10); for *Pekah*, see notes on 2 Kgs. 15²⁵.

3. *Shear-jashub* ('a remnant shall return'). Unlike the naming of
Isaiah's second son in 8¹⁻⁴, we can only speculate about the
circumstances in which the name *Shear-jashub* was given; it is
impossible, therefore, to be sure of its bearing on the crisis
which faced Ahaz. The name itself consists of a noun (*shᵉār*)
and a verb (*yāshûbh*) and the meaning of both is ambiguous.
Shear ('remnant') may describe either (i) a mere 'residue' to
which Judah would be at some future date reduced, or (ii) a
'remnant' which would be mercifully saved by God from some
future catastrophe. The verb, *jashub*, may mean either 'return
to God' or 'return home'. The context suggests that *Shear-
jashub* here is a warning and a threat, originally given during a
previous crisis and now presented again to Ahaz: Judah will
be doomed (reduced to a mere remnant) if it relies on power
politics instead of Yahweh (cf. 10²², 30¹⁵⁻¹⁷). It is widely held
that Isaiah taught the hopeful doctrine that Yahweh would
save a remnant of his people from destruction. In addition to
an improbable interpretation of the name *Shear-jashub* in this
passage, the following references are brought in evidence: 4³,
10²⁰, ²¹, 11¹¹, ¹⁶, 28⁵, 37³¹, ³². It is doubtful, however, whether
any of these may be safely ascribed to Isaiah himself. The
probability is that 'remnant' was reinterpreted as a word of
promise by those who were in fact 'left over' from destruction
during the period of the Exile (cf. Mic. 4⁶, ⁷, 5⁷⁻⁹; Zeph. 3¹¹⁻¹³;
Jer. 50²⁰).

4. Isaiah counsels Ahaz to keep calm and ignore Damascus and
Israel, who in any case are nearly burnt out. *Rezin* was the king

of Damascus (740–732), cf. 2 Kgs. 16⁵, ⁹; Pekah of Israel is contemptuously called *the son of Remaliah* (see notes on 2 Kgs. 15²⁵).

6. *the son of Tabe-el* was an Aramean prince whom Rezin and Pekah intended to make king of Judah.

7–9. Omitting the parenthetical note in 8*b* as a gloss, the oracle may be paraphrased: 'The plan of these little men will never be put into effect. After all, the capital of Syria (Aram) is only Damascus and the ruler of Damascus is merely Rezin. Similarly, the capital of Ephraim is only Samaria and the ruler of Samaria is merely the son of Remaliah.' *If you will not believe, surely you shall not be established.* This great utterance contains a play on two words from the same Hebrew root, *believe* (*tha'ᵃmînû*) and *established* (*thē'āmēnû*); only if Ahaz stood *firm* in God's sufficiency, would he be *confirmed* in his political position. This demand for faith epitomizes Isaiah's most distinctive contribution to the prophetic tradition (see pp. 321 f.).

7. 10–17 *The sign of Immanuel*

Most of the controversies which have raged over the interpretation of this passage are seen to be sound and fury signifying nothing once it is acknowledged that it does not use the word 'virgin' and has no bearing on the birth of Christ. Scholarly controversy about points of historical exegesis and the possibility that Isaiah was drawing on mythological material will, no doubt, continue. The view taken here is the simple one that the prophet's 'sign' was a way of affirming for the reassurance of the Judean king that within nine months his enemies would disappear and there would be peace. The circumstances and the implicit demand for faith in Yahweh are the same as those in 7¹⁻⁹.

10–12. Shortly after the incident with Shear-jashub, when Ahaz is still contemplating an appeal to Assyria, Isaiah invites the king to ask Yahweh for a *sign*—any kind of sign he cares to choose—to confirm the prophet's counsel that the way out of the crisis is faith and not a foreign alliance. A *sign* is any event, whether normal or abnormal, which signifies something beyond itself (cf. 1 Sam. 2³⁴, 10⁷, ⁹, 14¹⁰; Isa. 8¹⁸, 20³). Ahaz evades the issue by saying smugly that he prefers not to put God to the test.

13–17. Isaiah throws down his challenge to the king and his counsellors, the whole *house of David.* and, in a revealing phrase, declares that they are wearing out the patience of *his* God (v. 13). Such is the prophet's sense of being with Yahweh over against the people. They shall have a sign whether they want one or not. The sign offered is the normal birth in the near future of a son to a young woman and its significance lies in the child's name, *Immanu-el*, meaning 'God is with us' (cf. Gen. 16¹¹). By the time this child knows what he likes (that is to say, very soon), he will be able to enjoy such delicacies as *curds and honey* (v. 15; cf. Exod. 3⁸; Job 20¹⁷) and Damascus and Israel, of whom Ahaz is now so afraid, will be destroyed (v. 16). The imminent restoration of peace will surpass anything that has happened since the disruption of Solomon's Empire in 922 B.C. (v. 17, omitting *the king of Assyria* as a gloss). This is what faith in Yahweh offers as an alternative to the faithless and disastrous plan to make an alliance with Assyria. Different and more elaborate expositions of the sign have been proposed, which bring it closer either to traditional Christian interpretations, or to ancient mythological conceptions. Among the disputed points, the following may be noted: (i) *a young woman* (v. 14) of marriageable age is the meaning of the Hebrew word *'almāh* (cf. Gen. 24⁴³); *virgin* (RSV *mg.*) translates the Greek version, from which it was borrowed for Matthew 1²³. It has been suggested that this young woman was known at Court and may have been one of the wives of Ahaz. (ii) *curds and honey* (v. 15) have been interpreted as the diet of the desert and, therefore, as signifying a threat to Ahaz (cf. 7²¹, ²²). On the other hand, they have been seen as the food of the gods and thought to support the idea that the reference in these verses is to the birth of a divine redeemer, or at least a royal child of David's line. There is, however, no emphasis whatsoever on either the mother or the child. The sign is the birth and its significance is the name, Immanu-el, which points to the action of God. The possibility that v. 17 is a threat to Ahaz is much reduced when the prosaic note, *the king of Assyria*, is discounted as a marginal gloss.

8. 5–8a *Ahaz's false choice*

Ahaz rejected Isaiah's counsel that he should remain calm under the threat from Damascus and Israel and put his faith in Yahweh. Instead, he accepted the counsel of his political advisers that he should seek the protection of Assyria. As this oracle declares, the king's false choice was disastrous (see notes on 2 Kgs. 16[1–20]).

6. *the waters of Shiloah* refers to the channel ('the conduit of the upper pool', 7[3]) which brought water from the Spring of Gihon to the Pool of Siloam before Hezekiah had his underground tunnel constructed (see notes on 2 Kgs. 18[17]). This gentle stream admirably symbolizes the calm confidence in Yahweh (cf. 30[15]) which Judah had rejected in favour of the turbulent waters of Assyria. An alternative to the RSV rendering is to omit *Rezin and the son of Remaliah* as a gloss and translate *melt in fear before* as 'meltingly': 'this people have refused the waters of Shiloah that flow gently and meltingly.'

7, 8a. Judah has chosen the Euphrates, *the waters of the River*, whose torrents symbolize *the king of Assyria and all his glory* and will sweep devastatingly into Judah—*even to the neck* (cf. 30[28]). With the words, *its outspread wings*, the image changes from a destructive flood to a protective bird and a new oracle begins (vv. 8*b*–10).

8. 16–18 *Isaiah's withdrawal*

Between 734 B.C., when Ahaz appealed to Assyria, and 715 B.C., when Hezekiah succeeded to the Judean throne, Isaiah appears not to have engaged in any public affairs. These verses are thought to be the conclusion of the prophet's autobiographical memoirs which he wrote to accompany the collection of his early oracles. Their authenticity, however, is open to question.

16. *the testimony* and *the teaching* of the prophet were written on a scroll to be sealed and kept either by his *disciples*, or 'from those who can read' (cf. 29[11, 12]; Jer. 32[10–12]). These are the most probable interpretations of an obscure text.

17. Isaiah proposes to follow his own advice to Ahaz (7[1–9]).

18. The prophet and his children (cf. 7[3], 8[4]) are living witnesses to Yahweh's declared purpose, even though it is now ignored by the politicians.

9. 2–7 *The Man born to be King*

This well-loved Christmas lesson is a proclamation cast in the form of a psalm of thanksgiving. The form of the Hebrew verbs could mean either that the great event being celebrated has already happened or, though still in the future, may be thought of as having happened. Since we now know that far-ranging 'ideal' claims were made for Israelite and other oriental kings on their accession to the throne (see pp. 158 ff.), there is no difficulty in associating this proclamation of a new age with the actual birth of a Davidic prince or the actual accession of a Davidic king. It is probable, therefore, that the passage is celebrating an event which has already occurred. Most scholars take the view that this event is the *birth* of a prince and that the royal titles simply anticipate the child's accession to the throne. Others, however, interpret the event as the *accession* of a king and understand the references to his birth as a metaphorical way of describing his new royal status as Yahweh's 'son': 'You are my son, today I have begotten you' (see notes on Ps. 2[7]).

It is impossible to identify either the Judean king or the author of his praises. The language of the passage (like that of 11[1–9]) is drawn from the common stock of ideas about kingship and in most respects it is closer to the royal psalms than to the undoubtedly authentic oracles of Isaiah. It is reasonable, therefore, to ascribe it to the circles which preserved Isaiah's oracles and in so many other ways brought them into line with the dominant royal theology of Jerusalem (see pp. 320 ff.).

The continued use of this passage as a lesson for Christmas Day is an illuminating illustration of the way in which the ancient oriental ideas of kingship have been adopted and adapted to express the faith of God's people in the coming of his Kingdom.

2, 3. *The dawn of a new age.* It is possible that a myth about the invasion of the underworld by the sun-god has coloured the language of v. 2 (cf. Ps. 110³). For *Thou hast multiplied the nation*, it is preferable to read 'Thou has multiplied the rejoicing'. The people's rejoicing is like that at the end of harvest or a victorious battle.

4. The images for the oppression which God has now removed appear to be drawn from a yoke of oxen: the burdensome *yoke*, the bar *(staff)* on his shoulder, and the stick *(rod)* of his driver *(oppressor)*. *the day of Midian* was the day of Gideon's celebrated victory over the Midianites (Judg. 6–8).

5. The new age will be a time of peace and security from enemies. In 11⁶⁻⁸, even the animal creation shares the universal peace, as in the Ras Shamra texts: 'Baal shall sit on the throne of [his kingdom] . . . (when) the ox shall have the voice of the gazelle, (and) the hawk the voice of the sparrow' (G. R. Driver, *Canaanite Myths and Legends*, p. 119). For *every garment rolled in blood*, read 'every garment stained with blood'.

6. The reason for this sudden change of fortune is that *a child is born* (cf. Jer. 20¹⁵; Job 3³), who will wear on his shoulder 'an emblem of royalty' (rather than *government*). New names are now bestowed on the child, as on kings at their enthronement. There are four of them: *Wonderful Counsellor* (or, 'Ruler'); *Mighty God* (better, 'God-like Hero'); *Everlasting Father* (the god El is called 'father of years' in the Ras Shamra texts); *Prince of Peace*. These titles fall short of describing the king as divine, but they are nearer heaven than earth (see pp. 143 f.).

7. Read: 'Great shall be his dominion and endless the peace (or, good fortune).' *Justice* and *righteousness* are constantly ascribed to the king in the royal psalms (see notes on Ps. 72; cf. Isa. 11¹⁻⁹). *The zeal of the Lord of hosts will do this* belongs to the same tradition as 37³² and provides, therefore, a clue to the circles in which the whole passage was composed.

10. 5–15 *The arrogant boasting of Assyria*

This important oracle expresses two convictions and it is important to distinguish between them: (i) Yahweh was using Assyria as his instrument for punishing his own people (vv. 5, 6); (ii) Yahweh was about to punish Assyria for arrogantly assuming that by its power and political wisdom (v. 13) it determined the course of history. That was the prerogative of Yahweh alone (fig. p. 14). Both these convictions contribute to what is often called 'the prophetic interpretation of history', but the second is more distinctively prophetic than the first. The first, namely that foreign nations are used by the gods to punish their people, is found all over the ancient Near East. Thus, for example, the Assyrian *Epic of Tukulti-Ninurta* about 1220 B.C. explains that the Assyrians were able to plunder Babylon because the Babylonian gods, angry with the king of their people, fought on the Assyrians' side. At a later date, the Assyrian king, Esar-haddon (681–669), accounts for the destruction of Babylon by his predecessor, Sennacherib, in the following remarkably 'prophetic' terms: 'They (the citizens of Babylon) oppressed the weak, and gave him into the power of the strong. Inside the city there was tyranny, the receiving of bribes; every day without fail they plundered each other's goods; the son cursed his father in the street, the slave [abjured] his master, [the slave girl] did not listen to her mistress. . . . Marduk, the Enlil of the gods, was angry and devised evil to overwhelm the land and destroy the peoples' (quoted by W. G. Lambert, *Babylonian Wisdom Literature*, p. 5, from R. Borger, *Asarhaddon*, pp. 12–13). The more familiar Moabite Stone, erected by Mesha, king of Moab, about 830 B.C. (cf. 2 Kgs.

3⁴⁻²⁷), offers a similar interpretation of the invasion of his country by Omri (see p. 78): 'Omri, king of Israel, he oppressed Moab many days, for Chemosh was angry with his land.' Here, a Moabite king implies that Chemosh, his god, used Omri as the rod of his anger, as Isaiah claimed Yahweh was using Assyria (7²⁰, 10⁵, 28³; cf. Jer. 25⁹, 27⁶, 43¹⁰).

The distinctive feature of the prophets' interpretation of history is to be found in the second conviction of this passage, namely that Yahweh is sovereign over the nations and is able, therefore, to bring them to judgement. This was the presupposition of Amos (see notes on 1³–2¹⁶, 9⁷) and it is expressed by Isaiah with unambiguous clarity. In Amos, the nations were judged for inhuman cruelty; in Isaiah, the great Assyrian Empire at the height of its power is judged for daring to usurp Yahweh's control of the course of history (cf. 14²⁴⁻²⁷). Judah was insignificant, but Yahweh was universally sovereign. He did not simply intervene to protect or punish his own people from time to time; he ruled the nations according to a coherent and continuous purpose.

5, 6. *Ah* is altogether too polite: 'Shame on', or, 'A curse on' is more like it. Assyria, *the rod of my anger*, is the instrument Yahweh has used to chastise his own *godless nation* (cf. 7²⁰).

7–11. The Assyrian ruler, however, has his own very different ideas. Is he not the King of Kings (v. 8)? Capital cities have gone down like ninepins before him: *Calno, Carchemish, Hamath*, and *Arpad*, cities of Syria, had all been conquered (see notes on Amos 6²); *Damascus* had fallen in 732 B.C. and *Samaria* in 721 B.C. (see pp. 105–8). And if Samaria, why not Jerusalem? Its idol-gods were as useless as the rest (v. 11). Most scholars omit v. 10 as a corrupt gloss.

12. This prose note illustrates the notion of Zion's security from its heathen enemies which was current in the circles which edited Isaiah's oracles (cf. 29⁷; see pp. 157 f.).

13, 14. Isaiah represents the Assyrian king as using the confident language he had heard from political counsellors trained

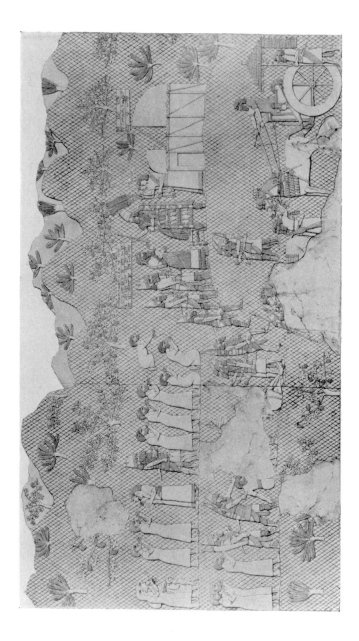

in the wisdom school of Jerusalem (see pp. 168–75). They too claimed *wisdom* and *understanding* and the ability to determine the course of events. Isaiah vigorously satirizes Assyria's ruthless and masterful imperialism: for *like a bull . . . thrones* (v. 13), read (perhaps) 'like a god I brought down their inhabitants'; he also grabbed the wealth of the nations as people rob birds' nests, without anyone making so much as a squeak (v. 14).

15. Isaiah replies to the Assyrian king and other clever statesmen in their own clever proverbial language (cf. 29¹⁵, ¹⁶; see pp. 183 f.). One of the proverbial sayings ascribed to the Assyrian sage Ahikar provides an illuminating parallel: 'Why should wood strive with fire, flesh with a knife, a man with [*a king*]?' (J. B. Pritchard, *Ancient Near Eastern Texts*, p. 429). Does the tail wag the dog? It is Yahweh who is the King of Kings and sovereign lord of history; the king of Assyria is a mere tool in his hands. The obvious implication is that when the tool has served its purpose it can be thrown away.

20. 1–6 *Isaiah's sign against reliance on Egypt*

This short biographical narrative records how Isaiah for three years went about Jerusalem stripped to the waist like a prisoner of war as a warning against joining an alliance with Egypt against Assyria. The Philistine city of Ashdod, encouraged by the expectation of support from Egypt, had become the centre of rebellion against Assyria and in 711 B.C. Sargon

---

SENNACHERIB: KING OF KINGS. This is part of a series of gypsum wall reliefs which Sennacherib (705–681) commissioned for his palace at Nineveh to celebrate the capture of Lachish by the Assyrian forces. It depicts the king outside the conquered city sitting in state on a high throne, his feet on a stool and a bow and arrow in his hands, receiving homage from the stricken population. An Assyrian officer and soldiers present the inhabitants of Lachish, who are shown kneeling, barefoot and dressed in ankle-length short-sleeved garments; their hair and beards are short and tightly curled. Behind the throne are two attendants holding fans. The inscription above the heads of the soldiers reads: 'Sennacherib, king of all, king of Assyria, sitting on his *nimedu*-throne while the spoil from the city of Lachish passed before him' (D. Winton Thomas, *Documents from Old Testament Times*, p. 70).

crushed and captured it. Not only did Egypt fail to send help, but actually handed over to the Assyrians the king of Ashdod who had fled south to seek protection. Isaiah's expectation that Egypt would be conquered by Assyria was not fulfilled for another fifty years (see p. 20).

This is the only recorded occasion on which Isaiah demonstrated his message in dramatic form, with the exception of the naming of his sons (7¹⁻⁹, 8¹⁻⁴). However we interpret the symbolic actions of Jeremiah and Ezekiel (see pp. 239 f.), there is no suggestion here that Isaiah's action was anything more than an urgent appeal to Hezekiah and his counsellors not to make an alliance with Egypt.

1. *Ashdod* was captured in 711 B.C. by *Sargon II* (722–705).

2. *at that time* refers to the beginning of Ashdod's rebellion three years earlier (cf. v. 3). For *by Isaiah*, read 'to Isaiah'. The *sackcloth* was presumably a rough outer garment (cf. 2 Kgs. 1⁸); we have no means of knowing whether this was Isaiah's regular dress, or whether he had adopted it because of its association with mourning (cf. 22¹²; 1 Kgs. 21²⁷; Lam. 2¹⁰); *naked* must mean merely in a loin-cloth.

3. *Egypt and Ethiopia* refers to the new (Ethiopian) XXVth Dynasty of Egypt (716–663).

6. *this coastland* probably includes Judah as well as the cities of the Philistine plain.

22. 1–14 *The judgement on Jerusalem*

In a poem of great anguish (cf. v. 4), Isaiah exposes the people's failure to see Yahweh's judgement in Assyria's siege of Jerusalem. Yahweh looked for penitence, but the people's only response was faithless panic in face of the emergency and reckless revelry as soon as it passed. There is no clear indication of the date of the incident, but many commentators refer it to Sennacherib's siege of the city and his sudden withdrawal in

701 B.C. (see notes on 2 Kgs. 18$^{13-16}$). There is undoubtedly a contrast between the prophet's attitude to Jerusalem's deliverance in this passage and that ascribed to Isaiah in 2 Kgs. 19$^{9-35}$ (especially vv. 32–34), but this only goes to confirm the unreliable character of the latter (see notes on 2 Kgs. 18–19). What Isaiah found in the events of 701 B.C. was not a proof that Zion was inviolable, but a proof that Yahweh was judging his people and that they had perversely failed to respond (see notes on 1$^{2-9}$).

1. The title is taken from v. 5, where *the valley of vision* may mean the valley of Hinnom (cf. Jer. 7$^{30-34}$; see pp. 103 f.).

3. This very obscure verse, describing, it seems, the desertion of the city by its leaders, may be reconstructed as follows: 'All your rulers have fled together, have fled from the bow (of the enemy); all your leaders turned aside and fled far away.'

5. This *day* of disaster for Jerusalem was the day of Yahweh's judgement and is described in the imagery of the Day of the Lord (cf. v. 12; see notes on 2$^{6-22}$).

6. For *with chariots and horsemen*, read 'Syria (Aram) mounted horsemen'. For *Kir*, see notes on Amos 1^5. It may be supposed that there were Elamite and Aramean contingents in the Assyrian army.

8b–11. In a piece of masterly description, the prophet points the contrast between the plans of men and the plan of God. Jerusalem's frenzied reaction to what was taken to be merely a military emergency was quite beside the point, as v. 12 makes clear. The royal palace, known as *the House of the Forest* (v. 8), had been an arsenal from Solomon's time (1 Kgs. 7^2, 10^{17}). The efforts to safeguard the city's water supply probably refer to Hezekiah's digging of the Siloam tunnel (see notes on 2 Kgs. 18^{17}).

12–14. Instead of a penitent response to Yahweh's judgement (v. 12), Jerusalem gave herself to feasting at the Temple (v. 13). To Isaiah, this frivolity was unforgiveable (v. 14).

28. 1-13 *Jerusalem's leaders will learn their lesson*

Isaiah is almost exclusively concerned with the ruling classes of Judah and here, in a scene of telling if sordid realism, he exposes their dissolute lives and defiant hostility. The threat from Assyria (vv. 11-13) suggests that the occasion was probably some time between the death of Sargon II in 705 B.C. and the siege of Jerusalem in 701 B.C., but a precise dating is impossible. The oracle against the leaders of Jerusalem (vv. 7-10) is appropriately introduced by the quotation of an earlier oracle directed against the irresponsible leaders of Samaria (vv. 1-4), who had been equally oblivious of their imminent fate in the last years of the northern kingdom (see notes on 2 Kgs. 17¹⁻⁶).

1-4. The capital city of Samaria is pictured as a garland of flowers decorating the heads of the drunken leaders of the northern kingdom; it is about to be trodden underfoot and to wither as quickly as a first-ripe fig. In vv. 1, 4, *the rich valley* should possibly be read as a reference to the fat paunches of the drunkards. In v. 2, *the Lord has one who is mighty and strong* means that Yahweh will use Assyria as 'the rod of his anger' (cf. 10⁵). The point in v. 4 is that the *first-ripe fig* (cf. Jer. 24²; Mic. 7¹) is a luxury so delicate that it withers as soon as it is handled.

5, 6. These verses of promise, coming between a threat to Ephraim and a threat to Judah, may be disregarded as an editorial intrusion (cf. 4²⁻⁶).

7-10. Jerusalem's leaders, including the priests and prophets of the Temple, like the leaders of Samaria, are a disgusting drink-sodden lot (vv. 7, 8). They reject Isaiah's teaching as 'kids' stuff' (v. 9) and sniggeringly compare it to learning one's ABC in school. The transliteration of the Hebrew, which is translated *precept upon precept . . . line upon line*, reveals a jingle with the letters 'ç' and 'q' in alphabetical order: *çaw lāçāw çaw lāçāw qaw lāqāw qaw lāqāw*. The phrase, *here a little, there a little,* probably echoes the teacher in class as he calls on one boy after another: 'The little one here, the little one there.'

11-13. Isaiah's immediate retort to the scoffers is that if they refuse to learn Yahweh's lesson from him they will learn it the hard way from the barbarous language of the Assyrians (v. 11). The lesson they refuse to hear is summarized in v. 12 (cf. 7⁹, 28¹⁶, 30¹⁵). When the Assyrians arrive as their teachers, then indeed they will be in the position of children learning their ABC (v. 13).

28. 14-22 *Yahweh's strange work of judging his own people*

This oracle of doom on the scoffing leaders of Jerusalem is closely related to 28¹⁻¹³. It contrasts the security of the house built on the rock of faith with the insecurity of those who seek shelter in alliance with 'the powers of death'. The parable of the two houses (Matthew 7²⁴⁻²⁷; cf. 16¹⁸) provides a most illuminating commentary on the whole passage and may, indeed, be indebted to it.

15. The *covenant with death* has not been satisfactorily explained. The reference may be to Mot, the Canaanite god of the underworld (*Sheol*), to which the leaders have turned for *refuge* and *shelter* (see pp. 45 ff.). The language of the verse is Isaiah's, but it is not inconceivable that he is repeating his opponents' contemptuous boasting that they are covered because the Devil will look after his own. It is possible, but not very obvious, that their *covenant* and *agreement* refer (as is usually maintained) to their plotting with Egypt. For *scourge*, read 'flood'.

16, 17a. It is probably no more than a coincidence that the prophet borrows an Egyptian word to describe the granite (*tested*) foundation stone which Yahweh will lay in Jerusalem. The RSV represents '*He who believes will not be in haste*' as an inscription on the stone. The statement may, however, be the first element of an interpretation of Yahweh's 'house of faith', founded on a rock against which the 'powers of death' (cf. v. 15; Matthew 16¹⁸) will not prevail. The firm foundation stone is the unwavering believer; its straight walls, built with *line* and *plummet* (cf. Amos 7⁷⁻⁹) stand for *justice* and *righteousness*. There is no indication as to who was to inhabit this house of faith, but it clearly represents an alternative to the Temple and denies rather than supports the belief that Zion is in itself a secure refuge (see pp. 148 f.).

17*b*–19. In contrast to the impregnable house of faith, the false *refuge* and *shelter* of the leaders of Jerusalem will be swept away by an overwhelming flood (cf. Matthew 7²⁴⁻²⁷).

20. A proverb describing an intolerable situation. The leaders have made their bed and must lie on it.

21. Yahweh will fight against his own people as he fought for David against the Philistines on *Mount Perazim* and in *the valley of Gibeon* (1 Chron. 14¹¹, ¹⁶). This indeed, is a *strange* and *alien* work.

29. 1–8 *A judgement on Jerusalem reversed*

This passage demands the kind of decision which is of crucial importance for the interpretation of Isaiah's teaching. It begins with an oracle of doom on Jerusalem (vv. 1–4) and ends with a proclamation of doom on the nations and of deliverance for Jerusalem (7, 8; for vv. 5, 6, see below). Either Isaiah changed his mind or somebody else changed his oracle. Those who take the first view usually ascribe the prophet's change of mind to his experience of the sudden withdrawal of the Assyrian forces besieging Jerusalem in 701 B.C., when, it is supposed, he came to believe in the inviolability of Zion (cf. 2 Kgs. 19³²⁻³⁴). This doctrine is taken for granted in vv. 7, 8 of the present passage. If Isaiah had in fact changed his mind on this occasion, one might have expected not a conventional reference to 'the multitude of all the nations' (cf. 17¹²⁻¹⁴), but a specific reference to Assyria. The reasons for preferring the second of the alternative views, namely that Isaiah's teaching has been changed by somebody else, are briefly as follows: (i) the 'doctrine of the inviolability of Zion' was almost certainly a belief originating

outside the prophetic tradition early enough for it to become a
commonplace of many pre-exilic psalms (see pp. 157 f.); (ii)
the clearest statements of this and other related 'doctrines'
current in the 'royal theology' of Jerusalem occur in those
oracles of the book of Isaiah which most clearly derive from
later tradition (see pp. 320 f.); (iii) while it is asking too much to
expect complete consistency of a prophet in changing circumstances, it is asking far too much to expect an interpretation
involving a complete reversal of a prophet's teaching to be
accepted without weighty evidence. If Isaiah had come to
believe that Jerusalem would be miraculously delivered, it is
unintelligible that he should have chosen to say so simply by
revising an old oracle of doom. On the other hand, it is entirely
intelligible that his editors should have brought the prophet's
teaching more into line with popular orthodoxy. The editing
of 31⁴, ⁵ provides another example of this process.

1. *Ariel* is clearly a cryptic name for Jerusalem (cf. v. 7). Its
use at the end of v. 2 favours the meaning given to the word as a
common noun in Ezek. 43¹⁵, ¹⁶, 'altar hearth'; since, however,
this reference is a pun, a primary meaning must be sought and
this is probably 'mountain of God'. *Add year to year; let the feasts
run their round* is an ironical summons to continue the futile
religion of the Temple (see notes on 1¹⁰⁻¹⁷ and Amos 4⁴, ⁵).

2. The 'mountain of God' will become 'an altar hearth' (cf. v.
6), or, possibly, 'a ghost' (see on v. 4), by enemy action (v. 3).

4. *like the voice of a ghost* depicts the weakness of the prostrate
city. It has been suggested that here (and as an alternative to
'altar hearth' in v. 2) there is a play on the connexion between
Ariel and the Akkadian word 'Arallu', which means 'underworld' or 'shade'.

5, 6. The change from doom on Jerusalem to doom on the
nations occurs at the beginning of v. 5, but some commentators
suggest that the end of v. 5 and v. 6 (*And in an instant . . . devouring fire*) were originally directed against Jerusalem. In view of
the city's already helpless condition in v. 4, this is improbable.

7, 8. The heathen nations besieging Jerusalem will vanish like a dream, especially like those dreams which are too good to be true.

31. 1–3 *The wisdom of men and the wisdom of God*

This brief oracle exposes the fundamental issue involved in the conflict between Isaiah and the politicians of Jerusalem over the question of alliance with Egypt between the years 705 and 701 B.C. (cf. 30¹⁻⁷ and p. 316). According to the wisdom in which they had been schooled (see pp. 166 f.), the politicians acted on the assumption that the course of events was governed entirely by forces under human control. According to Isaiah's passionate conviction, history was shaped by the righteous purpose and power of Yahweh, which no practical politics could replace or evade. The conflict was irreconcilable.

2. *And yet he is wise.* Yahweh possesses wisdom and this will find expression in action, as Judah, *the house of the evildoers*, and Egypt, its *helpers*, will discover when they *all perish together* (v. 3).

3. Instead of trusting in the power of God, Judah has put its confidence in the weakness of men (and their armed forces). The term *flesh* includes both animals and men who share the weakness of creatures (Gen. 6¹⁷; Isa. 40⁶, ⁷; Ps. 78³⁹); *spirit*, when, as here, it is contrasted with flesh, describes the character and the power of Yahweh (Joel 2²⁸; cf. Ps. 56⁴; Jer. 17⁵; 2 Chron. 32⁸).

JEREMIAH

Among the prophets, Jeremiah is *par excellence* the poet. His most characteristic utterances are the so-called 'confessions', in which he discloses a degree of mental conflict and emotional stress which he found almost intolerable (see notes on 11¹⁸–12⁶, 15¹⁰⁻²¹, 17¹⁴⁻¹⁸, 18¹⁸⁻²³, 20⁷⁻¹¹, ¹⁴⁻¹⁸). The cause of his suffering was a natural sensitivity, sharpened by his prophetic commission. He saw things without the tolerance inbred by tradition, or the compromise which most men accept as the price of ordinary human happiness. Although isolated from men, he was at all times overwhelmingly aware of the presence of God, but not, as Christians must affirm, of God as he really is. Like his spiritual master Hosea, Jeremiah had no doubt about Yahweh's goodness to Israel, as a husband to his bride (2^2, 3^4), or a father to his sons (3^{22}); but his own experience of Yahweh was primarily of power rather than love, of demand rather than grace (see notes on 15^{10-21} and 20^{7-18}). Despite the passionately intimate language of his prayers, Jeremiah knew Yahweh almost exclusively as the author of the message he was given to proclaim and that increased rather than eased his spiritual burden; for God's word to his people was like a scorching fire and 'a hammer which breaks the rock in pieces' (23^{29}). Yahweh is actual in Jeremiah's ordinary experience to a degree unprecedented in the prophetic tradition, but instead of imparting that quiet confidence which, for example, upheld Isaiah, he makes him shake and stagger like a drunken man (23^9). The terror which so conspicuously animates the oracles on the 'foe from the north' does not derive from the ferocity of the Scythians or the Babylonians; it is the terror of Yahweh's coming in judgement (see notes on 4^{5-31}). Not until the blow has fallen and some of the people have been deported to exile in Babylon, does Jeremiah attain anything like confidence and composure (see notes on 32^{1-15}). It is only then that we find a calm awareness of God as gracious: 'For I know the plans I have for you, says the Lord, plans for welfare and not for evil, to give you a future and a hope' (29^{11}; see notes on 29^{1-7}, 31^{31-34}).

Jeremiah seems almost to have welcomed the Babylonian exile, not so much as a punishment as a return to reality, which opened up the possibility of a genuine return to God (cf. 24^{1-7}). The contrast between reality and delusion, truth and falsehood, dominates his prophecy and is the key to his thought. Like his predecessors in the previous century, he, too, is incensed by injustice (see notes on 22^{13-19}) and profligacy (see notes on 3^{1-5}), but he particularizes about very few of Judah's failings. He is distinctive, rather, for his deep psychological penetration and for his despairing conviction that the whole of Judah's life is permeated by falsehood: 'falsehood and not truth has grown strong in the land'(9^3). It is *truth* that Yahweh looks for (see notes on 5^3), but in refusing to know him, his people have lost their hold on reality (cf. 2^8, 4^{22}, $5^{4, 5}$, 8^7, 9^{1-6}). The Hebrew word *sheqer*, meaning lie and falsehood, is used in the Old Testament rather more than a hundred times and no less than a third of these occurrences are found in the book of Jeremiah alone. No prophet was more sensitive to truth and untruth than he. Everywhere he looked, he found nothing but lies. The Canaanite cults to which the people had turned, with their 'orgies on the mountains', are mere *delusion* (3^{23}), like the gods they allegedly worshipped: '... you have forgotten me and trusted in *lies*' (13^{25}). The same falsehood has perverted the whole of Judean society:

> Every one deceives his neighbour,
>   and no one speaks the truth;
>   they have taught their tongue to speak lies;
>   they commit iniquity and are too weary to repent. (9^5)

The religion of the people, even when it is avowedly the worship of Yahweh, is nothing more than a conventional sham. They say, 'As the Lord lives', but 'they swear *falsely*' (5^2; cf. $7^{8, 9}$; see notes on Ps. 84). Their trust in the Temple and its futile sacrifices is mere deception (see notes on $7^{1-15, 21-26}$). They are also led astray from the truth by their teachers (cf. $8^{8, 9}$) and prophets. Of all the classes of the community, it is the prophets of Jerusalem who come in for the most scathing condemnation as the principal purveyors of falsehood: they 'walk in *lies*' (23^{14}; cf. 5^{31}, 14^{14}, $23^{25, 32}$, $27^{10, 14-16}$, 28^{15}, $29^{9, 21, 23, 31}$).

With terrifying clarity, Jeremiah penetrated every aspect of his people's falsehood and from a deep fund of human sympathy suffered agonies, because of their alienation from Yahweh and his own alienation from them (15^{17}, 16^1; see notes on $8^{18}-9^1$, $11^{18}-12^6$). His physical sufferings (20^{1-6}, 37^{11-15}, $38^{1, 13}$) were the inevitable consequence of his almost total estrangement from a people almost totally estranged from the truth of God. The qualification 'almost' is necessary, because the memory and preaching of a prophet without a friend in the world would have died with him. This is far from being the case with Jeremiah and all the evidence points to his having enjoyed the support and confidence of that circle of loyal and educated Yahwists whom we call the deuteronomists. The oracles of the prophet and the significantly detailed record of his life were preserved and edited in the literary and religious tradition from which also came the book of Deuteronomy and the books of Kings (see pp. 68 f., 213). The evidence for this conclusion, though indirect, is strong, and may be found in the characteristic idiom and religious viewpoint common to all three works. The little *direct* evidence that Jeremiah had supporters, who may have played a part in preserving his teaching, also leads us to the deuteronomists. The one person of whom the prophet speaks with unqualified appreciation is Josiah (see notes on 22^{13-19} and 2 Kgs. $22^{1}-23^{30}$) and, apart from his faithful disciple Baruch (see notes on 36^{4}), the only people in the record who consistently defend and protect him are a group of the king's senior officers connected with the family of Shaphan and, through Shaphan, with the promoters of the deuteronomic reform (see notes on 2 Kgs. 22^{3}). Despite the efforts of a great many scholars, it has not proved possible to isolate the editorial work of Baruch from the editorial work of the deuteronomists, nor, in much of the material, the original words of the prophet from the deuteronomic reports and discourses. As so often in St. John's gospel, we have to be content with the teaching of the master as it has been understood and presented by his disciple and friends.

Reservations about the tradition are, nevertheless, necessary, especially when it ascribes to the prophet convictions and forms of expression which coincide exactly with what we know to have been particularly characteristic of the deuteronomists themselves. In evaluating the tradition about Jeremiah, the crucial significance of Josiah and his reformation to the deuteronomists is the outstanding point at issue. While it is highly probable

that Jeremiah approved of their efforts to revive Mosaic Yahwism, it is legitimate to doubt whether we should accept the
assertion that he himself actually took part in the reform (see
notes on 11^{1-8}). It is even legiti_nate, on the same grounds, to
question whether Jeremiah was a prophet at all as early as
Josiah's reign (640–609), although the deuteronomists claim
that he was called in 626 B.C. (1^2, 3^6, 25^3, 36^2; see notes on 1^{1-3}).
There is no unassailable evidence pointing to this early date
(see notes on 4^{5-31}) and the lack of reliable data for Jeremiah's
direct experience of Josiah's reform tells against the view that
his ministry began before 621 B.C. No confident decision is possible, but it may fairly be said that the less popular date of 609
B.C. for the prophet's 'call' (cf. 1^3, 22^{10-19}, 26^1) is no more improbable than the generally accepted date of 626 B.C. It is good
to recognize what we simply do not know.

There is little doubt, however, that Jeremiah was actively
involved in four critical phases of Judah's final years as an
independent state. (i) *From the death of Josiah* (609) *to the Battle of
Carchemish* (605). This was the period after Assyria had been
finally liquidated, when the balance of power was precariously
held between the rising kingdom of Babylon and the temporarily resuscitated kingdom of Egypt, and Judah was completely in Egypt's pocket (see p. 20). It is to these four years
that we may ascribe Jeremiah's oracles on Shallum (that is,
Jehoahaz, see notes on 2 Kgs. 23^{31-33}), Josiah and Jehoiakim
(see notes on 22^{13-19}), the Temple sermon (see notes on
$7^{1-15,\ 21-26}$), and, perhaps, most of the poems on Israel's apostasy in chapters 1–5 (see notes). (ii) *From Carchemish to the First
Deportation* (597). The victory of the Babylonians and the routing of the Egyptians at Carchemish in 605 B.C. seem to have
convinced Jeremiah that Judah, too, was defenceless against
the new power, and, moreover, that military defeat was Yahweh's method of forcing his people to face reality (cf. 24^{1-10},
27^6, 28^{14}). For the rest of his life, therefore, he proclaimed that
on no account should the yoke of Babylon be resisted. Inevitably,
this apparently defeatist view involved him in violent opposition, persecution, and mental torture. The writing of the scroll,

which announced Babylon's imminent conquest of Judah (36²⁹), belongs to the year of Carchemish (see notes on 36¹⁻³²). Also to this period, we may ascribe the poet's agonized 'confessions' (see p. 348 and notes) and, perhaps, the oracles on 'the

THE BABYLON OF NEBUCHADREZZAR. The photograph shows some of the excavated ruins of the great Ishtar Gate, erected a quarter of a mile from the River Euphrates as part of the ambitious programme of public building in Babylon undertaken by Nebuchadrezzar II (605–562). The city to which the gate gave access from the north was about a hundred times the size of Jerusalem and enclosed by a formidable double wall. The first gate of the complex was flanked on each side by a huge square crenellated tower built of baked bricks and faced with glazed tiles tinted blue with powdered lapis lazuli. The tiles were decorated with thirteen rows of white and yellow 'dragons' and brown, green, and blue bulls, emblems respectively of the gods Marduk and Adad. The second gate, leading through the inner wall of the city, was flanked by even more massive blue (but otherwise undecorated) towers and gave access to a square gate-house 100 ft. deep. From this immensely impressive structure, worshippers emerged on to the long processional way which ran south in a straight line past the royal palace on the right into the heart of the city.

foe from the north' (see notes on 4⁵⁻³¹). It fell to Jehoiachin to face the consequences of his father's rebellion against Babylon (see notes on 2 Kgs. 24⁸⁻¹⁶). When the young king was exiled in the first deportation, Jeremiah offered no hope for his return (22²⁴⁻³⁰). (iii) *From the First Deportation to the Fall of Jerusalem*

(587). In Judah's final decade, the new Babylonian puppet ruler, Zedekiah, was torn between Jeremiah's unwavering counsel of subservience to the conqueror and the clamour of his pro-Egyptian political advisers and the nationalist prophets, who demanded the return of the exiles from Babylon and vigorous resistance. Jeremiah denounced an attempted alliance of petty Palestinian states against Babylon in 594 B.C. (27$^{1-11}$) and the lying assurances of institutional prophets, like Hananiah, who were inciting Jerusalem to rebellion (28$^{1-17}$; see notes on 23$^{9-32}$). It was also in this period that Jeremiah wrote his letter of encouragement to the exiles of the first deportation and condemned the prophets in Babylon who were trying to make them dissatisfied with their lot (see notes on 29$^{1-7,\ 24-32}$). Sometime during the nineteen months of the final siege of Jerusalem (January 588 to July 587), Jeremiah expressed his confidence in the people's eventual return to Judah by calmly buying a piece of family property (see notes on 32$^{1-15}$), but he maintained his conviction that all optimism about immediate relief was false (34$^{1-22}$), and (not surprisingly) was arrested and imprisoned as a deserter (see notes on 37^{1}–39^{10}). (iv) *After the Fall of Jerusalem* (587–582). After the fall of the city and his release from prison, Jeremiah appears to have lived at Mizpah with Gedaliah, the grandson of Shaphan and son of Ahikam, his former protector (cf. 26^{24}), whom the Babylonians had wisely made governor of Judah (see notes on 2 Kgs. 25$^{22-26}$). After about five years' peace, Gedaliah was assassinated by fanatical Judean nationalists and, against their better judgement, Jeremiah and Baruch joined a party which went down to Egypt. There the prophet disappears from history (see notes on 39^{11}–44^{30}).

I. 1-3 *Jeremiah and his ministry*

Jeremiah's father was *of the priests who were in Anathoth.* Anathoth is now identified with modern *Ras el-Kharrubeh* about two miles north-east of Jerusalem. Although it was to this village that Abiathar, the priest of David, was banished by Solomon

(1 Sam. 3$^{10-14}$; 1 Kgs. 2$^{26, 27}$), there is not the slightest evidence for the view that Jeremiah was one of his descendants. The first sentence claims that the prophet's call came *in the thirteenth year* of the reign of *Josiah* (640–609), i.e. 626 B.C. (see notes on 2 Kgs. 22^1–23^{30}). Rather awkwardly, the second sentence states that the word of the Lord *also* came in the reign of *Jehoiakim* (609–598) and continued to *the end of* (or, with the Greek, to *the fifth month of*) *the eleventh year of Zedekiah* (597–587), i.e. to 587 B.C., the date of the fall of Jerusalem (see notes on 2 Kgs. 23^{31}–25^{21}). It is possible that v. 2 was added later to push back the beginning of Jeremiah's ministry from 609 to 626 B.C.

1. 4–12 *Jeremiah's call and inaugural revelation*

This account of the initial experience through which Jeremiah became a prophet records features in common with the calls of Moses (Exod. 4$^{10-12}$) and Isaiah (Isa. 6$^{1-13}$). It is remarkable both for its brevity and for its restrained simplicity.

5. *Before I formed you in the womb* reflects the prophet's sense that his vocation must be inevitable, because it is otherwise inexplicable (cf. Isa. 49$^{1, 5}$; Galatians 1^{15}). *I knew you.* The verb means to know *personally* and so to be concerned with; it is used to describe Yahweh's choice not only of the prophet (cf. 12^3), but also of Israel as his own people (Hos. 13^5; cf. Gen. 18^{19}; see notes on Amos 3^2). Jeremiah was *consecrated* (set apart) as Yahweh's spokesman not to Israel only, but also *to the nations* (cf. v. 10; Amos 1^3–2^{16}).

6. *I am only a youth.* The word tells us little, since it covers an age-range from infant (Exod. 2^6) to young man (2 Sam. 18^5). Jeremiah explains his diffidence as did Moses (Exod. 4$^{10-12}$).

9. The touching of the *mouth* here is not to cleanse the prophet (cf. Isa. 6^7), but to empower him as a spokesman of Yahweh (cf. 15^{19}; Ezek. 2^8–3^3; Exod. 4$^{15, 16}$; 1 Sam. 3^{19}).

11, 12. The form of this 'revelation', since it is scarcely a vision, is like that found in Amos (see notes on Amos 7^1–8^3;

cf. Jer. 24³). As in Amos 8¹⁻³, the prophet's conviction becomes articulate through a familiar sight and a simple association of sounds. The Hebrew for *almond* is *shāqēdh* and for *watching* the word is similar—*shōqēdh*. Like the almond, which is the first tree to 'awake' after winter, Yahweh is 'awake' to fulfil his purpose and that was the assurance which Jeremiah was seeking.

2. 1–13 *Israel's appalling apostasy*

Jeremiah was as deeply convinced of Israel's special vocation as he was of his own. In view of all that Yahweh had done for his people, their drift into utterly worthless Canaanite religion was completely incredible and unintelligible. He is less moved by the idolatry and profligacy of the Canaanite cult than by its futility and falsehood. It is simply (to use one of his favourite terms) *a lie*.

1–3. Israel in the early days following the Exodus is depicted in ideal terms as Yahweh's *bride* (cf. Hos. 2¹⁴, ¹⁵), unwavering in her *devotion* (Hebrew, *ḥesedh*, see notes on Hos. 4¹), and (with a sudden change of metaphor) as *the first fruits* of Yahweh's harvest and, therefore, being exclusive to him, protected from the nations.

4–8. Like Hosea (9¹⁰), Jeremiah simply cannot understand why the Israelites forsook Yahweh as soon as he brought them into the land of Canaan and became like the gods they went after —*worthless* 'nothings'. Every kind of leader has proved unfaithful: the *priests*, the shepherds or *rulers* of the people, and the *prophets* (cf. 18¹⁸; Mic. 3¹¹; Ezek. 7²⁶). There is no agreement as to whether *Those who handle the law* (v. 8) is a further description of the priests, or refers to a separate group in the community— scribal teachers. The word *law* is not necessarily restricted to priestly law (see p. 204) and the suggestion that Deuteronomy is meant is no more than a guess.

9–13. Whether you go west or east, there is nothing to equal Israel's horrifying apostasy in forsaking Yahweh, *the fountain of living waters* (v. 13; cf. John 4¹⁰⁻¹⁵, 7³⁸), for gods as empty as *broken cisterns. Cyprus* lies to the west and *Kedar* to the east in the Arabian desert. Even the heathen do not change their 'no-gods', but the Israelites have abandoned *their glory* (v. 11), meaning, of course, Yahweh—'their Glory'.

3. 1–5; 3. 19–4. 4 *A plea for true repentance*

In Jeremiah there is no sense that the people's fate is determined by Yahweh's irrevocable decree; the way back to him is always open. In this oracle, the prophet continues the thought of 2^{1-13} and emphasizes the distinction between facile and fundamental penitence.

3. 1–5. *Israel, the faithless wife.* Like Hosea, Jeremiah contrasts the fidelity which Yahweh expects of Israel as his bride (cf. 2^2; Hos. 1–3) with her adulterous devotion to the gods of Canaan (cf. Hos. 2^{2-13}). The sexual licentiousness of the Canaanite cult, which included sacred prostitution (cf. Hos. 4^{12-14}; Deut. 23^{17}), gave added point to the metaphor. The first question (v. 1) assumes the answer 'No'; a man cannot remarry the wife he has divorced after she has married again. This reflects the official legal position as laid down in Deut. 24^{1-4}. Since, however, it is probable that the law was older than its formulation in Deuteronomy, Jeremiah's reference to it makes no contribution to the debated question as to whether he knew and approved of the book of Deuteronomy or the reform of Josiah. The Greek version represents 'that woman' instead of *that land* as polluted. The point is that Israel is too casual about both her apostasy and the possibility of her restoration.

2. Israel's profligacy on *the bare heights* is a reference to 'the orgies on the mountains' (3^{23}) at Canaanite high-places (cf. Hos. $4^{13, 14}$).

3–5. This shameless people has not responded to Yahweh's chastening (cf. Amos 4^{6-12}), but has simply presumed upon his good nature. *My father* (v. 4; cf. v. 19) was evidently used by a young wife in addressing her husband. The whole oracle is a masterly portrayal of Israel as a brazen little minx.

19, 20. These verses follow from 3$^{1-5}$. Contrary to the usual custom, by which neither wives nor daughters possessed any rights of inheritance (cf. Num. 27$^{1-11}$), Yahweh had treated Israel as a son (cf. Job 42$^{13-15}$) and given her the *pleasant land* of Palestine. But she had proved ungrateful and faithless.

3. 21–4. 4. In this dramatic dialogue, first, Israel is heard weeping and pleading to be taken back (v. 21); Yahweh replies with a summons to return (v. 22a); Israel then makes an abject confession of her sin (vv. 22b–25); and, finally, Yahweh affirms what a true return to him involves (4$^{1-4}$).

24. *the shameful thing* is the Canaanite god, Baal.

2. Read 'nations shall bless themselves in you, and in you shall they glory', instead of *in him* (cf. Gen. 12^3).

3. A current proverbial saying (cf. Hos. 10^{12}): plough up the weeds before sowing.

4. The prophet demands a circumcision of the heart (cf. Deut. 10^{16}), as Paul did later: 'The true Jew is not he who is such in externals, neither is the true circumcision the external mark in the flesh. The true Jew is he who is such inwardly, and the true circumcision is of the heart' (Romans 2$^{28, 29}$; NEB).

4. 5–31 *Disaster from the North*

A number of Jeremiah's oracles describe in a variety of vigorous images the coming of devastation from the north: 'Out of the north evil shall break forth upon all the inhabitants of the land' (1^{14}, 4$^{5-31}$, 6$^{1-8, \ 22-26}$, 8$^{14-17}$; cf. 5$^{15-17}$, 25^9). For two hundred years, many commentators have identified the enemy of these oracles with the Scythians, a people from the Caucasian steppes, who are believed to have marched through Palestine on their way to Egypt about 626 B.C. The authority for such a Scythian invasion (and the only authority) is a passage in the *History* of Herodotus (i. 105 f.), who dates it in the reign of the Egyptian king Psammetichus I (663–609). A growing number of scholars now reject this identification, generally on one or both of the following grounds: (i) the authenticity and date of the Scythian invasion of Palestine are not firmly established; (ii) a connexion between the enemy in Jeremiah and the Scythians is neither established nor necessary. The debate has gathered partisans on both sides, largely because of its bearing on a further disputed question—the date of the beginning of Jeremiah's ministry (see p. 352). It is obvious that the traditional dating of the prophet's call in 626 B.C. (cf. 1^2, 3^6, 25^3, 36^2) is strengthened by the acceptance of the Scythian identification (at least if the time of the invasion is reckoned to fit) and, equally, that it loses one of its supports if these oracles are either judged to have no historical reference or are associated with the coming of the Babylonians some twenty years later.

Unfortunately, these disputes about chronology have tended to push into the background the one issue of real substance which the interpretation of these oracles raises. Did the prophets take as their starting-point external events on the international scene and try to give them a theological explanation? Or was it the other way round? Did they begin with a conviction about the situation of their people in relation to God and interpret the inevitability of judgement in terms of the political situation? Between these alternatives, the choice must certainly go to the latter. Amos proclaimed judgement not because Assyria was on the march, but because Israel's conduct could not be allowed to continue. Isaiah denounced Judah not to explain contemporary political events, but because it faithlessly insisted on getting involved in them. If Isaiah had started with a 'realistic' political assessment of the international situation, he would never have prophesied Assyria's doom. Jeremiah, similarly, had no need of a Scythian invasion to stir him to pronounce coming judgement on the 'vile harlotry' of Judah, and it seems improbable that he knew of or appealed to any such instrument of Yahweh's punishment. His vision of the collapse of the world into primeval chaos (vv. 23–26) is drawn, not from any knowledge of a threatening military power, but from a tradition of mythology; and it is by no means improbable that much of the language of the related oracles was also taken from tradition (cf. Hos. 4³; Isa. 2⁶⁻²²; Joel 2¹⁻¹¹). This is certainly the most likely explanation of the emphasis in these poems on the *north* (1¹⁴, 4⁶, 6¹, ²², 25⁹), which in Canaanite mythology was the home of the gods (see notes on Ps. 48²) and came to be associated with divine and demonic forces (Ezek. 1⁴, 9²; Joel 2²⁰; Job 26⁷). We may, therefore, conclude that these oracles on 'the foe from the north' are intelligible without any specific historical reference and that the Scythian identification, while possible, is improbable and not very illuminating.

5–10. *The alarm is sounded.* Yahweh is bringing *evil from the north* as a judgement on Judah and the people are commanded to take cover and lament for the calamity (cf. 6²⁶).

5, 6. The text and translation are clumsy. It is better to understand a series of staccato commands to the people: '*Declare . . . proclaim . . . blow the trumpet . . . cry aloud . . . assemble . . . raise a standard . . . flee. . . .*'

7, 8. Since this is poetry, it would be improper to press questions of detail, although the verses present numerous difficulties. If this coming disaster is Yahweh's judgement and if it will utterly destroy Judah's cities, it is hard to understand why the people are commanded to flee to them for safety (cf. vv. 5, 6).

9, 10. Many scholars judge these verses to be secondary. *In that day* is a conventional introduction to a very conventional statement. *It shall be well with you* represents the false teaching of the institutional prophets (5³¹, 6¹⁴, 14¹³⁻¹⁶, 23¹⁷, 27¹⁴, ¹⁵, 28⁹; Mic. 3⁵; Ezek. 12²⁴; Isa. 30¹⁰); it is difficult to see why Yahweh is represented as being responsible for it.

11, 12. The blast of the scorching sirocco hardly emerges with full force from the RSV translation. The meaning is: 'Tell the people that they are going to be blasted by a wind from the desert too violent for the threshing-floor but not too violent for my judgement on them.'

13–18. After the image of the lion (v. 7) and the sirocco (v. 12), the foe from the north is depicted as an advancing army, packed as densely as *clouds* (cf. 6²³).

14. The verse is an aside and may well be a gloss.

15. *Dan* was Israel's most northerly city (cf. 1 Kgs. 4²⁵); *Ephraim*, also in the north, was nearer Jerusalem (cf. 6²⁴, 8¹⁶).

16, 17. It is more probable that *the nations* should be summoned to witness Judah's destruction (cf. 6¹⁸, ¹⁹), than that the prophet should *warn* them that the enemy is coming (v. 16). They are now closing in (v. 17; cf. 6²⁵).

19–22. Jeremiah's anguish is at once his own (v. 19), his people's (v. 20), and Yahweh's (v. 22). In v. 20, *my curtains* refers to the hangings of Judah's *tents*. The language of v. 22 is that of the wisdom schools (cf. 5²¹); the term *stupid* is almost exclusive in the Old Testament to the wisdom-book, Ecclesiastes.

23–26. In a poetic vision of tremendous power, Jeremiah sees the destruction of Judah in terms of the creation's reversion to primeval chaos. Yahweh in judgement is undoing his work as Creator. The terms *waste and void* are those used in Gen. 1².

27. *yet I will not make a full end* is an obvious bit of tampering from a prosaic editor.

28, 29. These verses use the conventional language for describing the Day of the Lord (cf. Zeph. 1¹⁴⁻¹⁶; see notes on Amos 5¹⁸⁻²⁰).

30, 31. Jerusalem, *the daughter of Zion*, like a rejected prostitute (v. 30), or a woman giving birth to her first child (v. 31), is helpless and terrified before her *murderers* (compare the description of the rape of Jerusalem by Babylon in 13²⁰⁻²⁷).

5. 1–14 *A nation such as this*

There is no need to dramatize Jeremiah's vain search for truth and justice in Jerusalem by representing it as his first visit to the city, or as the occasion on which he was forced to leave home. The capital was only half an hour's walk from Anathoth and must have been well known to the prophet. He sees it now, however, with new eyes and despairingly concludes that it is doomed.

1, 2. Yahweh directs Jeremiah to search Jerusalem for a single really upright man among all those who pretend to be religious (cf. Gen. 18²³⁻³³).

3. The prophet prays. In the Old Testament, *truth* is not an abstract, intellectual category, but a practical and moral one. If something is true, it is what it ought to be and, therefore, reliable and trustworthy. Thus, for example, the Hebrew root 'āman (from which we derive the word 'Amen') is used of a *verifiable* statement (Gen. 42²⁰), *genuine* seedlings (Jer. 2²¹), *reliable* witnesses (Isa. 8²), a man to be *trusted* with secrets (Prov. 11¹³), and God *faithful* to his character and 'as good as his word' (Deut. 7⁹; Isa. 49⁷; Ps. 31⁵). In this verse, the men of Jerusalem are not what they ought to be and have *refused to take correction*.

4, 5. The prophet here seems to be reflecting to himself, rather than addressing Yahweh. Since the common folk cannot be expected to have it and the men of distinction should, knowledge of God's *way* and *law* (or, requirement) is here clearly regarded as something which is taught and learnt (see notes on 31³¹⁻³⁴ and p. 174). But even the educated have kicked over the traces.

6. In three vigorous images, Jeremiah describes the judgement on apostate Jerusalem (cf. 4⁷).

7–9. Yahweh speaks to the people and exposes their ungrateful and unpardonable behaviour. Canaanite religion not only permitted but actively encouraged sexual licence (cf. 3², ²³).

10, 11. Yahweh's faithless vineyard is to be utterly destroyed (cf. 2²¹, 6⁹, 12¹⁰; Isa. 5¹⁻⁷); *but make not a full end* (or, at least, the word *not*) is a gloss (cf. 4²⁷).

12–14. In vv. 12, 13, Yahweh speaks to the prophet and quotes the words of Jerusalem's confident sceptics. *He will do nothing* is a legitimate paraphrase of the Hebrew 'Not he'; as Second Isaiah was always pointing out, a god who did nothing for all

practical purposes did not exist (cf. Isa. 45²⁰, 46¹⁻⁷; Zeph. 1¹²).
The prophets' proclamations of doom (cf. 28⁸) will prove to be
hot air. The final imprecation of v. 13 (*Thus . . . them*) is omitted
by the Greek. In v. 14, the Hebrew '*you* have spoken' could be
retained, if the oracle addressed to Jeremiah were to begin
with the words, '*Behold, I am making . . .*' and be understood as
what he then reported to the people. Yahweh's *words*, spoken
by Jeremiah, will burn them up. The ancient notion that words
had their own intrinsic power and once uttered became independent of the speaker (cf. Gen. 27²⁷⁻³⁸) is often reflected in
descriptions of the power of the prophetic word of God (Jer.
1⁹, ¹⁰, 23²⁹; Hos. 6⁵; Isa. 9⁸, 49², 55¹⁰, ¹¹; Ezek. 37¹⁻¹⁴). It is
possible, however, to exaggerate the significance of this language and to forget that ideas which were once magical (cf.
Num. 5¹¹⁻²⁸) became in prophetic thinking largely metaphorical (cf. Zech. 5¹⁻⁴; Wisdom of Solomon 16¹², 18¹⁴⁻¹⁶). The
prophets spoke to be understood and to change the situation,
not by the release of power, but through the moral response
of the people they addressed (see p. 240).

7. 1–15, 21–26 *The Temple and its alien religion*

Jeremiah's teaching in this chapter is that the Temple would
be destroyed and that sacrifice was no part of true Yahwism.
It is easier for us to record this conviction than to grasp
either its far-reaching implications, or the kind of courage
which enabled the prophet to proclaim it in the Temple Court.
From 26¹⁻²⁴ (see notes), where the occasion of the sermon is
described, we learn that Jeremiah was immediately arrested,
put on trial, and only narrowly escaped death.

The two passages on the Temple and its cult in this chapter
occur in the first section of the book of Jeremiah which has come
from the deuteronomic editor, but there is little reason to suspect that he is expressing his own views rather than those of the
prophet. Indeed, it is widely held that Jeremiah's denunciations ran so counter to the convictions of the deuteronomic
editor that it was only the actual destruction of the Temple in

587 B.C. which made him willing to include them in his record. This opinion assumes that the men of the deuteronomic school were deeply devoted to the Temple and is in line with the view that it was the deuteronomic reform under Josiah in 621 B.C. which encouraged the Temple-centred complacency Jeremiah so vehemently exposed.

Such a reconstruction of the matter is probably mistaken. On the one hand, the Temple was superstitiously regarded as a secure refuge many centuries before the deuteronomic school came on to the scene (see pp. 148 f.) and, on the other hand, the book of Deuteronomy and the deuteronomic edition of 1 and 2 Kings reveal an outlook which is much nearer the theology of the prophets than the theology of the Temple (see pp. 65 f., 220). If this view is correct, it is not in the least surprising that members of the deuteronomic school should have been willing to preserve Jeremiah's forthright preaching.

2. *Stand in the gate of the Lord's house.* Jeremiah delivered his sermon to the Temple worshippers 'in the beginning of the reign of Jehoiakim', i.e. 609 B.C. (see notes on 26^1).

4. The current catchphrase reveals the people's superstitious belief that the temple was Yahweh's dwelling-place and gave them complete immunity from danger. With incredible courage, Jeremiah declares that this is a lie.

5–7. Judah's only security from disaster is in righteousness of life and loyalty to Yahweh. On the *alien* (or 'sojourner'), see notes on Deut. 24^{14}.

9, 10. There is no formal appeal here to the Ten Commandments, but five of them are echoed (cf. Deut. 5$^{6-21}$). For *burn incense to Baal*, read 'sacrifice to Baal'. With passionate indignation, Jeremiah rejects the sense of security the people found in the Temple as being simply a security to sin.

11. The people take refuge in the Temple like robbers in a cave (cf. Matthew 21^{13}).

12–14. The Temple, therefore, will be destroyed like the ancient sanctuary of *Shiloh*, whose ruins may still be seen (v. 12; cf. 26⁶, ⁹; Ps. 78⁶⁰). Eighteen miles north of Jerusalem, Shiloh was the central sanctuary of Israel's tribal confederation during the period of the Judges (cf. Josh. 18¹, 21², 22⁹, ¹²; Judg. 21¹⁹⁻²¹), where the first temple of Yahweh was built and the Ark kept (Judg. 18³¹; 1 Sam. 1³, ⁷, ²⁴, 3³, ¹⁵). After its destruction (according to the excavators) in 1050 B.C., its place was taken by Jerusalem.

15. Those who complacently huddle in the court of the Temple will be cast into exile as the northern kingdom had been.

21–26. The deuteronomic editor gives no indication when these memorable words on sacrificial worship were spoken. In v. 21, Yahweh says in effect: 'Don't trouble to reserve any sacrifices especially for me; eat the lot yourselves.' *burnt offerings* were completely consumed on the altar, whereas other *sacrifices* were shared by the worshippers in a common meal (see pp. 135 f.).

22, 23. It is impossible to mistake the clear conviction of these verses that sacrifice was alien to Mosaic Yahwism (see notes on Amos 5²¹⁻²⁵ and Mic. 6⁶⁻⁸). What Yahweh did command was moral obedience.

24–26. The thought and language of these verses come from the deuteronomic editor.

8. 18–9. 1 *The prophet's sympathy with his people*

In this incomparable elegy, the broken-hearted prophet reveals his complete identification with the people whose incurable wound he was called to expose. Here is the human sensitivity we miss in Isaiah and find in the Gospels (cf. Luke 13³⁴).

19. *the daughter of my people* is Judah personified as a woman. Instead of *from the length and breadth of the land*, it is possible to translate 'from a far-off land', in which case we must suppose that Jeremiah is anticipating in his grief the exile of the people (cf. 9¹). This suggestion gives more point to the anxious

inquiries about the continued presence of Yahweh, as *King*, in Zion. It is generally agreed that the final question, *Why have they provoked me to anger . . . idols?* is a prosaic gloss from the deuteronomic editor.

20. The prophet uses a proverb to express his sense of Judah's hopeless plight. The *harvest* lasted from April to June; if that failed, there was still the fruit crop in September, known as *the summer*. If that failed too, disaster followed: *we are not saved*.

22. *Is there no balm in Gilead?* Comment is inevitably an intrusion, but this resinous product of Gilead in Transjordan (Gen. 37²⁵; Jer. 46¹¹) was much prized (Ezek. 27¹⁷) and credited with healing properties (Jer. 51⁸).

9. 1. In this final, passionate lament, Jeremiah implies that his people are as good as dead. In the Hebrew, this verse ends the chapter, as it should in the English versions.

11. 1–8 *Jeremiah and Josiah's reform*

This chapter is the storm-centre of scholarly controversy about Jeremiah's attitude to Josiah's reform, which continues unabated, alike for its intrinsic interest and for lack of reliable evidence. Three facts stand out as unassailable and generally relevant to the debate: (i) Jeremiah approved of Josiah (22¹⁵, ¹⁶); (ii) Jeremiah was conspicuously befriended by Shaphan and his family, and Shaphan was Josiah's Secretary of State (see notes on 2 Kgs. 22³); (iii) Jeremiah was approved of by the deuteronomic school, since otherwise they would not have edited his work. On these grounds, we may be reasonably certain that Jeremiah was sympathetic towards the aim of Josiah and the deuteronomists. However, we are not thereby justified in claiming that he played any direct part in the reform of 621 B.C. (see notes on 2 Kgs. 22¹–23³⁰), or that there is any authentic reference to it in his recorded teaching. Once it is acknowledged that there was a good deal of scribal teaching in the wisdom school of Jerusalem, it becomes far less probable that Jeremiah's much-debated attack on 'the wise' in 8[8, 9] is a hostile reference to those responsible for the deutero-nomic law (see p. 177). Equally, once it is acknowledged that the oracles of Jeremiah have been edited by the deutero-nomists, it is far from safe to conclude on the basis of 11[1–8], which is stiff with deuteronomic language, that the prophet made it his business to go preaching about Josiah's law book 'in the cities of Judah, and in the streets of Jerusalem'. The only fact about Jeremiah's part in or attitude towards Josiah's reform in 621 B.C. is that there are no facts. Arguments from silence are fraught with danger, but we may choose between the view that in this case it is evidence of the prophet's assent to the events of 621 B.C. and the view that it is evidence of Jeremiah's not yet having been called to be a prophet (see p. 352).

1. *The word that came to Jeremiah.* Anyone not committed to the view that Jeremiah *must* have had a hand in Josiah's reform is unlikely to conclude that this passage is anything more than a free composition of the deuteronomic editor.

2. *the words of this covenant* (cf. vv. 6, 8) is an expression charac-teristic of the deuteronomic editor (Deut. 29[1, 9]; 2 Kgs. 23[3]; Jer. 34[18]) and means the laws contained in the Deuteronomic Code. It has been suggested, however, that *this covenant* refers to the Sinai covenant (Exod. 24[1–11]) as something independent of, or even hostile to, Deuteronomy. This is improbable, since even the Exodus is described in deuteronomic language (cf. vv. 4, 7).

3. *Cursed be the man*: cf. Deut. 27[26].

4. The *iron furnace*, as a figure for Israel's bondage in Egypt, is peculiar to the deuteronomic editors (Deut. 4[20]; 1 Kgs. 8[51]).

5. The whole verse is deuteronomic. Yahweh's *oath* or promise of Canaan to the patriarchs (Gen. 12[7]) is referred to in Deutero-nomy with great frequency (1[35], 6[10], 7[13], 9[5], 11[9]); *a land flowing with milk and honey*: cf. Deut. 6[3], 11[9]; Josh. 5[6]; Jer. 32[22]; *as at this day*: cf. Deut. 2[30], 4[20], 8[18]; 1 Kgs. 3[6], 8[24]; Jer. 25[18], 32[20]; *So be it* ('Amen'): cf. Deut. 27[15–26].

7. *Obey my voice* is another familiar deuteronomic expression (Deut. 8²⁰, 13⁴, 15⁵, 26¹⁴, 28¹⁵). The Greek omits vv. 7, 8 (probably by accident).

8. It is probable that the deuteronomist is here explaining the Exile as the consequence of disobedience (cf. Deut. 28¹⁵⁻⁶⁸; 2 Kgs. 17⁷⁻¹⁸).

11. 18–12. 6 *The plot of Jeremiah's kinsmen*

Two loosely related passaged (11¹⁸⁻²³, 12¹⁻⁶), now in some disorder, reveal for the first time the external opposition and inner turbulence which characterize Jeremiah's existence. They reflect the isolation out of which his independence was born— the loss of the conventional and the familiar by which he found himself. There are six personal laments in the book of Jeremiah, of which this is the first (cf. 15¹⁰⁻²¹, 17¹⁴⁻¹⁸, 18¹⁸⁻²³, 20⁷⁻¹¹, ¹⁴⁻¹⁸).

18. It has been suggested that the last verse of this section (12⁶) should follow v. 18 to give the content of Yahweh's warning to Jeremiah.

19. Jeremiah was *like a gentle lamb* in the sense that, being ignorant of his fate, he put up no resistance (cf. Isa. 53⁷). For *the tree with its fruit*, read 'the tree when it is still in sap', i.e. young.

20. In an outburst of impassioned poetry, Jeremiah prays to be avenged. Only those who have equally committed their cause to God are in a position to criticize this recurrent feature of the prophet's prayer (12³, 17¹⁸, 18²³, 20¹¹).

21. *the men of Anathoth, who seek my life* (so read with the Greek) are said to have been incensed by Jeremiah's prophesying. Since he was nearly put to death after his Temple sermon (26⁷⁻²⁴) and went about saying that the flesh of sacrifice would not avert the people's doom (11¹⁵), the hostility of his priestly kinsfolk requires no complicated explanation (cf. Mark 3²¹; Luke 4¹⁶⁻³⁰; Matthew 10³⁴⁻³⁶).

12. 1–6. Jeremiah's disputation with Yahweh on the prosperity

of the wicked is only loosely attached to the preceding verses and (especially if v. 3 belongs with 11²⁰ and v. 6 with 11¹⁸) probably had an independent origin. *Why does the way of the wicked prosper?* Although this agonizing question springs from the prophet's personal experience (cf. v. 5) and its formulation here probably antedates comparable references in the Old Testament (Pss. 73³⁻¹², 37¹; Hab. 1¹³; Job 12⁶, 21⁷; Mal. 3¹⁵), the problem had been raised in educated 'wisdom' circles outside Israel many centuries earlier. For example, in the poem known as the *Babylonian Theodicy* (or, 'A Dialogue about Human Misery'), dated about 1000 B.C., we read: 'Those who neglect the god go the way of prosperity, while those who pray to the goddess are impoverished and dispossessed' (W. G. Lambert, *Babylonian Wisdom Literature*, p. 75).

3. If, as seems doubtful, this verse belongs to its present context, the wicked of v. 1 must be the prophet's personal enemies (cf. 11²⁰).

4. The thought is akin to that of the chaos poem of 4²³⁻²⁶ (cf. Hos. 4³), but its connexion with the present context is obscure. Instead of '*He will not see our latter end*', read with the Greek, 'God will not see our ways'. This sceptical denial (cf. 5¹²⁻¹⁴) comes, perhaps, from the prosperous wicked.

5. These two proverbial sayings represent Yahweh's reply to Jeremiah's expostulation. It is not an intellectual solution to the problem, but a challenge to face it with courage—for, indeed, there is worse to come. If the prophet cannot stand upright in favourable country, what will he do in difficult terrain?

6. This verse appears to belong to 11¹⁸⁻²³, probably after v. 18.

15. 10–21 *Jeremiah's lament and Yahweh's reply*

In this second lament, the prophet discloses the terrible burden and isolation of his ministry and in blaming God for his suffering approaches downright blasphemy. It should be noticed, however, that in the concluding verses, he records his awareness of Yahweh's stern rebuke no less faithfully than his initial sense of grievance. Jeremiah enables us to glimpse the cost of representing God among men and the agony of Gethsemane (cf. Mark 14³²⁻⁴²).

10. Like Job, Jeremiah laments that he had ever been born to be at odds with all the world (cf. 20¹⁴⁻¹⁸; Job 3¹⁻²⁶). 'Neither a borrower nor a lender be'; so the prophet had tried to avoid personal animosities.

11, 12. The RSV is based on a reconstruction of a very difficult text and represents Jeremiah as protesting that so far from deserving the hostility of his enemies, he has pleaded with Yahweh for them (v. 11; cf. 18²⁰). It is too much; his own *iron* cannot stand against the hard *iron from the north* (v. 12).

13, 14. These verses are an intrusion from 17³, ⁴.

15. *take vengeance for me*: see notes on 11²⁰.

16. Instead of *Thy words were found, and I ate them, and thy words became to me a joy*, read with the Greek: 'I have suffered reproach from them that despise thy words. Consume them, and let thy word be unto me a joy. . . .' The Hebrew expression *I am called by thy name* means 'I belong to you' (cf. 7¹⁰).

17. Jeremiah's isolation from society was the result of his prophetic vocation. The expression *thy hand was upon me* is often used to describe the ecstatic prophets' sensation of external compulsion (1 Kgs. 18⁴⁶; 2 Kgs. 3¹⁵; Ezek. 1³, 3¹⁴, ²², 8¹, 37¹; cf. Isa. 8¹¹), but here Jeremiah is describing a permanent state rather than an ecstatic moment. Conspicuously among the prophets, Jeremiah was personally identified with the word he proclaimed: *thou hadst filled me with indignation* (see notes on 20⁷⁻¹⁸).

18. Jeremiah's lament comes to a climax in the accusation that Yahweh is false and faithless, like a brook which does not supply the water it promises (cf. 2¹³, 20⁷; Job 6¹⁵⁻²⁰). The word *deceitful* is the negative of the word 'true' (see notes on 5³ and 20⁷).

19–21. Yahweh's reply to Jeremiah is a rebuke, a challenge, and a promise. He must turn away from this ignoble self-pity to God and then he will truly become his spokesman, divinely fortified against all the attacks of his ruthless enemies.

17. 9, 10, 14–18 *Taunts and self-torture*

It is illuminating to read the detached vv. 9, 10 as an introduction to the third of Jeremiah's personal laments (vv. 14–18). To the taunts of his enemies (v. 15) is added the torture of self-accusation. Jeremiah, it seems, had come to suspect his own motives in proclaiming the people's doom (v. 16). Was it spite, or was it prophecy? Was he speaking for God, or merely out of the unfathomable depths of his own heart?

9, 10. Who can tell, asks the prophet, what a man's true motives are? God alone knows.

14–18. The prophet begins to pray in the simplest terms for the healing of his own deceitful heart (v. 9), but is immediately side-tracked by the desire to deny that he needs it. Yahweh knows that he neither asked for nor wanted the doom he proclaims. The unnecessarily literal RSV translation of the second half of v. 16 merely means 'you know everything I said'. The imprecation of v. 18 comes from a man who is being taunted by his own kinsfolk and (what is worse) tortured by his own conscience.

18. 18–23 *The prophet's bitter prayer for vengeance*

The prayer of this fourth lamentation differs from the foregoing only in the intensity of its bitterness. Although the imprecation against his persecutors and their families is undoubtedly horrifying (vv. 21–23), we are not justified in denying its authenticity. It bears witness not to Jeremiah's understanding of God, but to that extreme sensitivity which everybody is ready to praise when it finds expression in the prophet's deep human sympathy (see notes on 8¹⁸–9¹). Here are two sides of the same coin; we cannot have one without the other.

18. This prose note identifies Jeremiah's opponents as those who support the established leadership of Judah (cf. 2[8]; Ezek. 7[26, 27]; Mic. 3[11]; Zeph. 3[3, 4]), without, however, giving any further details of the occasion and date of their scheming against the prophet. Jeremiah's teaching shook the very foundations of Judean society and so it is hardly surprising that its chief representatives—priest, political counsellor, and institutional prophet—combined forces against him. *Come, let us smite him with the tongue* means 'attack him by slander'. If this is correct, the Greek version of the following words is to be preferred, since it omits *not* and gives the meaning: 'and let us give heed to all his words', in order, that is to say, to catch him out (cf. 20[10]).

20. Jeremiah had actually interceded for his countrymen (cf. 15[11], 17[16]; see pp. 240 f.).

21-23. See note on 11[20].

20. 7-18 *Jeremiah's vocation and its cost*

This section records the last two (the fifth and sixth) of Jeremiah's personal laments (vv. 7-11, 14-18). The first is a classical statement of prophetic experience so terrifying in its extremes of compulsion to accept and freedom to reject that it seems impossible to conceive of this mode of revelation admitting of any further development. The second poem finds Jeremiah rejecting not God or his vocation but his own existence.

7-9. This is the most illuminating description in the Old Testament of the great independent prophets' overwhelming sense of divine constraint. They spoke because they had no alternative; they had not chosen a profession, but had been called by God. Their experience is analogous to that of Paul: 'Even if I preach the Gospel, I can claim no credit for it; I cannot help myself; it would be misery to me not to preach. If I did it of my own choice, I should be earning my pay; but since I do it apart from my own choice, I am simply discharging a trust'

(1 Corinthians 9¹⁶, ¹⁷, NEB; see notes on Amos 7¹⁰⁻¹⁷). *O Lord, thou hast deceived me.* The language is extremely strong: God has made a fool of Jeremiah, just as his opponents were hoping that he would be fooled into making a false move, so they could trap him (cf. v. 10).

9. The pressure of his message (cf. 23²⁹) and his opponents' mockery (v. 8) made him wish to abandon prophecy altogether, but the pressure of his divine vocation was greater. Jeremiah was torn and tortured, because in becoming God's spokesmen, the prophets suffered no diminution of personality but, rather, grew in sensitivity and self-awareness.

10, 11. Even Jeremiah's *familiar friends* (cf. 12⁶) were on the watch 'to seize upon some word of his as a pretext for handing him over' (Luke 20²⁰, NEB); but they will fail.

12, 13. These two verses are almost certainly editorial intrusions: v. 12 duplicates 11²⁰ and is a prayer; v. 13 is a fragmentary comment in the style of the psalms.

14–18. Jeremiah, like Job, curses the day of his birth (Job 3¹⁻²⁶).

16. The reference is to *the cities* of Sodom and Gomorrah (Gen. 19¹⁻²⁸; see notes on Amos 4¹¹).

17. Although it is extravagant for Jeremiah to blame the messenger who brought the news of his birth, *because he did not kill me in the womb*, it is no more so than the language of the poem as a whole.

22. 13–19 *Jeremiah on Josiah and Jehoiakim*

This courageous condemnation of the reigning king admirably illustrates the qualities which the independent prophets possessed in common. How it comes about that Jeremiah speaks with the accent of Amos is far from easy to explain, unless we suppose that they are both indebted to a common Yahwist tradition (see pp. 243–7). For Jehoiakim (609–598), see notes on 2 Kgs. 23³⁴⁻³⁷.

13, 14. These verses are valuable evidence for the social pretensions of the kings of Jerusalem, for the kind of palatial
building they regarded as a 'status-symbol', for the unscrupulous way they conscripted their subjects as unpaid labourers,
for the prophets' total rejection of these degenerate developments, and for their fearless integrity in speaking their mind.

15, 16. With withering scorn, Jeremiah asks Jehoiakim whether
it is 'keeping up with the Joneses' that proves him a king. This
'cedar-king' is not the man his father was. Josiah lived modestly,
ruled justly, and protected the poor: *and that is what is meant by
knowing God* (v. 16). This is one of the most illuminating verses
in the whole of the Old Testament. It summarizes the distinctive conviction of prophetic Yahwism that it is in right human
relations that God is known and served. The ancient world was
familiar (only too familiar) with religion; and it was also
familiar with morality. The startling novelty of prophetic
Yahwism is its assertion that the true God is indifferent to what
men think of as religion and more concerned than men about
morality. Morality is not social convention but knowledge
of God.

18, 19. This savage sentence on a savage king (cf. 36³⁰) was
contradicted in the event, at least according to one Greek text
of 2 Chron. 36⁸, which records that Jehoiakim was buried
decently and in order (cf. 2 Kgs. 24⁶). Since, however, this is
not prediction but prophetic affirmation, reinforcing the moral
judgement of the previous verses, the question of its literal
fulfilment is irrelevant and ought not to be raised.

23. 9–32 *Concerning the prophets*

Nearly all the information we possess about the institutional
prophets of Israel is derived from the independent prophets'
condemnations of them (in addition to this chapter, see Ezek.
13¹⁻¹⁶). It is therefore particularly ironical that attempts have
been made in recent years to deny that the great prophets can

be as sharply differentiated from their cultic namesakes as was formerly supposed. It has even been suggested, for example, that Jeremiah was 'on the staff' of the Jerusalem Temple. Anybody who believes that can believe anything. This is not to deny that the institutional prophets are more representative of Israelite prophecy *as a general phenomenon* than men like Amos, Hosea, Micah, Isaiah, and Jeremiah, and that in popular opinion and tradition the latter were simply regarded as an odd variety of the former. It is, however, unambiguous oracles such as those collected in this chapter which make it clear that the great prophets thought of themselves as men apart from prophets in general and this must be the starting-point of any serious attempt to understand them (see pp. 237–44).

9–12. Jeremiah is utterly shattered by the contradiction between what he knows of Yahweh's will and what he knows of the moral condition of his people, which is shared alike by prophet and priest.

10. For the idea that the natural order is affected by moral disorder, see notes on 12⁴.

11. The close connexion in Judah between *prophet and priest* is incontestable; what is contestable is the assertion of some recent scholars that it illuminates the role and preaching of prophets like Jeremiah (see pp. 234 f.). Just as prophetic guilds were to be found in the neighbourhood of the great sanctuaries in Israel (see notes on 2 Kgs. 2³, pp. 261 f.), so prophets were associated with the Temple and its priests in Jerusalem (Isa. 28⁷; 2 Kgs. 23²; Mic. 3¹¹; Zeph. 3⁴; Jer. 5³⁰, ³¹, 26⁷, ¹¹, 35⁴; Lam. 2²⁰). These Temple prophets probably took part in the conduct of worship, as some of the psalms are now thought to imply (see p. 141). Indeed, it was the belief of the Chronicler that the singers of the post-exilic Temple were their true successors (1 Chron. 25¹, ⁵; 2 Chron. 20¹⁴⁻²³, 34³⁰; cf. 2 Kgs. 23²). It should be noticed, however, that although Jeremiah associates prophet and priest with each other and with the Temple (*even in my house I have found their wickedness*, v. 11; cf. 5³¹), he

clearly distinguishes between them and uses language which suggests that, like 'the least' and 'the greatest', they stand at the opposite ends of a scale:

> For from the least to the greatest of them,
>   every one is greedy for unjust gain;
> and from prophet to priest,
>   every one deals falsely. (6¹³, 8¹⁰)

Even if their precise function is difficult to determine, Jeremiah's many references to prophets make it clear that in his day Jerusalem was swarming with them, but nothing he says allows us to suppose that he is to be reckoned among their number (2⁸, 5³⁰, ³¹, 6¹³, ¹⁴, 8¹⁰⁻¹², 14¹³⁻¹⁶, 18¹⁸, 27¹–28¹⁷).

13–15. The *prophets of Jerusalem* are worse than the paganizing prophets of Samaria, since instead of giving God's guidance to the people, they lead the way in wickedness. On *Sodom* and *Gomorrah*, see notes on Amos 4¹¹.

16–22. This further oracle on false prophets and their false optimism has been disturbed by the intrusion of vv. 19, 20, which also occur in 30²³, ²⁴.

17. '*It shall be well with you.*' On the *vain hopes* with which these self-made visionaries encourage the disobedient, see notes on 4¹⁰.

18. The *council of the Lord* (cf. v. 22) is a concept which is indebted both to the circles of the 'wise' (see notes on Prov. 3³²) and to pagan mythology (see notes on 1 Kgs. 22¹⁹⁻²³). In the latter, the gods are pictured as meeting in council and deciding the future course of events (cf. Job 1¹–2¹³). Jeremiah uses this model to describe the privilege of a true prophet; he is one who has been admitted to Yahweh's 'cabinet' and, therefore, has heard *his word* and has been sent to proclaim it (cf. vv. 22, 32; Isa. 6⁸). The fact that *sôdh* (the Hebrew for *council*) is used by Jeremiah in its more usual meaning of ordinary groups of people (6¹¹, 15¹⁷; see p. 187) should warn us against exaggerating the technical status of the term in the prophet's thought.

23, 24. The primary meaning of this detached oracle seems to be that Yahweh is omnipresent and therefore inescapable (see notes on Amos 9$^{1-4}$). In its present context, it may be intended to affirm that the false prophets cannot escape Yahweh's judgement.

25–32. *What has straw in common with wheat?* This last oracle of the series contrasts the deceitful dreams of institutional prophecy with the directness and power of Yahweh's word in true revelation (for v. 29, see notes on 5$^{12-14}$). *Dreams* were highly valued in the ancient Near East; men sought them by spending the night in temples, collected them in books, and employed professionals to interpret them (cf. 1 Kgs. 3$^{4-15}$; Gen. 40^8, 41$^{15, 16}$; Dan. 2$^{1-45}$). The Elohist tradition of the Pentateuch attaches great importance to dreams as the way in which God communicates with man (cf. Gen. 20^3, 28$^{11, 12}$, 31$^{10-13, 24}$, 46$^{1-4}$) and this emphasis probably reflects their status in northern prophetic circles during the ninth century B.C. (Num. 11$^{26-30}$, 12$^{6-8}$; cf. Gen. 20^7). Although, as is evident from the present passage, dreams remained the stock-in-trade of institutional prophecy throughout the pre-exilic period (cf. Jer. 27^9, 29^8; Deut. 13$^{1-5}$), they are totally foreign to the great independent prophets who, in terms of the contrast presented by the Elohist in Num. 12$^{6-8}$, stand not with the prophets but with Moses, to whom, it is said, Yahweh spoke 'mouth to mouth, clearly, and not in dark speech'.

26. 1–24 *Jeremiah's Temple sermon and its sequel*

This lively narrative describes how Jeremiah preached his decisive sermon against the Temple, of which a full account is given in 7$^{1-15}$ (see notes), and how, as a result, the ecclesiastical establishment of priests and prophets hauled him before the king's officials to be tried for treason. The civil authorities, with the backing (it is said) of certain elders who were able to quote a precedent in Jeremiah's favour, refused to yield to the clamour of the Temple hierarchy and acquitted the prophet.

1. *In the beginning of the reign of Jehoiakim.* Since the phrase *begin-ning of the reign* is the exact equivalent of a Babylonian expres-sion meaning the odd months between the king's accession and the beginning of the New Year from which the reign was formally dated, it is adequate to paraphrase: 'In the first year of the reign of Jehoiakim', i.e. 609 B.C. (see notes on 2 Kgs. 23³⁴⁻³⁷). The suggestion that Jeremiah launched his attack at Jehoiakim's actual enthronement during the New Year Festival is imaginative but implausible. The king's officers would surely have been present in the Temple on so great an occasion and not at their desks in the cabinet offices (v. 10; cf. 36¹²).

4–6. These verses give a deuteronomic summary of the sermon (see notes on 7¹⁻¹⁵).

7–9. *The priests and the prophets and all the people* accuse and seize Jeremiah in the Temple. For the Temple *prophets*, whom the Greek version simply calls 'false prophets', see notes on 23¹¹. *the people*, here on the side of the priests and prophets, are on the side of the king's officers later in the story (vv. 11, 12, 16).

10. *the princes of Judah* were not, as the translation suggests, members of the royal family, but senior government officials (cf. v. 24), who acted as magistrates 'at the gate' (see pp. 202 f.). It was at the *New Gate* of the Temple that Gemariah, one of the magistrates, had an office (cf. 36¹⁰).

12–16. The narrative of the trial and acquittal of Jeremiah, revealing the prophet's dignified assurance and restraint, pro-vides an illuminating background to the narratives of the trial of Jesus before Pilate (Mark 15¹⁻¹⁵; John 18²⁸⁻³⁸).

17–24. The magistrates' verdict in Jeremiah's favour (v. 16) is followed by the stories of two other prophets who had pro-claimed the doom of Jerusalem. The first about *Micah* provided a precedent for Jeremiah's acquittal (vv. 17–19) and the second, about the fate of *Uriah*, illustrated the grave danger from which Jeremiah had so narrowly escaped (vv. 20–23). The narrative is unexpectedly rounded off with the statement that Jeremiah owed his release to *Ahikam* (v. 24; cf. v. 16). Although it would be rash to rule out the possibility that Micah's prophecy of doom was remembered and used a century after it was first delivered, three features of the story suggest that it originated in later tradition: (i) The 'elders of the land' are shadowy figures who appear very suddenly and (in view of Jeremiah's acquittal by the magistrates) quite unnecessarily (v. 17). (ii) The oracle of Mic. 3^{12} is quoted exactly (v. 18) and this suggests deliberate literary composition, rather than a contemporary record of what the elders on the scene were able to remember. (iii) Hezekiah's piety and the deliverance of Jerusalem in 701 B.C., which are hinted at in v. 19, are celebrated at greater length in the deuteronomic history of his reign (see notes on 2 Kgs. 18–19). About the story of Uriah little can be said with confidence. It is anchored to history only by the names of *Jehoiakim* and *Elnathan*, one of the king's officers (v. 22; cf. $36^{12, 25}$), and has every appearance of being an early example of the legends which sprang up in great profusion later about the martyrdom of prophets (cf. 2 Chron. 24^{20-22}; Luke 11^{47-51}). The inconsequential note in v. 24 inspires confidence and suggests that the writer of the account as it now stands was at least an admirer of *Ahikam*, whose remarkable family played so central a role in the deuteronomist's story (see p. 351 and notes on 36^{1-32}; 2 Kgs. 22^3).

29. 1–7, 24–32 *Jeremiah's letter to the exiles*

Jeremiah's quietly confident letter to the exiles and Shemaiah's outraged reply illustrates the contrast between two different kinds of theology. Jeremiah's faith in Yahweh was sufficiently profound to be quite independent of Jerusalem and its cultic tradition; according to the popular view represented by Shemaiah, however, Judah's religion was unthinkable apart from the Temple. For Shemaiah, the return of the Jewish exiles from Babylon was an absolute necessity; for Jeremiah it was no urgent matter, although he was hopeful that some day it would occur.

1–3. Jeremiah's letter was addressed to *the exiles* who had been taken to Babylon in the first deportation of 597 B.C. (figs. pp. 128, 353). *Jeconiah* is an alternative form of Jehoiachin (cf. 24¹, 27²⁰, 28⁴), who surrendered to Nebuchadrezzar after a reign of only three months (see notes on 2 Kgs. 24⁸⁻¹⁷). The prophet's letter was taken by the king's officers on one of their diplomatic missions to Nebuchadrezzar, to whom Zedekiah (597–587) owed his throne. *Elasah* was a member of the great Shaphan family (see notes on 2 Kgs. 22³).

4–7. The prophet's letter urged the exiles to settle down in Babylonia and live their normal lives. They must ignore the spurious promises of the prophets who are stirring them to rebellion (cf. vv. 8, 9, 24–32) and *pray* for the Babylonian cities with whose welfare their own is now bound up. Never was so far-reaching a religious revolution expounded in so short a document. Jeremiah knew from his own experience and now just takes it for granted that communion with God was independent of the religion of the Temple and, therefore, unaffected by the exiles' removal to a foreign land (see notes on 2 Kgs. 5¹⁷, p. 264). This insight represents not only a turning-point for the future development of Judaism, but the triumph of a faith grounded in history over the sanctuary-based religion of the ancient Near East.

24–32. *Shemaiah*, a nationalist prophet among the exiled Jews in Babylonia, had written to *Zephaniah*, 'second priest' of the Temple (cf. 2 Kgs. 25¹⁸), rebuking him for not keeping Jeremiah under control and especially for allowing him to send his 'defeatist' letter to the exiles (cf. vv. 4–7). Zephaniah read this letter to Jeremiah (v. 29). His response is recorded in vv. 24–28. A further oracle addressed to the exiles, warning them against Shemaiah's false prophecies and declaring his doom, is given in vv. 30–32. *To Shemaiah* (v. 24). It is preferable to read 'Concerning Shemaiah', since the oracle of vv. 24–28 is *about* Shemaiah and his letter and is not addressed to him.

25. *Zephaniah*, the 'second priest', was clearly an important

figure in Jerusalem and was among those executed by Nebuchadrezzar after the fall of Jerusalem (cf. 21¹, 37³; 2 Kgs. 25¹⁸⁻²¹).

26. Nothing is known of *Jehoiada*, but another Temple overseer had put Jeremiah *in the stocks* (cf. 20¹⁻⁶). The phrase *every madman who prophesies* may reflect the common opinion of raving prophets in general (see notes on 1 Kgs. 18²⁹, p. 256), but since Shemaiah himself was a prophet (cf. v. 31), it is more probably a contemptuous description of independent prophets who, like Jeremiah, held 'eccentric' and treasonable opinions.

31. Shemaiah is dismissed as a false prophet whom Yahweh did not *send* to his people (see notes on 23⁹⁻³²).

32. *the good that I will do to my people*, which Shemaiah will be deprived of descendants to enjoy, reveals Jeremiah's confident expectation that the exiles would be restored (see notes on 32¹⁻¹⁵).

31. 31–34 *The New Covenant*

The essential affirmation of this familiar and influential oracle is the promise that Yahweh would inaugurate a new era in the relationship between Israel and himself, by endowing every member of his people with the capacity to respond to his will. It is Jeremiah's statement of the doctrine of grace (cf. Hebrews 8⁸⁻¹³, 10¹⁵⁻¹⁷; 2 Corinthians 3⁶, 5¹⁷).

At the beginning of the century, a vigorous battle was fought over the passage. A few scholars dismissed it as an insignificant composition by an exilic scribe, while the majority asserted that it was the highest expression of Jeremiah's conception of religion as the relation between God and the individual soul. The presuppositions underlying both these views are highly questionable. It cannot be assumed that scribal teaching was regarded by Jeremiah as inferior and alien; nor can it be taken for granted that 'individualism' is either the highest form of religion, or the goal which prophecy finally achieved in Jeremiah's teaching.

(i) It is now recognized that in this, as in many oracles of the book, we cannot disentangle the teaching of Jeremiah from the form in which his editors have recorded it. The degree to which it has been changed in this editorial process cannot, therefore, be determined, but there are good grounds for thinking that it has not been completely falsified. (ii) It is clear that the new covenant is represented as fulfilling the aims of those who tried to teach the law and that the primary contrast in these verses is not between two different kinds of knowledge but between two different kinds of *response*—disobedience and obedience. (iii) The subsidiary contrast is that in the future *all* Israel will know and take to heart Yahweh's teaching (cf. Isa. 54[13]: 'All your sons shall be taught by the Lord'), whereas at the present only a privileged minority ('the great' as distinct from the common folk, cf. 5[4, 5]) have the opportunity of learning 'the law of their God' and even they reject it. The consummation of the 'coming days' is not the individualizing of religion, but the universalizing of the knowledge of God. The teacher will be Yahweh; every Israelite will know his law by heart; and every Israelite will live by it. The emphasis falls on Yahweh's achieving his final purpose by empowering the whole of his people to respond to it (cf. Joel 2[28, 29]; Ezek. 11[17-21], 36[26-28], 37[1-14]).

31. The *new covenant* is to be made with the whole people of God and not simply with the individual. If, as some suggest, the phrase *and the house of Judah* is an editorial gloss, it nevertheless correctly interprets *the house of Israel* (cf. v. 33) as including the whole people.

32. The deuteronomic editors, who supplied the actual language of this oracle, were at one with Jeremiah and his prophetic predecessors in ascribing Israel's unique relationship with Yahweh to his gracious deliverance of the people from *the land of Egypt* (see notes on Deut. 7[7, 8] and see pp. 64-67). The pre-exilic prophets, however, did not use the formal term *covenant*. The clause *though I was their husband* (cf. 3[14]) is uncertain; the Greek, which was used by the writer of the Epistle to the Hebrews, has 'so that I abandoned them' (Hebrews 8[9]).

33. *I will write it upon their hearts*. The *law*, which expounded Israel's obligation as the people of God, will no longer be external to them and ignored by them, but will be set *within them*, made part of them and become, as it were, 'second nature' to them (see notes on Prov. 4²⁰⁻²³). It is not a new law which is promised, but the fulfilment of the purpose of the old law in the willing response of a people regenerated by Yahweh (cf. Ezek. 36²⁶⁻²⁸). *I will be their God, and they shall be my people* is the essential formula of Yahweh's covenant with Israel (cf. 7²³).

34. This verse makes the previous promises more explicit. To say that the law will be written upon the hearts of the people is to say that they will no longer need human teachers and that not only the privileged few but all men—*from the least of them to the greatest*—will be brought to the knowledge of God (cf. 6¹³; see notes on 5⁴, ⁵). This new covenant established by enabling grace marks a new beginning: *I will remember their sin no more*.

32. 1–15 *Jeremiah's confidence in Judah's future*

Jeremiah's purchase of a piece of family property, with all the regular legal formalities at a time when Jerusalem was besieged by Nebuchadrezzar's forces and on the point of capitulating, is excellent evidence for his confidence that despite appearances all was not lost (see p. 354). The significance of the whole episode, which clearly accounts for its preservation, is stated in the final verse: 'Houses and fields and vineyards shall again be bought in this land' (v. 15). The incident is also excellent evidence for the view that the symbolic actions of the great independent prophets were dramatic presentations of personal convictions, rather than irrational acts only once removed from their origin in imitative magic (see pp. 239 f.).

1, 2. The *tenth year of Zedekiah* means late in 588 B.C. The siege of Jerusalem began at the end of the ninth year of Zedekiah's reign in January 588 B.C. (see notes on 2 Kgs. 25¹⁻³).

3–5. These editorial verses represent a not very accurate attempt to sketch in the historical background of the chapter. Jeremiah was imprisoned not by Zedekiah, who was well disposed to him (cf. 37$^{16-21}$, 38$^{14-28}$), but by his officers for what they regarded as the prophet's treasonable activity (see 37$^{11-15}$, 38$^{1-13}$).

6–8. Apparently, Jeremiah's cousin Hanamel had fallen into debt and was forced to sell part of the family property at *Anathoth* (see notes on 1$^{1-3}$). To keep the field in the family, Jeremiah as next-of-kin was asked to buy it (cf. Ruth 4$^{1-9}$; Lev. 25^{25}; see p. 41).

9–14. This is the only record of a written contract in the Old Testament, although they must have been widely used in Israel, as they were throughout the ancient Near East. It is also the first example of a papyrus deed made out in duplicate, for which the evidence otherwise comes from Egypt over three centuries later. The point of making two copies, one *sealed* and the other *open* (vv. 11, 14), was to enable the document to be consulted without the risk of falsification. The sealed copy was the authoritative one to be opened only in case of a dispute. The use of *an earthenware vessel* (v. 14) for the safe-keeping of documents is well attested by archaeological finds and illustrated by the jars (two feet high and nearly a foot wide) in which the Dead Sea Scrolls were discovered in 1947. On *Baruch* (v. 12), see notes on 36^4.

15. Jeremiah interprets the sealing and preservation of the deeds of purchase as a sign that, despite Judah's imminent capitulation to Babylon, there was a future for the people in their own land.

36. 1–32 *Baruch's scroll*

The artistic unity of this chapter suggests that it is a deliberate composition by the deuteronomic editor, written with the two-fold purpose of demonstrating that Judah finally rejected Yahweh's warning through his prophet Jeremiah and of asserting the authority of the deuteronomic collection of his oracles. To what extent the writer draws on historical evidence from the lifetime of Jeremiah, it is quite impossible to determine. The information it gives must, therefore, be used with caution for any general statements about the recording and preservation of prophetic oracles. It cannot be said, for example, that prophetic oracles were here committed to writing for the first time and then only because the political situation in the last days of Judah demanded it, nor can it be said that the dictation of Baruch's scroll marks the end of the oral transmission of prophetic teaching. Nevertheless, even if this chapter was composed during the period of the Exile, it does at least indicate that it was not then unthinkable to describe a prophet as dictating his oracles to a scribe. Although in this case the making of a prophetic book is related to special historical circumstances, the writer never suggests that it was an innovation requiring explanation or apology. It is reasonable, therefore, to suppose that the oracles of earlier prophets had been similarly committed to writing (see pp. 244–7).

1–8. *The writing of the scroll. The fourth year of Jehoiakim* probably ended in September 605 B.C. Earlier this year, at the battle of Carchemish, Babylon had routed Egypt. Judah, having thus lost its only ally, was totally exposed to Babylon and the will of its new king, Nebuchadrezzar (605–562). The historical setting of this chapter is, therefore, one of acute crisis.

2, 3. The *scroll* was made by joining single sheets of papyrus. It was to contain all Jeremiah's oracles against Jerusalem (so read with the Greek instead of *Israel*) and Judah from the very beginning of his ministry (see notes on 1^{1-3}), and it represented a final bid to provoke Judah to penitence before it was too late (cf. v. 7).

4. *Baruch*, Jeremiah's faithful servant and scribe ($32^{12, 13}$; 45^{1-5}), had a brother in the king's service (51^{59}) and so, presumably, came from a fairly prominent Jerusalem family. After the murder of Gedaliah, he accompanied Jeremiah to Egypt (43^{1-7}).

5, 6. It is not surprising that Jeremiah was debarred from the Temple. Baruch is to go there in his place and read the oracles on a *fast day*, when a large crowd would be assembled.

9, 10. *The reading of the scroll in the Temple*. The *ninth month* of the calendar year (beginning in the spring) probably came early in the *fifth* regnal year of Jehoiakim (beginning in the autumn), that is to say, December 605 B.C. The fact that Baruch read the scroll *in the chamber of Gemariah the son of Shaphan the secretary* (presumably in the doorway) again illustrates the friendliness of the Shaphan family (see notes on 2 Kgs. 22³).

11–19. *The reading of the scroll in the Secretary's room*. After hearing Micaiah's report of the contents of the scroll, the king's officials (not *princes*) have Baruch brought in to read it to them. When they hear it, they are terrified (v. 16) and decide that they must go and inform the king immediately. It has been suggested that their purpose was to report Jeremiah as a menace to public morale, but, in view of the writer's emphasis on their friendly attitude to Jeremiah and Baruch (vv. 19, 20, 25), it is more probable that he wishes us to conclude that they were pious men who responded to Yahweh's warning as Jeremiah intended they should (cf. vv. 3, 7).

20–26. *The reading of the scroll to the king*. The detail of v. 22 confirms the interpretation of the *ninth month* (cf. v. 9) as December. The whole description of the scene, with the king's repeated action in v. 23, is intended to convey Jehoiakim's arrogant contempt for the prophet's words. All you needed to deal with prophecy was a penknife and a brazier. In v. 24, the writer explicitly contrasts the indifference of the king and his immediate courtiers (*his servants* are distinguished in the Hebrew from *the princes* of vv. 12, 19, 21) with the holy terror of the officers in v. 16 and also (by implication) with the horror of Josiah, who rent his clothes on hearing the contents of the deuteronomic law book (2 Kgs. 22¹¹). The appeal of the king's officers (v. 25), his plot to get rid of Jeremiah and its frustration (v. 26) round off the central section of a splendidly controlled and successful piece of writing.

27–32. *The rewriting of the scroll.* In v. 29, the writer at last comes out with the underlying cause of the whole incident. Strictly speaking, the oracle against Jehoiakim in v. 30 was not fulfilled, since he was succeeded by his son, Jehoiachin, who reigned for three miserable months before surrendering to the Babylonians (see notes on 22$^{18,\ 19}$ and 2 Kgs. 24$^{8-12}$). The concluding statement, *and many similar words were added to them,* has enticed many scholars into efforts to isolate the original 'book of Baruch' (sufficiently short to be read three times in one day) from the material added later. They have never met with much success.

37. 1–45. 5 *The last years of Jeremiah*

These chapters present an outline of the events of Jeremiah's last years, from the siege of Jerusalem (588 B.C.) to the assassination of Gedaliah (582 B.C.) and the final flight to Egypt (pp. 129–32). The following brief notes are intended as sign-posts to their content.

1–10. *The Babylonians will return.* In 588 B.C., when the Babylonians temporarily withdrew from Jerusalem on the arrival of the Egyptian army, Jeremiah warned Zedekiah that all hopes of escaping capture by the Babylonians were wholly unwarranted. The episode of 34$^{8-22}$ also belongs to this occasion.

11–15. *Arrest and imprisonment.* Taking advantage of the temporary withdrawal of the Babylonian army, Jeremiah left the city to visit his family property, but was arrested as a deserter and put into an improvised prison at the house of Jonathan.

16–21. *Secret interview with Zedekiah.* Zedekiah called Jeremiah for interview in the hope of receiving an encouraging oracle. Although all the king got was the awful truth, he responded to the prophet's plea and had him transferred to a more comfortable prison near the royal palace. Jeremiah's purchase of the family property probably belongs to this period (see notes on 32$^{1-15}$).

38. 1–13. *Rescued from the pit.* Jeremiah, with the king's helpless connivance, was thrown into a pit for advising people to give themselves up to the Babylonian army. He was rescued from certain death by a foreigner in the royal service (again, with the encouragement of the vacillating king).

14–28. *Second secret interview with Zedekiah.* Jeremiah reaffirmed his counsel that only by the king's surrendering to the Babylonian army could the city escape destruction. At Zedekiah's request, Jeremiah told a pre-arranged 'white lie' to the king's officers, whose suspicions were aroused by the interview.

39. 1–40. 6. *The fall of Jerusalem and the fate of Jeremiah.* The narrative of vv. 1–10 is virtually identical with the account in 2 Kgs. 25^{1-12} (see notes). The names in v. 3 may be read as follows: 'Nergal-sharezer *the Simmagir,* Nebushazban *the Rab-saris,* Nergal-sharezer *the Rab-mag*', the italicized words being the titles of Babylonian court officials. According to the largely legendary story of 39^{11}–40^6, Jeremiah was released from prison by the special favour of Nebuchadrezzar (cf. 2 Kgs. 25^{27-30}), gave a reassuring oracle to the Ethiopian who had rescued him from the pit (39^{15-18}), was taken to Ramah by a highly deferential Babylonian officer with a strongly deuteronomic prose style, and, finally made his way to Gedaliah, the newly appointed governor of Judah, whose headquarters were at Mizpah.

40. 7–41. 18. *Gedeliah's governorship and assassination.* This reliable record of Gedaliah's five years' conciliatory government and brutal murder in 582 B.C. is briefly summarized in 2 Kgs. 25^{22-26} (see notes). In 41^{4-10}, there is an account of Ishmael's inexplicable slaughter of the pilgrims to Jerusalem, which, incidentally, gives valuable (because rare) information about loyal Yahwists in the old northern kingdom and their continued reverence for the Temple. Ishmael's fanatical revolt against Babylon was brought to an end by Johanan and his forces, who for fear of indiscriminate Babylonian reprisals planned a flight to Egypt (41^{11-18}).

42. 1–43. 7. *Flight to Egypt.* On being consulted by Johanan and his followers about where to go (42¹⁻⁶), Jeremiah *at the end of ten days* replies that they must stay in Judah and not go down to Egypt (42⁷⁻²²). The prophet's counsel is rejected and he and Baruch are compelled to accompany the party to Tahpanhes, a fortress on the Egyptian border (43¹⁻⁷).

43. 8–44. 30. *Jeremiah in Egypt.* Interpreting a symbolic laying of foundation stones for the throne of the king of Babylon, Jeremiah proclaims that Nebuchadrezzar, as Yahweh's servant, will conquer Egypt and clear it of idolatry, as a shepherd gets rid of the lice in his clothes (43⁸⁻¹³). The oracle in 44¹⁻¹⁴ is a heavy deuteronomic discourse rebuking Jews scattered all over Egypt for their disobedience. The insolent utilitarian defence of the worship of the Queen of Heaven which follows (44¹⁵⁻¹⁹) provides early detail of a type of cult which has proved extraordinarily persistent. Another late deuteronomic discourse (44²⁰⁻²⁸) is sealed by a sign against the Egyptian king, Hophra (Apries), who was assassinated in 569 B.C. (44²⁹, ³⁰).

45. 1–5. *Final oracle to Baruch.* Despite the date (605 B.C.) given in v. 1, this complaint of Baruch, followed by Yahweh's rebuke and final promise, has a valedictory air about it and is appropriately placed at the end of the book.

CHRONOLOGICAL TABLES

By R. J. COGGINS

In the tables which follow, these points should be noted:

1. Precise dating in the history of Israel is impossible before the ninth century. In particular the biblical dates of the kings of Israel and Judah, given in 1 and 2 Kings, contain inconsistencies which have been resolved in various ways. The dates given here are therefore bound to be approximations. For discussion of the main problems, reference must be made to the appropriate sections of each volume.

2. Where names of prophets are given, e.g. Amos, Hosea, this should be understood as referring to the lifetime of the prophet and *not* to the composition of the book which bears his name. This can very rarely be dated with any certainty.

3. The column headed 'Archaeological Evidence' simply lists the main points at which archaeological discovery has thrown light upon the history of Israel. For fuller information, with translations where appropriate, reference should be made to such works as D. W. Thomas (ed.), *Documents from Old Testament Times* (Nelson, 1958), and J. B. Pritchard (ed.), *The Ancient Near East* (O.U.P., 1959).

DATE	ISRAEL	NEIGHBOURING POWERS — Egypt	NEIGHBOURING POWERS — Other	ARCHAEOLOGICAL EVIDENCE
1800				
1700	Abraham	Hyksos Period c. 1720–1550	Babylonian Power c. 1700	Mari Documents 1750–1700 — Law Code of Hammurabi c. 1700
1600				
1500		XVIIIth Dynasty 1570–1310	Hurrian (Horite) Power	Nuzu Documents — Tablets from Ras Shamra (Ugarit)
1400	Jacob — Descent into Egypt c. 1370		Hittite Empire	Tell-el-Amarna Letters
1300		XXth Dynasty 1310–1200 — Rameses II 1290–1224 — Merneptah 1224–1216	✗ Qadesh-Orontes c. 1286	Merneptah Stele
1200	Exodus c. 1250, Moses — Entry into Canaan c. 1200 — Joshua	XXth Dynasty 1180–1065 — Rameses III 1175–1144 — Defeat of the Sea Peoples		
1100	Judges Period		Rise of Philistine Power	Wen-Amon c. 1100
1000	Saul c. 1020–1000, Samuel — David c. 1000–961 — Solomon c. 961–922	XXIst Dynasty 1065–935 — XXIInd Dynasty 935–725 — Shishak 935–914		Gezer Calendar

PATRIARCHAL PERIOD

DATE	JUDAH	ISRAEL	Egypt	Assyria	Damascus	ARCHAEOLOGICAL EVIDENCE
	Rehoboam 922–915 Abijam 915–913 Asa 913–873	Jeroboam I 922–901		Revival of Assyrian Power		
900		Nadab 901–900 Baasha 900–877 Elah 877–876 Zimri 876 Omri 876–869 Ahab 869–850			Ben-hadad I ?900–860	Melqart Stele
	Jehoshaphat 873–849			Shalmaneser III 859–824 ✗ Qarqar 853	Ben-hadad II ?860–843	Black Obelisk of Shalmaneser
	Elijah	Ahaziah 850–849 Joram 849–842			Hazael 843–796	Moabite Stone
	Jehoram 849–842 Ahaziah 842 Athaliah 842–837 Joash 837–800 Elisha	Jehu 842–815 Jehoahaz 815–801 Joash 801–786		Adad-Nirari III 811–783		
800	Amaziah 800–783 Azariah (Uzziah) 783–742	Jeroboam II 786–746			Ben-hadad III ?796–770	Samaria Ivories and Ostraca
	Amos Hosea	Zechariah 746–745 Shallum 745 Menahem 745–738 Pekahiah 738–737 Pekah 737–732		Tiglath-pileser III 745–727	Rezin c. 740–732 Fall of Damascus 732	
	Jotham 742–735 Ahaz 735–715 Isaiah (active c. 742–700) Micah	Hoshea 732–724		Shalmaneser V 727–722 Sargon II 722–705 Sennacherib 705–681		Siloam Inscription Taylor Prism of Sennacherib
	Hezekiah 715–687	Fall of Samaria 721	XXVth Dynasty 716–663			
700	Invasion of Judah 701 Manasseh 687–642			Esar-haddon 681–669 Ashur-banipal 669–633?		
	Amon 642–640 Josiah 640–609 Zephaniah Jeremiah (active 626–c. 580) Nahum Habakkuk		Sack of Thebes 663 XXVIth Dynasty Psammetichus I 663–609	Fall of Nineveh 612	*Babylon* Nabopolassar 626–605	
	Jehoahaz 609 ✗ Megiddo 609 Jehoiakim 609–598		Necho II 609–593		✗ Carchemish 605 Nebuchadrezzar II 605–562	Babylonian Chronicle

NEIGHBOURING POWERS

DATE	JUDAH		Egypt	Babylon	Persia	ARCHAEOLOGICAL EVIDENCE
600	Jehoiachin 598–597 (deported) Jerusalem captured 597. First Deportation					
	Zedekiah 597–587[1]		Psammeticus II 593–588			Lachish Letters
	Fall of Jerusalem 587[1]; Temple Destroyed; Second Deportation		Apries (Hophra) 588–569			
	Third Deportation 581	Ezekiel				'Jehoiachin' Tablets from Babylon
	The Exile			A-mel-Marduk 562–560		
		'Deutero-Isaiah'	Amasis 569–525	Nabonidus 556–539 Fall of Babylon 539	Cyrus 550–530	Cyrus Cylinder
	Return of some Jews? 537				Cambyses 530–522 Darius I 522–486	
	Temple rebuilt 520–515	Haggai Zechariah 'Trito-Isaiah'?	Egypt conquered by Persia 525			
		'Malachi'			Xerxes 486–465 Artaxerxes I 465–424	
	Governorship of Nehemiah 445–433, 432–?					Elephantine Papyri
	Sanballat I, Governor of Samaria		Egypt independent 401		Artaxerxes II 404–358	Samaria Papyri
400	Ezra's Mission 398[2]				Darius III 336–331	
	Alexander the Great conquers Palestine 333–2				Conquests of Alexander: ✕ Granicus 334; ✕ Issus 333; ✕ Gaugamela 331	

[1] = or 586.

[2] This may also be dated at either 458 or 428.

HELLENISTIC PERIOD

DATE	JUDAH	NEIGHBOURING POWERS			ARCHAEOLOGICAL EVIDENCE
		Ptolemies	*Seleucids*		
300	Ptolemies rule Palestine	Ptolemy I Soter 323–285	Seleucus I 312–281		Zeno Papyr
		Ptolemy II Philadelphus 285–246	Antiochus I 281–261		
			Antiochus II 261–247		
		Ptolemy III Euergetes 246–221	Seleucus II 247–226		
			Seleucus III 226–223		
		Ptolemy IV Philopator 221–203	Antiochus III 223–287		
			⚔ Raphia 217		
200	Seleucids rule Palestine	Ptolemy V Epiphanes 203–181	⚔ Panium 198		
			Seleucus IV 187–175		
	Profanation of the Temple 167 (?168)		Antiochus IV Epiphanes 175–163		
	Maccabaean Revolt				
	Book of Daniel 167/4				
	Rededication of the Temple 164 (?165)				
		Rome	*Seleucids*		
	Hasmonean Rulers		Antiochus V Eupator 163–162		
	Judas Maccabaeus 166–160	?Qumran Sect established	Demetrius I Soter 162–150		Qumran Scrolls (?)
	Jonathan 160–143		Alexander Balas 150–145		
			Demetrius II Nicator 145–139,		
	Simon 142–134	Jewish Independence granted 142	129–125		
			Antiochus VI Epiphanes 145–142		
			(Tryphon 142–139)		
			Antiochus VII Sidetes 139–128		
100	John Hyrcanus I 134–104				
	Aristobulus I 104–103				
	Alexandra Jannaeus 103–76				
	Alexandra Salome 76–67				
	Aristobulus II 67–63				
	Pompey captures Jerusalem 63				
	Judah added to the Roman				
	Province of Syria				
	Hyrcanus II 63–40	Overthrow of Pompey 48			
		⚔ Philippi 42			
	Antigonus 40–37	⚔ Actium 31			
	Herod the Great 37–4 B.C.				

BIBLIOGRAPHY

The works marked ** are particularly recommended as an introduction to their subject and those marked * as also being suitable
for study in the preliminary stage.

I. INTRODUCTION

(i) *General*

***Oxford Annotated Bible*, ed. H. G. May and B. M. Metzger. Revised
Standard Version, with introductions, comments, cross references,
general articles, tables of chronology and of measures and weights,
and index (Oxford University Press, New York, 1962).

O. Eissfeldt, *The Old Testament: an Introduction* (Blackwell, 1965).

A. Weiser, *Introduction to the Old Testament* (Darton, Longman & Todd,
1961).

**G. W. Anderson, *A Critical Introduction to the Old Testament* (Duckworth, 1959).

*H. H. Rowley (ed.), *A Companion to the Bible* (2nd ed., T. & T. Clark,
1963; original ed. by T. W. Manson).

***Peake's Commentary on the Bible*, ed. M. Black and H. H. Rowley
(Nelson, 1962).

H. H. Rowley (ed.), *The Old Testament and Modern Study* (Clarendon
Press, Oxford, 1951).

M. Noth, *The Old Testament World* (A. & C. Black, 1966).

R. de Vaux, *Ancient Israel* (Darton, Longman & Todd, 1961).

*G. E. Wright, *Biblical Archaeology* (revised ed., Duckworth, 1962).

D. Winton Thomas (ed.), *Archaeology and Old Testament Study*
(Clarendon Press, Oxford, 1967).

J. Gray, *Archaeology and the Old Testament World* (Nelson, 1962).

*G. E. Wright and F. V. Filson, *The Westminster Historical Atlas to
the Bible* (revised ed., S.C.M. Press, 1957).

*L. H. Grollenberg, *Atlas of the Bible* (Nelson, 1956).

*H. G. May, *Oxford Bible Atlas* (Oxford University Press, 1962).

**H. H. Rowley, *Teach Yourself Bible Atlas* (English University Press, 1960).

J. B. Pritchard (ed.), *Ancient Near Eastern Texts* (2nd ed., Oxford University Press, 1955).

*D. Winton Thomas (ed.), *Documents from Old Testament Times* (Nelson, 1958).

*J. B. Pritchard (ed.), *The Ancient Near East in Pictures* (Princeton University Press, 1954).

The Interpreter's Dictionary of the Bible: An illustrated Encyclopedia in four volumes (Abingdon Press, 1962).

The New Bible Dictionary (The Inter-Varsity Fellowship, 1962).

(ii) *History*

M. Noth, *The History of Israel* (revised by P. R. Ackroyd, A. & C. Black, 1960).

*J. Bright, *A History of Israel* (S.C.M. Press, 1960).

Y. Aharoni, *The Land of the Bible* (Burns & Oates, 1966).

**E. L. Ehrlich, *A Concise History of Israel* (Darton, Longman & Todd, 1962).

(iii) *Economic and Social Developments*

R. de Vaux, *Ancient Israel*, Parts II and III (Darton, Longman & Todd, 1961).

*W. Corswant, *A Dictionary of Life in Bible Times* (Hodder & Stoughton, 1960).

*L. Koehler, *Hebrew Man* (S.C.M. Press, 1956).

**E. W. Heaton, *Everyday Life in Old Testament Times* (Batsford, 1956).

(iv) *Religious Traditions*

*G. E. Wright, *The Old Testament against its Environment* (S.C.M. Press, 1950).

*A. S. Kapelrud, *The Ras Shamra Discoveries and the Old Testament* (Blackwell, 1965).

J. Gray, *The Legacy of Canaan* (Brill, 1957).

*——*The Canaanites* (Thames & Hudson, 1964).

G. R. Driver, *Canaanite Myths and Legends* (T. & T. Clark, 1956).

S. H. Hooke (ed.), *Myth, Ritual and Kingship* (Clarendon Press, Oxford, 1958).

A. R. Johnson, *Sacral Kingship in Ancient Israel* (2nd ed., University of Wales Press, 1967).

R. E. Clements, *God and Temple* (Blackwell, 1965).

——, *Abraham and David* (S.C.M. Press, 1967).

G. von Rad, *Old Testament Theology* (vol. 1, Oliver & Boyd, 1962; vol. 2, 1965).

W. Eichrodt, *Theology of the Old Testament* (vol. 1, S.C.M. Press, 1961; vol. 2, 1967).

H. W. Robinson, *Inspiration and Revelation in the Old Testament* (Clarendon Press, Oxford, 1946).

H. Ringgren, *Israelite Religion* (S.P.C.K., 1966).

*N. K. Gottwald, *A Light to the Nations: an introduction to the Old Testament* (Harper, 1959).

**R. Davidson, *The Old Testament* (Hodder & Stoughton, 1964).

**P. R. Ackroyd, *The People of the Old Testament* (Christophers, 1959).

**G. W. Anderson, *The History and Religion of Israel* (The New Clarendon Bible, Clarendon Press, Oxford, 1966).

II. HISTORY

1 and 2 Kings

*N. H. Snaith, commentary in *The Interpreter's Bible* (Abingdon, 1954).

J. Gray, *I and II Kings* (S.C.M. Press, 1964).

**J. Mauchline, commentary in *Peake's Commentary* (Nelson, 1962).

G. von Rad, *The Problem of the Hexateuch*, chap. ix (Oliver & Boyd, 1966).

R. A. F. MacKenzie, *Faith and History in the Old Testament* (Oxford University Press, 1963).

For general histories, see under I (ii).

III. WORSHIP

(i) *General*

H.-J. KRAUS, *Worship in Israel* (Blackwell, 1966).

**A. S. HERBERT, *Worship in Ancient Israel* (Lutterworth Press, 1959).

*H. RINGGREN, *Sacrifice in the Bible* (Lutterworth Press, 1962).

R. DE VAUX, *Ancient Israel*, Part IV (Darton, Longman & Todd, 1961).

H. H. ROWLEY, *Worship in Ancient Israel* (S.P.C.K., 1967).

(ii) *The Psalms*

*A. R. JOHNSON, essay in *The Old Testament and Modern Study* (ed. H. H. Rowley, Oxford, 1951).

**G. W. ANDERSON, commentary in *Peake's Commentary* (Nelson, 1962).

S. MOWINCKEL, *The Psalms in Israel's Worship* (2 vols., Blackwell, 1962).

**J. H. EATON, *Psalms* (Torch Commentary, S.C.M. Press, 1967).

IV. WISDOM

(i) *General*

M. NOTH and D. WINTON THOMAS (ed.), *Wisdom in Israel and in the Ancient Near East* (Brill, 1955).

W. G. LAMBERT, *Babylonian Wisdom Literature* (Clarendon Press, Oxford, 1960).

W. MCKANE, *Prophets and Wise Men* (S.C.M. Press, 1965).

**J. C. RYLAARSDAM, essay in *Peake's Commentary* (Nelson, 1962).

G. VON RAD, *The Problem of the Hexateuch*, chaps. viii, xiv, xv (Oliver & Boyd, 1966).

W. M. W. ROTH, *Numerical Sayings in the Old Testament* (Brill, 1965).

*W. BAUMGARTNER, essay in *The Old Testament and Modern Study* (ed. H. H. Rowley, Oxford, 1951).

(ii) *The Book of Proverbs*

C. T. FRITSCH, commentary in *The Interpreter's Bible*, vol. 4 (Abingdon, 1955).

W .O. E. Oesterley, *Proverbs* (Westminster Commentaries, Methuen, 1929).

*J. C. Rylaarsdam, commentary in *Peake's Commentary* (Nelson, 1962).

**D. Kidner, *Proverbs* (Tyndale Old Testament Commentaries, Tyndale Press, 1964).

R. N. Whybray, *Wisdom in Proverbs* (S.C.M. Press, 1965).

V. LAW

(i) *General*

*W. Zimmerli, *The Law and the Prophets* (Blackwell, 1965).

M. Noth, *The Laws in the Pentateuch* (Oliver & Boyd, 1966).

A. Alt, *Essays on Old Testament History and Religion* (Blackwell, 1966).

J. J. Stamm and M. E. Andrew, *The Ten Commandments in Recent Research* (S.C.M. Press, 1967).

H. H. Rowley, *Men of God*, chap. 1 (Nelson, 1963).

(ii) *Deuteronomy*

*G. E. Wright, commentary in *The Interpreter's Bible*, vol. 2 (Abingdon, 1953).

*H. W. Robinson, *Deuteronomy and Joshua* (The Century Bible, T. C. and E. C. Jack, n.d.).

S. R. Driver, *Deuteronomy* (International Critical Commentary, T. and T. Clark, 1895).

G. von Rad, *Deuteronomy* (S.C.M. Press, 1966).

H. H. Rowley, *From Moses to Qumran*, chap. 6 (Lutterworth Press, 1963).

E. W. Nicholson, *Deuteronomy and Tradition* (Blackwell, 1967).

VI. PROPHECY

(i) *General*

J. Lindblom, *Prophecy in Ancient Israel* (Blackwell, 1962).

**C. Kuhl, *The Prophets of Israel* (Oliver & Boyd, 1960).

A. R. Johnson, *The Cultic Prophet in Ancient Israel* (2nd ed., University of Wales Press, 1962).

**R. B. Y. Scott, *The Relevance of the Prophets* (Macmillan, 1944).

M. Buber, *The Prophetic Faith* (Macmillan, 1949).

*N. W. Porteous, essay in *Record and Revelation* (ed. H. W. Robinson, Clarendon Press, Oxford, 1938).

——, essay in *Israel's Prophetic Heritage* (ed. B. W. Anderson and W. Harrelson, S.C.M. Press, 1962).

O. Eissfeldt, essay in *The Old Testament and Modern Study* (Oxford, 1951).

*H. H. Rowley, *The Servant of the Lord*, chap. 3 (2nd ed., Lutterworth Press, 1965).

——, *From Moses to Qumran*, chap. 4 (Lutterworth Press, 1963).

G. von Rad, *Old Testament Theology*, vol. 2 (Oliver & Boyd, 1965).

*R. E. Clements, *Prophecy and Covenant* (S.C.M. Press, 1965).

H. H. Rowley (ed.), *Studies in Old Testament Prophecy* (T. & T. Clark, 1950).

N. K. Gottwald, *All the Kingdoms of the Earth* (Harper & Row, 1964.)

G. Widengren, *Literary and Psychological Aspects of the Hebrew Prophets* (Uppsala Universitets Årsskrift, 1948).

*J. Muilenberg, essay in *Peake's Commentary* (Nelson, 1962).

*E. W. Heaton, *The Old Testament Prophets* (Pelican Books, 1958).

E. Nielsen, *Oral Tradition* (S.C.M. Press, 1954).

(ii) *Elijah and Elisha*

G. von Rad, *Old Testament Theology*, vol. 2, Part I b (Oliver & Boyd, 1965).

H. H. Rowley, *Men of God*, chap. 2 (Nelson, 1963).

(iii) *Amos*

*H. E. W. Fosbroke, commentary in *The Interpreter's Bible*, vol. 6 (Abingdon, 1956).

J. D. W. Watts, *Vision and Prophecy in Amos* (Brill, 1958).

R. S. Cripps, *The Book of Amos* (2nd ed., S.P.C.K., 1955).

S. L. Terrien, essay in *Israel's Prophetic Heritage* (ed. B. W. Anderson and W. Harrelson, S.C.M. Press, 1962).

(iv) *Hosea*

*P. R. ACKROYD, commentary in *Peake's Commentary* (Nelson, 1962).

J. MAUCHLINE, commentary in *The Interpreter's Bible*, vol. 6 (Abingdon, 1956).

A. C. WELCH, *Kings and Prophets of Israel* (Lutterworth Press, 1952).

**H. W. ROBINSON, *Two Hebrew Prophets* (Lutterworth Press, 1948).

H. H. ROWLEY, *Men of God*, chap. 3 (Nelson, 1963).

(v) *Micah*

**D. WINTON THOMAS, commentary in *Peake's Commentary* (Nelson, 1962).

R. E. WOLFE, commentary in *The Interpreter's Bible*, vol. 6 (Abingdon, 1956).

(vi) *Isaiah*

R. B. Y. SCOTT, commentary in *The Interpreter's Bible*, vol. 5 (Abingdon, 1956).

**J. MAUCHLINE, *Isaiah 1–39* (Torch Commentary, S.C.M. Press, 1962).

TH. C. VRIEZEN, essay in *Israel's Prophetic Heritage* (ed. B. W. Anderson and W. Harrelson, S.C.M. Press, 1962).

B. S. CHILDS, *Isaiah and the Assyrian Crisis* (S.C.M. Press, 1967).

(vii) *Jeremiah*

J. P. HYATT, commentary in *The Interpreter's Bible*, vol. 5 (Abingdon, 1956).

J. SKINNER, *Prophecy and Religion* (Cambridge University Press, 1922).

A. C. WELCH, *Jeremiah: his Time and his Work* (Blackwell, 1951).

J. BRIGHT, *Jeremiah* (The Anchor Bible, Doubleday, 1965).

**H. CUNLIFFE-JONES, *Jeremiah* (Torch Commentary, S.C.M. Press, 1960).

**H. W. ROBINSON, *The Cross in the Old Testament* (S.C.M. Press, 1955).

H. H. ROWLEY, *Men of God*, chap. 5 (Nelson, 1963).

INDEX OF SUBJECTS

Aaron, 73, 243
Abana, 263
Abel-beth-maacah, 102
Abiathar, 146, 354
Abibaal, 97
Abijam (Abijah), 65, 76 f.
Abilakka, 102
Abimelech, 34
Abraham, 157, 210, 256
Absalom, 2, 172
Accadian, 243
Achor, 59, 295
Acropolis (Athens), 217
Adad (Hadad), 108, 353
Adad-'idri (Ben-hadad II), 11
Adad-melech, 108
Adad-nirari III, 13, 15, 98
Adar, 128
Admah, 306
Administrative districts, 31 f., 86, 125
Adon, 127
Adoni-zedek, 146
Adoram, 72
Adrammelech, 103, 108
Aegean, 22
Africa, 159
Agriculture, 25, 39, 174
Ahab, 5, 11, 23 ff., 32 f., 45, 61 f., 65, 77 ff., 81–88, 92–95, 118, 143, 234, 249–55, 259 f.
Ahaz, 13, 16, 58, 102–5, 108, 116, 118, 123, 145, 227, 300, 308, 315 f., 321, 323, 331–5
Ahaziah (Israel), 62, 88
— (Judah), 88, 92–95
Ahijah, 61, 66, 70, 167
Ahikam, 120, 131, 354, 379
Ahikar, 167, 341

Ahithophel, 166, 172
Aleppo, 77
Allâh, 236
Allegory, 25, 326 f.
Alphabet, 29, 344 f.
Altar, 104, 135, 198, 271, 330
'amān, 362
Amaziah, 96, 143, 175, 281 f.
Amel-Marduk (Evil-Merodach),132
Amen-em-opet, Instruction of, 169 f., 186, 192 ff., 214, 310
Amman, 268
Ammon(ites), 1, 6, 16, 75, 97, 101, 103, 115, 118, 124, 127, 129, 266, 268
Amon-Re, 159
Amorites, 44, 117, 269
Amos, 35, 38, 55, 58, 85, 96 f., 99, 101, 107, 143, 146, 176, 178, 231 f., 237, 241–6, 248, 250, 264–85, 286, 299, 305, 307, 318–20, 322, 326, 329, 339, 355, 359, 373, 375
Amphictyony, 49
Amurru, 117
Anammelech, 108
Anat, 27, 44, 46 f.
Anathoth, 354, 361, 368, 384
Angels, 258
Anoint(ed), 4, 91 f., 145, 149, 151, 159, 162, 164, 258
Anti-Lebanon, 97, 263, 267
Anu(-melech), 108
Aphek, 11, 84
Apries (Hophra), 21
Aqhat, legend of, 27 f.
Arabah, 25, 33
Arabia, 11, 25, 33, 85, 104, 135, 138, 159, 235 f., 250, 357

Arallu, 347

Aramaic language, 77, 99, 114, 127, 167

Arameans, 1, 6, 10–13, 76 f., 82 ff., 91 f., 96, 102, 104, 107, 114, 248, 267, 289, 300, 333, 343; *also see* Damascus

Ararat, 115

Archaeology, related to the Old Testament, 5, 10, 23–27, 35 f., 78 ff., 82, 96, 98, 111, 128 ff., 132, 134, 174, 216, 226, 252, 278 f., 338 f., 340 f., 353

Architecture, 23–25, 27 f., 31, 35, 38, 52, 79, 140

Ariel, 347

Ark of Covenant, 72 f., 145, 147 f., 156, 162 ff., 255, 330, 365

Armenia, 115

Army, 4 ff., 30, 32, 34, 90–92, 217

Arnon, 12

Arpad, 114, 339

Arslan-Tash, 75

Asa, 7, 10, 54, 62, 76 f., 85

Asaiah, 121

Ashdod, 16, 20, 125, 267, 271, 316, 341 f.

Asherah, 44 f., 47, 75 f., 83, 95, 110, 116, 119, 122 f., 134 f., 189, 220, 234, 255, 293

Ashima(h), 107, 283

Ashkelon, 267

Ashur-banipal, 17, 20, 115 f.

Ashur-nasirpal II, 15

Asia, 235

— Minor, 20, 22, 25, 27, 226

Assyria(ns), 5–10, 13–17, 23, 25, 32, 39, 52, 56 f., 62, 69, 75, 81 ff., 85, 90 f., 96, 98–106, 108–11, 113–19, 122–6, 145, 148, 160, 167 f., 176, 200, 217, 239, 258, 267, 271, 277, 293, 300 f., 304–9, 311–19, 323, 331–4, 338

Astarte (Ashtoreth), 44, 71, 123, 190, 217, 293

Astrology, 116

Athaliah, 34, 85, 88, 94 ff.

Athens, 217

Athtar, 47

Avva, 107

Azariah, 98 f.; *also see* Uzziah

Azekah, 129 f.

Baal(ism), 27 ff., 32, 34, 44–48, 52, 83, 88 f., 93 ff., 97, 103, 108, 119, 122, 134 f., 139, 143, 154 f., 157, 171, 234, 249–57, 273, 286, 288, 291–9, 358, 364

Ba'ali-ra'si, 12

Baal-Milqart, 83

Baasha, 4, 10, 62, 76 ff., 81

Babylon(ians), 6, 16–21, 27, 40, 52, 56, 67, 101, 105 ff., 117 f., 123, 125–32, 147, 150, 155, 167, 169, 173, 182, 185, 190 f., 193, 200 f., 225, 239, 244, 258, 293, 338, 349, 352, 379, 388

Babylonian Chronicle, 128 f.

Babylonian Theodicy, 369

Baca, 162

Balikh, 267

Ban, 218

Barada, 263

Baruch, 174, 246, 351, 354, 384–7, 389

Bashan, 38

Beer-sheba, 78, 123, 257, 273, 283

Ben-hadad I, 10 f., 76 f.

Ben-hadad II, 11 f., 77, 82–85, 93

Ben-hadad III, 13, 267

Benjamin, 8, 71 f., 160 f., 300

Ben Sira, 170 f., 188, 195 f.

Beth-aven (Bethel), 299 f.

Beth-eden, 267

Beth-eked, 95

Bethel, 48, 64 f., 72 f., 75, 107, 122, 124 f., 143, 176, 233, 261, 271 ff., 299 f.

Beth-haggan, 93

Bethlehem, 163

Beth-shemesh, 39

Bit-adini (Beth-eden), 267
Black Obelisk, 90 f.
Boaz, 131, 140
Booths, Feast of, 137 ff.; *also see* Feast of Ingathering
Boundary stone, 40
Bozrah, 268
Bribery, 42
Bristol, 37
Bronze serpent, 110
Bull images, 48, 73 f.
Burial, 39, 268
Byblos, 23, 255

Calah (Nimrud), 15
Calneh (Calno), 277, 339
Calves of gold, 72 f.
Canaan(ites), land and people, 2, 5, 23, 30, 34, 39, 51, 56, 81, 95, 112, 145 f., 172, 201, 205, 209, 214, 221, 284
Canaanite craftsmanship and culture, 22 ff., 27 ff., 41, 169, 173, 185, 198 f., 201 f., 226 f., 229, 259, 269
— religion, 27–29, 32, 42–54, 63, 73, 76, 83, 87, 89, 93, 97, 103, 110, 116, 119, 122 f., 133 ff., 137–40, 148 f., 154–60, 163, 210 f., 215–18, 220, 222, 248–57, 272 f., 286, 291–9, 305, 314, 350, 356 f.
Caphtor, 55, 284
Capitals, proto-Ionic, 19, 23 ff., 80 f.
Carchemish, 20, 127, 339, 352 f., 385
Carthaginian inscriptions, 135
Chaldeans, 17, 127; *also see* Babylon
Chariots, 5, 278 f.
Chemosh, 71, 78, 124, 339
Cherith, 250
Cherubim, 15, 73, 156, 160 f., 163, 226
Cheti, *Instruction* of, 170
Chosen People, 156; *also see* Election
Christianity, 49, 51, 156, 189, 191, 197, 212, 296, 333 f.

Chronicler, 61 f., 95, 98 f., 119 f., 175, 217, 234, 257
Chronicles of the Kings, 60
Circumcision, 358
Communal Lament, 141, 160
— Thanksgiving, 141
Coniah (Jehoiachin), 127 f.
Conquest of Canaan, 197, 206, 212, 249
Coronation rite, 151 f.
Council of the Lord, 87, 154, 187, 376
Counsellors, 166, 172, 175 ff., 317, 331 ff., 372
Courts of law, 42, 199, 202 f., 259, 265, 273, 313
Covenant, 49 ff., 53 f., 59, 65 f., 71, 119, 122, 147 f., 162 ff., 205 f., 208, 215, 219, 293, 318 f., 367, 381 ff.; *also see* Davidic covenant
—, Book of the, 197–208, 223 f., 228 f.
Creation, 52, 150, 154 f., 165 f., 172, 179 f., 185, 188 ff., 191 f., 214, 273, 361
—, Babylonian Epic of, 185, 191
Crete, 194, 284
Cuneiform, 26 f., 128
Cuthah, 107
Cyprus, 80, 357

Dagon, 27, 29, 44, 46, 48, 135
Damascus, 1, 6, 8, 10–13, 15 f., 23, 25, 33, 61, 76–79, 82–86, 88, 90 f., 93, 96, 98, 100–4, 114, 258, 263, 266 f., 271, 300, 315–19, 321, 331–5, 339
Dan, 48, 64, 72 f., 75, 143, 361
Danel, 27 ff.
David, 1 ff., 6, 10, 17, 21, 23, 32, 78, 81, 85, 96, 112, 118, 126, 132, 233, 285, 297, 334, 346, 354
—, Court History of, 54, 172
Davidic covenant, 53, 65 f., 68, 72, 143, 145 f., 149–52, 158, 160, 162–4, 318, 322, 325, 336 ff.

Day of the Lord, 217, 274–7, 283, 305, 312, 319, 326, 343, 361
Dead Sea, 35 f., 97, 266
Dead Sea Scrolls, 27, 218, 384
Debir, 37 f.
Deborah, Song of, 1, 215
Debt, 194, 223, 229, 269
Deuteronomic history (1 and 2 Kings), 60–132
— school, 49, 54, 58, 63–69, 119 ff., 173, 351 f., 363–8
Deuteronomy, Book of, 51, 64 ff., 119 ff., 123 f., 173 f., 177, 187, 198, 202–30, 351, 357, 364, 386
Diblaim, 291
Divination, 104, 116 f., 119, 125, 236
Divorce, 294, 357
Dor, 102
Dragon, 155
Dreams, 377
Dyeing, 37

Ebal, Mount, 71
Ecclesiasticus, Book of, 171; *also see* Ben Sira
Economic development, 21–42, 89, 96 f.
Ecstasy, 86 f., 232–7, 241 f., 255 f., 282, 370, 381
Edom(ites), 1, 6, 11, 16, 24 f., 85, 88, 102, 104, 127, 129, 167, 266 ff.
Education, 54, 167–75, 206 f., 213 f., 245, 328 f., 344 f.
Egypt, 5 f., 10, 16 ff., 18–21, 24, 27, 32, 48, 61, 69 f., 71, 73, 75 f., 104 ff., 113 ff., 118, 125 ff., 129 f., 132, 143, 151 f., 176, 226, 255, 305 f., 316 f., 319, 341 f., 345, 348, 352, 385, 388 f.
Egyptian influence, 79 f., 88, 140, 159 f., 166 f., 169 f., 171, 173, 181 f., 185 ff., 192–5, 207, 214, 226, 253, 310

Ekron, 110, 125, 267
El, 27, 44, 46 f., 83, 135, 337
El Elyon, 52, 148, 156
El Hadad, 47
Elah, 4 f., 62, 81
Elamites, 343
Elasah, 120, 380
Elath (Ezion-geber), 24, 104
Election, 210 f., 215, 218, 270, 286 f., 304 ff., 307, 318 ff., 326 f., 349; *also see* Covenant
Elephantine colony, 107 f.
Eliakim, 113, 127, 132
Elihoreph, 167
Elijah, 41, 45, 61, 66, 82, 84, 89, 93 ff., 231 f., 245, 247–65, 291
Eliphaz, 191
Elisha, 61, 66, 91 f., 233, 239, 246–51, 258, 260–4, 291
Elishama, 167
Elnathan, 379
Elohist source, 377
Eltekeh, 113, 115
'ᵉmeth, 297
Endor, medium of, 116
Enthronement, 48, 148, 150
Ephod, 296
Ephraim, tribe of, 70, 160
Ephrathah, 163
Esar-haddon, 115, 338
Eschatology, 52, 59, 152, 158, 160, 217, 262, 274–7, 318, 326, 336 ff., 382
Eshbaal, 45
Ethbaal, 45, 83
Ethiopia(ns), 55, 114, 159, 284, 342
Euphrates, 20, 106, 125, 161, 168, 267, 335, 353
Evil-Merodach, 132
Exile in Babylon, 25, 37, 67 f., 126, 130 ff., 136, 139, 150, 206, 242 f., 245, 313 f., 332, 349, 368, 379 f., 387 ff.
Exodus from Egypt, 49, 55 f., 59, 64, 67, 138 f., 149, 160, 198, 202,

204 f., 208 f., 211, 218 f., 221, 224 f., 227, 232 f., 262, 269 f., 284, 288, 295, 304, 307, 318, 356, 367, 382
Ezekiel, 42, 132, 165, 231, 240, 284
Ezion-geber, 24, 33, 98, 102, 104
Ezra, 206

Faith, 227, 321 f., 333, 345
Family, teaching in, 51, 244
Fasting, 259 f.
Fate, 195
Father, teacher addressed as, 169, 323
Feast of Ingathering (Booths), 53, 72, 75, 137 ff., 143, 147 f., 150; *also see* New Year Festival
— of Passover, 119, 123 ff., 138
— of Unleavened Bread, 137 f.
— of Weeks, 137 ff.
Feasts, Festivals, 137 ff., 147–50
Fertility religion, 45–48, 89, 154, 250–7, 292 f.
First Fruits, 138
Flesh, 348
Flogging, 230
Forced Labour, 30 f., 72
Former Prophets, 69
Fort Shalmaneser, 19, 279
Fortifications, 7, 31, 57, 353
Fortune, 195

Galilee, 10, 77, 98, 102, 279
Gal'za, 102
Gate of city, 7, 31, 203, 353
Gath, 12, 267, 277
Gaza, 110, 125, 267
Geba, 30, 78, 123
Gebal (Byblos), 23
Gedaliah, 120, 127, 131 f., 354, 385, 387 f.
Gehazi, 264
Gehenna, 103 f.
Gemariah, 120, 378, 386
Gentiles, 132, 264, 275
Gerizim, Mount, 71

Gethsemane, 370
Gezer, 5, 30 f., 36 ff., 174
Gibeah, 233, 261
Gibeon, 36 f., 346
Gideon, 337
Gihon Spring, 111 ff.
Gilead, 102, 250, 268, 366
Gilgal, 49 f., 261, 272 f., 299
Gomer, 287–97
Gomorrah, Sodom and, 272, 306, 318 f., 323 f., 373, 376
Gozan, 106
Greece (Greek), 25, 51, 251, 315

Habakkuk, Book of, 239
Habor, 106
Hadad, 44, 75, 77, 108
Hadad-rimmon, 77, 104
Hadatu, 75
Hadyan, 77
Halah, 106
Hamath, 5, 12, 82, 96 ff., 107, 114, 277, 339
Hammurabi, Code of, 190, 200 f., 225 f.
Hanamel, 384
Hananiah, 129, 132, 242, 354
Hannah, 152
Hansen's Disease, 99
Haran, 125
Harmon, 272
Hatti, 128
Hazael, 12, 15, 91, 93, 96, 258, 267
Hazor, 5, 23 f., 29 ff., 36 f., 81, 102, 134, 140, 198
Hebrews, Epistle to the, 382
Hebron, 1 f.
Hena, 114
Hepatoscopy, 116 f.
Hermon, Mount, 155, 263
Herod, Temple of, 140
Herodotus, *History* of, 358
ḥeṣedh, 164, 219, 297, 302, 315, 356
Hezekiah, 5, 16 ff., 20, 36, 39, 54, 57, 61, 64, 108–16, 148, 167, 176,

181, 186, 195 f., 238, 289, 308, 315 f., 323, 335, 343, 379
Hiel, 83
High-places, 64, 133–9, 219 ff., 357
High Priest, 121
Hilkiah, 121
Hinnom, valley of, 103 f., 112, 343
Hiram, 23 f., 33
Hittite law, 200
Holiness Code, 223
Holy of Holies, 134, 140
— Land, 264
— War, 5 f., 86, 199, 210, 213, 215–19, 227 f., 275
Hophra (Apries), 21, 129, 389
Horeb, 205, 208, 249, 257 f.
Hosea, 4, 35, 45, 55, 59, 73, 93, 96 f., 99, 176, 179, 204 f., 213, 231, 237, 241, 244, 280, 285–306, 318, 322, 356 f., 375
Hoshea, 16, 102, 105 f., 161, 300
Host of Heaven, 47, 87, 116, 119
House of the Forest, 343
Huldah, 66, 68, 121
Humanism, 184, 230
Hushai, 172
Hydraulic engineering, 36 f., 108, 111 ff., 343
Hymns, 142

Ibleam, 93, 100
Ijon, 102
Imlah, 85
Immanuel, 333 f.
Individual Lament, 141, 152 f.
— Thanksgiving, 141
Instruction of Amen-em-opet, 169 f., 186, 192 ff., 214, 310
— *of Cheti the Son of Duauf*, 170
— *for King Meri-Ka-Re*, 169, 310
— *of Ptah-hotep*, 169, 187, 195
Inviolability of Jerusalem (Zion), 52 f., 148 f., 157 f., 164, 238, 313, 320 f., 339, 343, 346
Isaac, 256

Isaiah, 5, 35, 38, 54 f., 61, 99, 109 f., 113 f., 118, 146, 148 ff., 157 f., 166 f., 174, 176, 179, 196, 214, 227, 231, 234, 237 ff., 241 f., 248, 256, 307 f., 310, 315–48, 355, 359, 375
Ish-bosheth, 45
Ishmael, 132, 388
Ishtar, 90, 123, 293, 353
Ivories, 19, 24, 28, 79, 88, 216, 226, 271, 278 f., 292 f.
Ivvah, 114

J, Yahwistic source, 51
Jaar, 163
Jabbok, 72
Jabin, 29
Jachin and Boaz, 122, 131, 140
Jacob, 153, 163, 203, 210, 256, 283 f.
Jan-oah, 102
Jar handles, 33 f.
Jebusite, 110
Jeconiah, 380
Jedayah, 97
Jehoahaz (Israel), 12, 91, 96
— (Judah), 6, 20, 120, 127, 352
Jehoash, 13, 96, 289
Jehoiachin, 126 ff., 129, 132, 353, 380, 387
Jehoiada, 54, 95, 381
Jehoiakim, 20 f., 30, 32, 126 f., 352, 355, 364, 373 f., 378 f., 385 f.
Jehonadab, 94 f.
Jehoram (Judah), 85, 88 f., 104
Jehoshaphat, 24, 63, 85 f., 88, 92, 125
Jehu, 3 ff., 8, 12, 39, 49, 63, 66, 88–96, 100, 258, 289, 291
Jeremiah, 21, 25, 30, 45, 51, 54 f., 59, 95, 114, 119 f., 126 f., 129 ff., 146, 149, 152, 157, 174, 177, 179 f., 204 f., 212 f., 215, 231–47, 270, 281, 286, 313, 322, 348–89
Jericho, 37, 82 f., 130, 233, 248, 261
Jeroboam I, 48, 63, 69–76, 78, 143, 145

Jeroboam II, 4, 8, 13, 15, 35, 38, 96–98, 176, 265 f., 281, 286, 289, 291, 302

Jerusalem, plan of, 112; *also see* Inviolability of Jerusalem

Jesus, 196 f., 213, 215, 227, 327, 378

Jezebel, 23, 29, 45, 78, 82 f., 89, 93 ff., 143, 203, 234, 249 f., 254–9

Jezreel, 82, 91–94, 174, 250, 257, 259 f., 291

Joah, 113

Joash, 54, 95 f., 120 ff., 152

Job, 87, 182, 184, 191, 330, 370, 373

Johanan, 388 f.

Jonah, 66, 97 f.

Jonathan, 45

— (the secretary), 167

Joram (Israel), 12, 88, 90, 92 ff.

Jordan, 12, 33, 35 f., 72, 77, 92, 130, 205, 248, 261, 263, 268

Joseph, 165, 173

—, tribe of, 160, 273 f.

Joshua, 29, 70 f.

—, Book of, 32, 69, 125

Josiah, 6, 17, 20, 45, 54, 64 ff., 68 f., 108, 118–26, 129, 133, 149, 167, 212 f., 217, 351 f., 364, 366 ff., 373 f.

Jotham, 98 f., 103, 308

—, fable of, 34

Jubilee Year, 41

Judges, Age of the, 3, 6, 34, 49

—, Book of, 69

Kadesh, 155

Kaiwan, 277

Karnaim, 279

Kedar, 357

Kedesh, 102

Kenites, 95

Keret, 28, 123, 135

Kerioth, 268

Kidron Valley, 112, 122

Kings, Books of the, 60–132

King's Highway, 33

Kingship in Israel, 1, 21 f., 29–34, 89, 142, 143–6, 150, 151 f., 153 f., 158 ff., 165, 181, 184, 190, 202, 225 ff., 260, 286, 302 ff., 336 ff.

— of Yahweh, 52, 149 f., 152, 154 ff., 160, 165 f., 318, 324, 329 ff., 366

Kir, 55, 104, 267, 284, 343

Kiriath-jearim, 163

Kish, 233

Kislev, 128

Koran, 246

Lachish, 36 f., 111, 115, 129 f., 132, 175, 341

— Letters, 129 f., 175

Lamentations, Book of, 131

Landmark, 40

Laver, 105

Law, 42, 50, 54, 56, 171, 177, 188, 197–230, 282, 307, 356, 383

Lebanon, 30, 97, 155, 180 f., 267

Lebo-hamath (Lebweh), 97

Leontes, 97

Leprosy, 99

Levi, 221

Leviathan, 155

Levites, 73, 108, 206, 213, 221, 227 f.

Libnah, 115

Literacy, 174 f.; *also see* Education

Lo-debar, 279

Love, 215, 295 f., 349

Malachi, 204

Man of God, 251

Manasseh, tribe of, 160

— (Judah), 17, 45, 58, 69, 103, 115–18, 123, 125, 212

Marduk, 107, 190, 201, 353

Mari Texts, 236

Marriage, sacred, 48, 293

Mattaniah (Zedekiah), 129

Medes, 17, 118

Mediterranean, 25, 159, 161, 255

Megiddo, 5, 23 f., 30 f., 36 f., 39, 81, 93, 96, 102, 119, 125, 140, 226, 293

Melchizedek, 145 f., 156

Menahem, 16, 101, 107, 300

Mephi-bosheth, 45

Merchant shipping, 24, 33, 104

Merib-baal, 45

Merodach-baladan, 40, 117

Mesha, 338 f.

Mesopotamia, 104, 106, 108, 115, 117, 135, 159 f., 201 f., 236, 267

Metallurgy, 24 f., 33

Micah, 41, 53, 55, 58, 146, 157, 203, 231, 234, 237, 241, 244, 246, 250, 306-15, 375, 378 f.

Micaiah (prophet), 66, 85 ff., 330

— (scribe), 120, 386

Midianites, 33, 337

Milcom, 71, 103, 124

Millo, 70

Milqart Stele, 10, 77, 114

Miracle, 233, 236, 238, 248, 250-7, 262 f.

Mizpah, 7, 30, 39, 78, 132, 354, 388

Moab(ites), 1, 6, 8, 16, 78, 82, 88, 97, 124, 127, 129, 205, 221, 266, 268

Moabite Stone, 8, 78, 82, 124, 338

Molech, 103, 123 f.

Morality, 179 f., 266 ff., 274, 307, 374

Moresheth-gath, 306, 308

Mosaic Yahwism, 28, 43, 48-51, 53, 55, 58 f., 64, 66, 89, 137 f., 143, 146, 149, 157, 197, 202, 210-13, 217, 222, 227 f., 232, 237, 244, 247-50, 257, 265, 276, 286, 294 f., 302, 307, 314, 322, 352, 365

Moses, 48, 65, 110, 197, 202 f., 205 f., 208, 221, 227, 232, 241 ff., 257 f., 260, 262, 307, 355, 377

—, Blessing of, 203

Mot, 45 ff., 345

Mount Carmel, 12, 45, 249, 251, 253 ff., 257, 259, 284

Mount of Olives, 123

— Perazim, 346

Mourning customs, 46, 283, 342

Music, 233 f., 238

Mythology, 27 f., 45-48, 87, 155, 157 f., 189, 334, 337, 359 f., 376

Naaman, 99, 248, 263 f.

nābhî', 242 f.

Nabopolassar, 17, 21, 127

Naboth, 32, 41, 93 f., 174, 203, 248, 250, 259 f.

Nadab, 4, 62, 76

Nahar (River), 155

Nahum, Book of, 239

Naioth, 233

Name, significance of, 45, 154, 220

Naphtali, 11, 77

Nathan, 164

Nature study, 181 ff.

Nazirites, 34, 269

Nebat, 63

Nebuchadrezzar, 5, 21, 126 ff., 130, 132, 353, 380 f., 383, 385, 389

Nebushazban, 388

Necho II, 20 f., 125, 127

Necromancy, 116, 119, 133

Negeb, 98

Nehushtan, 110

Nergal-sharezer, 107, 388

New, significance of, 228

— Moon, 282

New Testament writers, 189, 191, 213

— Year Festival, 45, 75, 147 f., 150, 378; also see Feast of Ingathering

Nibhaz, 108

Nile, 108, 160, 283

Nimrud (Calah), 15, 17, 57, 79, 90, 102, 117, 145, 168, 217, 279, 293

Nineveh, 17, 111, 115, 118, 239, 341

Ninurta, 145

Nisroch, 115
nôqēdh, 266
North, significance of, 46, 157 f.,
    349, 353, 358–61
Numbers, Book of, 241
Nusku, 115
Nuzi tablets, 294

Obadiah, 254
Omri, 3 ff., 8, 11 f., 18, 23, 29, 32,
    62, 69, 78, 81 f., 85, 88–91, 101,
    143, 339
Ophir, 33
Oral tradition, 172, 244–7, 385
Orontes, 97, 107, 127, 277

Padi, 110
Parable, 179, 326 f.
Passover, 119, 123 ff., 138
Paul, 197, 285, 372
Pekah, 101 f., 300, 332 f.
Pekahiah, 101
Penuel, 72
People of the land, 6, 120, 127, 131
Pharisees, 197
Pharpar, 263
Philistines, 1, 6, 16 f., 44, 55, 98,
    102, 110, 127, 163, 266 f., 271,
    277, 284, 308, 316, 319, 346
Phoenicia(ns), 19, 22–29, 31, 33, 45,
    78, 80 f., 83, 88 f., 91, 95, 97, 113,
    124, 129, 140, 173, 185, 216 f.,
    236, 249, 251, 255, 267, 293
Pilate, 378
Pillars, 75 f., 95, 134 f., 296
Pool of Siloam, 111, 113, 130
Population, 21, 107, 131
Pottery, 33 f., 37
Prayer, 114, 152, 235, 240 f., 324,
    372, 380
Priests, 50, 122 f., 145 f., 203 f., 221,
    234, 298 ff., 356, 368, 372, 375 f.;
    also see Levites
Promised Land, 49, 205, 209 ff., 214 f.

Property, 32 f., 41, 194, 199, 228 f.,
    259 f., 310 f., 328, 383 f., 387
Prophecy, 66 f., 213, 231–47, 379
Prophets, bands and disciples of,
    50, 92, 245 f., 261 f., 281, 336
—, call of, 260 f., 281, 329, 352, 355
—, in relation to priests, 234 f., 350,
    375 f.
— — — to wisdom, 175–81, 204 f.
—, independent, 85 ff., 114, 208,
    237–44
—, institutional, 85–87, 121 f., 126,
    232–7, 254, 264, 281, 298, 312 f.,
    356, 360, 372, 374–8
—, symbolic acts of, 70, 239 f.,
    290 f., 333 ff.
—, tradition of, 244–7, 385
—, Yahwism of, 37 f., 55–59, 161
Prostitution, 76, 122, 190, 269, 286,
    291, 294, 296, 309, 357
Proverbial wisdom, 168 ff., 179–85,
    366, 369
Proverbs, Book of, 166, 170, 175,
    181 f., 184–96, 213
Psalms, 139–42, 146–64, 173 f., 220,
    234, 275, 347
Psammetichus I, 20, 358
Ptah-hotep, *Instruction* of, 169, 187,
    195
Pul (Tiglath-pileser III), 101

Qarqar, 5, 8, 11, 15, 82 f., 85, 91
Queen mother, 34, 75
— of Heaven, 189, 389
— of Sheba, 33
Qumran, 218; *also see* Dead Sea
    Scrolls

Rabbah, 268
Rabsaris, 111, 388
Rabshakeh, 111, 114
Rahab, 155
Ramah, 7, 77 f., 233, 261, 388
Ramat Raḥel, 25, 81
Rameses IV, 160

Ramoth-gilead, 12, 85 f., 91 ff., 234
Raphia, 18
Ras Shamra, discoveries at, 15 f., 22, 27, 34, 44 f., 76, 83, 108, 123, 135, 147, 154 f., 171, 185, 253, 266, 301, 337
Rechabites, 34, 95, 209, 269
Red Sea, 33, 104
Rehoboam, 61, 70 ff., 75 f., 104
Remaliah, son of (Pekah), 101, 333, 335
Remnant, 259, 323, 331 ff.
Resurrection rites, 47, 302
Rezin, 101, 332 f., 335
Riblah, 127, 130
Rimmon, 77, 264
Ritual drama, 158, 163, 256, 276
Royal psalms, 142, 336
— theology, 49, 51–55, 65 f., 150, 172, 212, 334–8, 347
Rwala Bedouin, 236 f.

Sabbath, 211, 223, 282
Sabeans, 159
Sacred lot, 86; *also see* Divination
Sacrifice, animal, 46, 52, 94, 135 ff., 145, 153 f., 203, 221 f., 238 f., 272 ff., 276 f., 302, 314 f., 324, 347, 350, 363 ff., 368
—, human, 83, 103 ff., 108, 119, 123, 314 f.
Sakkuth, 277
Salem, 157
Samaria, 16, 24 f., 32, 45, 78 f., 81 ff., 88, 99–102, 105–8, 124, 143, 179, 185, 202, 219, 254 f., 271 f., 279, 289, 307 ff., 333, 339, 344
Samaritan Ostraca, 32, 97, 175
Samson, 269
Samuel, 29, 34, 45, 50, 70, 233, 269
—, Books of, 69, 225
Saqqarah, Letter from, 114, 127
Sardinia, 24

Sargon II, 16, 105 ff., 114, 168, 217, 309, 316, 341 f., 344
Satan, 87
Saul, 3, 32, 45, 50, 145, 232 f., 235, 256, 282
Scribe, 166 ff.; *also see* Education
Scythians, 17, 349, 358 ff.
Sea (ritual), 105, 131
Seba, 159
Second Isaiah, 56, 59, 150, 214, 256, 318, 362
Sennacherib, 5, 16 f., 20, 57, 109 ff., 113, 115, 167, 316, 323, 338, 341
Sephar-vaim, 107, 114
Seraiah, 167
Seraphim, 330
Shallum, 4, 63, 100 f.
— (Jehoahaz), 127, 352
Shalmaneser III, 8, 11 f., 15, 82 f., 90 f.
Shalmaneser III, Black Obelisk of, 90 f.
Shalmaneser III, statue of, 144 f.
Shalmaneser IV, 98
Shalmaneser V, 106
Shamash, 201, 282
Shapash, 47
Shaphan, 120 f., 131, 167, 213, 246 f., 351, 354, 380, 386
Shear-jashub, 332 f.
Sheba, 2
Sheba (Arabia), 33, 159
Shebna(h), 39, 113, 167
Shechem, 34, 36 ff., 49 f., 70–73, 77, 169, 205 f., 213, 219
Shema, 215
Shemaiah (10th cent.), 66
— (exile), 379 ff.
Sheol, 284, 345
Sheshonk I (Shishak), 71
Shiloh, 70, 135, 152, 163, 365
Shimei, 165
Shishak (Sheshonk I), 18, 61, 71, 75 f.
Sib'e, 106

Sidon(ians), 12, 23, 83, 91, 129, 251

Siloam, water-works of, 36, 111 ff., 175, 335, 343

—, inscription of, 113

Sinai, 50, 155, 197 f., 205, 208, 258

Singers of Temple, 234, 375

Sippar, 107

Sirion, 155, 180

Slavery, 41 f., 101, 199, 224 f., 229, 267 ff., 296

So, 106

ṣôdh, 187, 376

Sodom, 272, 306, 318 f., 323 f., 373, 376

Sojourner, 230

Solomon, 1 f., 5 f., 10, 21, 23 f., 29 ff., 33, 43, 60, 65, 69–72, 75 f., 86, 89, 93, 97 f., 104, 112 f., 116, 123, 131, 134, 140, 143, 145 f., 156, 161 ff., 165 ff., 171–4, 181, 186, 195, 226, 334, 354

Son, king addressed as, 152; pupil addressed as, 186, 207

Song of Deborah, 1, 215

sôphēr, 166 ff.

Soul and body, 251

Spain, 24

Sphinx, 15, 19, 79, 226

Spirit, 3, 87, 95, 114, 151, 233, 238, 254, 263, 312 f., 348

Spring of Gihon, 111 ff.

Succoth-benoth, 107

Sumerians, 117, 145, 168, 185

Sun worship, 123, 201, 262

Syria(n), 1, 9, 10 n., 18 f., 82, 98 ff., 104, 106, 114, 126 f., 226, 253, 277, 315, 332 f.; *also see* Arameans

Syro-Ephraimitic Coalition, 102, 315 f., 331–5

Tabe-el, 333

Tabrimmon, 77

Tahpanhes, 389

Tappuah, 101

Tarshish, 24, 158 f., 326

Tartak, 108

Tartan, 111

Tartessus, 24

Taxation, 32 f.

Taylor Prism, 110 f.

Teachers, 168–75, 178, 203 f., 206 f., 213 f., 344 f.; *also see* Education

Tekoa, 265 f.

Tell en-Nasbeh, 7

Tell es-Saʿidiyeh, 35 f.

Teman, 268

Temple of Solomon, 8, 15, 23, 33, 45, 48 f., 51–55, 64, 73, 102–5, 112, 115–26, 130 f., 134, 139–50, 151, 153 f., 156–9, 161–4, 171, 174, 184 f., 204, 212, 217, 219–22, 225 f., 228, 234, 238, 266, 307, 312 f., 321 f., 324, 329 f., 343, 350, 363 ff., 375–9, 386

Temples, pagan, 27, 29, 171, 198

Ten Commandments, 202, 205, 208, 224, 297

Teraphim, 125, 296

Textiles, 25, 37

Thebes, 20

Thummim and Urim, 204

Thut-mose III, 159

Tibni, 4, 8

Tiglath-pileser III, 13, 15 f., 57, 75, 99–106, 168, 315

Tigris, 168

Tirhakah, 114 f.

Tirzah, 36, 38, 77, 81, 101

Tishbe, 250

Tithes, 32

Tombs, 39, 118

Topheth, 103 f., 123

tôrāh, 204, 206

Trade, 11, 24, 33, 37, 85, 88, 104

Transjordania, 86, 91, 97, 101 f., 268, 279

Tribute, 32

Truth, 350, 362

Tukulti-Ninurta, Epic of, 338

Tyre, 12, 23 ff., 27 ff., 33, 45, 82 f., 91, 97, 129, 165, 249, 251, 255, 266 ff.

Ugarit, 22, 27–29, 34, 171, 266, 280; *also see* Ras Shamra
Urartu, 115
Uriah, 378 f.
Urijah, 105
Urim and Thummim, 204, 235
Usury, 42
Uzza, 118
Uzziah (Azariah), 8, 15 f., 35, 98 f., 104, 266, 289, 315, 323, 330

Visions, 87, 236, 241 f., 261 f., 280 ff., 329 ff., 355 f.
Vizier of Egypt, 106, 169

Warfare, 57, 130, 153 f., 340 f.; *also see* Holy War
Wen-Amon, 255
Wine trade, 36 f.
Wisdom as ability, 165 f.
— as a person, 188–92
— and morality, 179, 194, 230, 282, 310
— and nature, 181 ff.
— and politics, 166 f., 175–8, 321 f., 348; *also see* Counsellors
— and prophecy, 175–81, 247, 267, 280, 322, 329

— outside Israel, 29, 168–71, 186 ff., 192–5, 214, 310, 341, 369
— schools, 54, 168–75, 206 f., 244, 341, 361, 366; *also see* Education
Women, status of, 224
Word, power of, 363
Worship, 133–64

Yahwist, the, 51, 172 f., 227
Yam (Sea), 155
Yaudi, 98 f.
Year of Release, 223

Zadok(ite), 146, 221
Zaphon (place), 36
— (north), 157
Zarephath, 251
Zarethan, 36
Zeboiim, 306
Zebul, 83
Zechariah, 4, 100
Zedek, 146, 325
Zedekiah (Mattaniah), 126, 128 ff., 132, 354 f., 380, 383 f., 387
— (prophet), 86 f., 239
Zephaniah, 380 f.
Zeredah, 70
Zimri, 4 f., 62, 81, 94
Zion, 53, 65 f., 148 f., 151, 157 f., 161 f., 164, 277, 313, 321 f.; *also see* Inviolability of Jerusalem
Zir-banitu, 107
Zoan, 166

INDEX OF SCRIPTURE REFERENCES

Genesis:

1^2	155, 191, 361
2^{10}	157
2^{18-23}	154
2^{24}	209
4^1	270
4^{17}	270
6^{17}	348
7^{11}	280
8^4	115
$8^{20, 21}$	136
9^2	298
10^{15-18}	218
12^3	157, 160, 358
12^7	210, 367
14^{18-20}	145, 156
14^{18}	157, 325
$14^{19, 22}$	52
15^{16}	117
$15^{17, 18}$	210
16^{11}	334
18^{18}	160
18^{19}	355
18^{23-33}	362
19^{1-28}	272, 373
19^{24}	257
20^3	377
20^7	235, 377
21^{22-24}	219
22^{18}	160
24^{43}	334
26^4	160
27^{27-38}	363
28^{10-22}	73
$28^{11, 12}$	377
31^{10-13}	377
31^{19}	125, 296
31^{24}	377
31^{34}	125, 266
31^{35}	125

Genesis (*cont.*):

32^{3-5}	244
33^{18}	71
35^{10}	256
$37-50$	173
37^{25}	366
39^8	270
40^8	377
$41^{15, 16}$	377
41^{25-45}	173
41^{39-43}	132
$41^{39, 40}$	165
42^{20}	362
46^{1-4}	377
46^{27}	94
49^6	187
49^{24}	163

Exodus:

2^6	355
3^{1-6}	260
3^1	258
3^6	256
3^8	334
$3^{13, 14}$	220
4^{10-12}	355
$4^{15, 16}$	243, 355
5^1	138
6^7	293
$7^{1, 2}$	243
10^9	138
12^{1-20}	138
$12^{3, 4}$	125, 138
12^{21-27}	138
12^{21-23}	124
$14^{13, 14}$	227
14^{16}	262
$14^{21, 22}$	262
17^6	258
19^{2-20}	50

Exodus (*cont.*):

$19^{5, 6}$	218, 325
19^{16-19}	283
20^{1-17}	297
20^2	202
20^{8-11}	282
20^{17}	224
$20^{22}-23^{33}$	197
20^{22}	205
20^{24-26}	135, 199
20^{25}	198
21^{2-11}	42, 199 f., 224
21^6	225
21^{7-11}	224
21^8	218
21^{12-32}	199
21^{12-14}	200
21^{26}	199
21^{32}	296
$21^{33}-22^{17}$	199
22^{7-9}	203
$22^{7, 8}$	200
22^{13}	271
22^{18-31}	199
22^{18}	200
22^{21-24}	193
22^{25-27}	42, 200
$22^{25, 26}$	269
22^{25}	229
$22^{26, 27}$	229
22^{28}	260
23^{1-9}	199, 201
$23^{4, 5}$	228
23^{10-19}	199
$23^{10, 11}$	223
23^{12}	282
23^{14-17}	137
$23^{14, 15}$	125
23^{16}	147
23^{20-33}	199

Exodus (cont.):		Leviticus (cont.):		Deuteronomy (cont.):	
24^{1-11}	50, 367	25^{35-38}	42	4^{10}	213, 258
24^7	197, 208	25^{39-43}	42	4^{13}	208
$25^{1, 2}$	220	26^{11}	324	4^{14}	213
29^{18}	315			4^{19}	255
$29^{27, 28}$	126	Numbers:		4^{20}	367
29^{40}	143	5^{11-28}	363	4^{23}	208
31^{12-17}	282	6^{1-21}	269	4^{25-31}	67
$32^{4, 8}$	73	$10^{35, 36}$	163	4^{31}	208
32^{25-29}	27	$11^{16, 17}$	262	4^{32-34}	207
33^{11}	208, 341	11^{24-30}	313	4^{35}	215
33^{17-23}	258	$11^{24, 25}$	262	4^{36}	207
34^{21}	282	11^{26-30}	377	4^{37}	218
34^{22}	137, 147	12^{6-8}	241, 377	4^{39}	215, 219
34^{28}	206, 258	12^6	236	$5-11$	205
40^{34}	330	13^{29}	117, 269	5^{1-33}	208
		15^{37-41}	215	5^{1-21}	205
Leviticus:		20	155	$5^{2, 3}$	208
1^5	203	20^{17}	11, 33	5^3	207
3^2	203	21^{6-9}	110	5^4	208
4^{24}	203	21^{13}	117	5^{6-21}	364
$10^{10, 11}$	204	22^{18}	264	5^6	219
13^{14}	99	23^{21}	149	5^{12-15}	211
13^{45}	312	24^{16}	52, 156	5^{12-14}	282
14^{12}	314	27^{1-11}	41, 358	$5^{14, 15}$	230
16^{13}	330	27^{21}	204	5^{15}	219, 225
17^7	123	28^{26}	138	5^{21}	224
17^{11}	222	33^{46}	291	5^{22-33}	205
18^{21}	103	34^8	97	5^{25-27}	207
18^{25}	311	35^{30}	260	5^{26}	208
19^{13}	230			5^{31}	213
19^{23-25}	228	Deuteronomy:		6^{1-9}	206, 213 ff.
$19^{35, 36}$	282	$1-4$	206 f.	6^1	206, 213
20^{2-5}	103	1^2	258	6^2	188
20^{14}	268	1^5	205, 225	6^3	367
22^{23}	137	1^6	258	6^5	207, 209, 219, 304
23^{5-8}	125	1^{17}	42	6^{6-9}	207
23^{9-14}	137	1^{19}	258	6^7	186, 211
23^{15-21}	137	1^{35}	367	6^9	174
23^{43}	139	2^4	268	6^{10-12}	217
$24^{1, 2}$	205	4^1	213	6^{10}	360
24^{14-16}	260	$4^{5, 6}$	207	6^{18}	208
25^{1-7}	223	4^5	213	6^{19}	217
25^{25-28}	41	$4^{7, 8}$	207	6^{20-24}	209
25^{25}	384	4^8	225	6^{20}	207

Deuteronomy (*cont.*):

6^{21-24}	211
6^{21}	219
7^{1-11}	210, 213, 215 ff., 227, 270
7^{1-5}	217, 220
7^{7-13}	215
$7^{7, 8}$	211, 224, 227, 382
$7^{8, 9}$	208
7^8	219
7^9	209, 214 f., 297, 315, 362
7^{12}	208
7^{13}	207, 210, 218, 315, 367
7^{15-26}	217
7^{17-26}	227
7^{17}	207
7^{18}	219, 225
$7^{23, 24}$	218
7^{25}	207
8^2	225
8^3	283
8^5	207, 209
8^6	208
8^{7-10}	207, 210, 221
8^{14}	219
8^{18}	208, 210, 225
8^{20}	208, 368
9^{1-5}	217
9^2	207
9^4	207
9^5	210, 367
9^7	219, 225
9^9	208
9^{11}	208
9^{15}	208
9^{26}	218 f.
10^{10-15}	211
$10^{12, 13}$	207, 214
10^{12}	207 f., 215
10^{15}	215, 218
10^{16}	358
10^{17}	207
10^{18}	215, 218

Deuteronomy (*cont.*):

10^{19}	219
10^{20}	209
11^{1-7}	219
11^1	215
11^2	207
$11^{8, 9}$	211
11^9	210, 214, 367
11^{10-12}	210, 221
$11^{11, 12}$	207
11^{13-21}	215
11^{13}	214 f.
11^{19}	213
11^{22-25}	217
11^{22}	208 f., 215
11^{26-28}	207
$12-26$	205
12^{1-19}	210, 219 ff.
12^{1-14}	64, 119, 211
12^3	119
12^5	116, 273
12^7	136, 210
12^{8-14}	213 f., 223, 227
12^{11}	220
12^{12}	207, 210
12^{15}	210, 220
12^{17}	137
12^{18}	207
12^{19}	221
12^{20}	207, 210
12^{28}	208
12^{29-31}	217
12^{30}	207
12^{31}	103
13^{1-5}	377
13^1	207
13^3	215
13^4	207 ff., 368
13^5	218
13^6	207
$13^{12, 13}$	207
13^{18}	214
14^1	209, 283
14^2	210, 218
14^{21}	230

Deuteronomy (*cont.*):

14^{22-29}	220 f.
14^{23}	220
14^{26}	210
14^{27}	221
14^{29}	42, 221, 230
15^{1-18}	222 ff.
15^{1-11}	223 f.
15^5	208, 368
15^6	207
15^9	207
15^{12-18}	42, 224 f.
15^{15}	211, 218 f., 225
15^{16}	215
15^{19-23}	212
16^{1-8}	119, 124 f., 138
16^2	290
16^3	138, 212
16^6	220
$16^{9, 10}$	137
16^{10-14}	230
16^{11}	210, 220 f.
16^{12}	219, 225
16^{13}	137
16^{14}	210, 221
16^{15}	210
16^{18-20}	203
$16^{21, 22}$	119
17^1	207
17^3	119
17^6	260
17^{8-13}	203
17^9	221
17^{12}	221
17^{14-20}	30, 66, 202, 225 ff.
17^{14}	207
17^{15}	223
$17^{18, 19}$	174
17^{18}	221
17^{19}	213
17^{20}	214
18^1	221
18^3	136, 221
18^{6-8}	123

E e

Deuteronomy (*cont.*):

18^6	210
18^7	221
18^{10}	103, 119
18^{11}	119
18^{12}	207
18^{15-19}	208
18^{16}	258
$18^{21, 22}$	235
18^{21}	207
18^{22}	66
19^1	217
19^8	210
19^9	208 f., 215
19^{10}	221
19^{14}	40 f., 194, 221
19^{16-19}	203
19^{17}	221
$19^{18, 19}$	223
20^{1-20}	217
20^{1-9}	218, 227 f., 321
20^2	221
20^{5-8}	207
20^{16-18}	218
20^{18}	207
20^{19}	207
$21^{3, 4}$	203
21^3	223
21^5	203, 221
21^8	218
21^{10-14}	217, 224
21^{15}	215
21^{17}	262
21^{18-21}	203
21^{23}	221
22^1-25^3	228 ff.
22^{1-4}	223, 228 f.
22^1	187
22^5	207
22^7	214
22^8	229
22^{13-19}	224
23^5	215, 218
23^7	219, 268
23^{9-14}	217, 228

Deuteronomy (*cont.*):

$23^{15, 16}$	229
23^{17}	119, 269, 291, 357
$23^{19, 20}$	42, 223, 229
23^{21-23}	221
24^{1-5}	224
24^{1-4}	357
24^4	221
24^5	217, 228
24^6	42, 229
24^8	221
24^9	219, 225
24^{10-13}	229, 269
$24^{12, 13}$	42
$24^{14, 15}$	181, 230
24^{14}	193, 230, 364
24^{17}	230
24^{18}	218 f., 225
24^{19}	230
24^{22}	219, 225
25^{1-3}	230
25^3	223
25^{13-16}	282
25^{16}	208
25^{17-19}	217
25^{17}	219, 227
25^{19}	225
26^{1-11}	131
26^1	221
26^2	220
$26^{3, 4}$	221
26^3	210
26^{5-9}	204, 219, 221
26^{11}	210, 230
$26^{12, 13}$	221
26^{12}	230
26^{14}	208, 368
26^{15}	210
26^{16}	211
26^{17}	208
26^{18}	214
27^{1-26}	205 f., 213
27^{2-8}	174
27^3	225
27^{11-26}	49, 56, 66

Deuteronomy (*cont.*):

27^{15-26}	367
27^{26}	367
28	206
28^1	207
28^{3-19}	119
$28^{12, 13}$	207
28^{15-68}	368
28^{15-19}	66, 121
28^{15}	208, 368
$28^{43, 44}$	230
28^{47}	210
28^{58}	208
29–34	206
29^1	367
29^9	367
29^{10-13}	230
29^{21}	225
29^{23}	306
29^{25-28}	208
30^{10}	225
30^{11-20}	207
30^{15}	218, 325
31^{9-13}	49, 205
$31^{12, 13}$	213
31^{17}	312
31^{26}	225
32^{14}	271
33^{2-29}	206
33^5	149
33^8	204
33^{10}	203
33^{17}	86, 164
34^{10-12}	208

Joshua:

3–5	163
3	49, 262
3^5	228
3^{10}	218
4	49
5^{10-12}	124
6^{26}	83
7^{20-26}	295

Joshua (*cont.*):

8^{30-35}	49, 260
$10^{1, 3}$	146
10^5	117
10^{11-14}	283
11^{1-15}	29
13^{14}	221
15^{21-62}	32, 125
18^1	365
18^{21-28}	125
21^2	365
21^{43-45}	221
22^9	365
22^{12}	365
24	49
24^{1-28}	71, 205
24^{11}	218
32^{20}	367

Judges:

1^{19}	84
3^7	76
3^{10}	3
4^{14}	227
4^{17-22}	95
5	215
$5^{4, 5}$	283
5^{13-18}	2
$5^{20, 21}$	283
5^{24-27}	95
5^{31}	147
$6-8$	337
6^{25-32}	76
6^{34}	3
8^{27}	296
8^{30}	94
9^{1-6}	71
9^{7-15}	34
9^{27}	137
11^{24}	124
11^{29}	3
12^{14}	94
13^{25}	3, 313
14^6	313
14^{19}	313

Judges: (*cont.*):

15^{14}	331
16^{17}	269
16^{23}	44
18^{31}	365
20^{18}	73
20^{23}	86
20^{26-28}	73
20^{26}	259
$20^{27, 28}$	86
21^{19-21}	137, 365

Ruth:

4^{1-12}	203
4^{1-9}	384
$4^{1, 2}$	273

1 Samuel:

1^{3-5}	203
1^3	365
1^7	365
1^{9-18}	152
1^9	135
1^{11}	269
$1^{14, 15}$	137
1^{22}	153
1^{24}	365
2^{12-17}	298
2^{13-16}	136
2^{27-36}	146
2^{34}	235, 334
3^3	365
3^{10-14}	355
3^{14}	136
3^{15}	365
3^{19}	235, 355
$4^{1}-7^2$	163
4^4	156, 161
4^{11}	235
5^{2-7}	44
6^7	228
6^{14}	261
$7^{1, 2}$	163
7^6	259
7^{16}	50

1 Samuel (*cont.*):

8^{1-22}	225
8^5	34, 202
8^7	149
8^{11-18}	30, 226
8^{12}	31
8^{14}	32
$9^{1}-10^{16}$	50
9^{5-10}	264
9^6	235
9^9	243, 273, 312
9^{11-25}	133
9^{16}	4, 151
9^{22-24}	136
9^{22}	135
10^1	4, 92, 151
10^{5-13}	313
$10^{5, 6}$	233
10^5	256, 261
10^6	256
10^7	334
10^8	50
10^9	334
$10^{10, 11}$	233
10^{10}	261
10^{17-27}	225
$11^{6, 7}$	313
11^6	3
$12^{7, 8}$	56
13^{8-12}	153
13^9	135, 145
14^{10}	334
14^{24}	259
$14^{34, 35}$	136
14^{34}	203
14^{36-42}	86, 204
15^{22}	314
16^{13}	92, 151
17^{12}	163
17^{45}	255
18^{10}	256
19^{13-17}	125
$19^{19, 20}$	261
19^{20-24}	233, 313
$19^{23, 24}$	256

1 Samuel (cont.):		2 Samuel (cont.):		1 Kings (cont.):	
19^{24}	234	$9^{1,\,3}$	219	3^4	145
20^5	282	10^2	219	3^{5-14}	165
20^8	219	$10^{16,\,17}$	11	3^9	181
$20^{18,\,19}$	282	11^{11}	228	$3^{12,\,13}$	181
20^{24-26}	282	12^{1-15}	327	3^{16-28}	202
21^5	228	$12^{5,\,6}$	202	4^2	145
23^{2-4}	86	12^{14}	235	4^3	167
23^{9-12}	86	14^{4-11}	202	4^6	72
$24^{6,\,10}$	151	14^{17-20}	145	4^{7-19}	32
$26^{9,\,11,\,23}$	151	15^{2-6}	202	4^{21}	1
26^{19}	264	15^{10}	92	$4^{22,\,23}$	32
28	116	15^{12}	166	4^{25}	361
28^6	235	15^{30}	309	4^{29-34}	181
$30^{7,\,8}$	86	16^{23}	166	5–8	145
		17^{1-14}	172	5^{1-12}	23
2 Samuel:		18^5	355	5^{11}	25
2^4	1, 151	18^8	295	5^{12}	181
2^8	45	18^{11-15}	2	5^{13-18}	30, 72
3^{10}	2	19^{43}	2	5^{14}	72
4^4	45	20^1	2, 72	6–7	116
5^3	2, 151	20^{25}	145	6^{23-28}	73, 156, 163, 226
5^5	2	21^8	45	7^2	343
5^{6-9}	2, 157	21^{17}	164	7^7	202
5^8	113	23^5	53	7^{13-47}	23
5^{11}	23	24^{1-9}	2	7^{13-22}	140
$5^{23,\,24}$	236	24^7	23	7^{15-22}	122, 131
5^{24}	227	24^{22}	261	7^{23-39}	105
6	147, 162 f.	24^{25}	136	8	147, 162 f.
6^{2-15}	163			8^2	75, 137
6^2	156, 255	1 Kings:		8^5	145
$6^{12,\,13}$	137	1–2	172	8^6	156
6^{14}	145, 296	1^{20}	172	8^8	68
6^{17-19}	145	1^{32-48}	151	$8^{10,\,11}$	330
6^{18}	255	1^{34}	92	8^{13}	148
6^{19}	296	1^{35}	2	8^{23}	219
7^{4-17}	53	1^{39}	151	8^{25}	66
7^{8-16}	152, 164	1^{50}	271	8^{27-30}	220
7^{14-17}	149	2^9	165, 181	8^{27}	148
7^{14}	152	2^{19}	34, 75	$8^{33,\,34}$	67
8^{1-14}	1, 6	$2^{26,\,27}$	145 f., 355	$8^{44,\,45}$	153
8^2	78	2^{28}	271	8^{46-53}	67
8^{15}	202	2^{30}	244	8^{51}	367
8^{17}	145, 167	2^{35}	34	8^{62-64}	105, 145
9–20	172	3^{4-15}	377	8^{65}	97

1 Kings (*cont.*):

Reference	Page
9^{4-9}	66
9^{6-9}	67
9^{10}	23
9^{11}	23, 32
9^{15-19}	5
9^{15}	23, 31, 70
9^{21}	68
9^{22}	72
9^{25}	145
9^{26-28}	24, 33
10^{1-13}	33
10^{1-10}	159
10^{1}	181
10^{11}	33
$10^{14}-11^{8}$	226
10^{15-22}	4
10^{15}	33
10^{17}	76, 343
10^{18-20}	24, 226
10^{22}	24, 33
10^{26}	5
10^{29}	101
11^{4}	65
11^{5-7}	123
11^{5}	124
11^{7}	103, 124
11^{11}	208
$11^{12, 13}$	65
11^{23-25}	10
11^{26-40}	69 ff.
11^{28}	72
11^{29-39}	61, 66, 72
11^{29}	228
11^{32}	72
11^{33}	65, 124
11^{36}	65, 68
11^{40}	71, 75 f.
11^{41}	60
12	60
12^{1-20}	71 f.
12^{1}	49, 72
12^{4}	30
12^{15}	61, 66
12^{16}	2

1 Kings (*cont.*):

Reference	Page
12^{17}	71
12^{18}	30
12^{19}	267
12^{21}	71
12^{25-33}	48, 72 ff.
12^{25}	49
12^{28-33}	143
$12^{32}-13^{34}$	124
13^{1}	145
13^{2}	66
13^{6}	235
13^{18}	258
14^{1-18}	61
14^{1-6}	234
14^{1-3}	264
14^{8}	65
14^{17}	78
14^{19}	60
14^{21-31}	75 f.
$14^{23, 24}$	110, 122
14^{23}	83, 116, 135, 296
14^{25-28}	18
14^{25}	61
14^{29}	60
14^{30}	8
15^{1-8}	76
$15^{3, 4}$	65
15^{3}	65
15^{5}	65
15^{9-24}	62
15^{9-15}	54, 76
15^{11}	65
15^{13}	34, 45, 72, 75
15^{14}	64
15^{16-22}	7 f., 10, 76 ff.
15^{16}	8
15^{18}	33, 83, 114, 264
15^{20}	11
15^{21}	81, 101
15^{22}	30
$15^{25}-22^{40}$	62
15^{25-32}	76
15^{26}	63
$15^{27, 28}$	4

1 Kings (*cont.*):

Reference	Page
15^{27}	6
15^{29}	61
15^{34}	63
$16^{1, 2}$	4
16^{8-20}	4
16^{8-14}	81
16^{9-15}	94
16^{15-28}	78 ff.
16^{15}	6
16^{20}	61
$16^{23, 24}$	78
16^{29-34}	81 ff.
16^{31-33}	45
16^{31}	24, 25
16^{32-34}	143
16^{32}	95
$17-19$	61, 82
17^{1-24}	249 ff.
17^{1}	254
17^{14}	254
17^{17-24}	235, 237
17^{18}	234
17^{22}	315
18^{1-46}	45, 251 ff., 273
18^{3}	32
18^{7}	234
18^{12}	261
18^{13}	262
18^{15}	161, 271, 318, 323
18^{19}	76, 234, 236, 262
18^{20-40}	249
18^{26-29}	135
18^{28}	46
18^{29}	234, 381
18^{30}	235
$18^{36, 37}$	235
18^{42}	236
18^{46}	370
19^{1-18}	249, 257 ff.
19^{10}	235
19^{13}	236
19^{16}	4, 92
19^{19-21}	258, 260 ff.
20	61, 77, 82

1 Kings (*cont.*):

20^{1-34}	83 ff.
20^{1-20}	11
20^2	94
20^{23}	264
$20^{24,\ 25}$	11
20^{26-43}	11
20^{34}	11, 33, 77, 86
21	61, 82
21^{1-24}	41
21^{1-20}	248, 250, 259 f., 307, 328
21^{1-16}	32
21^1	82
21^{8-14}	203
21^{8-12}	174
21^{19}	88, 93
21^{20}	255
$21^{21,\ 22}$	66, 95
21^{23}	94
21^{27}	342
22	61, 77, 82
22^{1-40}	8, 85, 234, 239
22^{1-36}	12
22^2	63
22^3	92
22^{5-12}	236
22^5	121
22^6	262
22^{10-12}	236
22^{10}	256
22^{11}	164, 239
$22^{13,\ 14}$	270
22^{19-23}	95, 330, 376
22^{19}	149, 154, 255
22^{38}	260
$22^{39,\ 40}$	62, 82
22^{39}	24, 61, 79, 82, 271
$22^{41,\ 42}$	62
22^{41}	63
22^{43}	64
22^{47-49}	85
22^{47}	6
22^{48}	24

1 Kings (*cont.*):

22^{52}	63

2 Kings:

$1-2$	249
1	88
1^{2-17}	61
1^3	258
1^8	260, 342
1^{10}	257
1^{13}	234, 254
1^{15}	258
$2-13$	61
2^{1-18}	246, 250, 261 ff.
2^3	233, 235, 248, 254, 281, 375
2^7	262
2^8	260
2^{14-25}	248
2^{14}	260
2^{16}	262
2^{20}	228
3^2	134
3^{4-27}	8, 88, 248, 338
3^{4-20}	236
3^4	266
3^5	82, 267
$3^{11,\ 12}$	86
3^{11}	86, 273
3^{13-20}	234
3^{15}	236, 254, 370
3^{27}	103
4^{1-44}	248
4^{1-7}	41, 233, 251
4^1	262
4^7	251
4^9	251
4^{21}	251
4^{23}	235, 282
4^{27}	235
4^{32-37}	237, 251
4^{34}	251
4^{38}	233, 261 f.
4^{43}	262
5^{1-19}	248, 263 f.

2 Kings (*cont.*):

5^1	99
5^{16}	238, 313
5^{17}	380
5^{18}	104
5^{19-27}	281
5^{26}	233
6^{1-23}	248
$6^{1,\ 2}$	262
6^1	233
6^9	233
6^{12}	233
6^{17}	235
$6^{24}-7^{20}$	12
6^{32}	233
8^2	251
8^3	202
8^{7-15}	93, 248, 258
$8^{7,\ 8}$	234, 264
8^9	254
8^{11}	251
$8^{12,\ 13}$	258
8^{12}	101, 254, 268
8^{18}	8, 64, 85
8^{19}	65, 68
8^{20-22}	88
8^{25-29}	8
8^{25-27}	88
$8^{26,\ 27}$	8
8^{27}	64
$8^{28,\ 29}$	92
8^{28}	12, 88
9^{1-13}	91 f.
9^{1-6}	4, 248, 258
9^7	242
9^{11}	234, 256
9^{13}	93
9^{14-28}	92 ff.
9^{20}	91
9^{26}	260
9^{27}	8, 100
$9^{30}-10^{27}$	93 ff.
$9^{36,\ 37}$	260
10^{10}	66
10^{12-14}	8

2 Kings (cont.):

10^{16}	258
10^{18-27}	135
10^{19}	234, 236
10^{29}	73
10^{30}	100
$10^{32, 33}$	12, 91, 94
11^{1-20}	34, 95, 226
11^{4-20}	89
11^{12-20}	151
11^{12-18}	122
11^{12}	120, 151 f.
11^{14}	122
$11^{17, 18}$	54
11^{18-20}	120
12^3	64
12^{4-16}	121
12^9	122
12^{10}	121, 167
$12^{17, 18}$	12, 96
$12^{20, 21}$	96
13^{3-7}	91
13^3	12
13^{4-6}	98
13^5	13
13^7	12
13^{14-21}	248
13^{14-19}	236, 239, 248
13^{14}	262
13^{19}	240, 251
13^{22}	12
13^{23}	98
13^{25}	13, 96
14^{1-3}	62
14^3	65
14^4	64
14^{8-14}	8
14^9	6, 96
14^{11-14}	96
14^{22}	24, 98
14^{23-29}	96 ff., 266
$14^{23, 24}$	62
14^{25}	13, 279
14^{28}	13
15^{1-7}	98 f., 266, 323,

2 Kings (cont.):

	330
15^4	64
15^{8-31}	99 ff., 160, 300, 304
15^{16}	268
$15^{19, 20}$	32
15^{19}	16, 61, 107
15^{25}	332 f.
$15^{29, 30}$	106
15^{29}	16, 332
15^{35}	64
15^{37}	13, 103
16^{1-20}	102 ff., 300, 316, 323, 332, 335
16^2	65
16^3	108, 116, 123 f., 315
16^4	64
16^{5-8}	13
16^5	333
16^8	33
16^9	13, 267, 333
16^{10-18}	145
16^{12-16}	145
16^{15}	153
$16^{17, 18}$	33, 131
17^{1-6}	18, 105 ff., 161, 300, 304, 344
17^{7-18}	368
17^{7-12}	65
17^{9-12}	299
17^{13}	67, 242
17^{16}	87
17^{17}	103
17^{23}	242
17^{24-33}	105 ff., 300, 304
17^{24}	114, 309
17^{28}	143, 188, 214
17^{30}	283
17^{31}	103
$18-25$	60
$18-19$	316, 323, 343, 379
18^{1-8}	16, 108 ff.

2 Kings (cont.):

18^{3-5}	46
18^3	65
18^4	145
18^{12}	65
$18^{13}-20^{19}$	61, 323
$18^{13}-19^8$	108 ff.
18^{13-16}	343
18^{13}	17, 323
$18^{15, 16}$	33
18^{17}	335, 343
18^{18}	167
18^{21}	18
18^{24}	5
18^{26}	77
$18^{31, 32}$	39
$19-20$	248
19^{1-7}	241
19^{9-35}	343
19^{12}	267
19^{14}	148
19^{15}	73, 156
19^{32-34}	346
19^{34}	65
$19^{36, 37}$	108 ff.
20^{1-11}	238
20^{20}	61, 111
21^{1-26}	115 ff.
21^{2-9}	64
21^3	45, 122 f.
21^5	123
21^6	103, 125
$21^{7, 8}$	66
21^7	76, 122
21^8	65
21^{10-15}	67
21^{10}	242
21^{11}	269
21^{20-22}	64
$21^{23, 24}$	6, 120, 226
21^{23}	32
22^1-23^{30}	54, 118 ff., 351, 355, 366
22^1	6, 118, 127, 131
22^2	65

2 Kings (*cont.*):

22^3	131, 167, 247, 351,
	366, 379 f., 386
22^{8-10}	167
22^8	121
22^{11}	386
$22^{16, 17}$	68
22^{20}	68
23^2	375
23^3	367
23^{4-25}	64
23^{4-14}	145
23^4	43, 121
23^7	291
23^8	78
23^9	221
23^{10}	103
23^{11}	262
23^{13}	103
23^{15}	143
23^{16}	66
23^{21-23}	138
23^{24}	296
23^{25}	65, 68
$23^{26, 27}$	68
23^{27}	66
$23^{29, 30}$	68
23^{29}	20
23^{30}	6, 127
$23^{31}-25^{30}$	126 ff.
$23^{31}-25^{21}$	355
23^{31-37}	226
23^{31-33}	352
23^{33-35}	6
23^{34-37}	373, 378
23^{35}	32
24^1	21, 114
24^2	67, 242
$24^{3, 4}$	66
24^6	374
24^7	21
24^{8-16}	353, 380
24^{8-12}	377
25^{1-12}	388
25^{1-3}	383

2 Kings (*cont.*):

25^{13}	122
25^{18-21}	381
25^{18}	122, 380
25^{19}	30
25^{22-26}	354, 388
25^{27-30}	388

1 Chronicles:

2^{55}	95
$3^{15, 16}$	129
$4^{14, 21}$	37
4^{23}	33
8^{33}	45
9^{40}	45
10^{10}	44
14^{11}	346
14^{16}	346
17^{13}	152
21^1	87
22^{10}	152
22^{15}	165
25^{1-8}	234
25^1	375
25^5	375
27^{25-31}	32
27^{33}	166
28^2	163
28^6	152
29^3	218
29^{18}	257
29^{23}	145

2 Chronicles:

2^7	165
11^{15}	123
11^{16}	72
13^{1-22}	76
13^{13-18}	293
14^{9-15}	293
15^1	313
$17-20$	85
$19^{6, 7}$	201
19^{8-11}	203
20^{1-30}	293

2 Chronicles (*cont.*):

20^{1-23}	217
20^{1-19}	153
20^{14-23}	234, 375
20^{14-17}	154
20^{14}	313
$21^{16, 17}$	267
23^{13}	122
24	96
24^{20-22}	379
24^{20}	313
$25^{15, 16}$	175
26	98
28^{18}	102
$28^{22, 23}$	103
28^{23}	104
30^6	257
32^{2-5}	111
32^8	348
32^{30}	111
32^{33}	118
34^{3-14}	120
34^3	120
$34^{6, 7}$	119, 125
34^{30}	375
34^{31}	122
35^{18}	124
36^8	374

Ezra:

1^2	244
4^2	107

Nehemiah:

3^8	37
5^{1-5}	41, 224
7^{65}	204
$8^{7, 8}$	206
8^{13-18}	139
9^{30}	313
11^{35}	37

Job:

$1-2$	87, 376
1^6	154

Job (cont.):		Psalms (cont.):		Psalms (cont.):	
3^{1-26}	370, 373	$2^{8, 9}$	159	40^{6-8}	314
3^3	337	2^8	156, 158	$42-43$	146
4^8	176, 179	3	141	42^2	153, 161
6^{15-20}	370	4^6	153	42^4	161
7^{12}	155	5	141, 152 f.	44	141
8^{11}	178	5^2	149	45	142 f.
9^{4-12}	196	5^3	162	45^1	173
9^{13}	155	5^7	161	45^5	159
$10^{21, 22}$	284	6	141	45^6	143
11^7	196	7	141	45^7	145
12^6	369	7^{17}	156	45^8	271
$12^{7, 8}$	182, 298	12^5	141, 234	46	142, 146, 157
12^{17-20}	177	12^6	141	$46^{4, 5}$	148, 157
13^{28}	179	13	141	46^4	156 f.
$15^{7, 8}$	191	15^5	42	46^6	152, 158
15^8	187	18	141 f.	46^{8-10}	152, 158
19^{19}	187	$18^{6, 7}$	309	47	142, 146, 150,
20^{17}	334	18^6	153		155 ff., 161, 162
21^7	369	18^{7-15}	283	47^2	52, 148
23^7	324	$18^{13, 14}$	154	$47^{5, 8}$	330
24^2	40, 179, 194	18^{43-45}	159	$47^{8, 9}$	152
24^3	229	18^{50}	151	47^8	150
26^7	360	20	141 f., 145, 153 f.	47^9	162
$26^{12, 13}$	155	20^6	151	48	142, 146, 148 f.,
29	190	21	142		151, 157 f., 313
29^4	187	$21^{4, 5}$	145	48^2	149, 360
29^{12}	179	21^7	149, 156	48^{4-8}	152
29^{16}	193	21^{8-12}	152	48^4	156, 159
30^{25}	315	22	141	48^8	325
31^{13-15}	230	22^{12}	271	50	314
31^{21}	273	23^6	167	51	141
33^{14}	178, 267	24	147	51^{15-17}	314
37^{22}	158	24^6	153	51^{18}	157
$38-39$	182	24^{7-10}	149	54^1	154
$39^{5, 6}$	179	26^8	164	55^{14}	187
40^5	178	27^4	148, 161	56^4	348
$42^{5, 6}$	330	28	141	64^2	187
42^{13-15}	358	29	142, 150, 154 f.	65	147
		29^{4-9}	283	66	141
Psalms:		$29^{10, 11}$	284	67	147
2	142, 149, 151 f.	30	141	68^4	155
2^2	145, 162, 164	31^5	362	68^5	193
2^6	149, 191	32	141	68^{7-10}	149
2^7	145, 336	37^1	369	$68^{15, 16}$	149

Psalms (*cont.*):

68¹⁶	149
68²⁴, ²⁵	147
72 142, 145, 149 f.,	
158 ff., 190, 338	
72⁵	145
72⁸⁻¹¹	151 f., 156
72⁸	283
72¹⁷	157
73³⁻¹²	369
73¹¹	52
74	141
74²	157
74¹²⁻¹⁷	155
75¹⁰	164
76	157
76²	149, 157
76³⁻⁶	158
78	149
78³⁹	348
78⁶⁰	365
78⁶¹	164
78⁶⁷⁻⁷²	149, 164
79	141
80	141, 143
80³	153
80⁸	149
80¹⁸	302
81	143
81², ³	147
81¹⁰	149
82¹	87, 154
83³	187
84 142, 146, 157,	
161 f., 299, 350	
84¹	148, 153
84³	149
84⁹	151
85⁴⁻⁷	302
85⁸⁻¹³	234
87	146, 157
89	142
89¹⁻⁴	53
89⁷	87, 187
89⁹, ¹⁰	155

Psalms (*cont.*):

89¹⁰, ²⁰	145
89¹⁸	157, 162
89¹⁹⁻³⁷	53, 164
89²⁰⁻²⁷	159
89²⁴	149, 154
89²⁶, ²⁷	143, 152
89²⁸⁻³⁷	149
89³⁸, ⁵¹	151
91¹⁴⁻¹⁶	234
92	141
93	150, 156
93¹⁻⁴	155
93¹	157
94¹⁷	141
95⁻100	142
95²	153
95⁶	164
96	150, 156
96¹⁰	157
97	150, 156 f.
98	150, 156
99	150, 156
101	142
102	141, 152
107¹¹	52
109	141
110	142, 151
110¹	145, 150, 161
110²	152
110³	337
110⁴	145, 156, 325
110⁵, ⁶	159
111¹	187
112⁵	42
118	141 f.
118¹⁹, ²⁰	147
118²⁶, ²⁷	147
120	141
122	146, 157
124	141
130	141
132 142, 145, 147,	
149, 162 ff.	
132¹⁻⁵	156

Psalms (*cont.*):

132¹	148
132¹⁰	145, 151
132¹¹, ¹²	152
132¹³, ¹⁴	149
132¹⁷	279
137⁷	268
139⁷⁻¹²	284
139¹³	191
140	141
143¹¹	302
144	142
145⁻50	142
145¹³	155
148	182
149²	149
149⁵⁻⁹	142

Proverbs:

1ᴸ⁻9¹⁸	186
1²	207, 323
1⁵	166
1⁷	188
1⁸	186, 204, 323
1⁹	215
1²⁷	179
2¹	186, 214
2⁵	297
2⁶	188
2⁷	186
2¹⁵	193
2¹⁶⁻¹⁹	190
3¹, ²	214
3¹	186, 204, 214
3³	215, 297
3⁷	329
3¹¹	207
3¹⁹, ²⁰	188
3²¹⁻³²	186 f.
3²¹	190
3²²	180, 187
3³²	270, 376
4¹	186, 207, 323
4⁴	213 f.

Proverbs (*cont.*):

4^{10}	186, 214
4^{11}	213
4^{20-27}	187 f.
4^{20-23}	383
4^{20}	186
5^{1}	186
5^{6}	193
5^{13}	213
6^{1-3}	194
6^{6-11}	182
6^{16-19}	178
6^{20-35}	190
6^{20-23}	204
6^{20}	186, 214
$6^{21, 22}$	215
6^{23}	213 f.
$6^{27, 28}$	178
7^{1-27}	189
7^{1-3}	188
$7^{1, 2}$	214
7^{1}	186
7^{2}	204
7^{3}	215
7^{6-27}	190
7^{10-23}	294
8	186, 188 ff.
8^{20}	196
9^{4}	179
9^{5}	283
9^{13-18}	189
9^{16}	179
$10^{1}-22^{16}$	181, 186
10^{2}	195 f.
$10^{8, 10}$	179
10^{8}	214
11^{1}	282
11^{4}	195
11^{5}	196
11^{13}	187, 362
11^{14}	166
11^{15}	194
11^{16}	195
11^{28}	195
11^{29}	179

Proverbs (*cont.*):

12^{2}	168
12^{5}	166
12^{10}	270
12^{15}	183
12^{27}	195
12^{28}	192
13^{11}	195
13^{13}	214
13^{14}	204
14^{15}	184, 190
14^{17}	186
14^{22}	297
14^{23}	195
14^{28-35}	184
15^{8}	314
15^{18}	194
15^{22}	187
15^{24}	192
15^{27}	195
16^{6}	297
16^{10-15}	184
16^{11}	179, 282
16^{32}	194
$17^{10, 16}$	190
17^{18}	194
17^{24}	184, 190
17^{27}	194, 323
19^{11}	194
19^{12}	184
19^{16}	214
19^{18}	207
20^{1}	179
20^{2}	184
20^{8}	184
20^{10}	207
20^{16}	194
20^{18}	166
20^{19}	187
20^{21}	195
20^{23}	179, 182
20^{26}	184
20^{28}	184, 297
21^{1}	184
21^{3}	314

Proverbs (*cont.*):

21^{17}	195
21^{27}	207, 314
22^{4}	195
22^{8}	176, 179
22^{16}	195
$22^{17}-24^{22}$	186, 192 f.
$22^{17}-23^{12}$	186, 192
$22^{17}-23^{5}$	192 ff.
22^{17-21}	188
22^{22}	179
$22^{24, 25}$	187
22^{28}	179, 310
22^{30}	192
23^{1}	184
23^{9}	193
23^{10}	179, 194
23^{29-35}	179
24^{6}	166
24^{9}	207
24^{20}	164
24^{23-34}	186
$25^{1}-29^{27}$	181, 186, 195
25^{1-10}	195 f.
25^{1}	108
25^{8-10}	193
25^{9}	187
25^{14}	187
25^{15}	194
26^{5}	329
26^{12}	329
26^{16}	329
26^{20}	183
27^{7}	183, 328
27^{13}	194
27^{18}	183
28^{2}	323
28^{11}	329
28^{16}	214
28^{20}	184
28^{26}	183
29^{7}	270
29^{14}	179
29^{17}	207
29^{20}	193

Proverbs (*cont.*):

30	186
30[2, 3]	323
30[4]	178
30[15-31]	178, 267
30[18, 19]	182
30[24-31]	182
31[1-9]	186
31[4, 5]	179
31[10-31]	186
31[26]	204

Ecclesiastes:

2[8]	218

Isaiah:

1[1]	146, 323
1[2-9]	316, 319, 322 ff., 343
1[2-4]	320
1[2]	255, 267
1[3]	179, 182, 320
1[9, 10]	318
1[9]	272, 318
1[10-17]	52, 244, 314, 319, 322, 324, 329, 347
1[10]	204, 323
1[13]	282
1[15]	312
1[18-20]	319, 322, 324 f.
1[21-26]	313, 319, 321 f., 325
1[23]	42
1[24]	255, 318
1[27-31]	320
2[2-4]	320, 322
2[6-22]	275, 319, 322, 326, 328, 343, 360
2[7-11]	322
2[7]	36
2[10]	318
2[12]	255
2[19]	318
2[21]	318
3[1-4][1]	319

Isaiah (*cont.*):

3[1-15]	322
3[1]	318
3[8]	322, 329
3[12]	320
3[13-15]	244
3[14, 15]	38
3[14]	328
3[15]	307, 312
3[16]–4[1]	322
3[16, 17]	271
3[16]	322
4[2-6]	320, 344
4[3]	322
5[1-24]	319
5[1-7]	161, 244, 319 f., 322, 326 f., 362
5[3]	146
5[6]	295
5[8-24]	319, 322
5[8-24a]	328 f.
5[8-10]	259, 307
5[8]	41, 194
5[13]	320
5[18-23]	177
5[19-21]	322
5[19]	318, 323
5[21]	322
5[23]	42, 193, 307, 313
5[24]	204, 318, 323
5[25-30]	322
5[26]	318
6[1-13]	87, 241, 318 f., 322, 329 ff., 355
6[1-5]	149
6[1]	99, 315, 326
6[3]	318
6[5]	52, 318
6[7]	355
6[8]	376
6[9-13]	291
6[10]	320
7[1-17]	322
7[1-9]	13, 104, 227 f., 316, 319, 321, 331 ff.,

Isaiah (*cont.*):

	336, 342
7[2]	318
7[3]	111, 321, 323, 331, 335 f.
7[4, 5]	101
7[6]	102
7[9]	345
7[10-17]	316, 333 f.
7[13]	318
7[20]	56, 244, 318, 339
7[21, 22]	334
8[1-4]	247, 322, 332, 342
8[2]	362
8[3]	242
8[4]	336
8[5-8a]	316, 322, 335
8[6]	320
8[11, 12]	320
8[11]	270, 370
8[14]	6
8[16-18]	316, 322, 335 f.
8[16]	204, 246 f.
8[17]	331
8[18]	334
8[20]	204
9[2-7]	320, 322, 336 ff.
9[4]	275
9[6]	190
9[7]	318
9[8]–10[4]	319, 322
9[8]	363
9[16]	320
10[1, 2]	42
10[5-15]	58, 316, 318 f., 322, 331, 338 ff.
10[5]	56, 259, 339, 344
10[9]	277
10[13-19]	279
10[13]	167
10[15]	179
10[17]	323
10[19]	174
10[20, 21]	332
10[20]	323

Isaiah (*cont.*):

10^{22}	332
10$^{24-27}$	318, 320, 323
10^{24}	157
10$^{27-32}$	307
11$^{1-9}$	320, 323, 336, 338
11^2	190
11$^{6-9}$	48
11$^{6-8}$	337
11$^{10-16}$	320
11^{11}	332
11^{16}	332
12$^{1-6}$	320
13$^{2-22}$	275
14$^{9-20}$	284
14^{13}	158
14$^{24-27}$	158, 316 f., 323, 339
14$^{28-32}$	319
14^{32}	158, 320
17$^{1-11}$	323
17$^{1-6}$	319
17$^{12-14}$	158, 320, 323, 346
18$^{1-7}$	319
18$^{1-6}$	16, 316, 323
19$^{1-15}$	319, 323
19$^{11-15}$	176
19^{11}	167
20$^{1-6}$	16, 239, 316, 319, 321, 323, 341 f.
20^2	309
20^3	334
22$^{1-14}$	316, 319, 321, 323, 342 f.
22^1	229
22^4	320
22^6	104, 267
22^{11}	111, 130
22^{12}	342
22^{13}	244
22$^{15-22}$	323
22^{16}	39
22^{22}	318
23^8	39

Isaiah (*cont.*):

27^1	155
28$^{1-2}$	323
28$^{1-13}$	316, 319, 344 f.
28^3	339
28$^{5,\ 6}$	320
28^5	332
28^7	375
28$^{9,\ 10}$	174
28^{11}	320
28$^{14-22}$	316, 319, 321, 345 f.
28$^{14,\ 15}$	322
28^{14}	320
28^{16}	321, 345
28^{17}	280
28^{21}	318, 320, 328
28$^{23-29}$	179, 323
29$^{1-8}$	238, 319, 346 ff.
29$^{1-4}$	323
29^1	318
29$^{5-8}$	320 f., 323
29^6	255
29$^{7,\ 8}$	158
29^7	339
29$^{9-12}$	323
29$^{11,\ 12}$	336
29^{12}	174
29$^{13-16}$	176
29$^{13,\ 14}$	320, 323
29^{13}	214
29$^{15,\ 16}$	179, 323
29$^{17-24}$	320
30$^{1-7}$	113, 316, 348
30$^{1-5}$	323
30$^{1,\ 2}$	317
30$^{8-14}$	323
30^8	247
30^9	204
30^{10}	311 f., 360
30^{11}	323
30$^{15-17}$	316, 323, 332
30$^{15,\ 16}$	322
30^{15}	227, 323, 335, 345
30$^{18-26}$	320

Isaiah (*cont.*):

30^{22}	296
30^{28}	335
30^{33}	103
31$^{1-3}$	5, 113, 154, 167, 176, 316, 321, 323, 348
31^1	322 f.
31$^{4,\ 5}$	158, 321, 323, 347
31^5	320
31$^{8,\ 9}$	320
32$^{1-8}$	320
32^5	328
32$^{9-14}$	323
32$^{15-20}$	320
33$^{17-24}$	320
34$^{1-17}$	275
34$^{5-7}$	268
36^1–39^8	323
36–37	158
37^2	242
37$^{31,\ 32}$	332
37^{32}	338
37$^{33-35}$	320
37^{35}	318
38^1	242
38$^{5,\ 6}$	318
38$^{9-20}$	323
39^3	106, 242
40$^{1-11}$	87
40^4	309
40$^{6,\ 7}$	348
40$^{9-17}$	150
40^{26}	154
40^{28}	196
42^1	313
42^4	204
42$^{5-17}$	214
42^5	255
43$^{5-7}$	59
43$^{15-21}$	150
43^{15}	52
43$^{16-21}$	59
43$^{18,\ 19}$	56
43$^{22-24}$	314
44^6	255

430   INDEX OF SCRIPTURE REFERENCES

Isaiah (cont.):		Jeremiah (cont.):		Jeremiah (cont.):	
44^{9-20}	256, 299	1^{4-12}	355 f.	$5^{4, 5}$	174, 350, 382 f.
45^{13}	59	1^{4-10}	241	5^{12-14}	240, 369, 377
45^{18}	255	1^5	242, 270	5^{14}	241, 270
45^{20}	363	$1^{9, 10}$	363	5^{15-17}	358
46^{1-7}	363	1^{11-14}	282	5^{20-29}	180
46^7	256	$1^{11, 12}$	241	5^{21}	361
47^4	255	1^{14}	358, 360	$5^{30, 31}$	375 f.
47^{13}	167	1^{18}	120	5^{31}	350, 360, 375
48^{20-22}	59	2^{1-13}	356 f.	6^{1-8}	358
49^1	355	2^{1-8}	50	6^1	360
49^2	363	2^2	349, 357	6^9	362
49^5	355	2^{5-7}	204	6^{11}	187, 241, 270, 376
49^7	362	2^8	45, 204, 350, 372, 376	$6^{13, 14}$	235, 376
49^{8-13}	59			6^{13}	376, 383
$49^{22, 23}$	152	2^{13}	370	6^{14}	239, 287, 360
49^{26}	163	2^{20}	48	$6^{18, 19}$	361
51^4	204	2^{21}	161, 362	6^{19-21}	314
51^6	255	2^{22}	325	6^{19}	204
51^7	204	2^{23}	45	6^{20}	159
51^{9-11}	150, 155	2^{30}	180	6^{22-26}	358
52^7	52, 150	3^{1-5}	349, 357 f.	6^{22}	360
53^7	368	3^2	48, 291, 362	6^{23}	360
54^{10}	219	3^4	349	6^{24}	361
54^{12}	162	3^6	352, 359	6^{25}	361
54^{13}	382	3^8	174	6^{26}	360
55^3	53	3^{14}	382	7^{1-26}	146
$55^{10, 11}$	363	$3^{16, 17}$	149	7^{1-15}	238, 350, 352, 363 ff., 377 f.
$55^{12, 13}$	59	$3^{19}-4^4$	357 f.	$7^{8, 9}$	350
58^{3-9}	314	3^{19-22}	323	7^9	45
58^{5-7}	314	3^{22}	349	7^{10}	313, 370
59^{21}	313	3^{23}	350, 357, 362	7^{12-14}	307
60^3	132	4^2	161	7^{14}	313
60^{16}	163	4^{5-31}	349, 352 f., 358 ff.	7^{16}	240
61^{1-3}	313	4^6	360	7^{18}	189, 296
63^{1-6}	268	4^7	362	7^{21-28}	314
65^{10}	295	$4^{9, 10}$	239, 255, 312	7^{21-26}	350, 352, 363 ff.
66^{1-4}	314	4^{10}	376	7^{21-23}	52, 276
66^{23}	282	4^{19}	241	7^{21}	135
		4^{22}	180, 350	7^{22}	137
Jeremiah:		4^{23-26}	179 f., 359, 369	7^{23}	383
1^{1-3}	352, 354 f., 384 f.	4^{27}	362	$7^{25, 26}$	242
1^1	289	5^{1-14}	316 ff.	7^{30-34}	343
1^2	352 359	5^2	161, 350	7^{31}	103
1^3	352	5^3	180, 297, 350, 370		

Jeremiah (*cont.*):

8^2	123
$8^{4, 5}$	179
8^7	180, 182, 350
$8^{8, 9}$	177, 204, 350, 367
8^{10-12}	376
8^{10}	177, 376
8^{14-17}	358
8^{16}	361
$8^{18}-9^1$	350, 365 f., 371
9^{1-6}	350
9^1	365
9^3	350
9^5	350
$9^{23, 24}$	180
10^{6-12}	166
$10^{6, 7}$	52, 152
10^{10}	52
10^{12-16}	180
11^{1-8}	352, 366 ff.
11^2	146
11^{14}	241
11^{15}	314, 368
$11^{18}-12^6$	348, 350, 368 f.
11^{18-20}	152
11^{20}	372 f.
12^{1-6}	152
12^3	270, 355, 368
12^4	375
12^6	373
12^{10}	362
13^{1-11}	239 f.
13^1	228
13^{20-27}	361
$13^{22, 23}$	179
13^{23}	182
13^{25}	350
14^{11}	241
14^{13-16}	235, 360, 376
$14^{13, 14}$	235
14^{13}	287
14^{14}	235, 350
14^{21}	149
15^{10-21}	234, 241, 348,

Jeremiah (*cont.*):

	368–71
15^{11}	372
15^{15-21}	152
15^{17}	187, 350, 376
15^{19}	355
16^1	350
17^2	135
17^{5-11}	182
17^5	348
$17^{9, 10}$	371
17^{11}	180
17^{14-18}	152, 348, 368, 371
17^{15}	328
17^{16}	372
17^{18}	368
17^{23}	180
$18^{3, 4}$	37
18^{13-15}	180, 183
18^{13}	273
18^{18-23}	348, 368, 371 f.
18^{18}	177, 204, 356, 376
18^{19-23}	152
18^{20}	241, 370
18^{23}	368
19^{1-15}	239
19^5	45, 103
19^{13}	123
19^{14}	242
20^{1-6}	350, 381
20^2	242
20^{7-18}	238, 241, 349, 370, 372 f.
20^{7-13}	152
20^{7-11}	348, 368
20^7	370
20^9	270
20^{10}	372
20^{11}	368
20^{14-18}	152, 348, 368, 370
20^{15}	337
21^{1-10}	241
21^1	381

Jeremiah (*cont.*):

22^3	42
22^{10-19}	352
22^{10-12}	127
22^{10}	122
22^{13-19}	127, 349, 351 f., 373 f.
22^{13-17}	313
$22^{13, 14}$	30
$22^{15, 16}$	181, 366
22^{16}	193
$22^{18, 19}$	387
22^{24-30}	353
22^{24}	127
$23^{7, 8}$	56
23^{9-32}	234, 238, 281, 354, 374 ff., 381
23^9	349
23^{11}	234 f., 298, 378
23^{13}	45
23^{14}	235, 272, 350
$23^{16, 17}$	235
23^{16}	235
23^{17}	287, 360
23^{18}	87, 241, 330
$23^{18, 22}$	180, 187
23^{21}	235
23^{25-32}	235 f.
23^{25}	350
23^{26}	235
23^{27}	45
23^{29}	241, 349, 363, 373
23^{30}	235
23^{32}	350
24^{1-10}	352
24^{1-7}	349
24^1	37, 129, 380
24^2	344
24^3	356
25^3	352, 359
25^9	56, 339, 358, 360
25^{10}	164
25^{13}	242
25^{30}	267
26^{1-24}	363, 377 ff.

Jeremiah (*cont.*):

26^{1-16}	238
26^1	352, 364
26^{4-16}	242
26^5	242
26^6	365
26^{7-24}	368
26^7	375
26^9	365
26^{11}	375
26^{17-19}	313
$26^{18, 19}$	308
26^{23}	39
26^{24}	120, 131, 354
$27-29$	126, 129
27^1-28^{17}	239, 376
27^{1-11}	354
27^6	56, 339, 352
27^9	377
27^{10}	350
27^{14-16}	350
$27^{14, 15}$	360
27^{18}	235, 241
27^{20}	380
28^{1-17}	354
28^4	132, 380
28^{5-8}	242
$28^{8, 9}$	239
28^8	363
28^9	235, 360
28^{14}	352
28^{15}	350
29^{1-7}	349, 354, 379 f.
29^1	242
29^3	120
29^8	312, 377
29^9	350
29^{11}	349
29^{19}	242
29^{21}	350
29^{23}	350
29^{24-32}	238, 354, 379 ff.
29^{26}	92, 256
29^{31}	350
30^2	247

Jeremiah (*cont.*):

$30^{23, 24}$	376
31^4	273
31^{21}	273
31^{31-34}	51, 59, 188, 349, 362, 381 ff.
31^{34}	215
32^{1-15}	239 f., 349, 354, 381, 383 f., 387
32^{6-15}	41
32^{9-15}	174
32^{10-12}	336
$32^{12, 13}$	385
32^{29}	123
32^{35}	103
33^{19-22}	53
34^{1-22}	354
34^7	129
34^{8-22}	387
34^{8-16}	42, 224
34^{18}	367
35^{1-19}	95
35^4	234, 375
35^{13}	180
35^{15}	242
36^{1-32}	246, 353, 379, 384 ff.
36^2	352, 359
36^4	174, 351, 384
36^{10}	120, 378
36^{11}	120
36^{12}	167, 378 f.
36^{25}	379
36^{26}	87
36^{29}	353
36^{30}	374
37^1-45^5	387 ff.
37^1-39^{10}	354
37^{1-10}	241
37^{3-10}	129
37^3	381
37^5	130
37^{6-10}	21
37^{11-15}	350, 384
37^{15}	167

Jeremiah (*cont.*):

37^{16-21}	384
37^{17}	129
38^{1-13}	350, 384
38^4	130
38^{14-28}	129, 254, 384
38^{24-28}	32
$39^{11}-44^{30}$	354
39^{14}	120, 131
40^6	120, 131
40^7-43^7	131
$40^{9, 10}$	131
$41^{4, 5}$	119
41^{12}	36
42^2	241
42^{20}	241
43^{1-7}	385
43^{8-13}	239 f.
43^{10}	56, 339
44^4	242
44^{15-19}	189
45^{1-5}	385
45^1	242
46^1	242
46^2	20
46^{11}	366
47^1	242
48^{22}	291
48^{37}	283
49^7	167
49^{18}	272
49^{23-27}	13
50^{20}	332
50^{35}	167
51^8	366
51^{57}	167
51^{59-64}	239 f.
51^{59}	385
52^{11}	130
52^{17-23}	131
52^{28-30}	131
52^{28}	129

Lamentations:

1^8	294

Lamentations (*cont.*):		Ezekiel (*cont.*):		Daniel:	
2^8	117	15^7	284	1^{1-21}	169
2^{10}	342	16	286	2^{1-45}	377
2^{20}	234, 375	16^{21}	103	2^{47}	264
$4^{4,\ 5,\ 10}$	130	16^{38-40}	294	2^{48}	132
4^6	272	16^{46-58}	272	3^{28-30}	264
4^{20}	145, 151	17^4	39	4^{1-3}	264
$4^{21,\ 22}$	268	20^{26}	103	4^{34-37}	264
		21^{21}	236, 296	6^{25-28}	264
Ezekiel:		22^{12}	42	7^{9-13}	87
1^2	132	22^{26}	204, 313		
1^3	370	22^{29}	230	Hosea:	
1^4	360	23	286	$1-3$	357
2^2	313	24^{15-27}	240	1^1	289
2^8-3^3	247, 355	24^{17}	312	1^{2-9}	287-91, 293, 295
3^{12}	313	25^{12-14}	268	1^2	286, 288
3^{14}	270, 313, 370	27^{1-36}	25	1^4	93, 289
3^{22}	370	$27^{8,\ 9}$	165	$1^{6,\ 7}$	288
3^{24}	313	27^{10-25}	25	$1^{10}-2^1$	287 f.
4^{1-17}	240	27^{13}	268	2^{2-15}	287 ff., 293 ff.
5^{1-17}	240	27^{15}	271	2^{2-13}	357
5^{12}	284	27^{17}	25, 39, 366	2^{2-5}	288 f.
6^{1-7}	284	27^{23}	267	2^2	286
$7^{26,\ 27}$	372	28^3	29	2^4	286
7^{26}	120, 177, 204, 356	$28^{4,\ 5}$	165	2^5	286
8^1	370	30^{1-19}	275	2^{6-13}	288
8^{14}	291	34^{23-27}	160	$2^{6,\ 7}$	296
8^{16}	123, 262	36^{26-28}	382 f.	2^8	45, 139, 273, 298
$9^{2,\ 3}$	174	37^{1-14}	363, 382	$2^{10,\ 11}$	314
9^2	360	37^1	370	2^{11}	282, 296
10^4	330	37^{15-23}	240	2^{13}	45, 276, 296
11^1	313	$38-39$	158, 275	$2^{14,\ 15}$	59, 286 ff.,
11^9	284	$38^{19,\ 20}$	298		297 f., 304, 356
11^{17-21}	382	40^{5-16}	31	2^{16-23}	287 f.
12^{1-20}	240	$40^{19,\ 20}$	116	$2^{16,\ 17}$	45
12^{14}	284	$43^{15,\ 16}$	347	2^{19}	297
12^{24}	287, 360	44^{10-14}	123	3^{1-5}	289, 293, 295 ff.
13^{1-23}	281	44^{23}	204	$3^{1,\ 2}$	288
13^{1-16}	374	44^{24}	203	3^1	215, 291
$13^{2,\ 3}$	235	45^{10-12}	282	3^{3-5}	294
$13^{6,\ 7}$	235	45^{13-16}	32	$3^{3,\ 4}$	288
13^9	187	45^{21-25}	138	3^5	288
13^{10-12}	287	45^{25}	137	4^{1-3}	179, 288, 297 f.
13^{10}	235, 312	47^{8-12}	157, 160	4^1	286, 297, 302, 315
13^{19}	264, 281, 307, 312	47^{15}	97	4^2	286

Hosea (cont.):

4³	182, 360, 369
4⁴⁻¹⁹	288, 298 ff.
4⁴⁻¹⁴	314
4⁵	285
4⁶	204, 297, 328
4⁷, ⁸	302
4¹⁰	286
4¹¹	179
4¹²⁻¹⁴	48, 286, 357
4¹³, ¹⁴	357
4¹⁴	179, 269, 291
4¹⁵	50, 143, 161, 267, 272, 293, 300
4¹⁶	182
5¹⁻⁷	288
5¹	176
5⁴	286, 299
5⁵	283
5⁶	285, 302, 314
5⁸⁻¹⁵	288 f., 300 f.
5⁸	267, 299
5⁹	285
5¹⁰	40, 176, 179, 194, 285
5¹²	179, 244
5¹³⁻¹⁵	301, 304
5¹³	286
5¹⁴	285, 306
5¹⁵⁻6⁶	288
6¹⁻⁶	301 f.
6¹⁻³	244
6¹	285
6⁴⁻⁶	286, 306
6⁴	297, 303
6⁵	363
6⁶	296 f., 314
6⁷⁻⁷¹⁶	288
6⁹	49
6¹⁰	286
6¹¹	293
6¹¹ᵇ⁻7¹²	289, 296, 302 ff.
6¹¹ᵇ⁻7²	306
7¹, ²	286

Hosea (cont.):

7¹	288
7⁵	179, 328
7⁸	286
7¹⁰	283
7¹¹	176, 179, 182, 286, 301, 305 f.
7¹⁴	256
7¹⁶	305
8¹⁻¹⁴	288
8¹	285
8⁴⁻⁶	286
8⁴	4, 176
8⁵, ⁶	73
8⁷⁻¹⁴	288
8⁷	176, 179
8⁸⁻¹⁰	304
8⁹, ¹⁰	286, 301
8⁹	176, 179, 182, 286, 305 f.
8¹¹⁻¹³	314
8¹³	302, 305
8¹⁴	35, 285 f.
9¹⁻⁹	288
9¹	48, 286
9³	295, 305
9⁴	302
9⁵	137, 276
9⁶	305
9⁷	92, 256, 285
9¹⁰⁻¹⁷	288
9¹⁰	45, 285, 295, 356
9¹⁵	50, 176, 285
10¹⁻⁸	288
10¹, ²	296
10¹	161
10⁵, ⁶	286
10⁵	73, 267, 299
10⁶	301
10⁸	267
10⁹⁻¹⁵	288
10¹¹	293
10¹²	297, 358
10¹³	176, 179, 286, 301
11¹⁻¹¹	304 ff.

Hosea (cont.):

11¹⁻⁹	287
11¹⁻⁴	209, 288, 295, 323
11¹	50, 215
11²	45
11⁵⁻⁷	288
11⁵	306
11⁶	285
11⁸, ⁹	287, 303
11⁸	272, 288
11⁹	288
11¹⁰, ¹¹	287 f.
11¹¹	179, 182
11¹²	293
12¹	286, 301
12²	293
12⁶	297
12⁷, ⁸	286
12⁷	39, 179, 282
12⁸	35
12⁹	50, 56, 288, 295, 297
12¹¹	50
12¹³	286, 295
13¹	45
13²	73
13⁴, ⁵	288
13⁴	50, 286, 295
13⁵	355
13⁷⁻¹⁶	288
13⁷, ⁸	182, 285, 306
13⁹	285
13¹⁰	176
13¹¹	285
13¹³	179
13¹⁴	218
13¹⁶	285
14¹⁻⁹	287 f.
14³	179, 286, 301
14⁹	179

Joel:

2¹⁻¹¹	217, 275, 360
2²⁰	360
2²⁸, ²⁹	313, 382
2²⁸	348

Joel (*cont.*):

3^{4-8}	267
3^{9-21}	158
3^{16}	267
3^{18}	157

Amos:

1^1–2^{16}	266 ff.
1^1	265, 281, 289
1^2	284
1^3–2^{16}	265, 329, 339, 355
1^3–2^8	178, 302
1^{3-5}	284, 299
1^3	153
1^5	104, 284, 343
1^{6-8}	284
1^{13}	101
2^{6-8}	97
$2^{6,\,7}$	193
2^6	41
$2^{7,\,8}$	265, 276, 314
2^7	291
2^8	42, 229
2^{9-11}	265, 305
$2^{9,\,10}$	45
2^9	117
2^{10}	50
2^{12}	311
2^{14-16}	283
3^{1-8}	270
$3^{1,\,2}$	50
3^1	273
3^2	55, 58, 265, 320, 355
3^{3-8}	178, 244
$3^{4,\,5}$	182
3^7	87, 187, 242
3^8	242
3^9–4^3	271 f.
3^{10}	97, 265
3^{12}	265, 373
3^{14}	283
3^{15}	24, 35, 88, 97, 265, 279
4^{1-3}	265, 307

Amos (*cont.*):

4^1	38, 97, 193, 310
4^2	283
4^4–5^{15}	272 ff.
$4^{4,\,5}$	265, 276, 314, 347
4^4	135, 143, 220
4^5	137
4^{6-12}	357
4^{11}	306, 324, 373, 376
4^{12}	56
4^{13}	284, 309
$5^{1,\,2}$	56
5^1	265
5^2	244
5^3	178
5^{4-15}	276
5^{4-6}	274
$5^{4,\,5}$	314
5^4	273
5^5	50, 143
5^7	97, 279
$5^{8,\,9}$	273, 284
5^{10-13}	97, 307
5^{10}	193, 203, 311
$5^{11,\,12}$	265
5^{11}	35, 97
5^{12}	203, 265
$5^{14,\,15}$	255, 274
5^{14}	312 f.
5^{15}	203, 265
5^{16-27}	274 ff., 305
5^{18-20}	319, 326, 329, 361
5^{18}	265, 312
5^{19}	178, 283
5^{21-25}	314, 365
5^{21-24}	265
5^{25}	178
6^{1-14}	277 ff.
6^1	273
$6^{2,\,3}$	178
6^2	339
6^{4-7}	265
6^{4-6}	328
6^4	35, 88, 97, 271, 279
6^8	283

Amos (*cont.*):

6^{12}	178, 265
6^{13}	97
6^{14}	97
6^{24}	24
7^1–8^3	241, 280 ff., 355
7^{1-9}	283, 320
7^2	240
7^3	265
7^5	240
7^6	265
7^{7-9}	346
$7^{7,\,8}$	117
$7^{8,\,9}$	265
7^8	178
$7^{9,\,10}$	265
7^9	283
7^{10-17}	373
7^{10-13}	176
$7^{12,\,13}$	264
7^{12}	312
7^{13}	73, 143, 272
$7^{14,\,15}$	241 f., 265
7^{14}	266
7^{15}	260, 264
7^{16}	311
8^{1-3}	265, 283, 356
8^2	178, 293
8^{4-14}	282 f.
8^{4-7}	97, 274
$8^{5,\,6}$	265
8^{10}	276
8^{14}	107, 161, 327
9^{1-8a}	283 f.
9^{1-4}	377
$9^{5,\,6}$	273, 283
$9^{7,\,8}$	55, 265
9^7	50, 104, 178, 265, 267, 320, 339
9^{8b-15}	284 f.
9^{11-15}	266
9^{13}	160

Obadiah:

12	268

Micah:

1–3	308
1^1	289, 306, 308
1$^{2-9}$	308 f.
1$^{2-4}$	308
1^6	307 f.
1^7	308
1^9	307
1$^{10-16}$	307
1^{14}	306, 308
1^{16}	307
2$^{1-11}$	309 ff.
2$^{1-5}$	259, 328
2$^{1, 2}$	41, 194, 307
2$^{3, 4}$	307
2$^{8-10}$	307
2^{10}	307
2$^{12, 13}$	308
3$^{1-12}$	312 f.
3$^{1-4}$	307
3$^{2, 3}$	309
3$^{5-12}$	238
3$^{5-8}$	242, 307
3$^{5-7}$	236
3^5	234, 264, 281, 287, 360
3^8	238, 254, 267
3$^{9-12}$	238
3^{11}	42, 56, 177, 193, 204, 235 f., 264, 281, 307, 356, 372, 375
3^{12}	53, 307, 314, 379
4–5	398
4^4	39
4$^{6, 7}$	332
4$^{11-13}$	152
5$^{7-9}$	332
5^{13}	296
6–7	398
6$^{1-5}$	398
6$^{6-8}$	239, 301 f., 308, 310, 314 f., 324, 365
6$^{6, 7}$	136
6^6	314
6^7	103

Micah (*cont.*):

6$^{9-16}$	308
6$^{10, 11}$	282
7$^{1-4}$	308
7^1	344
7^3	42
7$^{11-17}$	152

Nahum:

1$^{3-5}$	155
1^{12}–3^{19}	118
3$^{5-7}$	294
3$^{8-10}$	20

Habakkuk:

1^{13}	369
2^2	247
2$^{6-20}$	239
2^{20}	309
3$^{4-15}$	155
3^6	309

Zephaniah:

1^2–2^{15}	275
1$^{2, 3}$	298
1^5	123
1^{11}	39
1^{12}	328, 363
1$^{14-18}$	217
1$^{14-16}$	361
3$^{3, 4}$	372
3^4	375
3$^{11-13}$	332

Haggai:

2$^{11-13}$	204

Zechariah:

1$^{18-21}$	86
2^{12}	264
3$^{1, 2}$	87
3^{10}	39
5$^{1-4}$	363
7^{12}	313
9^3	25

Zechariah (*cont.*):

9^{10}	283
12^{11}	77
13$^{4, 5}$	281
13^4	260
13^6	256
14$^{1-21}$	158
14^5	266
14^8	157, 160
14^9	39, 52, 150, 152

Malachi:

1$^{2-5}$	268
2^7	204
3^2	325
3^5	230
3^{15}	369
4^5	262

APOCRYPHA

Wisdom of Solomon:

16^{12}	363
18$^{14-16}$	363

Ecclesiasticus:

7$^{4, 5}$	196
19^{10}	196
24^{23}	188
26^5	267
31$^{12-18}$	195
38^{24} 39^5	170 f.
39^1	188
48^{10}	262
51^{23}	171

NEW TESTAMENT

Matthew:

1^{23}	334
5^{22}	104
5$^{25, 26}$	196
6$^{2-4}$	272
6^7	324
7$^{24-27}$	345 f.
10$^{34-36}$	368
11^{14}	262

Matthew (*cont.*):

16^{14}	262
16^{18}	345
17$^{3,\,4}$	262
17$^{10-13}$	262
21^{13}	364
23^{5}	215
26$^{59,\,60}$	260

Mark:

1^{24}	251
3^{21}	368
9$^{4,\,5}$	262
9^{43}	104
12$^{28-33}$	213, 315
12^{30}	215
14$^{12-16}$	138
14$^{12-15}$	125
14$^{32-42}$	370
15$^{1-15}$	378

Luke:

1^{17}	262
4$^{16-30}$	368
9^{8}	262
9^{61}	261
11$^{47-51}$	379
12$^{16-21}$	273
13^{34}	365

Luke (*cont.*):

14$^{7-10}$	196
14$^{15-26}$	227
14^{20}	228
18$^{29,\,30}$	227
29^{20}	373

John:

1$^{1-14}$	191
1^{21}	262
3$^{19-21}$	303
4$^{10-15}$	356
4$^{16-19}$	251
7^{38}	356
12$^{46-50}$	303
18$^{28-38}$	378

Acts:

20$^{9-12}$	251

Romans:

2$^{28,\,29}$	358
11^{22}	285

1 Corinthians:

1^{24}	191
1^{30}	191
9$^{16,\,17}$	373

2 Corinthians:

3^{6}	381
5^{17}	381
11^{24}	230

Galatians:

1^{15}	355

Ephesians:

5^{25}	296

Colossians:

1$^{15-17}$	191
2^{3}	191

Hebrews:

1^{3}	191
8$^{8-13}$	381
8^{9}	382
10$^{15-17}$	381

1 John:

4^{19}	218

Revelation:

4^{11}	191
20$^{9,\,10}$	158
22^{13}	191

PRINTED IN GREAT BRITAIN
AT THE UNIVERSITY PRESS, OXFORD
BY VIVIAN RIDLER
PRINTER TO THE UNIVERSITY

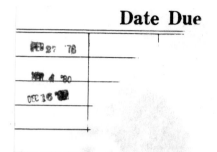

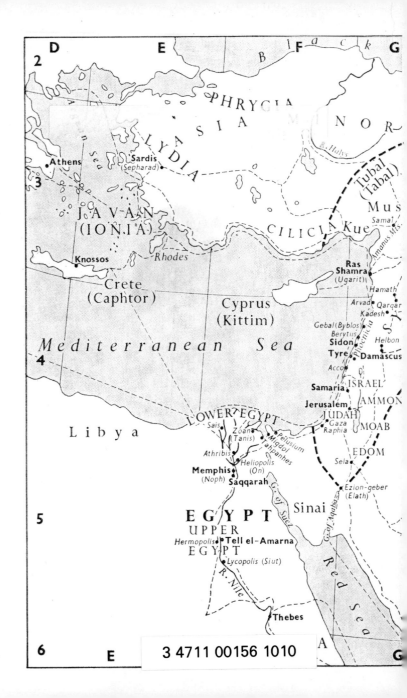

D 2   **E**   B *l* a *c* k   **F**   **G**

PHRYGIA

A S I A   M I N O R

R. Halys

LYDIA

•Athens

Sardis (Sepharad)

3

Tubal (Tabal)

Mus

J A V A N (I O N I A)

Samal

•Knossos   *Rhodes*

CILICIA Kue

Amanus Mts.

Ras Shamra (Ugarit)

Crete (Caphtor)

Hamath

Cyprus (Kittim)

Arvad   Qarqar
Kadesh

Gebal (Byblos)
Berytus
Sidon

Helbon

M e d i t e r r a n e a n   S e a

Tyre   •**Damascus**

4

Acco

Samaria   ISRAEL

AMMON

Jerusalem

JUDAH

L i b y a

LOWER EGYPT

Sais   *Zoan* (Tanis)

Gaza
Raphia   MOAB

Pelusium
Migdol
Tahpanhes

EDOM

Athribis

Sela

Heliopolis (On)

Memphis (Noph)
Saqqarah

Ezion-geber (Elath)

5

E G Y P T

Sinai

UPPER

Hermopolis •**Tell el–Amarna**

E G Y P T

G. of Suez
G. of Aqaba

Lycopolis (Siut)

Red Sea

R. Nile

•**Thebes**

6   **E**   3 4711 00156 1010   A   **G**

The Lightning Queen

LAURA RESAU

Scholastic Press / *New York*

Library of Congress Cataloging-in-Publication Data available

ISBN 978-0-545-80084-6

10 9 8 7 6 5 4 3 2 1   15 16 17 18 19

Printed in the U.S.A.   23
First edition, November 2015

Book design by Abby Dening

For Bran, who lights up my world

Table of Contents

CRACKLE: Mateo; The Hill of Dust, Oaxaca, Mexico; Present Day   1

RUMBLE: Teo; The Hill of Dust, Oaxaca, Mexico; Long, Long Ago   9

DROP: Mateo; The Hill of Dust, Oaxaca, Mexico; Present Day   89

GUST: Teo; The Hill of Dust, Oaxaca, Mexico; Long, Long Ago   93

HUSH: Mateo; The Hill of Dust, Oaxaca, Mexico; Present Day   201

BOOM: Teo; The Hill of Dust, Oaxaca, Mexico; Long, Long Ago   205

BURST: Mateo; The Hill of Dust, Oaxaca, Mexico; Present Day   253

ZAP!: Mateo; Suburban Maryland; Present Day   271

Author's Note   305

Mexican Spanish–English Glossary and Pronunciation Guide   313

Mixteco–English Glossary and Pronunciation Guide   317

Romani–English Glossary and Pronunciation Guide   319

Acknowledgments   321

About the Author   325

CRACKLE

Mateo

THE HILL OF DUST,
OAXACA, MEXICO

Present Day

TUG OF MAGIC

At the brink of every summer, something yanks me toward the Hill of Dust. Something like fishing line, spooling out from the heart of the hill, across Mexico and all the way up to Maryland, zipping through cul-de-sacs, searching me out, trailing bits of magic all the way. It doesn't even matter if I'm holed up in our basement rec room, lost in Xbox with my buddies . . . somehow the string finds me and ties itself to a place smack in my center.

Then it reels me back in.

Its pull is strong on the first airplane, even stronger on the second, and stronger still on the bus bumping its way into the mountains. And at the foot of the Hill of Dust, the pull is so strong, my sneakers barely touch the ground, and I'm nearly floating up the dirt path to the very tip-top. Finally, I lurch straight into its heartbeat.

Which is where I am now, sitting on a small wooden chair across from Grandpa Teo in his healing hut. I'm missing Xbox already, but mostly just buzzing from the journey. Mom's right across the muddy courtyard, inside the adobe kitchen, catching up with her great-aunts and great-uncles. You'd think a robotics engineer might feel out of place here, but she always settles right in. After all, this is where she grew up with Grandpa and Grandma before she went to college in Maryland, before she married her American boyfriend, before they had me.

Since Dad has to work, it's usually just me and Mom who come here. Every visit gives me that swooping, soaring feeling, like a Ferris wheel ride. And somehow, this space here—Grandpa's small, old healing room—is the hub.

It's dark, cave-like, and mostly empty except for an altar covered in ancient things like tin-framed saints, and fresh things like white flowers, and glowing-sweet things like candles. It all feels outside of time—the packed dirt floors and clay walls and film of incense smoke coating everything. I bet I could've been sitting here fifty years ago and it would've felt the same.

Grandpa and I stare at each other, which is both weird and not weird. It's like looking into a mirror, seeing myself when I'm old, only subbing an Orioles cap for his palm hat, and a Ravens jersey for his white collared shirt. All my gray-haired relatives say he was my spitting image when he was twelve, especially the crazy-thick eyelashes.

"Mateo," his voice rumbles, deep as the engine of Dad's old pickup truck. His eyes widen, like he's been waiting all year for this moment. "I need your help."

Whoa. My help? This is new. I just got here and we usually have small talk first. School, soccer, and guitar lessons on my end. Corn harvest, baby goats, and weather on his end. "Sure, anything, Grandpa."

He takes something from his shirt pocket, raises it in the candle's glow. It's some sort of necklace . . . a string of coins. Coins that flash here and there, kind of shimmering like far-off city lights.

I peer closer. The coins are freshly polished but old, the stamped faces worn smooth, the words foreign, nothing like Spanish or English.

He holds the necklace before me, letting it swing back and forth. I wonder if he's mesmerizing me like one of those old-fashioned hypnotists with pocket watches.

Sure enough, with every sway of the coins, the heartbeat of magic grows stronger, louder, ringing in my ears, booming through my blood. "Um, what's going on, Grandpa?"

His face beams like a little kid's, all fresh and new. "It's a long story," he says. "A path paved in wonder. A path that stretches to long, long ago." He speaks Spanish, which I know, thanks to Mom, but his words are so much different from hers. Hers are about car pools and errands, while his are lines that sound snatched right from poems and songs.

He leans closer, the coins shining spots of light onto his face like a field of fireflies. "Mateo, can you believe in the impossible?"

The pulse is growing louder, moving lower, then higher, practically a full-blown melody now. A picture of swirling, silver ribbons pops into my head. Something's happening, and it's awesome and crazy . . . but mostly awesome, I think. *Can you believe in the impossible?* I ask myself.

"Open your hand," he says, and lets the necklace spiral into my palm.

And now my heart's really thudding because sure, I've seen magical stuff here, just more like glimpses from the corner of my eye. But these coins crackling in my hand—well, this is something different. Sparks are jumping into my palm, zooming through my arm like tiny fireworks, and exploding in my chest.

Now sweat's dripping from my cheeks and an earthquake's rolling through my bones. I manage not to freak out, just barely, because Grandpa Teo's voice is comforting, like syrup streaming over pancakes, promising something delicious to come.

"Now turn away from the movie of your own life, Mateo. And look at the movie of mine."

As he speaks, his words somehow beam light onto an imagined screen, flooding the room with people and places from long, long ago. "*Mijo*, you are about to embark on a journey of marvels. Of impossible fortunes. Of a lost duck, three-legged skunk, and blind goat—all bravely loyàl. Of a girl who gathered power from storms and sang back the dead. Of an enchanted friendship that lifted souls above brutality."

He pauses, tilts his head. "Perhaps there will even be an intermission or two. But as of yet, there is no end. That, mijo, will be up to you." He winks, clears his throat, and begins.

"There was once a girl called the Queen of Lightning . . ."

I hang on to the humming, zapping necklace, and just before I slip completely into his movie, I wonder: *Okay, just what kind of help does Grandpa Teo need?*

RUMBLE

Teo

THE HILL OF DUST,
OAXACA, MEXICO
Long, Long Ago

SECRET PATH

*E*sma, Queen of Lightning, rolled into my life like the first wild storm at the end of dry season. Her caravan wound up the mountain in four horse-drawn wagons, kicking up clouds of dust all the way through the valley. I watched it with the other children, all of us parched as the earth, thirsty for . . . *something.*

"Who is it?"

"Are they coming here?"

"All the way out here?"

"But why?"

The who, we soon discovered, was the Gypsies.

The why was uncertain; no visitors came here, just the occasional patient hoping to be healed by my grandfather. Yucundiachi—the Hill of Dust—was a cluster of adobe and wood huts surrounding a single stone cathedral, perched on the peak like a lonely bird, waiting. Our village was not on the way to anywhere. And there was little reason to seek it out.

Yet by some miracle, the Gypsies must be headed here. Like fate, the road led only here. There was simply nowhere else to go.

On bare, calloused feet, we ran toward this ribbon of dust snaking up, up, up to our village. The closer we came, the more the caravan's colors shone through the haze—royal greens and golds and reds, painted blooms and swirls—a brilliant relief to the dry, cracked grays and browns that life had become. I drank them up, these Gypsies who came like sparkling rain-drops, a thrill of colors and flowers, a pulsing promise.

They didn't look like us, not Mixteco, or like other country Oaxacans. They didn't even look like the city Mexicans I'd seen . . . no, these visitors were something else entirely. The women were walking gardens, wearing long, flowered skirts, flowered shirts, flowered scarves in their hair. And the men glinted, sporting gold necklaces, coins galore, and mustaches as large as small animals.

But that's not when I first noticed Esma, Queen of Lightning. It was that night, the night of my first movie, when I truly saw her in all her electric glory.

And nothing was ever the same again.

That night, the projector beam sliced through the air as if a square had been snipped in the sky, channeling light from some secret place, as if these Gypsies knew of a hidden tunnel straight to the stars. The beam stretched to the side of the cathedral, where a makeshift screen of white sheets was hung, illuminated and dancing in the breeze. The clicking of the projector accompanied the chirping of crickets and flutter of moths. The generator hummed and croaked like a giant toad.

My entire village had gathered in the dusty plaza—the adults on wooden chairs they'd carried from their houses. The women shone in their nicest *huipiles*, woven with red zigzag patterns, and the men wore gleaming white shirts and pants, their freshly washed faces bright beneath palm hats. Children darted around, wild with anticipation. I sat in the dirt, hugging my knees, watching it all, thinking of secret paths to the moon.

"Teo!" my cousin Lalo shouted at me. "Come sit back here with us!"

I pretended not to hear. I wanted my front-row view, away from the silliness of my cousins. I was only eleven, still young enough for silliness, but the events of the past year had made me weary. My cousins called me a few more times, then gave up.

A Gypsy man my grandfather's age stood before the crowd. He twirled the tip of his massive mustache, patted the waterfall of glittering coins tumbling across the lapels of his ragged suit jacket. Once all eyes were on him, he removed his strange, tall hat with a flourish and gave a deep bow. "May I introduce myself to you, kind people. I am Ivan, Master of the Traveling Cinema, Duke of the Impossible Caravan. And we shall bestow upon you, dear friends, magic beyond your wildest dreams."

That was the gist of it, at least. His thick accent made his Spanish words as garbled as turkey squawks. Since most adults in the audience spoke only Mixteco and barely understood Spanish, his meaning was lost on many. But the words didn't matter because the dramatic curves of his mustache were enough to enchant us. It was as sleek as a muskrat, an elegant creature perched on his lip with a graceful life of its own. As the mustache danced over the Duke's mouth, two other men attended to the projector, and the Gypsy women wove through the audience, collecting our fifteen centavos. For those of us who had no money, which was nearly everyone, they kindly accepted freshly woven hats or baskets as payment.

The Duke bowed again, and we clapped and whistled in anticipation. He pulled something from his pocket, a white orb—an exotic fruit, maybe—and munched on it as he breezed back to the projector. A sharp, biting smell pierced the air.

Now came voices, crackling from the speakers, then words on-screen that few of us could read. Hardly anyone had gone to school, and those of us who had only attended for a short time. Six years ago, a one-room schoolhouse had been built in a nearby town, but along with it had come a beautiful, cruel teacher. She'd scared off every child on the Hill of Dust within a year. Although I'd lasted longer than most, I could only pick out a few easy words here and there on the screen. It didn't matter; soon enough, the story started and swept me away.

My pulse raced and I tried not to blink so that I wouldn't miss even a second. It was my first-ever movie, *Nosotros los*

Pobres—We the Poor. It starred Pedro Infante—whose neat little mustache didn't hold a candle to the Duke's—and his spunky daughter, Chachita, and the dramas of their village, far more exciting than our Hill of Dust.

During the songs, a girl's voice joined the actors'. A real girl's voice, from somewhere in the back. No one from my village, I was certain; it had to be a Gypsy. Her voice sounded surprisingly *right*, completing something that had been missing. At the funny parts, her laugh rose above others, a cackle of wild abandon.

I looked back, squinting through the beam of light. A girl stood beside the projector, mouthing the words, every single one. Her face mirrored the expressions on the actors' faces, only hers were even more dramatic, the way she flung her braids, raised her proud chin, widened her eyes. The night breeze caught her headscarf, made it flutter like wings lifting into flight.

I hadn't seen so much . . . *aliveness* . . . in a long time.

After the movie, the rest of my village was abuzz, wondering what film we'd see tomorrow, because rumor had it the Gypsies would stay two more nights! Parents ushered children back home, some half-asleep on their shoulders, some holding hands. I missed the cozy nighttime feeling of someone's hand in mine. My sister's. My mother's.

I would never touch my sister's hand again. And probably not my mother's. My mother wasn't dead, not exactly, but she was one of the only people who'd stayed at home that night. For nearly a year, she hadn't been interested in having fun or holding hands. She wasn't even interested in the *possibility* of ever being interested again. As usual, my grandfather stayed with her, worried to leave her alone. I wished he had come, too. This past year, he was the only person who made me feel at ease.

"Let's go, Teo," my aunt Perla said, half-heartedly trying to herd me with Lalo and my other cousins, but I drifted away to the edge of the milpa. Through head-high cornstalks, I watched the lingering Gypsies. Soon, all the other villagers had left. But I wouldn't let the aliveness of the night end, not yet.

The Duke was busily tending to the long spiral of film, while the projector's beam tunneled light through darkness. And the girl—she left the projector and ran toward the screen in a strange, loping gait, carrying a violin with one hand. Standing before the sheet, she tossed up her arms and let them swoop down in a deep bow, then raised her violin and eked out a melody at once mournful and cheerful. She held the bow and moved her fingers over the strings in an odd way, slightly lopsided, the same way she ran.

She belted out a song in her language, an impossibly huge voice for a small girl. She looked no older than me. Her voice was a storm, rolling in low, gathering strength, spinning and swirling into something high and keening with a life of its own. It was beautiful and wild and a little scary, as if she were channeling all the power of rainy season at once. I sucked up her raindrop notes like a half-shriveled plant.

Afterward, she took another deep bow and, in perfect Spanish, announced, "*¡Gracias!* I am Esma, Queen of Lightning!"

The other Gypsies paid her no heed; she could've been a moth fluttering around for all they cared. They were talking among themselves, carrying the equipment toward their camp. But I lingered in the shadows, soaking her in, wishing I had even a drop of that aliveness inside me.

It wasn't until the next morning that I would discover the fate of the Queen of Lightning was already woven into my own. For life.

FORTUNE

*B*efore dawn, I awoke at the rooster's first cries. For a moment, I lay there on my *petate,* rubbing my thumb over the woven palm, listening to early birds chirping and my aunts slapping tortillas in the kitchen hut. My mother snored lightly by the far wall. Had last night been a dream?

Uncertain, I crept outside, into the darkness. Half-asleep, I stumbled toward the Gypsies' camp by the river. Yes, they were there, asleep inside their circle of wagons around the ash-filled fire pit. A spontaneous smile broke out over my face. It felt strange; my mouth hadn't arranged itself like this for a long time.

All morning, along with every other child on the Hill of Dust, I followed the group of Gypsy women and children as they walked from house to house. My eyes kept landing on that girl, the one from last night who'd shot electricity right through me.

We discovered they were offering to tell fortunes in exchange for food—small bags of beans or corn or eggs. When they made it to our house, I was almost bursting. My cousins and I quieted our dogs, shooed away our turkeys and chickens, darted ahead to clear a path for the visitors.

Standing in the center of our dusty courtyard, the girl spoke to us in bold and perfect Spanish, just as she'd addressed her invisible audience the night before. "Amigos, I am Esma, Queen of Lightning." She raised her arms dramatically, speaking with the confidence of a true queen. She wore her dark hair in two thin braids, woven with tiny shells and ribbons and draped over her shoulders, while the rest of her hair was tucked back in the blue-flowered scarf. A fringe of bangs framed her forehead, and around her neck hung strands of beads, shiny brown and black and red seeds, sprinkled with glittering coins. She exuded queenliness.

Chin high, she announced, "May I present to you my royal court."

The blank expressions of the other Gypsies made me realize they didn't understand her words in Spanish. They simply nodded, then continued chattering among themselves in their own language.

With a flourish, Esma motioned to the eldest and largest woman. It looked like a field of wildflowers had blown away and stuck to her skirt and blouse and apron and headscarf. "My grandmother, Roza, Mistress of Destiny!"

The woman's nose filled most of her face, as if it were in the spotlight, and the other features—squinty eyes, shriveled lips, brown-spotted cheeks—were all forced into the shadows. The nose was a mountainside, shadowing the rest of her face, with crevices and nooks and caverns of its own. It twitched in a kind of greeting.

"And my ladies-in-waiting," Esma continued, motioning with her chin to four women who looked in their teens or early twenties.

They nodded, and, in broken Spanish, mumbled, "*Buenos días.*"

"Amigos, I shall serve as your translator this afternoon, as the Mistress reads your fortunes from her magical cards, passed down for generations. Now, in exchange for this rare opportunity, we only ask for food in return—what you see fit as payment for this once-in-a-lifetime opportunity . . ."

Esma rambled on as I murmured the translation in Mixteco. Language had always come easy for me, and my family on the Hill of Dust turned to me to translate on the rare occasions we had visitors. I'd learned Spanish the first years of my life, back in my father's village, closer to Mexico City. Stubbornly, I'd held on to the language. It was the only piece of my father left.

As Esma talked, she began looking straight at me. Blushing, I looked back, and found I could almost guess her next singsong word before she said it. Soon we were engaged in a strange dance with words, her in the lead, and me following without thinking, simply letting speech flow from her mouth to mine.

It was as if our words moved to music only the two of us could hear.

I could have gone on like this forever, but the other young Gypsy women were growing antsy, shifting from one leg to another and muttering among themselves. Clearly, they didn't understand Esma's words. And they didn't care.

At the limits of her patience, one of the women smacked Esma on the head. Another scolded her. The others grumbled in agreement.

Esma, Queen of Lightning, scowled.

So these were not her ladies-in-waiting. Just the opposite. And it appeared they only put up with her for her language skills.

The Mistress of Destiny gave a thunderous snort and, in a raspy voice, hushed the others.

Esma raised her chin and asked us, "Are you interested, amigos?"

As this was the most exciting thing that had happened in our village since—well, since ever—my aunts and uncles and cousins all nodded eagerly.

Grandfather studied our visitors with eagle eyes, being the only one who hadn't fallen completely under the Gypsies' spell. He spoke little Spanish—mainly Mixteco—but he'd come to rely on me as his translator for out-of-town patients. This had its advantages, he'd told me. When you don't know the language others speak, you watch their faces, their eyes, their movements—all of which say worlds more than flimsy words.

To my surprise, instead of setting out chairs for our guests in the courtyard, Grandfather escorted them into his healing hut. "*Por favor,* come in," he said in choppy, Mixteco-accented Spanish.

The Gypsies looked surprised as well. As we walked inside, the Mistress of Destiny said something to Esma, who translated softly. "Thank you. Most places we go, no one invites us in."

When I passed her comment to Grandfather, he crinkled his eyes at Roza. "Most outsiders don't show our people respect. To them, we're backwards *indios*. Indians who know nothing. Yet you treat us as royalty. So we, in turn, will treat you as such."

"Most outsiders distrust us," Roza replied, meeting his gaze. "To them, we are sneaky thieves. But you treat us as royalty. So we, in turn, will treat you as such."

While Esma and I murmured translations, Grandfather and Roza locked eyes, as if they shared a secret joke. As if their faces, so very different, were somehow mirrors.

The adobe hut barely fit us inside—about twenty people, pressed shoulder-to-shoulder, all the way back to the altar at the far wall, where beeswax candles flickered. As always, the earthy, sweet scents of copal incense and pine filled the dark room. The dirt floor was cool on my feet, a welcome relief from the relentless sunshine.

Slowly, with old-man movements, Grandfather dragged an empty table to the center of the room. I helped him carry several chairs from along the wall to the table. He offered them to the women, who nodded politely and sat with toddlers piled on their laps.

Roza, Mistress of Destiny, spread a shiny cloth over the table—red silk with coins and gold beads sewn into the fringe. Ceremoniously, she placed a deck of worn cards in the middle.

Once I looked past the central feature of her face, I saw that her eyes were similar to Grandfather's—watching carefully, picking up tiny details that slipped by those of us focused on words and obvious things like noses. Her gaze slid over every item in the healing hut—the colorful pictures of saints and Virgin Marías, the green bundles of herbs, the golden candles, the clay incense burners . . . and over my entire family.

My entire family except for my mother, that is, who was most likely staring into space in the kitchen.

Meanwhile, my youngest aunt, Perla, returned with cups of steaming chamomile tea and set them before our guests.

Esma said, "Amigos, who will go first? Who has a question for the Mistress of Destiny?"

I did. I had questions that had been growing and whirling like a dust storm inside of me. A year earlier, when the water had swept away my sister, it had also stolen a piece of my soul. The piece that felt happiness. In its place was an empty space— cold and dark and fearful. *Will I find that piece? Or grow a new piece? Will I ever feel alive again? Will life ever feel strong and good again?*

But the words wouldn't form on my tongue.

Meanwhile, my aunts were tittering and whispering among

themselves. My uncles elbowed each other, urging each other on. Finally, Aunt Perla volunteered. She asked shyly, "Will I marry soon?"

The Mistress of Destiny seemed to expect this question. She motioned for my giggling aunt to deal out cards. From her pocket, Roza pulled out a gleaming black pipe and wedged it into her mouth. She didn't light it, only chewed thoughtfully on its stem. Peering at the cards, she aahed and hmmed, huffing deeply in and out of flared nostrils, and finally speaking in a voice as gruff as a man's.

Aunt Perla held her breath as Esma translated to Spanish easily, like a spool of thread unwinding, and I, in turn, spun the words into Mixteco. "Dear girl, within the year, you shall be married to a strong and handsome man with eyes the color of the finest brown horse. He shall have ample hair, the color of the blackest night."

My aunts squealed. Of course, everyone in my village had black hair and brown eyes; every man was strong from working in the fields all day; and handsome was in the eye of the beholder.

"And that's not all!" The Mistress of Destiny placed a finger at the side of her nose, apparently lost in a trance. "Within the following year, you shall have a beautiful baby, a boy with big brown eyes and black hair."

A round of giggles broke out, and Aunt Perla rocked with so much glee she nearly fell off the chair. "I'll give you an entire chicken for that fortune!"

And on it went, marriages and baby predictions for the younger women. For the older ones and the men, vague predictions like, *You will have a run of bad luck followed by marvelous luck, so keep your faith.* Or, *You will make a deal with someone that will bring you good fortune.*

By the time it was my turn, over an hour had passed, and everyone else was buzzing with their own fortunes and not terribly interested in mine.

Esma smiled at me—a dazzling smile of white, even teeth. "Your turn! The boy who translates like the wind!"

I blushed, looked down as I walked to the chair.

She asked, "Do you have a special question for Roza, Mistress of Destiny?"

I'd been going over my questions for the past hour, and distilled them down to one. *Will I ever feel alive again?*

I willed myself to speak it. But no, I couldn't, not in front of everyone.

"No special question?" Esma prompted.

I shrugged. "Anything is fine."

"Now what is your name, amigo?"

"Teo," I replied softly.

"Teo," she repeated. "The boy with the eyes."

I lowered my gaze, embarrassed. My eyes were like two mud puddles encircled by long, dark, thick reeds of lashes. That's how my sister had described our eyes; she'd had the same. A trait we got from our father, whose face I barely remembered now, except for those lashes.

When I lifted my gaze to meet Esma's eyes again, I saw that hers were the color of rain, silvery and flashing, like mica-flecked stones after a storm.

"Deal the cards, Teo."

I obeyed. They were well-worn around the edges and looked like they'd been chewed on, drooled on, and spit out by children and animals over the decades. Each featured a hand-painted scene—a majestic lady, a gold goblet, silver swords, a black cauldron, a yellow sun, a white horse, a red heart.

Esma watched Roza respond to the cards. Her nose twitched. To the right, to the left, and then did a lively dance. Her nose had not made this particular series of moves before.

I looked beyond, at her eyebrows, which were pressed together in confusion. Her shriveled lips stuck out in a puzzled pout. She blinked and squinted at Esma, Queen of Lightning. Then she squinted at me, gnawing at the stem of her pipe. My pulse sped . . . something big was coming, I was certain.

The others—Gypsies and villagers alike—were chattering and didn't notice the strange reaction; it was only me, Esma, and my ever-observant grandfather.

Finally, Roza shook herself like a dog in the rain, took a breath, and gave my fortune. As Esma translated, she seemed disappointed, and failed to conjure up any drama. With a sigh, she said, "You are kind and gentle and stronger than you know. If you do something bold, you will be rewarded."

My heart sank. Just another vague fortune.

At the prompting of my cousins, I translated, my voice flat. I turned to Roza and, with a weak smile, said, "Gracias." Then I stood up to fetch her payment.

Grandfather put his hand on my shoulder, pressing me back down. He looked at the fortune-teller, past her nose and into her slits of eyes. Still watching her, he murmured, "Teo, ask her your true fortune."

I looked at him, confused.

"Go ahead, son."

I swallowed, then said to Esma, in my most polite voice, "Excuse me, señorita, my grandfather would like the Mistress of Destiny to tell me my true fortune."

Esma's right eyebrow shot up, straight into her bangs. "Your true fortune?"

I nodded. "My true fortune."

TRUE FORTUNE

*E*sma gave me a sideways grin, then translated my request to her grandmother. My true fortune.

In the shadow beneath the Mistress of Destiny's nose, a smile spread, revealing two crooked teeth above and three below. The pipe was clenched firmly between them. Her eyes crinkled and she nodded at Grandfather in a gesture of respect before speaking.

This time, as Esma listened, her eyes sang. She translated, swiftly, with trembling excitement. "I will tell you what I truly saw, but I will also tell you that it is impossible. That is why I . . . *adjusted* the fortune. There are such things as false truths and honest lies, my friends."

I was on the edge of my seat now. I wiped my damp palms on my pants.

Roza continued, dropping her voice to the lowest rumble, the purr of a mountain lion. And as the Mistress of Destiny spoke, Esma's jaw fell open. The Gypsy women stopped their chattering and tea sipping and stared at Esma. Then at me, then back at Esma. With expressions of disbelief, they shook their heads, muttering a harsh word that bounced among them.

Finally, Esma raised her chin, drew in a breath, and climbed, in her lopsided way, onto her chair. Standing tall on top of it, she towered over us.

"According to the always-accurate prediction of the Mistress of Destiny's cards, this boy—what's your name again?"

"Teo."

"This boy, Teo, and I, Esma, Queen of Lightning, are on the path to being loyal friends for our long lives!" She paused to let this sink in. And then she continued, eyes wildly alive. "And if our friendship lasts, we will save each other when no one else can. This is our destiny!"

For a moment, my heart stopped. Then I stammered a translation for Grandfather, whose face lit up brighter than a sunrise. He gave a nod of approval to Roza, Mistress of Destiny.

My aunts and uncles and cousins were exchanging doubtful looks. "Impossible," they murmured, most in Mixteco, a few in Spanish. It was probably the same word the Gypsies were murmuring. *Impossible.*

Esma, on the chair, bellowed, "I, Queen of Lightning,

specialize in the impossible!" She smiled at me, held out her hand, and declared, "Join me, Teo, my new friend for life!"

I stood motionless, all eyes on me. I didn't take her hand, because what if she pulled me up there? What if she was crazy? What if *crazy* was the word her people were muttering?

Then I whispered, "I'll be back in a minute." Legs shaking, I stumbled out into the sunshine, then across the patch of dirt, and into the dark kitchen.

There by the hearth fire was my mother, hair messily unbraided, huipil filthy, and expression vacant. Draped over her head, a black shawl hid her eyes in shadows. She held a sweet potato in one hand and a knife in the other, unsure what to do with them. A year ago, she would have been dashing around the kitchen, shooing out the chickens that were now pecking around her still feet. I looked at her, wishing she would look back at me. She didn't.

I took three of my circles of goat cheese to use as payment and wrapped them in banana leaves. On the way out the door, I paused. "Mother, if I told you I'd be lifelong friends with a Gypsy girl, what would you say?"

She looked at me blankly, as if I were speaking another language. Impossible to understand. For her, after what had happened to my sister last year, everything was impossible. Getting up from her petate in the mornings, making tortillas, doing the simplest of chores. The smallest task, like talking to her son, was impossible. Even if she could answer my question, I knew her response. *Impossible.*

I left her in the kitchen and headed across the patch of dirt, through the squawking cluster of chickens and turkeys, and back to the healing hut. My cousins and aunts and uncles were just leaving, still giddy, while the Gypsies were putting away their things.

The Impossible Caravan, that was the name of this troupe. Did *impossible* describe the incredible wonders they'd brought all the way out to the Hill of Dust? Or did they—the Queen of Lightning in particular—hold the magical key to making the impossible happen?

Esma was humming a lively tune as I walked over and handed her the payment. "Cheese," I said, "from my goats."

"Gracias, querido amigo," she said, radiant.

Tingles crept over my skin. Dear friend, she'd called me. Where my mother was emptied of life, this girl was overflowing.

"Gracias, gracias, gracias," she sang.

I nodded. "Gracias to you."

She locked eyes with me. "It's not impossible, Teo."

I paused. "They think it is," I said, motioning to her people and mine.

She scoffed. "*They* just accept things how they are. *They* would say we're only staying here one more day and we might never come back and Romani girls aren't friends with boys of any kind and Rom aren't friends with *gadjé* and if I am friends with a *gadjo*, then I'll be impure and they'd disown me and—"

"Gadjé? Gadjo?" I asked, trying to keep up. "Romani? Rom?"

"The Rom are us. The Romani people. Gypsies. And gadjé are you all. Anyone who isn't Romani. A gadjo."

"I see." I struggled to understand. "But how can they argue with the Mistress of Destiny?"

Esma twisted a braid around her ring-bedecked finger. "It's true, my grandmother has power, but traditions run deeper than predictions. For centuries, things have been this way. It would take more than a single fortune to change that." She paused, letting her silver eyes pierce mine. "But we'll do it, my friend!"

As Esma reached her hand toward mine, one of the Romani women snapped at her and whacked the side of her head. It was a hard slap, but not enough to damage more than her pride. The women frowned, ready to leave and waiting on her.

I had more questions, but there wasn't time. I just said, "I hope our fortune comes true."

"Teo," she said fiercely, "hope is for squash heads. You and me, we won't sit around and hope. We'll make our fortune come true. Nothing is impossible. Not for me. And not for you either, now that you are my loyal friend for eternity."

Pure craziness. Yet my unasked question had been answered. All at once, life thrummed with possibility.

I searched for what to say next, but one of the women slapped Esma's head again, and another grabbed her by the elbow and dragged her away.

From the doorway, I watched them leave. The other women trudged, except for Roza—who waddled, her hips rivaling her nose in enormity—and Esma, who danced away in a peculiar lope, as if she simply refused to walk like everyone else.

Suddenly, she wrestled her arm away, turned around, and called out, "See you soon, Teo, my lifelong friend!"

Her defiance earned her another smack.

No matter. Esma, Queen of Lightning, tossed back her head and sang out to the dust-baked mountains: "Nothing is impossible!"

DUCKLING

*Y*our mind plays tricks on you when you're alone pasturing goats, way out in *el monte*. Among the spiky agave and fanning palms and rock outcroppings, you hear things that aren't there. Voices, wails.

My sister, Lucita, used to wander el monte with me and our goats. We'd been doing it for years, nearly every day, since we were six or seven. As twins, we'd looked alike—wide faces and strong cheekbones and those muddy, reedy eyes. She'd always been the more fragile one—smaller, slighter, prone to sickness.

But what she'd lacked in physical strength she'd made up for a hundred times over in spunk and imagination and curiosity. She'd been the one who'd come up with the crazy games we'd play along the dried, cracked riverbeds. She was the one endlessly interested in the world, peering at petals of succulents and insect wings and glittering mica. She was the one who was most alive.

Until she wasn't.

Today, as always, I tried to keep my goats away from the swath of green that meandered with the river, down the mountainside, all the way past my village. Giant trees with thick, bright canopies lined the water, precious shade in the otherwise roasting-hot hills.

Despite its promise of a cool drink or a refreshing foot soak, I stayed away from the stream. It was narrow now, at the end of dry season—just an arm span wide—but I'd seen it transform into something raging and terrible in mere minutes.

That day, nearly one year ago, Lucita had yelped and sputtered, flailing her limbs, struggling to keep her head above the waves. It had been a flash flood, at the seam between dry and rainy season. Trying to save our baby goat, she'd been swept downstream. I'd leapt in and grabbed for her, but the water tore her away. The spirit of the stream pulled her under, and I tried, I tried, I tried, but I couldn't save her.

My grandfather found me unconscious on the riverbank. Hours later, Lucita's body floated up, caught on a fallen branch, lifeless.

And now, every day, her screams lived on in the rush of the stream, a reminder that I hadn't saved her. That maybe if I'd paddled harder, searched longer, I could have.

In three days, it would be her *cabo de año*—the first anniversary of her death. My family was supposed to honor her along with our entire village. The idea made me queasy. Another reminder I'd let her die.

I lowered the brim of my palm hat over my eyes, licked my dry lips. But today, instead of Lucita's wails, I imagined Esma's voice, echoing through the mountains. *Friends for life! Nothing is impossible!*

Of course, that wasn't true. Bringing my sister back to life was impossible. And being lifelong friends with a Romani girl? Even if her people didn't frown on friendships with outsiders, how do you become best friends in a couple days? And what about saving each other? I wasn't strong enough to save anyone.

My goats refused to stay away from the stream. They were thirsty and I had to let them drink. As they lapped at the water, I stood twenty paces away, just in the outer fringe of shade. Ignoring my parched throat, I scanned the bush-straggled hills for Esma. Maybe she would come out here to search for me.

A noise rose over the water's wails and the echoes of Esma's words.

Squeaking. High-pitched and rhythmic and urgent.

It was coming from the shore. I took a few tentative steps toward the river to investigate. A tiny baby duck, no bigger than my fist, was stumbling in a circle on the sandy bank. It had no true feathers yet, only furry down, brown with splotches and stripes of gold. Its shiny black beak was open wide, emitting loud cheeps. It tried walking, but something was wrong, and its legs buckled after a few steps.

Strange. I'd rarely seen ducks on this river before, and never baby ducks. I searched the brush for its mother, or siblings, but none were in sight. For a long time, from my spot high on the banks, I watched it getting up, wobbling, then falling down, squeaking the whole while. As it stumbled dangerously close to the water, I held my breath, whispering, "Move, move. Away from the water."

And then the baby bird tumbled in, and a small current engulfed its body. "Swim, swim!" I urged, but it fell over and squealed in panic. Downstream it floated like a tiny, battered twig.

Without thinking, I scrambled down to the water's edge, reached in, and pulled out the duckling. It was shivering and squeaking, and looked even tinier soaking wet. And then, realizing what I'd done, I started shaking. I wrapped it in my shirt, then sat with it, both of us trembling, waiting for its mother. She would help; she'd protect it.

Hours passed. My trembling stopped. The duck's shivering calmed. Its eyes closed and its peeping vanished and it fell asleep against my chest.

Its mother never came.

As the sun started dropping, setting the sky aglow, I thought about what to do. If I left the baby duck here alone, it would be eaten by a fox or die when the temperature fell at night. So I carried it home, nestled against my chest.

At the outskirts of town, I passed the Romani camp, where women were bent over buckets and pots, washing and preparing food, chattering loudly. Men dozed on berry-red carpets spread out in the shade. I didn't see Esma but did hear violin notes soaring above the circle of wagons, and I paused to listen, wondering if it was her. If the swirling, jeweled colors of the wagons were transformed into music, this would be it, this vibrant, spiraling melody.

The baby duck woke up and started cheeping, probably hungry. I rushed home, corralled the goats, and handed the little fluff ball to Grandfather. "Why, I haven't seen a duckling like this in years," he remarked, cupping it in his palms. "They don't often come around here, just a vagrant one, here and there. A whistling duck, I'm guessing."

"Whistling?"

He smiled. "You'll find out why in a few months."

"So we can save it?" I asked.

He examined it, feeling its wings and legs with gentle fingertips. "Nothing broken. Just bruising, soreness." He raised an amused eyebrow and pointed to my shirt. "Your reward for doing something bold," he observed.

I looked down at my shirt. Yellow-green duck poo covered the front. Reward? "That first fortune the Mistress of Destiny told me—it was true?"

Grandfather tilted his head. As a healer, he knew things, things deeper and wider than most people knew. It was as though most people saw only a small black-and-white photo of the world, but he saw what was outside the frame, too, and in full, dazzling color. That's how my mother had explained it to me once, the wisdom of her father. That was before she gave up.

"Perhaps it was true," he said. "Or perhaps you made it happen. Perhaps without the fortune, you wouldn't have saved the duck." He paused. "I know being near the river is hard for you, son. It took courage to help this creature."

I cupped the duck close, a tiny bundle of pulse and breath. I felt the aliveness contained, against all odds, in this chirping ball of fluff.

"Let's get some food in our girl!" Grandfather said.

"Girl?"

"That's my guess."

"I'm naming her Thunder," I said over her squeaking.

Grandfather laughed. "She is pretty noisy."

Together, we mixed dried, crushed corn kernels with water and fed it to her in a tiny gourd. We let her splash around at the edge of the narrow irrigation ditch that flowed between the edges of our courtyard and bean field. Then we made her a soft bed with a pile of old rags in a fruit crate.

Beyond our little courtyard, the pink sunset melted into gold, then cooled into purple shadows of dusk. I drank cinnamon-chocolate *atole*—corn mush—with my cousins by the light of the kitchen hearth fire. Then I walked with them over to the church plaza, carrying Thunder in my shirt, not trusting anyone else to hold her. She was snug in a sling I made from my sister's old shawl that had sat untouched, folded in a corner, until now. I'd tied it around my neck and stuffed in plenty of rags to capture the globs of poo that Thunder dropped every few minutes.

I also brought along a tiny gourd of atole since she squeaked for more food every half hour. I settled with her in the front row and waited for the magic to begin. Even if she made a commotion, the noise of the projector and generator and music and actors would drown it out.

The film was a western, starring Luís Aguilar, whose tiny, tame mustache paled beside the Duke's. Esma, Queen of Lightning, knew all the words and songs in this film, too. As she whooped at the exciting parts, I longed to do the same. This time, after the movie, instead of belting out an impromptu song, she walked over to where I sat. Stray bits of light flashed off her coins like lightning. "Hello, my friend for life."

"*Buenas noches*, señorita." I felt a little nervous and rested my hand on Thunder, sleeping inside the sling, right over my heart. Then, after a deep breath, I said, "Let's do it. Let's make our fortune happen."

"Of course!" she declared, matter-of-factly. "We should've started today. I looked all over for you!"

She'd looked for me? A warmth spread through me, rich and sweet as cinnamon-chocolate atole.

"Where will you be tomorrow?" she asked.

"Pasturing my goats in el monte."

Behind her, a young Romani woman was approaching like a furious whirlwind.

I spoke quickly, pointing east with my chin. "Over there. Follow the river from your camp up to the mountains. But not too close. The water's dangerous. There's a boulder shaped like a sleeping dog, just beside a big tree. I'll meet you there in the morning."

She grinned, and then noticed Thunder, who was now poking her beak out of the sling. Esma tilted her head, curious, but just as she was about to speak, the Romani woman grabbed her ear and tugged her away.

At least she didn't get smacked this time.

"Until tomorrow, my lifelong friend!" she called back cheerfully, waggling her fingers like a cinema star. "And your baby goose, too!"

"Duck!" I called out.

"Duck!" she called in return.

It felt like a handshake, the seal of a promise.

6

SCREAM

*T*hat night, I put Thunder's crate right next to my petate in the spot where my sister used to sleep. The little duck squeaked and rustled around and tried to jump out of the box. So I laid my hand over her, and she settled down and slept most of the night, with just a few peeps here and there.

Her noise didn't bother my mother, who slept across the room with a blanket over her face, as if it could block out the world. Since last year, she wanted to sleep all the time. She would sleep and sleep and sleep until one of my aunts came in and splashed cold water on her face and dragged her into the kitchen. It was hard to remember how my mother had been before—slapping tortillas into circles well before dawn, laughing and calling me and Lucita "lazybones" when we wandered groggily into the kitchen, greeting us with smiles and cups of steaming atole.

But if I followed my memory back even further, there was another time—when Lucita and I were five or six—that our mother had slept late and let her huipil grow stained and her hair messy. It happened after our final trip to Mexico City to sell baskets and hats with my father, the last time his hand held mine. Months later, when Grandfather found our mother all crumpled to pieces, he moved her and Lucita and me back here, to the Hill of Dust, so he could care for us and heal her sorrows.

And it had worked. After a year or so, my mother had returned to herself. Mostly.

But now, looking back, I could see that a piece of sorrow had lodged inside her, waiting for the next tragedy to swallow her whole. And try as he might, Grandfather couldn't seem to heal her this time.

The next morning, my mother slept right through the barrage of hungry squeaks that woke me. My hand was still cupping Thunder's tiny, downy back. It was good to feel something so soft and alive, so close to me all night.

Outside, in the courtyard, I fed her atole and let her play a bit at the edge of the irrigation ditch, just a trickle of water now. Then I stuck her in the sling with rags, had a breakfast of eggs and beans and tortillas with my cousins, and headed into el monte with the goats. Humming a tune, I meandered toward my meeting point with Esma, weaving a new palm hat on the way—payment for tonight's movie.

I was halfway to the rock when I heard a piercing scream. A girl's. My heart stopped and then started again, wild and pan- icked. Could it just be the memory of Lucita's screams? I'd relived her screams before, but they'd never been quite so loud . . . and *real*. I kept walking, my pulse jagged, nausea oozing through me. I covered my ears with my palms. *Stop, stop, stop.*

But when I released my hands, the shrieks had grown louder, tearing through the valley, coming from the stream. My head spun; black stars filled my vision. My instinct was to run away, shielding my ears.

And then, a thought: *What if it's a real girl? An alive one? What if it's Esma?*

I remembered the second part of our fortune. *You two will save each other when no one else can.* Was it my time to save my friend for life? So soon?

The fortune made me brave. I drew in a breath, scanned the river for people, but I couldn't see past the thick foliage along the banks. Cupping my hand over Thunder, I ran toward the screams. They stabbed the air like thin, freshly sharpened blades.

There, at the banks of the river, in the shade of a giant tree, was Esma, mouth open wide, screaming.

And swirling. Her long skirt spun out around her; her arms flew out and up. Her hair had burst loose from its scarf and flailed out in a nut-brown halo. Her face was uplifted, her jaw open wide enough to gulp the sky.

Clearly, she did not need saving.

I watched her a moment as my heart flip-flopped.

Then I noticed three small children near her, toddlers playing in the dappled light at the sandy shore. One had a finger up his nose, another was drooling and gaping at Esma, and the third was banging two sticks together. All the while, Esma spun lopsided, screaming in her own revolving world.

Finally, I stepped into her view, just outside the arc of her arms and skirt and hair.

Her wails stopped. She slowed and stood still, wavering, wobbling, dizzy, and then her eyes focused on me and she smiled. "Buenos días, Mamma Duck!"

"You all right, señorita?" I asked, unsure how I felt about my new nickname.

"Yes. Why?"

"I thought—I thought you needed me to save you. Because of our fortune . . ." My voice faded.

She laughed. "Oh, I don't need any saving. Never have, never will. Just interested in the loyal-friend-for-eternity part."

I blinked. What a relief. But I *had* managed to save a duckling. Maybe I *was* stronger than I realized, just like my false fortune said. Maybe someday far, far away, I'd actually save the Queen of Lightning herself.

She bugged out her eyes, then crossed them, then bugged them out again. "Why are you staring at me like that, Teo?"

I blinked again. "It's just—you were screaming like it was the end of the world."

"Oh, that. That's just what I do, Teo. See, wherever we go, I find a good place to scream. Not too close to camp. Don't want the others to hear. Near a stream is good—rushing water drowns out my noise." She tapped two dented tin buckets lying on their sides. "And it's a handy excuse—fetching water. Far upstream, where it's freshest." She gazed at the stream as if it were her second best friend.

I glared at the stream, positioned myself at a safe distance, just close enough to rescue any toddlers who might fall in. The stream was calm today, all gentle currents, and no wider than I was tall. Still, you never knew.

The kids were staring at me, curious. The girl said, "Ga? Ga?" and the boy said, "Da? Da?" and the other boy said, "Ba? Ba?"

I waved to them, then looked back at Esma, who was flushed and breathing hard from so much swirling and screaming. "Why do you scream?"

"Try it," she said. "You've swallowed plenty of screams. I can tell."

I didn't try it. Instead, I asked again, "Why do you scream?"

She picked up the rose-splattered scarf that had fallen from her hair, twirled it in the air like a lasso. "You met the *boria* at your fortune."

"The boria?"

"The wives of my uncles and father—the ones who enjoy smacking me and calling me squash head. I swallow as many screams as I can—twenty-two is my limit—and then I drag these three little squash heads away from camp—I'm in charge of them—and I let loose the swallowed screams."

I furrowed my brow, looked at the ground. "You scared me."

"Oh, sorry, Teo."

If we were best friends—or even pretending to be—there were certain things she had to know. "Last year, in that stream, my sister drowned."

Esma said nothing.

I forced myself to continue. "She screamed, but I couldn't save her."

For the first time, Esma, Queen of Lightning, was speechless. She sat down on the boulder, rearranging the scarf in her tangled hair.

I perched beside her, appreciating the cool rock beneath me. I watched the toddlers squealing and tugging on the goats' tails as they lapped at the water. "Ga! Da! Ba!" the children sputtered, mouths wide open in delight.

"You shouldn't let those kids there," I said. "The spirit of the stream could snatch them under."

Esma thought for a moment, then announced, "Teo, my screams scared away every last evil spirit. Even the slipperiest of the sneakiest."

I eyed her doubtfully.

"Look, Teo, I've been screaming like this for years now. And I can tell you, at every scream, the bad spirits turn around and run off covering their ears."

I raised my eyebrows. "You see the spirits?"

"The Gypsy Queen of Lightning can do anything!"

She *was* convincing. "Why are you called that?"

She slapped her right leg, entirely covered by her long skirt. "You've noticed my limp, I presume?"

I wasn't sure what the polite answer was. "I noticed you walk like—like you're dancing."

She grinned. "Now I can see why we're best friends for life." She whacked her leg again. "Lightning strike. The doctor said the lightning should've killed me, but I tamed it instead. I've been the Queen of Lightning ever since."

As Esma talked about her powers, Thunder began squeaking in the sling. I pulled out some crushed corn from the basket strapped to my back, sprinkled it into the gourd, added a little water, then set Thunder down to dig in. I took out the rags and washed them downstream. My heartbeat, I noticed, was not as frantic as it usually was so close to the water.

Esma watched me curiously. "Is it common in your village to carry around pooping ducks?"

"I'm the first," I said, grinning. And I told her about finding Thunder yesterday.

"You're noble, Teo," she said. "Savior of baby ducks. You should be my knight."

"But I'm a—" I tried to remember the word for *outsider* she'd used yesterday. "Gadjo," I said. "Can't only Rom be part of your royalty?"

"Nothing is impossible, my friend."

48

I stared at a thin string of clouds above the far mountain. What seemed impossible was that someone as bold as Esma would want me as her friend. She was lightning; I was a wisp of a cloud, a puff of dust. I couldn't imagine a time when she'd need to be saved by someone like me. I asked, "How are we going to make our fortune happen?"

Her eyes gleamed. "Well, I've been thinking. My people are supposed to leave tomorrow. That's what my grandfather says, and he's the leader."

"The Duke? Biggest mustache ever?"

"That's the one. But we have to convince him to stay longer so we can plant the roots of our lifelong friendship."

"So how do we convince him?"

She tapped her chin, thinking.

There was silence, except for the rush of the stream and the toddlers' shouts of "Da! Ga! Ba!" and Thunder's contented peeps now that her stomach was filled. She wandered around, always within an arm's reach of me, just pecking in the wet sand and pebbles. She had a little limp and trouble with balance, but seemed much better than yesterday.

Something about this little duck reminded me of Lucita. The pluckiness in its eyes. I glanced at Esma. "I wish you could come to my sister's cabo de año."

"What's that?"

"The one-year anniversary of her death. It's in three days."

She raised an eyebrow. "Is that something that would plant roots of a lifelong friendship?"

I nodded. "My sister would've liked you."

"Why?"

"Because you're so . . . alive."

"Alive," Esma mused. "Well, tell that to the boria. They call me a squash head and tell me I'm crazy and slow in the mind."

"Well," I admitted, "you are crazy—"

She reached out and lightly slapped the rim of my hat. "Hush, you squash head."

"But you're good crazy," I added quickly. "And your mind— it's faster than . . . than lightning."

She smacked her leg again, so hard I winced. "They say my mind is as lame and broken as my body." She held up her right hand. The last three fingers were curled tightly in on themselves, like unfurled leaves. "It's not just my leg."

In my translations during Grandfather's healing sessions, I'd seen all manner of injuries and illness, yet I couldn't figure out how lightning could cause these particular problems in Esma. "Did the lightning do that, too?"

She looked at her fingers, then lowered them, tucking them into the folds of her skirt. "Yes."

She stood up on a boulder, and now I could see the effort it took with her weak leg. But it didn't stop her. She straightened tall like a pine tree and spoke to the valley below.

"They said, 'You'll never be able to walk again, squash head,' and I said, 'I'll dance!'"

Pausing dramatically, she tossed a braid over her shoulder.

"They said, 'You'll never be able to hold a broom, squash head,' and I played the violin!"

She gazed at the mountaintops, like an actress on-screen. "They said, 'No man will ever pay a bride-price for you, squash head.'"

I broke in. "Bride-price?"

She looked down at me and her voice lowered, as if she were telling me a secret the valley couldn't hear. "It's what the husband's family pays to his new wife's family to make up for them losing a good worker. You know the boria? Well, they left their own families when they were about thirteen years old to get married and live with their husbands, my uncles and father."

"But why wouldn't anyone pay a bride-price for you?" I couldn't help blushing as I asked. After all, we were talking about marriage.

She seemed unfazed. "The women in our boria say no man would want me. That I'll just have to let them boss me around and call me squash head until I die."

"And what do you tell them?"

Her answer came as a bellow that echoed through the valley. "I tell them, 'Someday I will be a famous singer! I will be paid a thousand times the bride-price a man would have given. I will be loved not by one man but by hundreds, thousands! By men and women and children and anyone who hears my songs.'"

She packed every word with soul-shaking emotion. Just listening to her made my life larger, as if I were being projected onto a sheet on the side of the church right along with her. As if our story were epic, a music-drenched tale of tears and laughter and heart-swelling triumph.

Turning to me, she narrowed her eyes fiercely. "Then I told them, 'And no one will call me squash head!'"

My heart raced. She was a lightning storm so bright I had to look away. So I did, and that's when I noticed what the toddlers were doing.

"Esma," I said, cringing. "Your cousins are eating duck poo."

She jumped in alarm, then scrambled down the boulder to the children. She tried wiping the yellow-green goop from their mouths and chins.

"Oh," she muttered, "I'm such a squash head." She wrinkled her eyebrows. "Think it'll make them sick?"

I shrugged. I'd never had any duck-poo-eating patients with Grandfather.

She groaned. "My people don't like poo-covered animals, and definitely don't like their children eating poo."

"Most people wouldn't," I pointed out.

"But they have this idea about *marime*. Impure things. Ideas you gadjé wouldn't understand. Let's just say the boria would tear out my eyeballs if they knew."

Da started crying, and she patted his back. "Think the poo is making him cry?"

I was a little hurt by her comment about us gadjé not understanding. Flatly, I said, "He's just mad you made him stop eating it."

She rocked Da, and just as his cries let up, Ga and Ba started wailing. Now spit bubbles and mucus and tears were smeared over their faces, mixing with the dust, creating muddy streaks along with the poo. Not a pretty sight.

Esma looked miserable.

"Let's go to my grandfather," I said. "He's a healer. He'll know what to do."

She hesitated. "My family wouldn't like that either."

"Why not?"

She let out a breath. "You know how . . . *disturbing* it felt to watch my cousins eat duck poo?"

I nodded.

"Well, that's how my people would feel if they knew I went to a gadjé home. I mean, if I went for something other than business reasons." She averted her eyes. "They think spending time with gadjé would make me marime. Unclean."

I tried not to feel offended. Slowly, I said, "I'm . . . unclean? And being with me is like . . . eating duck poo?"

"That's how *they'd* feel," she said quickly. "Not me. Listen, Teo, I like being with you. And your baby duck, poo and all. And when my family tells me I can't do something, I do it." She stuck out her chin. "So let's go, my friend for life!"

She filled one bucket and I filled the other, and we hurried into town along the river, currents rushing, water sloshing, kids crying, goats bleating, duck squeaking, *friend for life* echoing.

And no dead sister wailing.

THUNDER'S POO

*I*t took a while to get all the goats and toddlers back to town. At her camp, Esma dropped off the buckets of water, then quickly told the boria she'd found a good spot for berry picking. She grabbed an empty red pail, and before anyone could protest or offer to come with her or smack her head, she and the toddlers were walking toward my house, supposedly to pick berries. "Not lying," she assured me. "Just creative storytelling."

By the time we reached the courtyard, Da and Ga and Ba were still fussy—maybe because it was hot and they were tired; maybe because Thunder's poo was churning around in their stomachs.

My aunts, in the kitchen, didn't see us cross the patch of dust to my grandfather, who was repairing a fence. He looked up, surprised, and greeted Esma with a handshake. In accented Spanish, he said, "Buenos días, Queen."

She greeted him back. "Buenos días, Doctor."

Then, to Grandfather, I said in Spanish, "Her little cousins ate Thunder's poo. Will they be all right?"

He surveyed the toddlers' filthy, tearstained faces, then gave me a baffled look. I switched to Mixteco and repeated myself, adding that poo made her people feel extra disturbed.

He raised a brow, then took some ears of dried corn from a pile and set them in front of the children. They grabbed the cobs, banged them against each other, open-mouthed and intent. Meanwhile, he peered into their eyes. "Tell me, Teo, was the poo fresh or old?"

"Fresh, very fresh."

His eyebrows furrowed. "More green or yellow?"

I thought about it, then conferred with Esma. "Yellow," she said nervously.

Grandfather frowned gravely. "Goopy or runny?"

Esma and I discussed the consistency. "Goopy."

A wide grin spread over Grandfather's face. It crumpled into a laugh. He shook his head and wiped his eyes, and that's when I knew Esma's cousins would be all right. I laughed, and then glanced at Esma, and she laughed, too, relieved.

"Let's all have some mint tea together," Grandfather said, patting my back. "If their stomachs are upset, the tea will calm them. They'll be fine."

Esma played with the toddlers and their corn while I gathered fresh mint from our garden. I brought the bundle of leaves into the kitchen, where two of my aunts bustled around, roasting red chilies and garlic for salsa. My mother stood in the center, holding the broom, motionless.

"Mother, could you boil water to brew this mint?"

She offered me only an empty look. Beneath the shadows of her shawl, her eyes were red and watery from the chili smoke, but she didn't bother wiping them. If the river had stolen a bit of my soul along with Lucita's, it had taken most of my mother's. There wasn't much left.

Sighing, Aunt Perla said, "I'll do it," and took the herbs from my hands.

My other aunt huffed that nearly every woman she knew had lost a child or two, and they didn't use it as an excuse to laze around.

Ignoring her, Aunt Perla patted my back, then kindly offered me *panela* to sweeten the tea.

I bit the inside of my cheek and waited for the water to boil. After the tea had brewed and cooled a bit, I joined Esma and Grandfather and the toddlers outside, where we sat and sipped from chipped clay mugs. I'd snuck in extra panela to make the tea sweet for the toddlers. It worked. They guzzled it down, then went back to inquiring about their corn. "Da? Ga? Ba?"

Meanwhile, in broken Spanish, Grandfather told Esma about the disgusting things I'd eaten as a toddler. Kitten throw-up, chicken droppings, owl pellets.

I refused to translate, but Esma caught the gist without my help. She made faces and laughed. I was a little embarrassed,

56

but mostly I wished she could stay forever. Or at least a few more days. But how? Especially now that I knew how her people felt about Rom and gadjé mixing. For nonbusiness reasons, at least.

After the tea, Da, Ga, and Ba curled up in the shade, sleeping in a pile like puppies.

Esma finished her tea and wandered around the courtyard. She stopped under the tree in the corner, in front of a colorful sawdust mosaic framed in wood. The flowered border was done, but the inside remained to be finished.

"Pretty," she said. "What is it?"

"It's for my sister's cabo de año. Grandfather will fill in the rest with more flowers and stars and birds and things."

Esma cocked her head. "When did you say this party was?"

"In three days. And it's not exactly a party," I admitted. "I mean, it's in honor of a dead person. But we'll have sweet tamales and cinnamon-chocolate," I added, to make it sound more cheerful.

As she stared at the picture, her mind gears were turning. "Think your grandfather could put a Romani wagon in the picture? I mean, he can still do flowers and birds, but they'd be painted on the wagon."

"I guess," I said, wondering where she was headed. "Why?"

Her eyes shone. "Think you could invite my people?"

Excitement bloomed inside me. "Maybe. But would they come? I thought they didn't approve of spending time with gadjé."

"This would be for business relationship reasons. We can call it the Romani Business Appreciation Event."

"Are we clean enough for your people to eat the food we make?" I couldn't help it; a little resentment crept into my voice.

She shrugged. "As long as the drinks are sweet enough and no one sees Thunder pooping all over your shirt, my people should be fine."

The corner of my mouth turned up. "I'll sneak extra panela in the chocolate."

"Great! Now go ahead," Esma urged. "Tell your grandfather."

I translated most of it into Mixteco, but there was no equivalent for Romani Business Appreciation Event. I wasn't sure how he'd react; he was always adamant about being honest, and this involved some . . . creative storytelling.

"Romani Business Appreciation Event?" Grandfather repeated. And then he threw his head back, and the laughter spewed out. "Yes. I think Lucita would like combining her cabo de año with this, don't you?"

I nodded. "Definitely." This was the first time in a year I'd been able to talk about Lucita with a smile.

"This evening," Grandfather said, "after the movie, I'll formally invite the Rom."

I hugged him. "Grandfather," I whispered, "you really think I'll be Esma's friend forever?"

"I can tell you this," he said in my ear. "Somehow, the Queen of Lightning put the spark of life back inside you." He looked at Esma, standing expectantly at my side. "It's true, you have the power to save each other. I'll do what I can to make your friendship last."

INVITATION

*T*hat night, moon shadows stretched long through the pines where the Rom's wagons circled a bonfire. Sweet smoke drifted and swirled above, past the golden flames and into the cool smattering of starlight. Music rose, a cascade of violin notes and hands clapping in rhythm, sticks drumming against tin buckets, and above it all, a soaring voice. It was a song without words, a kind of trilling melody, a soul cry that soared and dove and soared again.

It was Esma, I was certain.

In the darkness, Grandfather and I walked unseen to the edge of their circle, watching the young women dance, their arms raised, faces aglow, jewelry flashing, skirts and braids whirling. It felt as if we had stumbled across something secret and ancient. I put my hand over Thunder, who was trying to squirm out of the sling, as if she wanted to join in. Esma had said she'd be disowned if she befriended gadjé. And now, watching her people, I understood what a loss it would be for her to give up this life. Even if the boria did call her squash head all the time.

When one of the men noticed us, he said something to Esma's grandfather, the Duke. And the Duke said something to his wife, the Mistress of Destiny, who sat on a tree stump with her knees splayed, pipe bobbing, foot tapping in time with the music. Her nose twitched in surprise, and her eyes squinted at us, puzzled. As word spread through the group, people stopped their music and dancing one by one. To my dismay, Esma stopped singing, too, and set down her violin. But the secret look she gave me made up for it.

Grandfather and I introduced ourselves and begged pardon for interrupting them.

The Duke reintroduced himself as Ivan, Duke of the Impossible Caravan, Master of the Traveling Cinema. Ceremoniously, he twirled the tips of his enormous mustache and welcomed us into their firelit circle.

We sat on little wooden chairs. The Duke pulled another white orb from his suit pocket—maybe a peeled apple; it was hard to tell in the dim light. He bit into it and munched, then stuck it back into his pocket. Noticing our curiosity, he pulled out another one, unbitten, and offered it to us. As he leaned in, I smelled it, the sharp odor that stung my eyes. Onion.

Grandfather and I shook our heads politely.

The Duke, still munching, said something passionate in

garbled Spanish. Esma clarified, lacking his enthusiasm. "Raw onions," she sighed. "Supposedly his secret to good health. Strength. Long life. He snacks on them all day long."

Moving swiftly, she grabbed two porcelain cups from a low, round table draped with a gold-fringed cloth. On the table sat an enormous, shiny silver vessel, with a spout that Esma opened with her pinkie. Transfixed, I watched as steaming, honey-colored liquid poured out, into the cups.

"Tea," she announced, placing the cups in our hands.

I sipped. It was a strange, dusky taste—nothing like the pale yellow chamomile tea I was used to. No, sipping this was pure magic, as though I were somehow sipping a night of Romani music and dancing and films. My insides warmed, suddenly golden.

In Mixteco, Grandfather said, in his most formal voice, "Thank you for the tea. And for bringing joy into our hearts and a spark into our souls." I translated in my own most formal voice.

Duke Ivan gave a little bow. Grandfather and I bowed back.

Roza, Mistress of Destiny, just chewed on her pipe and watched us with sharp eyes.

Grandfather said, "We are planning a special occasion in your honor . . . the Romani Business Appreciation Event."

Once I translated, Ivan's eyebrows shot up. After a stunned moment, he said, "Señor, before I was born, my father came by boat across the ocean. All the way from Hungary he came, to find a safe place for his family. Back then, he did metalwork."

The Duke paused and reached over to touch his wife's coin neck-laces. "My father's art," he said proudly. "Despite his extraordinary talents, we were often refused service in the cities . . . unjustly arrested . . . spat upon." The Duke traced a jagged scar on his cheek. "Some people have even thrown stones at us."

I strained to understand his Spanish, as tangled as over-grown bean vines, past and present intertwined. But the meaning behind the scar was clear, and it set off a wave of fire in my center. I felt like a brittle, fragile twig, set aflame and tossed in a flooding river. Burning and drowning at once. Powerless.

I looked away from his scar, into my amber tea. My heart thudded. Sweat broke out. I couldn't breathe. And all the while, I tried not to think of the other time I'd felt like this, after what had happened to my father.

After a pause, the Duke continued. "So we mostly stay away from cities. Since we moved from metalwork to the traveling cinema, we only go there to rent reels and sell hats and baskets. We travel to the tiniest of tiny villages, where we are treated best." He smiled, patting the coins over his chest. "And your Hill of Dust, this is the first place to hold an event in our honor. For that, we are grateful."

I sipped the golden tea, and it calmed me just enough to sputter a translation.

Grandfather's eyes crinkled with compassion. "My people embrace you as true friends. We, too, have suffered such indignities."

I held my breath, wondering if he, in turn, would tell details of these indignities. The first, the biggest, the most terrible would be about my father. My insides began to burn and drown again. I gnawed at the inside of my cheek.

Thankfully, Grandfather moved the topic back to our invitation. "Three nights from now, we will join together in respect and gratitude. The event will occur at our house, over there, three houses west of the church."

Ivan returned his smile, then raised his shoulders and sighed. "Thank you for this great honor, my friend, but we must decline. We leave tomorrow morning. You see, we've already shown all the films we've brought. We would have no way of making money for three more days. Alas, we would lose money, as we must rent these films by the week."

Grandfather sipped his tea, unruffled. "My people would happily offer more baskets and hats to watch the same movies again."

The tips of Ivan's swirling mustache rose. "Why thank you, kind sir, but we would have nothing to eat. We've already told your fortunes in exchange for food. We have nothing else to offer."

Again, I translated, sweat pouring from my armpits. I glanced at Esma, but she didn't look concerned. And Grandfather only smiled, as if he'd expected this glitch.

"Our family," he said, "has a fruit grove not far from here. Oranges, mangoes, limes, papayas, avocados. You are welcome to eat as much as you can pick."

Ivan sighed, fingering the rim of his hat. "Thank you, friend, but we cannot live on fruit."

Again, my heart caved. Living on fruit gives you terrible stomach cramps, it's true. Lucita and I had tried it the first time our mother crumbled. After what happened to our father, we stayed in his village for months. His relatives tried to help us, but there was a drought, and the corn harvest was bad, providing hardly enough for even half the tortillas we needed. Our mother forgot to feed us, so Lucita and I scavenged for fruit, making ourselves sick. That's when Grandfather journeyed to the village and, finding us half-starved, brought us to my mother's native home on the Hill of Dust.

"True, one cannot live on fruit," Grandfather agreed, sipping his tea, "but we've had a good corn harvest, enough to share with you." His eyes twinkled. "We also have a patch of wild onions. The sweetest you've ever tasted. The biggest you've ever seen. You're welcome to as many as you like."

This caught the Duke's attention. You could almost see him drooling at the thought of pocketfuls of onions. He raised a finger, pausing to confer with the Mistress of Destiny.

I studied their expressions and movements, remembering what Grandfather always said about gestures speaking louder than words. I peered past Duke Ivan's grandiose mustache and saw the uncertainty in his eyes, the torn movements of his mouth. He looked to his wife for guidance, and she, miraculously, seemed to be convincing him to stay.

The Mistress of Destiny waved her pipe in the air, said

something bold. Then she walked over to Esma and tugged on her braid, speaking in a gruff voice melting with tenderness. Gently, she tapped the side of Esma's head. She said something to Duke Ivan, and the commanding look in her eyes made it clear that Roza, Mistress of Destiny, was the true leader.

Doing his wife's bidding, Duke Ivan turned to Grandfather. "It would be our honor to attend the Romani Business Appreciation Event."

"Thank you," Grandfather and I said at the same time.

Duke Ivan continued. "Please send your grandson tomorrow morning to show our women where to gather the food. Our granddaughter, Esma, will come along to translate."

Grandfather nodded. "My grandson, Teo, will help them gather as well."

As we bid the Rom good night, I saw Grandfather and Roza exchange glances, and I wondered if she, too, saw the world in full color, saw outside the frame that limited the rest of us. Once we left, violin notes and Esma's voice flew up into the night, far above any stones and scars and burning and drowning. Her song was free and joyful, a rising flock of birds. The magic of the tea lingered on my tongue, the taste of possibility.

SQUASH HEAD

*O*n the way to the fruit tree grove the next morning, the toddlers followed me like baby ducks, sputtering "Da? Ga? Ba?" and tugging at my clothes and reaching for Thunder, who they knew was in my sling. The Mistress of Destiny twitched her nose at me and muttered something in a low voice to Esma.

Esma eyed me cautiously. "My grandmother said she's not even going to ask how my cousins are already friends with you and your duck."

Thank goodness the toddlers couldn't talk. I met Roza's suspicious gaze and offered her an innocent smile.

When we reached the onion patch, we dug them up with sticks and knives. The women looked impressed at their size, but grumbled as they stuck the onions in sacks.

"They're not fans of my grandfather's stench," Esma whispered. "But it's true, he never gets sick."

Later, in the woods by a mostly dried riverbed, we picked low-hanging mangoes from trees and gathered the ones on the ground, stuffing them into burlap sacks. Some mangoes were already old and rotten, filling the air with a sweet scent of decay. Plenty were ripe, small but full of juicy, honeyed promise.

An hour or two passed quickly, and although I couldn't talk openly to Esma, we exchanged the secret glances of best friends. When the young women said they were tired and ready to go, I pointed out mangoes higher in the branches. "You all can rest beneath the trees while I climb up and toss more down."

"I'll help!" Esma said.

One of the young women scowled at her and said something sharply. She pointed to Esma's lame leg, her curled-up fingers. Her meaning was obvious: You can't climb trees.

Esma raised her chin and loped over to the biggest mango tree in sight. She grabbed a low limb and heaved herself up, tossing her weak leg over the branch. Panting with the effort, she paused to catch her breath. It took her a while, but she managed to climb halfway up the tree, until she was hidden in the canopy. I scampered up after her, careful with Thunder asleep in my sling.

As birds chirped in the branches, Esma and I talked softly, occasionally tossing mangoes down to the women below. Wrapped in a cocoon of leaves, I felt like it was only Esma and me, in our own green world.

After devouring three rosy-orange mangoes, Esma asked, "Why does your family let this fruit fall and rot?"

"My mother used to bring Lucita and me here to gather it and sell it at the market. But since my sister died, my mother stopped caring. About the fruit, about me, about anything. It's like she died with my sister."

Esma's face grew tender as a new leaf. "What about your father?"

Her question was a fireball that knocked me into a raging river. At least, that's what happened inside me. On the outside, my face turned stony and my fist clenched a mango.

Could I tell her the truth? It would hurt; it would burn; it would steal my breath away. Still, I had to. This was my loyal friend for eternity.

"One day," I began, "when I was little, we were selling palm hats in Mexico City—my parents and sister and me. We were crossing a really wide street. The cars were whizzing by so fast, and there were so many lanes . . . like the river flooding in the worst storm of rainy season. We were all holding hands, running across . . . then Lucita dropped her orange."

I paused. I'd never talked about this with anyone but Grandfather. But Esma was listening with her raindrop eyes wide. "The orange, it rolled backward. Lucita ripped her hand from mine. She tried to pick it up. I stopped to help her. My hand—I felt it tear out of my father's. He turned back. And his face was—it was all fear. That's when I saw the car. So close, racing toward us. My father pushed us out of the way."

Esma was leaning in close now, her face wild with concern. *She's here with me,* I realized, *right here inside this burning-drowning memory.* And her gaze was like a hand holding on to mine, tight and determined.

My voice lowered and crackled and almost didn't make it to the end. "There was a screech and a thump. The car—it hit my father. And then everything goes fuzzy. I remember blood and tears on his eyelashes. I remember that orange, round and perfect. I remember the driver standing over my father, talking to another driver. Calmly. Too calmly. And most of all, I remember their words."

Esma's head was cocked, waiting. "What?" she said finally.

The words came out of my mouth, stinging and smoking. " 'It's just an indio.' Then the other man—he shrugged and said, 'What's one less indio?' They dragged my father to the side of the road. They wiped his blood from their shirts with handkerchiefs. Then they got back into their cars and drove off."

"And your father?" Esma whispered. Her voice was a rope I hung on to so I wouldn't drown.

"I tried to stop his bleeding. But I couldn't. I couldn't save him."

Once I finished, I felt something dripping over my hand. I looked down. I'd squeezed the mango so tight that juice had burst out like blood.

Esma took the scarf from her hair and wiped the nectar from my hand, gently, as if it really was blood and I really was hurt. Then she looked me straight in the eyes and said, "You couldn't save him, but you'll save other people. Lots of them."

"I'm too weak, Esma."

"Weak? Look what you did to that mango!" she said, balling up her sticky, wet scarf and tucking it in her pocket. "And you saved Thunder! Nothing is impossible for you!"

She settled back into the crook of two branches, peeled another mango, and bit into the juicy tip. With her headscarf off, her hair flew out in wild waves. "My mother's dead," she said matter-of-factly. "She died in childbirth. I was her first and only baby. My dad remarried. See that woman down there?" She poked her head through a gap in the leaves and pointed. "The one in the green dress?"

I spotted her and nodded. She was the one who whacked Esma and called her a squash head the most.

"That's my stepmother." Narrowing her eyes, Esma dropped a mango, which fell through layers of leaves, landing squarely on the woman's head.

"Ow!" came an annoyed shout. And then something like, "Watch out, squash head!"

Esma smiled, satisfied.

It was mean, but the woman deserved it. I said, "I've been watching how they act around you, Esma."

Her face darkened. "And?"

"They're jealous."

She nearly spit out her mango. "Jealous?" she said, wiping nectar from her chin.

"They wish they had lightning inside, too."

She barked a laugh. "I don't think so."

"And your grandmother, the Mistress of Destiny," I continued.

Esma looked at me, her expression suddenly vulnerable. She cared what her grandmother thought, I realized. That was whose opinion mattered.

"When she taps your head, it's like a hug. When she tugs your braid, it's like a kiss. And when she calls you squash head, it's like she's really saying 'I love you.'"

Esma's eyes shone, and she blinked quickly, then sniffed. Softly, she said, "I wish we could stay up here all day."

"Let's do it!" I said.

"Spending all day in a tree with a gadjo would definitely make me marime." Quickly, she added, "At least, that's what *they'd* say."

I remembered that word. *Unclean. Impure.* It still made blood rush to my face, hot and indignant.

"And if that happened, my grandfather could disown me, kick me out of the family. Then I'd never see my grandmother again."

I took this in. "Your grandmother's the one who's really the boss." I paused. "You know she's on our side, right, Esma?"

"Well, she did give us our true fortune," Esma admitted. "After your grandfather asked her to. But then why didn't she stand up for us? Why didn't she argue with everyone who said it was impossible?"

"She knows that if she tells you something is impossible, you'll do it."

"True." Esma plucked a few more mangoes and breathed in the flowery scent before dropping them below. She stuck out her chin. There, in our cave of fluttering leaves, her eyes met mine. "Thanks for everything, my friend for life. And I mean it. You really are. Even without the fortune, you would be."

I reached out and tugged her braid, then tapped her lightly on the head. It was the first time I'd touched her, and it felt like the opposite of burning and drowning. It felt like flying through a cool, bright, wide-open sky. "Thank *you*, squash head."

CURSE

*I*n the freshness of the next two mornings, I led Esma and Roza and the boria and toddlers along winding trails to more fruit trees and onion patches. The Duke was enchanted by the giant, sweet onions and eager for more. Grandfather had arranged for my cousins to cover my morning chores so that I could act as guide. Later, in the afternoons, when the Romani women were preparing peppery stews, Esma would tell them she was going to fetch fresh water and leave with the toddlers and a tin bucket. She'd find me and the goats, and together we'd all gather by the river.

On our last full day together, she dipped her feet in the water, and then I dipped in mine, and then we were up to our knees and splashing and soaking wet and laughing. The currents were gentle and sweet and cool, and afterward we lay on the boulder and watched the leaves' shifting patterns above us.

Every so often we glanced at Da and Ga and Ba to make sure they weren't indulging in more duck poo.

I'd noticed that Thunder didn't poo too much unless she'd recently eaten, so I let her crawl on me when she had an empty stomach. She waddled on top of me with her little webbed feet, over my chest, then nibbled at the collar of my shirt and hair and earlobe. Her personality had been coming out, more and more—feisty, demanding, and fiercely loyal.

"She really thinks you're her mamma," Esma said. "I bet she'll still be following you around when we come back."

"Next year?"

She nodded. "Listen, Teo, we have to make it happen."

I agreed, but I didn't know how. The onions would be a big draw, but they weren't enough.

On the way back into town, we took a detour so I could show her a cluster of rock mounds. "Look, Esma. These are ruins from our ancestors, the ancient Mixtecos."

"It's like buried treasure!" she cried.

I scanned the ground, found small bits of obsidian knives and pottery. Archaeologists from Mexico City had taken the biggest statues away to put in a museum where folks from the Hill of Dust would never see them again. When I was little and we'd sell baskets in the city, I'd seen people lined up at the giant museum, eagerly paying to see our ancestors' crafts. Yet on the street, these same people wouldn't meet our eyes across the woven baskets we sold. And they would warn their children not to play with the dirty indio kids.

Now that burning-drowning feeling was coming back, so I looked up at Esma's face, all lit up with delight. It made me feel better and breathe better. I dropped the pieces of glassy obsidian and red pottery into her hand. "You can keep them," I told her, knowing there were thousands more pieces just like them around here.

Excited, she tucked the little treasures into her pockets. Biting her bottom lip in concentration, she dug around with a stick, overturning small rocks, searching for more. From underneath one, a scorpion skittered out, and I jumped back, pulling her with me.

But it didn't bother her. Bravely, she kept digging and, minutes later, uncovered part of a carved stone face.

"Look, Teo!" Brushing away more dirt, she carefully pulled out an entire statue, unbroken.

It was small enough for her to cradle in her palm. It looked like a raccoon wearing a giant crown of corncobs. "What is this?" she asked in awe, blowing off the dust.

"We call them *diositos*—little gods. People say they're good luck. Most of us have one or two at home. But don't tell the priest about it," I added with a smile. He wasn't a fan of our diositos. "You should keep it, Esma."

Suddenly, her face blazed with an idea. "I've got it!" she shouted. "You and your grandfather can present this to our people. Tell them it's a good luck gift from your village."

I eyed the statue, doubtful. "You think it will make them come back?"

"Oh, we'll add . . . some creative storytelling."

I tilted my head, waiting.

"We Rom are experts at it. Of course, we usually use it on you gadjé."

I gave her a look.

She bit her lip, thinking hard. "So, Teo, you'll give them the diosito and here's what you'll say." She climbed onto a rock mound—what was once part of an ancient temple. She held up the statue, threw back her shoulders, and boomed, "Dear Romani friends, please accept our gift to you. If you return in one year, this diosito will bring you the best of luck. Your food will taste especially delicious. Your movies will have extra magic to entrance your audiences. People will flock to your shows like ants to honey. You will be showered with money like a rainstorm."

I climbed up beside her on the rock and straightened tall. I shouted, "Good fortune will follow you like a baby duck follows its mother. The largest and sweetest onions will be yours."

She grinned. "But if you don't return, dear Romani friends, your entire family will be cursed."

"Cursed?" I recoiled. Grandfather always warned that healers never use their powers for evil.

"It's just pretend!" Esma assured me. "Listen, tell them this." Her voice grew ominous, and her eyes shifted like shadows. "If you do not return within a year, your voices will change into croaks of mournful toads."

She let out a belch. I stifled a laugh.

"Your hair will turn into spikes, like a cactus." She stretched out her braids, widening her eyes.

I couldn't resist adding, in my spookiest voice, "Your tongue will shrivel like a worm in a desert."

Her voice rose in a creepy howl. "Your sweat will smell like an angry skunk."

I widened my own eyes. "Your poo will turn greenish yellow and goopy."

At this, she collapsed into laughter, and once she recovered, gasped, "Oh, they'll do anything to avoid that curse. I know it."

ROMANI BUSINESS
APPRECIATION EVENT

*T*he night air was thick with the promise of rain, rich with the smells of sweet tamales and cinnamon-chocolate, smoky with a hundred flames of beeswax candles. Everyone in town, Mixteco and Romani alike, had gathered at our home for Lucita's cabo de año. People overflowed from the courtyard, spilling into every corner of our huts, out past our squash and bean patch, to the edge of our milpa and the fringes of our herb garden. An expanse of stars hung over the fields and mountains around us, with my home at the warm, golden center.

The Rom seemed to be genuinely enjoying our refreshments. At first they kept to themselves in a cluster, but then the chocolate and sugar and candle smoke and mist conspired to make everyone light, happy, brave enough to mingle with strangers . . . who were no longer strangers after a week here. In broken Spanish, Rom chatted with Mixteco, and Mixteco with Rom, and the language was just broken enough that the Rom didn't realize this was actually an event for my sister, and the Mixteco didn't realize that the Rom thought they were honored guests for a Romani Business Appreciation Event.

Grandfather put his hand on my shoulder and said, "They are like us, outsiders in Mexico. Both of our people have little voice in the government. City folk consider us backward. We live on the fringes, the wilds of our country. So it is with the Rom."

He nodded to himself, watching our guests. "Duke Ivan told me the Rom have traveled for many centuries and scattered around the world, yet they speak the same language and keep their traditions strong. Our people, the Mixteco, were here before the Spaniards came, before this place was even called Mexico. We too survived, our language survived, our customs survived. And perhaps that is why our village welcomes these Rom with open arms, because we see ourselves in them."

I looked at Esma and her grandparents, who were admiring the sawdust mosaic of the flowered caravan. And I wondered if the key to her people surviving had been separating themselves from outsiders—gadjé. Maybe that's what bonded them together as they danced around their bonfires, night after night for hundreds of years.

Esma and her grandparents met our eyes and ambled over. In his flowery speech, Duke Ivan thanked us, offered us some of the onions—which we all politely refused—and bid us good night as he took an enormous bite of one.

Esma shot me a pointed look.

The statue! I had to give it to them before they left. Esma and I had decided this would be the perfect time to give the gift. The curse would seem spookier in the flickering candlelight and ghostly mist.

I pulled the little diosito from my pocket, my palms damp. I tried to channel Pedro Infante and all the other bold actors I'd seen on-screen the past week. I said, "Dear Romani friends, my sister died a year ago today. She would have loved the movies you've shown. She would have loved the aliveness you've brought. She would have loved . . . you."

I placed the statue in the Duke's free hand, the one that wasn't occupied by an onion. "Please take this ancient diosito that our ancestors made many years ago."

Glancing at Esma's eager face, I launched into the speech I'd memorized, about the good luck the statue would bring. By now my cousins had gathered, sensing something exciting was happening. Lalo understood enough Spanish from his year at school to do a rough Mixteco translation—a word here and a word there.

Esma translated to her own people while Duke Ivan nodded and smiled, extra big at the mention of onions. In return, Grandfather nodded and smiled.

I'd told him about this part. But not the next.

I took a deep breath and, trying to make my eyes scary and my voice haunting, explained the curse that would befall them if they didn't return.

On hearing Lalo's choppy translation, Grandfather gave me a strange look, but I kept going.

Duke Ivan must have understood some of my ranting; I could tell from the way his mustache fell into an upside-down arc over a deep frown. And as Esma translated, making her voice eerie, Duke Ivan's face darkened more with every gory detail. With effort, he swallowed his mouthful of onion and put the remaining half onion in his jacket pocket, looking woozy.

Here was a man who did not like curses. His hand went to his throat at the part about the toads, to his mustache at the part about the spiky hair, and to his paunch at the part about the duck poo. He now held the statue at arm's length, thoroughly disturbed.

Maybe we'd overdone it. Maybe we'd ruined everything.

Roza, on the other hand, wore an expression of skeptical amusement, at least when Duke Ivan wasn't looking at her. While she watched Esma's theatrical translation, the Mistress of Destiny's nose twitched, as if trying to hold back laughter. It was like a volcano, bubbling up and threatening to explode. Finally it gushed out, this lava rush of laughter, but she covered it up, feigning a coughing fit.

She made such a commotion that Ivan patted her back, concerned. Eventually, she calmed down and wiped her eyes and sniffed. Beyond the giant nose, her moist eyes crinkled in enjoyment. She tapped Esma's head, tugged her braid, and whispered something to her, which I could only guess involved the word *squash head*.

Then the Mistress of Destiny turned to her husband. I figured they must be debating whether to accept the statue. With a sigh of exasperation, she grabbed the statue, kissed it, pressed it to her bosom, then issued a firm and unshakeable order.

Duke Ivan grimaced, sighed, and turned to Grandfather and me. "Thank you for the gift, my friends." He shook our hands, leaving sharp traces of onion juice. "We will be certain to return next year to avoid the unpleasantness of the curse."

His wife elbowed him. He added, "And of course, we look forward to enjoying your company once again."

Esma brightened and declared, "I would like to play a song in honor of Lucita."

She wedged her violin beneath her chin and eked out a melody, mournful and beautiful, something that brought to mind caves and candles, beams of light cutting through the night, white sheets waving like magic in the breeze. Her voice rose in an open-mouthed, wordless song, as though she'd converted lightning and stars into spiraling notes, waves of sorrow and waves of joy, waves of losses and waves of wishes.

I looked at my mother, sitting with my aunts outside the kitchen, and wished she could feel it, too, this aliveness all around us. I wished she could feel my sister's presence in the music and mist. I could. It was a soft and whispery presence, something comforting that would always be with me.

STORM

The next day, beneath a heavy white sky, the Rom packed up their camp and loaded their wagons. Everyone on the Hill of Dust came to see them off.

Esma walked over to me and Grandfather, under the guise of thanking us for the Romani Business Appreciation Event. "Well, my friend for life, this is it. The roots of our friendship are planted deep."

I nodded, my lip quivering. If I opened my mouth, I might crumble to bits.

She looked furtively behind her, and seeing that her family was busy packing, she leaned toward me. For one heart-thrumming moment, I thought she might hug me good-bye. Instead, she bent toward my sling, cupped her hands over Thunder, and kissed her downy head. In return, Thunder peeped and nibbled at her ear.

Esma giggled. Still standing close, she stared at me, as if memorizing my face. And then, "Teo, before we leave, can you ask your grandfather something important?"

"Sure. What?"

"Ask him if I'm going to be a famous singer one day."

Confused, I said, "Why don't you ask the Mistress of Destiny?"

Esma lowered her voice. "Here's a Romani secret, never to be divulged. Promise?"

"Promise."

"As far as I can tell, most Romani women aren't true fortune-tellers. They just pay close attention, make good guesses, tell the gadjé whatever they want to hear."

I swallowed hard. So this whole friends-for-life thing was invented? Crushed, I asked, "The Mistress of Destiny made up my true fortune?"

"No!" Esma cried vehemently. "Here's the strange thing! After paying so much attention, my grandmother sometimes sees glimpses of real things, real fortunes. Like she did with you." Esma paused. "Once she told me my true fortune."

"What was it?"

"She said I'd be a famous singer. That was a long time ago, when I was little, before—before the lightning strike. I asked her about it later and she said, 'No, squash head, you imagined it.' But, Teo, I remember, I remember she had that same look in her eyes that she did when she saw your true fortune."

"Why would she lie?"

She lowered her head. "Because if I become a famous singer—it means I'll be marime. I'd have to leave my family forever."

After spending a week with Esma and her people, the gravity of this decision sank into me. Becoming a famous singer would get her disowned. Becoming my friend for life would get her disowned. I remembered how joyful she looked, dancing and singing and playing music around the fire with her people.

"Esma, do you really want to make these fortunes come true? Do you really want to be a famous singer?" I forced myself to continue, my voice raw. "Do you really want to be my friend for life?"

"Yes," she said, without hesitation, her chin jutting, determined, in the air. She glanced at Grandfather. "Your grandfather, he has powers like my grandmother. That's how he knew she was hiding your true fortune. So please, ask him, will I be a famous singer?"

Once I translated, my grandfather regarded her. Then he took her hand—the one with the curled-up fingers—and gave a deep bow, a gesture of true admiration. "Queen Esma," he said, "it doesn't take a divination to see that whatever it is you want, you will make it happen."

And then, Esma's stepmother called out for her and stomped over, smacking her head, then pulled her away by the ear.

Moments later, the horses were hooked to the wagons, and the Rom were walking beside them, loaded with packs of their own. They waved good-bye, and we bid them farewell. The

Mistress of Destiny pulled something from her pocket—the diosito—and held it up as she waved, looking directly into my eyes. In broken Spanish, she said something along the lines of, "Here's hoping none of us is croaking like a toad or pooping like a duck next year."

Somehow Grandfather caught the gist of her words and laughed a deep belly laugh.

The caravan began its descent down the mountain, with Esma bringing up the rear, carrying a satchel in front and Da on her back and holding Ga's and Ba's hands. "Good-bye, my friend for life! Until next year!"

"Good-bye, Queen of Lightning!" I called after her.

As she grew smaller, loping away in that crooked dance of hers, my eyes burned and my chin trembled. Once she turned the curve, I ran up into the hills, into el monte. I perched on a high lookout, where I could watch the caravan wind down into the valley, on to their next village. At the horizon, clumps of stone-gray clouds were rolling in, and a deep rumble sounded in the distance.

Lightning illuminated the entire sky. I tucked myself farther back against the rocks, under the overhang, watching the first storm of rainy season draw near. The rain came, first a few drops, then walls of water. Safely under the overhang I sat, feeling the air's new coolness. Bolt after bolt of lightning crackled against the dark sky, flashes of wild energy.

Water slid down the mountains, gushing mud, and far below, the river swelled and roared. Tucked far above in my mountaintop nook, I imagined Esma and her people taking refuge inside their wagons, sheltered from the howling and pounding. I heard Esma's shouts in the crashes of thunder, her screams in the wind, alive and whirling with possibility.

And I screamed, at first wordless, open-mouthed screams. Dozens, maybe hundreds that I'd swallowed over the past year. Then, when I was all screamed out, words formed, words for Esma. "I will see you again. And one day, I will save you, too."

DROP

THE HILL OF DUST,
OAXACA, MEXICO

Present Day

13

FIRST INTERMISSION

$\mathcal{M}$ ateo, how about some food?" The question comes from a distant place, some other world.

"Huh?" My voice sounds strange and hoarse.

I blink and focus on Grandpa's head, which is tilted in concern. "Food?" he repeats, making an eating gesture.

It's like a spell has been broken, like there's a glitch in the movie I'm watching and it's suddenly just . . . stopped.

"Food," I echo, staring down at the coin necklace in my hand. It feels almost alive, something with a heartbeat. "Why food?"

He grins. "Thought I heard your belly rumbling."

"Oh." I listen, embarrassed. Yup. My gut's making a storm of its own.

"And, mijo," he says, "there are some strange noises coming from your pocket."

"What?" Oh. Right. My phone. It's sounding message alerts in the form of my favorite guitar riff. I silence it without even seeing how many texts I've missed or what time it is. This is the longest I've gone without checking my phone. Well, at least outside of sleeping, plane rides, and school.

The weird thing is, I don't care. I still have one leg in the world of his story, and I want to climb back in. All I can think about is Esma, somewhere out there. I pool the coin necklace from one hand to another, like a deck of cards. "Did she come back, Grandpa?"

He stands up slowly, without a word. Then he takes some new candles from his altar, lights them, and smushes them over the ones that have burned out. The room brightens.

He sits down again, and his eyes shine with reflections of flame, like tiny mirrors. And my stomach grumbles fade and he starts talking and the movie plays on . . .

GUST

Teo

THE HILL OF DUST,
OAXACA, MEXICO
Long, Long Ago

SPARK AND FLASH

*O*ne year later, the Rom came at sunrise, when the sky was a riot of pink and gold, when the air was fresh and cool and full of hope. For months, I'd been glancing at that bend in the road, far down the valley, at the foot of the Hill of Dust, waiting, waiting, waiting. And at the moment their trail of wagons and horses and scarves and coins rounded the curve, the sun peeked above the mountains and shone long rays across the valley, through wisps of hearth smoke, onto their caravan.

I'd been crossing the courtyard for breakfast, but at the sight of the Rom, I sprinted down the road.

Until a flurry of whistles flew at me.

Months earlier, Thunder's cute peeps had changed to piercing whistles. Her beak had bloomed bright pink with a yellow patch, like a slice of rosy mango. Her feathers had grown in a rich coppery brown on her neck and back. Black feathers had sprouted on her belly, and a patch of white feathers spotted her now-black wings. Her neck stretched long and proud, and she strutted around on tall legs as though she were boss of the world, even though she barely reached my knee.

Her high-pitched twitters were easy to translate. *Slow down, Teo!*

Reluctantly, I slowed down.

In her whistle language, she scolded me as she waddled up. *Don't you dare leave us behind!*

Yes, *us.* There were two new members of my rescued-animal club.

Spark, a baby goat born blind, whose *baah* of protest was barely audible over Thunder's scolding. *Please slow down, please?* Spark was saying in her timid voice. *What about little me?* She meandered along, her nose and ears quivering in the breeze, trying to compensate for her lack of vision. She was white with honey speckles and the softest ears I'd ever felt, a tender velvet that your fingers couldn't resist smoothing.

And then there was Flash, the newest member: a three-legged skunk, just a few months old, who I'd found as a baby caught in a trap. When it was clear he'd never survive in the wild, Grandfather removed the skunk's stink glands so that he could live with us. Now, Flash scampered back and forth along the road, curious about every twig, every bug. He was a slippery, roly-poly thing, always on the move, devilishly weaseling here and there. He was only still when sleeping, and only then could you fully appreciate the beauty of his shiny, coal-black fur with the perfect, milk-white stripe running down the center of his back to the tip of his bushy tail.

Relenting, I slowed even more, letting all the animals catch up. Sometimes it felt as if each of them held a little piece of Lucita's soul—Thunder's bossiness, Flash's playfulness, and Spark's tenderness. I was bound to them, and we were as loyal to each other as family.

But slowing down for the animals meant my cousins had time to catch up, too. "Hey, wait for me!" Lalo shouted. He was just a couple years younger but still whined like a little kid when he felt left out. "Where are you going, Teo?"

"Nowhere," I called back. I wanted to greet Esma and her people first, have them to myself for a bit. Soon enough they'd be mobbed.

Of course, Lalo followed me anyway, and then little red-faced Chucho caught up, too. When they caught sight of the caravan, Chucho yelled so loudly the entire village must have heard. "THE GYPSIES!"

For someone so small, he had a giant mouth. Within moments, children appeared like bees on sweet rolls. They ran ahead to the Rom, as I hurried my animals along. The adults soon abandoned their chores and followed, too, jostling past. I picked up Flash so he wouldn't get stepped on. Thunder shot warning whistles at anyone too close to the goat—her own large, furred, four-legged baby.

Now the nervousness set in. What if Esma had changed? Gotten a new best friend for life? Forgotten about our fortune altogether? Or what if she needed to be saved? Could I do it? Maybe rescuing animals was practice for saving the Queen herself one day.

I continued down the dirt road, trying to calm my thudding heart. But even the morning birds were chirping with the thrill of the Rom coming. What would I say to Esma? She was just minutes away now, three more switchbacks down the road. I peered at the valley where the villagers had already reached her caravan. They were petting the horses, running their hands over the carved swirls of the wagons, reaching out to shake the Rom's hands.

I was squinting, searching for Esma, when I noticed footsteps and the pungent smell of shoe polish. A rough voice said, "*Hola*, Nephew." It was my uncle Paco, who'd recently returned from working for three years in Mexico City. The way he talked about it, you'd think he was mayor of that place.

He'd had a round paunch before but now was thin, almost caved-in looking, with bloodshot eyes. He claimed it was lack of sleep from the ruckus out here in the boondocks—roosters and crickets and dogs. Supposedly he'd gotten used to sleeping to the civilized sounds of buses and automobiles and streetcars out the window. *Real glass* windows, he was quick to point out. He rejected farm chores and spent most of the day polishing his shoes, which was another reason for not working—he didn't want to dull the shine.

Thunder didn't like him. When Uncle thumped me on my back—a little too hard—she spewed out a string of disapproving whistles. He gave a vague kick in her direction, which only served to sharpen her whistles to a shrill siren.

"Shh, Thunder," I said. If Uncle didn't calm down soon, she might bite his ankle. You didn't want to get on Thunder's bad side, especially when she was protecting her little family.

"So, Nephew," he said, walking stiffly in his shiny shoes. They were so small and pointy, I had to wonder how he crammed his feet into them. "What's all the fuss about?"

I answered softly. "The Rom are here. The Gypsies."

He reeled. "You all permit them in our village?"

I blinked. Why wouldn't we? "They're our friends," I said. "We welcome them."

Uncle shook his head. "You all really are as ignorant as city folk say."

My muscles tensed. Why had he even come back to the Hill of Dust, only to insult us?

"In the city, we scorn the Gypsies." He spit on the ground, a yellow glob of phlegm. "They're all dirty beggars. Sneaky, out to steal kids and every last centavo."

I swallowed hard, wishing I could pick up the pace and leave Uncle behind, but then I'd also be leaving behind Spark and Thunder. I patted Flash as he wriggled around in my shirt, patches of black-and-white fur peeking out here and there.

"Well, Uncle," I said finally. "I don't know about the Rom in the city, but this caravan is good and honest. They show us movies in exchange for hats and baskets. And they tell our fortunes. You'll see."

"Right, and they pick your pockets while you're busy watching. Or ransack the houses you leave empty. Now in the city . . ."

I blocked him out, tired of hearing about the wonders of the city—electricity, phones, radio, television. But it pained me to hear him insult my friend for life and her people. I racked my mind for an excuse to get away from him.

As I thought, I stroked Flash, who was creeping around my neck now, nibbling at my collar with sharp, tiny teeth.

Uncle stopped his ranting and said, "Is that a skunk on your neck?"

I gave him a bewildered look. "You've never noticed Flash before?" But as I said it, I realized that of course he hadn't. He was so absorbed in his own complaints, he barely noticed the goings-on of daily life around him. "Yes," I said. "He's a skunk. Only three legs, but he manages."

Unaware that Flash's stink glands were no longer intact, Uncle took a step away and wavered there, watching my skunk warily and muttering about backward villagers like me.

Thunder took advantage of his distraction to waddle over to Uncle's left shoe and let out a goopy, greenish-yellow stream of poo on the freshly polished leather.

She half-flew, half-waddled away before he could kick her. She sat at the edge of the road, fluffing her tail feathers, indignant, watching Uncle's reaction from the corner of her eye. He was livid, jumping around and cursing, and finally stormed off toward our home, probably to spend the morning removing every last trace of duck poo from his precious shoe. Once he disappeared around the bend, a satisfied Thunder strutted back to my side.

Through the mesquite leaves, a breeze rippled, like the light sound of Lucita laughing at my duck's antics. Grateful that Thunder had freed me of Uncle, I rounded the last curve and found myself at the edge of the crowd swarming the Rom— practically the entire village. This time, everyone greeted our visitors warmly, eager for the wonders they'd brought. My people spoke with the Rom in broken Spanish, asking what they'd seen in their travels over the past year.

I breathed in the rich horse smells, the scents of amber tea and fringed carpets and far-off lands that clung to the wagons. The acrid scent of the Duke's onions cut through the dusty haze. My eyes lingered on the wagons' golden spirals, the deep red and turquoise flowers, all of it more ornate than even the gilded, angel-speckled ceiling of our village cathedral. I tried to glimpse inside one of the wagons, through the blue curtains, but it was too dark and stayed hidden in mystery.

Searching for Esma, I wove through the throng, eyes skimming over the flower-clad boria with babies strapped to their backs. There were Da and Ga, whose hair had sprouted out in waves, like agave leaves. There were the men with gold jewelry sparkling in the sun. There was the nose of Roza, Mistress of Destiny, twitching and dancing with delight over her pipe. And there was the Duke's mustache, prancing around as he smiled and laughed and munched his onion. The warmth of familiarity filled me, and I hugged Flash tightly as I took it all in.

Finally, I spotted Esma. She looked the same as I remembered, only taller, and with a different dress and scarf—all royal ruby reds, poppies and roses and dahlias. And more necklaces of beads and shells and coins; it looked like a thousand jewels had spilled from a treasure chest hidden beneath her scarf.

On seeing me, a smile lit up her face like a sunrise, more dazzling than in my memories. On her hip, she held Ba, who sputtered off words in Romani, his sounds now broadened beyond *ba*.

As she set him down and loped toward me, I drank her in like a glimmering red glass of *agua de jamaica*. She came close, and for a moment I thought she'd throw her arms around me. But she said, "My friend for life! I missed you!"

I nodded, overcome with the miracle of Esma in front of me, in the flesh. This was the moment I'd dreamed of all year. She stood so close I could smell the spice of her breath— cinnamon and sweet tea and unknown scents.

"Me, too," I whispered. And then I added with a shy smile, "Queen Esma."

She stared at me for a while, a huge grin on her face, and I tried to look back but it was too much, like looking at the sun. "Your eyelashes grew," she observed.

I blushed, stared at my feet.

She spotted Thunder, who was prissily preening herself. "Your duck grew up! And look at your new little creatures!" She petted Spark's soft ears, watching Flash wriggle in my arms.

Then she took Ba's hand and smoothed it over the silk of Spark's fur, murmuring something in Romani.

Then, like a dark shadow, her stepmother closed in, frowned, and snatched up Ba. She bonked Esma's head and dragged her away by her elbow.

I sighed. That was one thing that hadn't changed.

With her other hand, Esma waved vigorously. "See you tonight, Teo!" she called back. "I have a surprise!"

SURPRISE

*A*s the projector beam illuminated moths and bats, I knelt on the dusty ground with Spark's head in my lap. Thunder settled at my side, her beak resting drowsily on my knee. In front of me, Flash played with a bit of string, pouncing on it like a cat. When he got too rowdy, Thunder let out a grumpy barrage of whistles.

I kept glancing over my shoulder, searching for Esma, wondering what her surprise could be.

Excitement hung in the plaza like electricity, even more so than last year. Most everyone on the Hill of Dust had been looking forward to this day all year. As the Duke and his sons fiddled with the projector, spooling spirals of film, nearly all of my village sat on the edge of our little wooden chairs. In eager voices, people speculated on what this new movie might be, and mused over questions they'd ask tomorrow at the fortune-telling.

My cousins Lalo and Chucho insisted on sitting beside me, vying for a prime place to rub Spark's ears. Nearby sat Aunt Perla and her new husband and my other aunts and uncles and cousins, each with freshly woven hats on their laps. My mother was at home, as usual, shrouded in her shawl, huddled over her cardboard box of treasures.

This was something new she'd started this past year. She'd place the worn box on her lap like a baby, then carefully pick up a necklace, admire it, put it back. Next, she'd choose a fancy spoon, which she'd admire, then tenderly set down. And on it went with a silver candlestick, a tin box, a picture frame, gold earrings, and a random smattering of other shiny possessions. Grandfather suspected my mother deemed it safer to love things she could keep protected in a box. He gave her healing teas and did cleansing ceremonies for her, but she only cared about the contents of her box.

And Grandfather, he rarely left home now, claiming he wanted to keep an eye on my mother and the animals. But there was more to it. I tried not to notice how just crossing the court-yard left him breathless and limping.

The movie started, and everyone hushed. When the star actress came on-screen, I gasped. A stab of recognition shot through me. Those heart-shaped lips, those impossibly long, curved eyebrows, that soft, dark cloud of wavy hair. The sight made my legs quake, my stomach churn, a cold panic grip me.

This was Maestra María, the teacher I'd had during my stint in first grade. Or at least the spitting image of her.

Six years earlier, on that first morning of school, I'd thought, *Oh, how beautiful!* But before the first lesson was over, I'd witnessed the evil hidden beneath all that beauty. And by the afternoon, I'd fallen victim to her wrath, and trudged home in tears. It had been the same day after day: One of us students offended her somehow. In retaliation, Maestra María would raise a long, curved eyebrow like the bow of an arrow, just before her attack. Her weapon of choice was not an arrow but a wooden ruler, an innocent tool until you saw how ruthlessly she wielded it. To this day, her memory struck an instinctive fear, a reflex to cower and flee. I suspected a gaping hole where her heart was supposed to be.

Wincing, I forced myself to watch the film, noting that this actress wasn't quite identical to Maestra María. I was somewhat reassured by the slight difference in nose length and chin width and curve of her shoulders. Yes, it must have been a different woman altogether, but she proved just as heartless, and moved her eyebrows in a similarly vicious manner.

La Mujer Sin Alma—the Woman Without a Soul—the Heartless Woman. This was the name of the movie and the main character. She was a beautiful and evil lady who made rich men fall in love with her. Compared to my teacher, she was sneakier with her evildoing, and targeted grown men rather than innocent children, yet both she and Maestra María lacked a soul.

Afterward, everyone was still shivering and marveling over the horrid, gorgeous movie star—whose real name, someone said, was María Félix. Another María, I noted. Although, in fairness, half the women I knew had María as one of their names.

I was relieved when the movie ended. I liked the funny ones with songs and silly mustached men better. While the others were picking up their chairs and bidding each other good night, I spotted Esma at the edge of the cornfield. I hoped she would sing and play violin while her people packed up the film, as she had last year.

But no, she was standing there, staring at me. Silver eyes glittering, she motioned for me to join her. And she disappeared into the tall stalks.

Heart pounding, I stood up and strolled over to the milpa, as casually as I could with three animals at my heels. A bossy duck, three-legged skunk, and blind goat usually attract attention, but everyone else was still under the movie's spell and didn't notice me slip into the cornstalks.

A few rows back, I stumbled right into Esma. Embarrassed, I staggered backward.

With a grin, she grabbed my hand and steadied me. She led me deeper into the shadows of the field, where no one could hear or see us. Her hand was warm, and I could feel her lightning pass into my palm and spread through my body.

When she released my hand, I was breathing hard.

"Teo, my friend for life!"

"Esma, my queen," I whispered, my voice soft beneath the crickets' chorus.

She greeted my animals, cooing and fussing over them, and then stood up to smile at me. Her teeth glowed as white as a crescent moon.

I swallowed hard. "What's your surprise?"

She pulled a small card from her pocket. "Look!"

I held it up, out of the shadows, against the sky. There were letters and swirls and stars. I could sound out a few short words, thanks to my time in school six years earlier. *Of, the, a . . .* words that didn't tell me anything useful. "What does it say?"

Her shoulders fell. "You can't read, Teo?"

I looked away, ashamed. "No." And feeling the need to defend myself, I added, "Hardly anyone can read in my village. The kids work all day." I didn't say that the beautiful and evil Maestra María had terrified me—and most of the others who had dared go—into quitting school.

Esma tapped her finger to her chin. "Then we'll have to find another way."

"But what is it, Esma?"

"A business card." Eyes flashing, she tossed a shell-laced braid over her shoulder. "See, Teo, one night my family was showing films near Mexico City, and I was singing and playing violin after the movie, just fooling around. I didn't think anyone was paying attention. And when I stopped, a man and his wife came up to me, clapping."

Esma's eyes were wide as she spoke, her hands and arms making sweeping gestures, painting pictures of her words. After a dramatic pause, she continued. "Teo, the man was a music agent! He said I could be a star! A famous singer!"

I was speechless. Of course, *I* knew she could be a famous star. But it was something else altogether to hear about another person recognizing her talent. Someone who could make a difference in her life. I wanted to be the one to save her. Or at least help her.

This was her dream. Yet I remembered what it would mean for her—leaving her family forever. And for me—if she left her family and settled in the city, I'd probably never see her again. But she had to leave. If she stayed with her people, she'd have a life full of squash-head insults and bops to the head. I kept my thoughts to myself and said only, "That's your dream."

"Yes!" Esma's chin jutted out in that fierce way. "Then the Duke came over, and when the man asked him about training me for a professional career, he said, 'Absolutely not' and walked away. But the woman slipped me this card and whispered that if I ever decided to try, I could live with them until I made enough money to put me on my feet."

Esma cradled the card against her cheek. "I was hoping you'd read it," she said.

"Well," I said, "we'll find someone who can. My uncle just got back from working in Mexico City. Maybe he can read a little."

She paused, shook her head. "I wanted you to teach me to read."

I furrowed my eyebrows. She wanted my help, yet I couldn't give it. "Why, Esma?"

She raised her arms, palms upward, as though channeling celestial light. "Reading is like lightning."

I tilted my head. "Lightning?"

"Power, Teo. If I'm going to be out on my own in the gadjé world, I need to know how to read. So no one takes advantage of me."

"Doesn't anyone in your family know how to read?"

She shook her head, adamant. "My people don't read, don't approve of their kids reading. They say we'd become marime, part of the gadjé world."

That word again, *marime*. Impure. My gaze fell to the ground, where Flash was nibbling on Spark's ear. "Well, I can't help you, Esma. I'm sorry."

She looked at me wildly. "Nothing is impossible."

Cringing inside, I thought of Maestra María, that terrible, elegant eyebrow arching upward.

"I know!" Esma said. "Why don't you start going to school now? Then next year when I come back, you can teach me."

I rubbed my temple, remembering Maestra María's ruler, the sting, the hot, humiliating tears, the bruise that lasted days afterward. "But who would herd the goats and do my chores?"

"You'll find a way."

And then she dropped to the ground and held her palm out to Thunder, who crawled right into her lap. She started petting Spark, letting the goat nuzzle against her. She reached out to Flash, unafraid of the possibility of stink.

"He can't spray," I assured her. "My grandfather removed his stink glands."

"Pobrecito," she said, touching his nose to hers. "Poor little guy. Three legs and no stink. You'll just have to find a new weapon, huh?"

"He has one," I said, motioning to my duck. "Thunder. Our grumpy guard duck."

Esma's laughter rang out, a melody like raindrops on leaves. "Think she could guard me from the boria?" she joked. "Next time my stepmother tries to whack me, Thunder can fly up and bite her hand."

"Actually, ankles are her specialty." I grinned. "And greenish-yellow poo on shoes."

As we talked, I settled beside her, only a sliver of space between us. I breathed in the smell of earth and corn and leaves and night, and the spice and wood smoke that clung to her. She smelled like the promise of distant lands, of adventure, of possibility. I reached over and stroked the animals' fur and feathers, and our fingers brushed, and more lightning passed into me.

"My powers flare up when I'm with you," she said.

"I know," I said softly. "I feel it in your fingertips."

And there in the dappled moonlight, with creatures warm and breathing, and lightning passing between the places our skin touched, we told each other all the things that best friends share.

She showed me her new beads and shells and coins, like blooms on vines winding around her neck, her wrists, in and out of locks of her hair. Some she'd found at the sea, she said, and some in the jungle, and some in pine forests, and some in deserts.

She told me how her stepmother wouldn't let her sleep in the wagon anymore and made her sleep outside instead, even during storms. It was a good thing, too, because thanks to her lightning powers, one night, camping beside a river, she awoke hours before dawn, knowing something bad was about to happen. Then she saw the river rising, fast, and using her talent for screaming at the top of her lungs, she woke the others. They moved to higher land just before the water flooded the valley.

Another night, they were camped in a field with some other Romani caravans near Mexico City, when Esma woke up smelling gasoline and smoke. She saw that someone had lit fire to the dried grasses, and the flames were zipping toward their wagons. Again, her screaming skills paid off, and within two seconds, she'd woken up everyone in camp. They moved their wagons just before the flames could engulf them. Esma narrowed her eyes and said, "I knew who set the fire—I saw him—a man who'd fought with my father earlier that evening. But later that night, there was a storm, and the man's house was struck by lightning." She grinned, triumphant. "Lightning avenged me!"

And on and on we went, exchanging stories. Hers were more exciting than mine, and mostly involved her saving herself and her entire caravan from doom. She definitely didn't need anyone to save her, not with lightning powers on her side.

At first I was nervous, and my words came out stuttering, but soon they flowed between us like warm honey. I told her about my animals' antics, how when Flash got grumpy, he'd raise his tail in anger, assuming he was spraying his offender, then strut smugly away. I told her how I saw Lucita in my animals, in starlight, in sunlit clouds, in the paths of hummingbirds . . . and how happy, mixed with sad, it made me.

Esma told me she'd composed secret songs about missing me and Thunder. She sang them lightly, under her breath, and shivers and sparks danced over my skin, through my blood.

In whispers, we talked until the church bell struck midnight. And then she said, "Alas, my friend for life, I must bid you farewell. The boria will be wondering why there's no squash head around to whack."

"What'll you tell them?"

She thought for a moment, cradling Flash in her arms. "That I encountered a vicious skunk and had to stay perfectly still so it wouldn't spray me."

"Creative storytelling," I said.

"Well, Flash *is* pretty vicious," she laughed, as the skunk ran up her arm and nibbled at a red ribbon woven into her braid. She handed me Flash and stood up, adjusting her headscarf. "Until tomorrow, Teo."

Esma left first, just in case anyone was still in the plaza, and I stayed with my animals, warm in the afterglow of her lightning. I wondered if I could face the beautiful, evil Maestra María again, in order to make Esma's dream come true. It wasn't exactly saving her, but it was close. And as I thought, a question took shape in my mind—the perfect question for tomorrow's visit from Roza, Mistress of Destiny.

Back home, I poked my head into Grandfather's room. He'd waited up for me. I was touched; lately he'd been going to sleep earlier and earlier, sometimes before twilight, skipping supper altogether.

"Teo! Come in!"

He sat on his petate, leaning against the adobe wall, smiling with tired eyes. He looked small, huddled in his poncho; lately he'd gotten chilled so easily. His room smelled of earth and incense and herbs and wool and beeswax—Grandfather's unique combination of scents.

"Tell me about the movie, Teo," he said, reaching out to smooth Spark's ears. Once you started petting her ears, it was hard to stop.

I told him about the beautiful, heartless woman with the alluring eyebrows. "She looked just like that teacher I had," I added, then fell quiet, remembering Esma's request.

Grandfather stroked Flash's fur for a long moment. "Is there something more?"

It was as if he could peer into my mind, the spaces between words.

"Esma wants me to go back to school."

He tilted his head, surprised. "And?"

"Well," I said, looking away. "I don't know. I have the goats and my chores."

He studied my face. "Your cousins could help. Lalo could take over your chores, and Chucho could do Lalo's. They're old enough now."

I looked down. "People like us—we're not welcome in school. I can't stand how the teacher treats us."

For a moment, he was quiet. Then he said, "You already speak Spanish. This gives you a voice. And when you learn to read, your voice will be stronger. So strong you will be able to demand the teacher's respect. Not just for yourself, but for others."

"Maybe," I said, unconvinced. My voice felt like a dusty whisper now. I made a last grasp at an excuse. "But what about helping with your patients?"

He shrugged. "I only have energy for a few patients a day anyway. And since Paco is back in town, he can help translate."

I didn't like the idea of Uncle Paco in the healing hut instead of me.

Reluctantly, I asked, "You think the patients would feel comfortable with him?"

"No, but I think sometimes if you give a person a role, he steps up to it. And anyway, you learning to read is more important." His eyes twinkled. "And Esma is still your friend for life, isn't she?"

I nodded quickly. I thought of Esma and Maestra María. At the heart of it, my loyalty to Esma was greater than my fear of the *maestra*. I wasn't so much of a coward to be scared of a teacher, was I? I was twelve years old now. What could she do to me?

16

SOMETHING STUPID

In the angled morning sunlight, I was scattering corn for the turkeys when a cluster of Romani women and children strutted up our path. Roza's nose did a happy jig as my entire family gathered in the courtyard, eager for their fortunes. "Buenos días," she said in her choppy accent, and then something that Esma translated as, "It's marvelous to be back!"

Aunt Perla stepped forward, holding her new husband's hand. Before their marriage, he'd been a widower for years. Now they lived just a few houses down, but she made sure to be here bright and early so she could show him off to the Rom. "Look!" she squealed. "My husband. Strong and handsome, with brown eyes and black hair." She squeezed his bicep, ruffled his hair. "Just like you said!"

The others looked doubtfully at her husband. True, his eyes were brown, but his hair was more gray than black, and his predominant feature was not muscle but a large gut hanging over his waistband. And handsome? Well, that was stretching it. His teeth looked stolen from a horse, so big that his mouth never quite closed. And then there was his chronically stuffed nose, certainly not mentioned in the fortune. Yet my aunt believed he was handsome, and he doted on her like she was a princess.

She patted her round belly. "And you were right! A baby!"

Roza nodded, twitching her nose, unsurprised but obviously pleased. Esma translated the boria's polite murmurs of congratulations.

My grandfather hobbled out. "Welcome, Mistress of Destiny. We hope your people will come again to our . . . special yearly event. It's in three days."

Upon hearing the translation, Roza nodded, let her hand linger in his, patted it with her other one. "It would be our honor."

Grandfather led us all into the healing hut, and as I unstacked chairs for our guests, he lit candles.

The fortunes were similar to last year—marriages, babies, bouts of good luck, bouts of bad luck, things lost and found. When my turn came, I perched on the wooden seat across from Roza and Esma, twisting the hem of my shirt.

"And what is your question, Teo, my friend for life?" Esma asked, exuberant.

Softly, I translated. My relatives raised their eyebrows, curious about my friendship with this Romani girl. My cousins giggled and made jokes and low whistles.

A blush warmed my face. I looked at Esma for a moment, then flicked my eyes to Roza. "Mistress of Destiny," I asked, "should I go to school?"

There was another flurry of murmurs and baffled whispers.

Roza looked amused at the question, her mouth widening into a five-toothed smile. "That's a new one. Haven't heard that before."

As Esma translated back and forth, her eyes glittered with hope.

I dealt the cards as Roza instructed and watched her nose flutter as her gaze swept over the cards—a jumble of swords and cauldrons and goblets and royalty and suns and moons that meant nothing to me.

She shook her head and muttered something.

Esma's shoulders sank, and a shadow passed over her face. She took a deep breath and began arguing with Roza. After a storm of impassioned words flew between them, Roza smacked Esma's head lightly and tugged her braid and gave her a command.

Esma hesitated before translating, her voice bitter. "No, you shouldn't go to school. It's a . . . it's a waste of time." She blinked back angry tears.

Pipe bobbing, Roza studied her granddaughter. Her nostrils expanded to nearly double their size as she sucked in a long breath. After a moment, her nose calmed and her eyes softened. She spoke again, resigning herself to something.

A smile broke out over Esma's face. She translated, giddy. "You shouldn't go to school. No child should. But the fact is, you will! You will go to school! For reasons more noble than most. You will learn to read. And it will change your life. And the lives of others!"

Roza narrowed her eyes and pursed her lips and added something else.

Esma suppressed a smile as she said, "The Mistress of Destiny would like to make it very clear that in her own opinion, however, school is not recommended."

With a glint in his eye, Grandfather nodded at Roza and said, "Thank you for that true fortune."

"You go next," Lalo said, urging my grandfather forward.

I stood up to offer the seat.

He shook his head. "I'm an old man. Fortunes are for the young."

But Chucho and my other cousins pushed. "Come on, come on, Grandfather."

With a sigh, he consented and sat down, looking almost sadly at Roza. With trembling hands, he dealt the cards.

Roza gazed at the cards, then at his face, deep creases at the corners of his eyes from years of smiles, and between his brows from years of compassion for others' pain. And lately, from some of his own pain.

Her nose held perfectly still, motionless as a statue. Something passed between the two of them. Something beyond words, something that remained unspoken. She laid her hand over his. "Your grandson will bring you great joy."

Grandfather appeared relieved. "He already does." He added, "He also brings me three-legged skunks and baby ducks and blind goats."

Laughter filled the room, and as if on cue, Flash squirmed out of my arms and onto the table, attempting to gnaw at the fortune cards. Then Thunder spewed out a wave of curmudgeonly whistles, as if to say, *Quiet down, now!* She didn't like crowds or closed-up spaces or noise . . . unless she was making it herself. With all the ruckus, Spark the goat began to *baah* and stumble around, confused.

Embarrassed, I scooped up Flash and set him firmly in my lap, then drew Spark in close, stroking her ear.

As my cousins joked about my animals, Grandfather and Roza continued to stare at each other, in silent conversation. Despite the commotion, her nose remained still as a leaf on a windless day.

And then Uncle Paco entered the room, limping slightly from his too-tight footwear. "What's going on here?" he bellowed in Spanish.

Thunder gave him an unwelcoming whistle and stood between me and my uncle, protectively.

Roza broke her gaze with Grandfather. Like the hair on the back of a dog, her nose stood up, tall and ready for a fight.

I groaned inside. I'd been hoping Uncle had slept in late this morning, as he did most mornings, lost in dreams of sewage pipes and television.

"Well?" he demanded. And again, louder now, "What are these people doing in my home?"

My relatives didn't answer, simply looked the other way as if that could make him disappear. The odor of shoe polish oozed through the room.

"Answer me!" he shouted in Mixteco first, then in Spanish. He swung his arms around wildly, nearly hitting Aunt Perla in the face. Her husband pulled her in close, gaping at Uncle.

Esma cracked the silence, her head high. "We're reading fortunes, señor."

He glared at her, then at the others. "I'll tell you what they're doing! They're getting you in a crowded space and distracting you so these little Gypsy brats can pick your pockets." He pointed to Da, Ga, and Ba, who were more interested in picking their noses than any pockets.

His rant continued, a furious mix of Spanish and Mixteco. "Criminals, all of them. I've seen Gypsies in the city, how they work, like sneaky foxes. They'll even steal your kids."

Esma kept her chin jutting bravely out, and translated not a word. But her people's offended expressions made it clear they understood the gist.

My stomach was in knots. We'd worked so hard to forge a friendship, not just between me and Esma but between our people. What if my uncle ruined it all?

Grandfather spoke. His voice sounded more fragile than ever but had a calmness that commanded attention. "Son," he said to Uncle, "these are honored guests. There is a respect among us. I ask you to show them this same respect."

This, Esma did translate, with a flash of pride.

Uncle barged through the crowd to the table. "So read my fortune," he challenged. "Do it now."

Esma whispered words to her grandmother. Roza seemed unruffled. The tip of her nose had somehow turned up, as if it were looking down on Uncle. If a nose could be indignant, this was it.

Tapping her pipe against her teeth, she instructed him to shuffle and deal the cards. He did so, roughly, banging them on the table.

She stared at the cards, then at him. Her words were slow and solemn.

Esma translated, "Your insides are torn up, broken."

Uncle shifted uncomfortably in the chair. All my relatives listened carefully, watching his reaction.

Esma's translation continued. "Beware of doing something very"—and here Esma paused and seemed to hold back a smile, but then she rearranged her face into something solemn—"very stupid."

At that, Uncle erupted, all rage and clumsiness. He flipped the table over. Cards scattered. Roza held her ground like a mountain, with Esma at her side, but the other Romani women gasped and skittered backward with the toddlers. My aunts pulled away, against the wall, holding their own children. My uncles lunged toward Uncle Paco, trying to restrain him.

But he shook off their hands.

Anger rippled through the room. Even Flash the skunk was arching his back and stamping his feet in outrage. Fists were clenching, eyes narrowing. Someone would get hurt if this wasn't stopped. And the Rom might leave forever. I had to do something.

I looked at Esma for inspiration, at her gleaming silver eyes, at her fierce, proud jaw framed by braids and shells and coins. And I thought about what she would do in my place. I felt her lightning in my blood.

I righted the chair, stepped onto it, and held up my skunk, whose bushy tail was already raised and ready. I spoke loudly, from my belly, staring straight at my uncle. And I aimed Flash's bottom right at him.

My cousins and other uncles and aunts were surprised but unafraid, knowing that except for his penchant for nibbling at clothes and grain sacks, my skunk was harmless. Esma murmured something to her relatives, which made them relax. Now only Uncle Paco looked wary.

My voice thundered, low and strangely commanding in Mixteco. "Uncle, my skunk has no patience for . . . stupid things. He's just about to spray."

That was like a bucket of cold water on Uncle's head. He fled the room.

I lowered Flash, who promptly began biting at a loose thread on my sleeve.

Over the next hour, my relatives fetched payments of eggs, vegetables, and corn for their fortunes and chatted with the Romani women. The children picked up the cards from the floor, eager to touch their magic. Eventually, my aunts and uncles and cousins trickled out to return to their chores, and the Romani women and children headed outside and down the path, leaving only Roza and Esma and Grandfather and me. We lingered at the doorway, half in the sunshine.

A tiny snort of laughter escaped from Roza. Esma pressed her lips together to keep her own laughter from bursting out.

Grandfather said, "Your fortunes appear true, Mistress. My son did something very stupid indeed. And as a result, my grandson has given me great joy."

"And school?" Esma asked, looking at me hopefully.

Bolts of lightning were still flowing through my blood, making me brave . . . for the moment at least. I glanced at the Mistress of Destiny, chomping on her pipe, awaiting my response. Maybe this could be my way to save Esma. And maybe, if Grandfather was right, to save my future self.

"Looks like I'm going," I said. "Even if it's not recommended."

THE HEARTLESS WOMAN

*I*n the half light of dawn, sneezing and rooting through dusty junk in our storeroom, I found a yellowed notebook with only a few warped and water-stained pages left. A search through more odds and ends revealed a pencil stub, shorter than my thumb, which I sharpened with a knife.

The church bell rang six chimes. Time to leave for my first day of school. I rubbed my eyes, still groggy from staying up late after last night's movie with Esma. We'd met again in the shadows of the cornfield, whispering stories from our year apart. My body felt exhausted, but the precious hours with Esma were worth it, especially since I couldn't see her again till later this afternoon.

Quickly, I tossed my supplies into a small satchel along with a few tortillas and a lime and goat cheese for lunch. Still sipping their morning atole, my aunts and uncles waved and wished me well, while my cousins skulked, annoyed they had to take over my chores. And my mother—she slept, shutting out the world.

On the walk over the caked-brown hills, I tugged at my clothes, uncomfortably small. These were the pants and shirt I wore to weddings and baptisms, since they had only a few patched holes. I'd washed the shirt yesterday, and it hadn't dried completely. I shivered in the cool morning air. My mother used to wash and patch my clothes, but she barely left her room now, either sleeping or rifling through valuables in her cardboard box.

I'd tried to make Thunder and Spark and Flash stay home with Grandfather, but five minutes into the walk, they'd appeared at my side. Little did they know they had an hour's trek ahead of them—narrow pathways through patches of prickly trees, across dried riverbeds, around spiky palm fans. Little did they know a heartless woman would be waiting at our destination.

Even though they slowed me down—Spark with her blind meandering, Flash with his lopsided darting, and Thunder stopping to groom at every trickle of water—I was glad for the company. I needed their support. Not a single kid from my village had even stayed in school till Christmas. Now it was May, late in the school year. Would anyone even be there besides me and Maestra María? What if all her fury was focused on me alone?

But as I approached the one-room adobe building perched on a hill, I spotted a cluster of students under a tree.

"Buenos días," they murmured in Spanish, friendly enough.

"*Yo'o naa yo*," I said, greeting them in Mixteco. "*Nixi yo'o?*" How are you?

With a furtive glance at the schoolhouse, they mumbled answers in Spanish. "*Más o menos.*"

So-so.

A little boy whispered in Mixteco, so softly I could barely hear, "She doesn't like us speaking our language."

I glanced at the others, who nodded gravely. Their weary faces made it clear: They were dreading another school day. There were twelve of us in total, all boys from other villages, mostly six or seven years old. I was the oldest, over a head taller than the rest.

From a safe distance, I peeked inside the classroom. There, writing on the blackboard, was Maestra María. She looked just as I'd remembered, just as stunning as the Heartless Woman herself.

Last night, the Rom had shown another María Félix film— *La Devoradora*. The Devourer. And now, I was on the verge of being devoured. My insides twisted.

Yet the maestra was so pretty it took my breath away. Her waist was small, her skirt full and powder blue, reaching just past her knees. She wore shiny patent-leather shoes with little heels that made her ankles look as graceful as a deer's. Her creamy sweater was trimmed with pearls and looked feathery soft, so unlike the coarse cotton and wool the women of my village wore. Silky brown curls fell around her shoulders.

"Hey," one of the older boys said to me. "Why are these animals with you?"

I told them about rescuing Flash and Spark and Thunder, and they listened, curious, but when Maestra María rang the bell, they fell silent and marched inside like a funeral procession.

I followed them, so nervous about the teacher that I didn't notice my animals following me.

Not until I saw Maestra María's horrified expression. "Get those foul creatures out of my school," she hissed.

"Sorry, Maestra," I stuttered. I was already rattled, and the school day hadn't even started yet. Breathless, I settled my animals outside.

"Please, please be good," I begged them. "Thunder, keep an eye on Flash." In response, she gave an irritated series of whistles.

I kissed Flash's nose. "Just sleep, all right?" I pleaded. He was nocturnal, at his craziest at night, and took catnaps throughout the day.

I gave Spark's ears a final rub, which instantly calmed me. I didn't have to worry about her; she'd just lie there, docile, obeying Thunder's orders.

Pausing, I watched Flash wriggle in and out of Spark's legs, entertained for the moment. It was my last chance to grab my creatures and run home. But Esma's silver eyes and golden coins flashed before me, and I forced my legs to walk back into the classroom.

Maestra María strode up to me, placing a manicured hand on her hip. Her eyebrow shot up. And her red-stained, heart-shaped lips twisted into a frown. "Aren't you old enough to know not to bring filthy animals into school? In fact, aren't you too old for school?"

I felt suddenly self-conscious. She didn't seem to remember me from six years earlier. Probably for the best—this way I didn't have to explain why I'd quit.

"I need to learn to read, Maestra," I said, looking at the packed dirt floor.

"Why now?"

My mind was a blank, so I told her the truth, already kicking myself as I did. "A-a Gypsy said I was destined to come to school." Silently, I added, *Although it was not recommended.*

"A Gypsy?" the maestra spat, her elegant nose wrinkled in disgust. "They're as ignorant as indios."

My face burned. I glanced around the room. Except for her, everyone here was indio. Mixteco, specifically.

She frowned. "Sit down there."

And if I'd had any hope that she might have softened, after the morning was over it was clear that she was, if anything, more evil than ever. Minute by minute, I felt I was sinking further and further, and it grew harder and harder to breathe.

She had us copy words and letters and make the sounds. None of the students were actually reading yet, since everyone else had dropped out before they'd gotten that far along. I tried to help the younger children, but the maestra shot me the evil eye when I spoke with them. One little boy, Benito, was hope-lessly confused and too scared to ask her for help, so he asked his older brother Marcos, in Mixteco, about the instructions.

Before he could answer, Maestra María had trained her evil eye on him like an arrow and arched her eyebrow like a bow. Benito couldn't have been more than six or seven; he still had all his baby teeth.

"I told you," she said, "none of that uncivilized language in my classroom. Ten smacks. Benito, put out your hand."

His eyes filled with tears as he extended his hand on his desk. It was small and pudgy with lingering baby fat, and his knuckles were still just dimples.

The maestra took a ruler from her desk and smacked the boy's hand. Once. Tears streamed down his cheeks and he cried out. Twice. Now the boy was sobbing, trembling. Three times. Snot and tears covered his face, and his eyes were wide with fear.

I watched. My blood burned while the air pressed on me like water, dark and dense and suffocating.

She held up her hand for another smack.

I couldn't stand it, this burning and drowning. I leapt up, bursting through the surface of something. Taking the boy in my arms, I held his hand gently in mine.

I breathed. My heart still galloped, but air filled my lungs and cooled my blood and cleared my head. My eyes met hers. "That's enough, Maestra."

I turned to Benito and comforted him in Mixteco. "*Taxiini, taxiini.*"

She took a menacing step toward me. "Who are you to come in here and tell me how to run my classroom?"

"He's just a little boy." I wanted to say more but stopped myself. I could just walk out, never come back. But I couldn't leave Benito here to fend for himself.

And there was Esma. What would she say if I hadn't made it through a single day?

"He has seven more smacks," Maestra María said coldly. "Go back to your seat."

I steeled myself, kept my arms firmly around Benito. "No."

"No?" Her eyebrow rose higher still, until it had nearly reached her hairline. "Shall I do *your* hand instead?"

I swallowed hard, looked at the boy's hand. Red welts were forming after only three strikes.

"Yes," I said. I pressed my cheek to his head, then led him to his seat. Then I sat down, laid my hand on the desk, squeezed my eyes shut, and breathed.

There was a crack, a bolt of pain like fire that shot through my entire body. My hand wanted, more than anything, to pull away. I forced it to stay. I blinked back hot tears, braced myself for the next blow.

And it came. I breathed. I blinked. I clenched my jaw.

Then came another. And another. I bit my tongue to hold in the cries.

I looked at Benito, still shaking, tears streaming down his plump cheeks. Better me than him.

I thought of Esma, of the moment she'd been struck by lightning, how it must have burned and ached, and how, in the end, she came out stronger. She came through with powers. And like Esma, I held my head proud and tall and jutted out my chin.

Once, on the sixth strike, I did cry out.

Immediately, a commotion of wings rustled outside the open window. Thunder fluttered up, shrieking alarm whistles. Seeing that I was in danger, she flew into the room, landed on a desk in a fury of feathers.

Her whistles were so loud and shrill that kids winced, pressing their palms against their ears in wild-eyed shock. Maestra María had been holding the ruler up, poised for the next blow. She froze. At the sight of an enraged duck hurtling toward her, her eyes widened and her jaw dropped.

Thunder was in full attack mode. Like a raging storm, she half-flew, half-waddled toward the teacher. Her bright pink beak was wide open in a savage war cry. Her spindly legs were an orange blur, her wings a streak of white and black as she swooped forward.

Maestra María was now pressed against the chalkboard, shielding her face with her arms.

Just before Thunder reached that elegant, silk-covered ankle, I grabbed her.

A few feathers floated in the air as Maestra María put her hand to her chest, speechless. Her eyebrows were too stunned to rouse themselves into an arch.

I took that opportunity to deposit my duck outside. "Shh, calm down, Thunder, I'm all right. I can handle it."

I buried my face in her feathers, reached my uninjured hand out to stroke Spark's ears, let Flash slither around my neck. For a moment, I stayed like that with my animals, my hand throbbing. *Could* I handle it? I could just grab my animals and run, right now.

But Esma's lightning had filled me, and it was here to stay. No, I couldn't run away, because she wouldn't run away.

Slowly, I walked back into the building, as a prisoner would return to his jail cell. Only, like Esma, I held my head high. I imagined I was flying.

Inside, the maestra was closing the window and latching it firmly. Just outside, Spark was *baahing*, confused, while Thunder was whistling and grumbling under her breath, and Flash was scratching at the pane, trying to find a way in.

Over her shoulder, Maestra María said, "Bring that creature back here and you'll have duck stew for dinner."

For the rest of the afternoon, my hand ached. It was red and swollen and would surely be bruised, but nothing was broken. It would heal. I didn't think it could handle more beatings like this one, though. And this had only been six strikes, not the full ten. Thunder had saved me from the last four blows.

After school, I found some aloe, sliced it open with my fingernail, and placed the sticky leaf gently over Benito's swollen knuckles.

"Thanks," said his older brother Marcos, his arm around the little boy. "Wish I'd been brave enough to stand up to the maestra."

"No problem," I said, blushing. I wasn't brave, not really. Esma was the brave one. I'd just been lucky enough to have some of her lightning rub off on me.

I pressed gooey aloe to my own aching hand as my animals and I walked home. On the way back, I stopped at every creek to dip my hand in the cool water, as my animals splashed and poked around for insects and grains to munch on.

As I walked, I had plenty of time to imagine terrible things that could befall Maestra María. She could catch a mean case of lice and bedbugs and fleas all at once. She wouldn't be able to stop itching, not even to sleep, and definitely not enough to come to school. She'd have to shave off her hair to get rid of the relentless lice and burn her mattress to get rid of the bedbugs. Still, the fleas wouldn't leave her in peace. Moths and worms would eat holes in all her clothes, so she'd have to wear brown corn sacks. There she'd be, tossing and turning on the dirt, plagued by nightmares and itchiness, bald-headed and covered in welts, wearing a corn sack. And then a skunk—with intact stink glands—would spray her. Yes, she would end up wallowing in itchy, foul-smelling misery.

Shame crept through me along with my vengeful thoughts, but they did make me feel better, for a little while at least.

As I turned the bend to my house, I examined my welted

hand. Hopefully no one at home would notice. If Grandfather knew, he might not let me return to school. He was as protective as Thunder, only less boisterous.

With every jarring step, my hand throbbed with the Mistress of Destiny's words: *School is not recommended.*

18

LETTERS IN THE DUST

*C*oming home, I spotted Da, Ga, and Ba chasing a turkey in our courtyard. And just past them, in the shade, stood Esma, laughing and sipping drinks with Grandfather. My heart nearly jumped out of my chest. Esma and her cousins, *here*?

Somehow, she and Grandfather were chatting despite the language difference. They were surveying the half-finished mosaic for the commemoration of the second anniversary of my sister's death—also known as the second annual Romani Business Appreciation Event.

Unseen, I watched them for a moment, mesmerized by Esma's wrist, how her bracelets clinked as she swirled her arm in conversation. I'd been planning to soak my hand in cool water, nurse it with herbs until the swelling went down. But Esma's presence here was an unexpected gift, and I couldn't waste a minute of it. I tossed the aloe into the bushes and wiped the goop from my flesh, wincing. The hand was still red and swollen, so I stuck it in my pocket as I walked toward her.

My animals reached her first and nuzzled her leg. Within seconds, Flash had wrapped himself around her shoulders, poking his nose inside her headscarf.

"Teo!" she called, loping toward me. "How was school?"

I smiled and shrugged, not up for creative storytelling, but eager to spend time with her. "I have some things to teach you."

She clasped her hands together and, unable to contain her thrill, she twirled around, letting her skirt and hair flare out.

Grandfather insisted I relax and chat with Esma while he hobbled to the kitchen to fetch milk for Spark and *agua de papaya* for me. Da, Ga, and Ba toddled over to Spark and pulled at her ears. They were steadier on their feet and stronger in their grasp this year. They shouted exclamations in Romani as Spark patiently tolerated their tugging and poking. Meanwhile, Thunder waded into the irrigation ditch, fluffing her feathers, out of the toddlers' range, but close enough to keep an eye on them.

I squatted and smoothed the dusty ground with my good hand. Keeping my wounded hand in my pocket, I picked up a stick and wrote the letter *A*. Esma found her own stick and knelt beside me, copying *A* in the dirt.

We went through the alphabet, letter by letter. She focused hard, biting her lip, memorizing the sounds. She barely noticed the children and skunk and goat pattering over the letters.

"This is like magic!" she kept murmuring. "Now I get it! It's a code for the sounds."

Although my hand throbbed, the rest of me buzzed with her contagious excitement. These moments together were bursts of electricity that would keep me lit up through our times apart.

When I wrote her name in the dirt, she let out a yelp of joy. "It's like when my people leave markers on the roadside for other caravans—twigs and branches and bones, all tied and notched in special ways. But this, the alphabet, these letters, they're amazing! You can say anything!"

As she worked on copying and practicing sounds, Grandfather put his hand on my shoulder and offered me a mug of agua de papaya.

"Thank you," I said, sipping the cool, sweet juice, feeling his kindness fill me. He'd sensed that something went wrong today, I was sure of it.

That's when Uncle Paco appeared, limping out from his room, holding shoe polish in one hand and a rag in the other. When he caught sight of Esma and the children, he glared.

I held my breath, praying he wouldn't cause another scene.

Esma stopped writing, mid-letter, and eyed him, not in fear but as a challenge. Lightning danced over her skin, and her unspoken words were *Just try me, just try and you'll see who's stronger.*

My mind scrambled for a way out of the situation, a way to avoid hurt feelings and anger. But Uncle said nothing and continued on his way to a pile of metal pipes on the hill.

Sick of hearing his complaints about the lack of plumbing, my other uncles had brought him a bunch of pipes and told him to have at it. Uncle had made a half-hearted attempt to build a sewage system but had soon given up. Now he sat on a pipe and polished his shoes, watching us like a raptor.

"Teo," Esma said, glancing at him warily, "the boria was mad about his outburst yesterday. They told my uncles. They wanted to leave town, but my grandmother convinced the Duke to stay. At least until the Romani Business Appreciation Event."

"Good," I said, relieved.

Her eyes pierced into mine. "But we have to make sure your uncle doesn't make another scene. If it happens again, we'll leave the Hill of Dust forever. We can't stay in places we're not welcome. The police look for any excuse to arrest us."

I chewed on my fingernail, glancing at Uncle atop his pile of pipes.

Grandfather shuffled over. "Look at your hand, son."

My wounded hand. I'd forgotten to hide it. Quickly, I set down my drink and tried to cover the welts. The agua de papaya spilled all over the letters we'd just traced, turning them to mud.

"What happened?" he asked.

"Nothing," I said quickly, watching the liquid absorb into the dust.

Grandfather nodded. He would have let it go. At least until I was ready to talk to him about it. That was his quiet way.

But not Esma. "Your hand?" she asked. "Are you hurt?"

Seeing my troubled expression, Grandfather said, "I'll

make a poultice for you, son." And he shuffled to the herb garden behind the kitchen.

Esma grabbed my wrist. Her eyes widened as she took in the angry welts. "What happened?"

"It's not a big deal."

"I'm your best friend for life. You have to tell me."

"This doesn't change things, Esma. I'm still going back to school tomorrow."

"This happened at school? Did you get in a fight?"

She wouldn't relent, so I told her. I told her about the teacher insulting my language and people, about her hitting the boy, about me taking his place.

Esma's face reddened; her eyes turned to fire. Her entire body was smoking, flaming. Lightning shot out of her every pore, like the sky during a ferocious storm, all wild electricity.

When Esma finally spoke, it was with unwavering certainty. "That teacher will never hurt you or any other child again. I'll make sure of it."

"Esma," I said softly, "forget it. She hates Gypsies even more than indios."

"Good. I'll use that to my advantage."

"Esma," I tried again, "you can't stop her. She's been like this for years. She's even worse than the Heartless Woman. It's hopeless."

Her eyes burned. "Nothing is impossible, my friend for life."

I eyed her hesitantly. "What do you have planned?"

"Oh, I'll come up with something."

My skunk sniffed out the spilled papaya drink and scrambled over, trying to lick it up, and then just deciding to roll in it. Da, Ga, and Ba laughed.

After that, I tried teaching Esma more sounds, but the mood was broken, and although her teeth were biting her lower lip, now her concentration wasn't on the letters but on her plot against Maestra María.

Soon, Esma said she had to go, gathered the toddlers, and called back, "See you tomorrow at sunrise, my friend for life."

"Sunrise?" I sputtered.

"Oh, yes! I'm going to go to school with you."

A tingle shot through my chest. Part of it was a jolt of happiness at the idea of walking to school with Esma. And part of it was dread over what Maestra María would do to her. I swallowed hard. "How will you get away from your family?"

She shrugged. "I'll leave before they wake up. I'll do some creative storytelling when I return. They'll probably smack me and call me squash head for it, but they do that anyway."

I watched her and her cousins leave as a muddy, sticky Flash tried climbing up my leg. Grandfather stood at my side and offered me a new glass of agua de papaya.

"That teacher of yours had better watch out," he said, chuckling. "She'll meet her match in the Queen of Lightning."

MEETING HER MATCH

So, what do you have planned?" I asked Esma nervously the next morning on the way to school. I'd tried questioning her after the movie last night, but she'd insisted I go straight home and rest up for our big day.

She grinned as she dance-walked beside me. "I'll know when I see her."

I bit my cheek and tried to focus on the simple miracle of walking over the hills with Esma in the early light. Now she was singing out the letters of her name in rhythm to our steps. I could pretend we did this every day. The only thing missing was my entourage of animals. Cringing at the thought of duck stew, I'd made them stay home with Grandfather.

But I couldn't forget what was to come, her face-off with the Heartless Woman. "Really, Esma, what are you planning?"

She swirled in a circle. "Probably I'll just give her a big whack and call her squash head."

My insides jumped. "What?"

"Kidding. I'll think of something."

"I have to admit," I said, hopping over a rock, "when she was hitting Benito, I did imagine grabbing the ruler and whacking her myself." And then I confessed all the misfortunes I'd envisioned befalling the teacher, including stinkification by skunk.

Esma plucked a leaf and smiled devilishly. "I think a curse is in order."

I frowned. "You know how I feel about curses."

"Oh, Teo, this won't be a real curse."

"But if your victim believes in them," I argued, "they're still bad."

"Teo," she said firmly, "this curse will be glorious! You'll see."

And she gave another lopsided twirl for good measure.

Little Benito was in the school yard, clinging to the tree, with his older brother Marcos patting his back. "He's scared to go inside," Marcos whispered in Mixteco, glancing warily at the maestra through the doorway.

Benito loosened his panicked grip when he saw Esma. He stared, taking in her layers of red and pink and purple flowers and beads and shells and coins and braids. "Who's that?"

By now a small, curious crowd had formed. "This is Esma," I said, "Gypsy Queen of Lightning."

"Gypsy?" the boys echoed.

"But aren't Gypsies bad?" one of them whispered.

I was conjuring an indignant response in my head, when Esma did something that took my breath away.

She opened her mouth wide and sang. She sang softly enough not to announce her presence to the maestra inside. Her song was only for us, the small crowd of boys around her, drinking in her voice, enchanted.

When she finished, the boys exchanged glances, speechless.

"My people have a saying," Esma announced, silver eyes glinting. "Bad people don't sing." She waited a moment, letting it sink in. And then, "Decide for yourselves who's bad, amigos."

At that moment, the teacher rang the bell. Immediately, the other students filed inside.

Esma waited just outside the doorway, hidden around the corner. I hovered beside her.

"Go on in," she insisted.

I had the nearly irresistible urge to tug her braid. "Be careful, Esma."

"Go," she ordered.

I did. I found my seat and pulled out the water-stained notebook and pencil stub. My heart drummed in anticipation.

We'd just finished pledging allegiance to the flag when Esma strode in like a force of nature.

"Buenos días, Maestra," she declared, as if onstage.

Standing behind her desk, Maestra María regarded her headscarf and coin necklaces with suspicion. "Who are you?"

"Esma," she responded coolly, putting her hands on her hips, "Queen of Lightning." She moved toward the maestra.

Understanding dawned over Maestra María, and she took a step backward. "Are you—are you a *Gypsy*?"

Esma nodded, enjoying this. "But we call ourselves Romani."

An uncomfortable hush had fallen over the class.

"You'll have to leave," the maestra said, raising a bow-and-arrow eyebrow.

I sucked in a breath. Maestra María had overcome her shock and was readying for attack.

Esma raised her own eyebrow, making no move to leave.

The students watched with bated breath.

Maestra María reached for the ruler on her desk, but Esma snatched it up first.

And then, the Queen of Lightning loped over to the nearest empty desk and climbed right onto it. She towered over us like a statue in a church alcove. Her headscarf grazed the ceiling. She raised her arms like bird wings. "I have come to place a Gypsy curse on you, Maestra María."

The teacher glanced around, unsettled. "Get down from there!" Her voice was shrill, laced with fear. "Get out, you horrid girl!"

Esma smiled, as if the teacher had paid her the highest of compliments. "My dear maestra, here is your curse." She narrowed her eyes and pointed the ruler at the woman.

"Lice!" Esma boomed. "Thousands of them! They will dwell in your hair, make a meal of your scalp."

The children gasped. The maestra clasped a hand to her mouth.

Esma continued. "Bedbugs! Thousands of them! They will crawl over your sleeping body, sucking your blood and leaving a red sea of bumps."

The students murmured to one another in giddy disbelief.

Her voice rose again. "Fleas! Thousands of them! They will dance over your flesh, make you scratch until you bleed, even after you've shaved your head and burned your bedclothes."

The maestra stumbled backward against her desk.

Esma kept going. "And as you are lying in the dirt, miserable and bald and itching, a skunk will wander over and spray you. Liberally! And there you will wallow in your miserable cloud of stink."

The maestra tried speaking, but she was drowned out by Esma, who raised her chin higher still. "There's more! Every tear you produce in a child will be another link chaining this curse to you."

More whispers rippled through the students.

"HOWEVER!" Esma thundered. A hush fell over the room, an electric silence.

"However," she continued, in a now eerily quiet voice, "each teardrop you *prevent* will *cut* another chain in the link. And if you prevent enough teardrops, one day, you may free yourself of the curse."

There was silence as Esma punctuated her speech with a dramatic pause. And then, dignified, she climbed down and placed the ruler on the desk. With a sideways glance at the maestra, she said, "I suggest you use this wisely."

Then she did her lopsided walk-dance out of the room.

After Esma left, the maestra locked the door and called out the window, "And don't come back!" before locking it, too.

The rest of the day was hot and stuffy in the closed-up schoolroom, but the atmosphere among the students was exuberant. All day, the maestra trembled, though she tried to appear composed. She lost her temper quickly, but checked herself before yelling too much. And she didn't smack a single child all day.

The ruler stayed exactly where Esma had left it on the desk.

20

UNEXPECTED VISITOR

*K*icking up dust, whizzing past agave, I raced home from school, unencumbered by my animals, hoping Esma would be waiting for me again. But no, I saw only Grandfather in the courtyard, rubbing Spark's ear with one hand, and with the other, sprinkling colored sawdust onto the mosaic beneath the tree. Esma must be back at her camp, I figured, eating the peppery stew I'd smelled while passing her camp.

On seeing me, my animals and Grandfather hobbled and waddled and scampered toward me. "It wasn't an easy task," he said, laughing. "They kept trying to sneak away and run after you." Then he listed everything Flash had gotten his sharp little teeth into—sacks of beans and corn, junk in the storeroom, crates of fabric scraps, and even my mother's box of treasures. But no lasting harm done, he assured me.

As I petted the animals, I told Grandfather about Esma's visit to school.

"Well, son," he said slowly, "I still don't approve of curses, you know. Even pretend ones." He broke into a grin. "But this one sounds pretty glorious, all right."

I couldn't wait for night to fall, to see Esma at the movie, the last one her people would show this year. Tomorrow would be the Romani Business Appreciation Event, and the morning after that, they planned to leave.

At sunset, I was sipping chili-laced atole with my cousins in the courtyard when a car—an actual car, curvy and shiny and sky blue—wound up the Hill of Dust. I'd heard the unfamiliar hum of the motor, and then Chucho had spotted the car chugging up the mountain. Within moments, my entire family except my mother and grandfather was ogling it. Even Uncle Paco paused in his shoe shining to stand up on the abandoned sewage pipes and squint down the valley.

The car stopped at the cathedral, where the road ended in the dusty plaza. Since there were still a couple hours till the movie, the stretch of dirt was empty. But now a crowd was forming around the car, mostly kids and curious adults.

Out of the driver's seat stepped Maestra María.

Panic exploded through me. Quickly, I ducked behind a tree. What if she'd come to exact vengeance on Esma and her people? My heart thundered; sweat trickled like rivers over my skin. I gathered my animals close, made them huddle beside me, hidden.

Meanwhile, people oohed and ahhed at the maestra's beauty—surely people who'd never met her before. "She looks just like the Heartless Woman!" they murmured in Mixteco, excited. "She must be a movie star!"

As enthralled as they were, they were also too intimidated to approach her. Of course, the children who'd been to school hung back like cowering animals. A survival instinct.

I sucked in a breath and poked my head around the tree, hopefully hidden by low-hanging leaves. The maestra was looking around, probably for the Romani camp.

Of all the people to come to her aid, Uncle Paco stepped forward. "Señora, you look lost. Can I help you?" He was attempting a gentlemanly voice, but it came out sounding oily.

The maestra resisted shooting him her usual evil eye. After all, she needed his help.

"Yes, señor," she said, all business.

I strained to make out her words.

"I was told there was a"—her lips pursed—"*brujo*—a witch—of some sort in this town."

"A *brujo*?" Uncle repeated, confused.

"Yes," she said, shifting awkwardly from one foot to the other. "Someone who could remove a curse."

"You mean a *curandero*? A healer?"

"Whatever. An elderly señor by the name of Teodoro."

Uncle's face lit up. "That's my father, señora!"

"Good." She gave a quick nod. "Will you take me to him?"

Eagerly, Uncle nodded. He tried to take her elbow but she

shrugged it out of his grasp, with a threatening arch of the eyebrow. They walked slowly, thanks to her high heels and his too-pointy shoes.

This gave me time to take a back shortcut to warn Grandfather that the Heartless Woman was coming—of all places—to our home.

"You can't let her in!" I argued with Grandfather, glancing furtively over my shoulder across the courtyard. It was hard to see down the path in the twilight, but it still looked clear; thankfully, the maestra was taking a while. "You know how many kids she's terrorized? Probably hundreds over the years!"

"Oh, Teo, it takes strength to move past your hurt to help someone." Grandfather spoke calmly, unrushed. "Especially someone you think you hate. But sometimes that is the very person who needs your help the most." He paused, cocked his head. "Perhaps this teacher is ready to change. If you lift up one soul, she will lift up others. And on and on it goes. This is what you do as a healer."

"I'm not a healer," I said bitterly. "I'm just a translator."

"You'll rise to the occasion when needed, son." Grandfather patted my shoulder. "People tend to do that. Surprise you. If you give them a chance."

"But, Grandfather, she's evil!" I insisted. "There's no heart there to heal!" And then, quickly, I closed my mouth. She was walking up the path in the evening shadows beside Uncle.

Grandfather invited Maestra María into the healing hut and lit some candles. Uncle followed her in like a devoted puppy. I hovered at the door, about to slip away, when Grandfather said, "Stay, Teo. Translate."

Reluctantly, I walked inside, folded my arms tight across my chest.

In the flickering light, the maestra eyed me uneasily. "You're the new boy at school."

I breathed in the beeswax and herb scents that always calmed me and tried to meet her gaze. It was like looking into the eyes of a snake. "I'm Teo," I said flatly. "I'll be the translator. My grandfather speaks Mixteco."

She hesitated, wringing her hands. "I don't know about this . . ."

"I'll translate," Uncle said, stepping closer to the maestra.

She recoiled, even less enthused about that option. "I'll go with Teo."

Uncle's shoulders fell and he glared at me. "I'll just watch, then."

"We can handle it, son," Grandfather said, ushering him outside and shutting the door.

"Have a seat," I told the maestra and motioned to a wooden chair. She sat on the front of the seat, ready to hop up and run out at the last minute.

I positioned chairs for Grandfather and me across from her. She wore a sour expression, as though she smelled something bad. *Leave*, I wanted to hiss at her. *Get out of my home.*

"Señor," she said to Grandfather, "I came to ask you to remove a curse."

He nodded as I translated. "Tell me more about this curse."

She shrank down, embarrassed. "Go ahead, Teo, tell him."

Of course, he already knew every gory detail of the glorious curse, but I repeated it anyway, relishing the stinky, itchy details.

Grandfather watched her with sympathy, and when I finished, he patted her shoulder.

At his touch, she buried her face in her hands and crumbled into tears.

Sudden bursts of tears were common in Grandfather's healing hut, so I shouldn't have been so stunned. There was something about this safe, candlelit place that had created a well-worn path for long-hidden tears. Most of all, it was Grandfather's gentle words, his compassionate touch, his way of gazing *into* people. He coaxed out their vulnerable side.

I'd had no idea Maestra María even had a vulnerable side.

Sniffing, she opened her purse and dabbed at her ruined makeup with a handkerchief. "Please, señor, can you remove it?"

He kept his hand on her shoulder and spoke kindly. "My daughter, they say no one but a Gypsy can remove a Gypsy curse."

As I translated, I made a half-hearted effort to capture his kindness in my voice, even though my hand still ached from her beating.

At the news, she murmured, "Oh, no, I was afraid of that." A new round of tears leaked out.

"But have you considered another option, daughter?" he said with smiling eyes.

"What?"

"Severing the curse by preventing children's tears."

She blinked. "How on earth would I do that?"

"Simply offer them kindness."

"You don't understand, señor. I have a class of little wild animals that I have to train and they can't even speak a civilized . . ." Her voice trailed off. She was probably remembering that I was one of those wild animals and that my grandfather couldn't speak a so-called civilized language.

"Perhaps," Grandfather said tenderly, "I can teach you some kind words in our tongue so that you may comfort the children."

She shook her head. "I can't speak that language. Not at school. The whole point is to teach them Spanish, the language of our country."

Grandfather tilted his head. "Their young minds are clever enough to learn both, so why not give them that gift?"

Rubbing her face, she said in a low voice, "My instructions are to beat their language out of them if I have to. I could be fired for allowing it in my class."

"Be brave," Grandfather said quietly. "Do what feels right in your heart, my daughter."

Again, she wiped her eyes, leaving dark smears of makeup, as if a mask were melting off. "You think if I use these words I'll break the curse?"

"Yes, my daughter. Of course, you'll need to keep using them so that the curse will not reattach. It will take practice to develop this new habit."

She let out a quivery breath. "All right."

Over the next hour, my grandfather and I taught her how to say words in Mixteco—*please, thank you, love, good, hug. Ñamani, tatsavini, kuu ini, yeu, sikita'an.*

Her pronunciation was horrible. I winced, hearing how she butchered our language. Yet as she struggled, Grandfather put his hand on her shoulder and told her in Mixteco, "Yeu. Good job, daughter. Clever student."

She laughed. But when she repeated his words, they came out harsh and choppy and without feeling.

"Imagine each word is a petal, daughter," Grandfather said. "A feather, something soft and light and tender."

She repeated the words, now in the same soothing tone as Grandfather's, and although her face was a mess of tear-smeared makeup, it looked pretty in a whole new way.

The words floated around like petals and feathers, until she smiled and said, "I think I can remember now. Thank you." She stood up, opening her purse. "How much do I owe you, señor?"

He shook his head. "You are my grandson's teacher. This is a gift to you."

I murmured the translation.

A few more tears slipped out. Still, she didn't leave.

He touched her shoulder again. "Is there something else, Daughter?"

She glanced at me and back at him. "I—I wasn't always like this. So bitter." Her words came from a deep place.

Sometimes words come from near the surface, and they sound flat and wispy. Then there are words that come from the caves of a person's soul—at least that's how Grandfather explained it. And these words were coming from a hidden place inside the maestra. They smelled musty and damp and true.

She sank back down into the chair. "My husband and I dreamed of having lots of children. But the years passed, and none came. We had a nice house, a nice car, nice clothes. But it wasn't enough. I needed a child. Then my husband died. I was grieving, but I had to work to keep my lifestyle. So I took this job, but it's torture spending all day with these children who aren't mine."

I translated under my breath as she spoke, trying to keep the shock from my voice. So there was a heart inside her after all—a shattered heart, its pieces encased in steel, but a heart all the same. I reminded myself she was the same evil woman who had beaten my hand just yesterday.

Maybe evil was simply pain in disguise.

"Pobrecita," Grandfather said. "Poor thing, you've been through so much. But I will help you. I'll give you soul cleansings and herbs that will sweeten and soften your heart, melt the wall around it."

The maestra nodded, sniffling and wiping her eyes.

We followed him into the smoke-filled kitchen, where my aunts were busy cooking beans over the hearth fire, grinding chile for salsa, patting *maza* into circles for tortillas. As Grandfather gathered the herbs, I introduced the maestra. She stood awkwardly, too tall for the squat kitchen. But she looked better now, refreshed after all her crying.

Politely, she greeted my aunts and asked, "Are one of you Teo's mother?"

My aunts looked at one another, shook their heads. "She's in there," Aunt Perla said, pointing with a spoon across the courtyard.

Maestra María smiled at me. "Perhaps I should say hello, tell her what a fine translator of a son she has." She was trying to be kind. But how could she know that meeting my mother would just lead to discomfort at best, misery at worst?

I took a breath. "Please, go ahead, Maestra," I said. "I'll help Grandfather finish with the herbs."

She gave me a strange look, and I glanced away. I couldn't bear to see people try to talk with my mother. I could forget about her craziness, let her dissolve into shadows, but when new eyes saw her, I had to remember.

The maestra bid my aunts good night, then walked across to the doorway of my mother's room. I turned away, unable to watch.

I focused on getting the dried herbs together, and by the time Grandfather and I had tied them with twine—all eight varieties—we went into the courtyard. Several minutes had passed, and I couldn't imagine what she'd been doing. My mother wasn't a conversationalist.

Sure enough, when Maestra María emerged from the room, she looked shaken. Sadly, she said to me in Mixteco, "Tatsavini." Thank you. The words floated to me like petals, strangely comforting.

She reached into her bag and pulled out a small notebook, brand-new, and a long, freshly sharpened pencil. "Since your grandfather won't accept payment, I hope you will accept a gift."

Holding the present gingerly, I thanked her. "Tatsavini."

Grandfather handed her the bundle of herbs. I translated his instructions to drink the tea twice a day, and to return to see him every evening for a week for spiritual cleanings to sweep away her bitterness.

She took his hand, held it in hers. "Tatsavini," she said, like the brush of a feather.

After Grandfather and I bid her farewell, and he disappeared into his room to rest, Uncle appeared from the shadows, reeking of shoe polish. The maestra was just teetering down the path when he took her elbow. "I'll walk you back to your car," he said.

"Oh, I'm fine," she said, continuing past the moonlit agave.

But Uncle followed her, insisting, "It's dangerous to walk by yourself. There are Gypsies lurking about."

As they walked into the darkness, I pressed my nose to the open notebook, breathed in the new-paper-and-glue scent. Even after she vanished, ghosts of rose petals lingered all around me.

STOLEN

*L*ater that night, laughter filled the plaza, rising into the night air above the Hill of Dust. Beside me, my cousins were rolling around in the dirt, clutching their bellies, shaking with laughter. The adults were laughing so hard they were crying. And I was laughing with more abandon than I had since Lucita and I would tickle each other as kids.

The audience was bigger than ever. Some of the other students had come with their families, a long walk from their villages. Little Benito and his brother Marcos were here with their own entourage of cousins and brothers and sisters.

The film was about a man named Cantinflas, whose mustache was short and missing the middle part, so it was just two ridiculous patches of hair on either side of his lips. He was a *pobre,* poor like us, but he found hilarious ways to put the powerful and rich in their place.

All was happy until an hour into the movie, when a man's shadow suddenly appeared in front of the screen.

He was just a silhouette. Who was it? He raised his hands and shouted something, something I couldn't hear well over the voices and music blaring from the speakers. He spoke in Spanish, and cursed often—that much I could tell.

From the audience came shouts of *Boo* and *Go away!*

But the man stayed, pacing and ranting before the screen. With a start, I recognized his telltale pointy-shoe limp and smug voice. Uncle Paco.

Nausea spread over me. I took hold of Flash and stroked him, in case I'd have to use him as a weapon again. I glanced back at the Duke, saw him grimly stick his half-eaten onion in his pocket, stop the projector, turn off the speakers.

The image paused on a close-up of Cantinflas's face cocked in a funny, sidelong expression beneath his pointy hat. But no one laughed now. The only sounds were the hum of the generator, the chirp of crickets.

Finally, Uncle Paco left the screen area, and I breathed out in relief. But now he was dragging someone—a woman—up there with him. She shielded her eyes from the projector beam.

My mother! She looked small and lost, helpless as he gripped her elbow.

A prickly heat filled me. Part of me wanted to run up and protect her, lead her back home to her safe little room. Another part wanted to shrink down and hide in embarrassment.

Instead, I hugged my animals and stayed seated.

"There is a thief here," Uncle shouted. "Someone stole this woman's prized earrings."

My mother's earrings? Stolen? I could picture them vividly—large, dangling half moons made of delicate, spiraling gold threads. A gift from her own mother on her wedding day. Who would take them from her box?

Grandfather appeared, panting, and touched Uncle's shoulder. In a low voice, in Mixteco, he spoke to his son.

Uncle shrugged him off, nearly knocking him over.

That did it. I leapt up and bolted forward. I held Grandfather steady and then carefully sat him down on my chair. Next, I retrieved my mother, slipping her arm from Uncle's hand, and led her to sit beside Grandfather.

Oblivious, Uncle was still ranting. "The Gypsy thieves stole it! They robbed a poor, vulnerable woman, my own sister!"

"What's going on?" I whispered to Grandfather.

He was still breathing hard from the walk over. "After you and the others left for the movie, son, your mother came to me, crying. She was checking her box like she always does and noticed the earrings were missing." Grandfather shook his head sadly. "Paco heard her and immediately accused the Rom."

Now Uncle was flailing his arms toward the Duke and Esma and Roza, all standing back near the projector. "That girl there! The lame girl! She was sneaking around our home."

He pointed directly to Esma.

Her eyes widened in shock, but she kept her head high. Once she translated for her grandparents, the Duke's chest puffed out angrily. His mustache leapt in indignation, the tips cocked back like fists ready to punch. He waved a large, threatening onion in the air, as if he might hurl it at Uncle. Roza bristled, shouting what I could only imagine were Gypsy curses as she pointed a finger at Uncle Paco.

My heartbeat filled my ears, along with the hot rush of blood. What could I do? The Duke had said if there was another scene, he would leave with his people and never come back. How could I stop this?

Esma stepped into the projector beam, suddenly illuminated, like a ghost. She was entirely lit up—her hair, her headscarf, her skirt, the coins and beads on her necklace. She declared, "I did not steal from this family. They are my friends." She raised her chin even higher in defiance. "And I am not the Lame Girl. I am Esma, Queen of Lightning."

Uncle took a menacing step toward her. She held her ground.

Now her uncles and the Duke came to her side. He had an onion in each hand now, grasping each so tightly his knuckles were white. His mustache twitched as if it could barely hold itself back.

A fight? If there was a fight, my friendship with Esma would be severed forever. My insides were sinking down, down. But I forced myself to stand tall, holding Flash ready.

And then, Benito walked to Esma's side. His brother followed. Each took her hand in a gesture of solidarity. In Mixteco, Benito belted out, so everyone could hear, "She's good. She helped us. And anyway, bad people don't sing!"

Then the other students emerged from the audience to stand at her side. Inspired, people from my village came to her side, until nearly everyone on the Hill of Dust was facing Uncle Paco. Heart swelling, I joined them with my animals.

My relatives stood up, their loyalty split, but finally walked to Esma's side. Everyone except for two uncles, who firmly took hold of Uncle Paco and led him away.

He struggled, red-faced. "I'm bringing the police tomorrow!" Uncle yelled. "They'll be happy for an excuse to put this trash behind bars."

After he was gone, people found their seats and quieted down, and the Duke smoothed his mustache and started the movie again. Yet I couldn't pay attention, couldn't rouse any laughter at the funny parts. I put my hand on my mother's. She sat, transfixed, not laughing at the jokes either, simply watching Cantinflas's antics in a slack-jawed daze.

Grandfather, looking exhausted, rested his hand on her other hand.

"You think she misplaced the earrings?" I whispered.

He shook his head. "I don't know, Teo. I don't know what to think."

I stroked Spark's ears and glanced back at Esma, who was standing with the Duke by the projector. "You think the Rom will leave? Before our gathering tomorrow night?"

"Who knows." He stood up shakily, casting a small shadow on the screen. "Let's get your mother home."

"We have to do something, Grandfather!"

He looked at me for a long moment. "All right, Teo. After your mother's settled back home, we'll pay the Rom a visit."

Later that night, Grandfather and I walked down the deserted, dark street toward the Rom camp. There was a distinct lack of music and dancing and singing, a stark contrast from our visit to their camp last year. And last year, Grandfather hadn't paused to catch his breath every few steps.

At the edge of the ring of wagons, I called out, "¡Buenas noches!" And then, peering inside the circle, I noticed the bustle of activity. By the light of the bonfire, the Rom were rolling up carpets and filling sacks with pots and utensils. Packing up?

When they caught sight of us, chatter rippled through them. Soon the Duke appeared, and then Roza and Esma. Her hair was disheveled, her face tearstained, her shoulders slumped, as if all the lightning had drained out of her.

Something was wrong, very wrong.

"Come in, friends," the Duke said in heavily accented Spanish, his mustache hanging down, forlorn. He gestured at tree stumps by the fire. "Please, sit down."

The table and chairs must have been stashed inside a wagon already. I sat, and a plume of smoke blew right into my face, stinging my eyes.

"I'm sorry we have no tea ready to offer, but as you can—" Esma's voice cracked as she translated. "As you can see, we're leaving at dawn."

"We have to avoid the police," Roza said apologetically, turning her pipe over in her thick hands. "They don't treat us fairly. That's why we stick to villages like yours, out here in the mountains. But now, with that man falsely accusing my granddaughter . . ."

Esma sniffled and wiped her eyes, reluctantly translating.

"Don't leave!" I said. "Please! I'll find the thief, prove Esma's innocence. Just give me another day, please!"

Grandfather added, "I will make sure my son doesn't contact the police."

The Duke looked at Roza with doubt. Esma looked at her with a last wisp of hope.

The Mistress of Destiny's nose twitched as she considered and then conferred with the Duke, shaking her head.

"My grandfather says no," Esma said softly, after her grandfather spoke. "It's not worth the risk. He's—we're sorry."

Our eyes met, and another tear slipped from hers. Her tears scared me. This was not a girl who let go of hope easily. Seeing her like this, I understood she'd begged and pleaded with her grandparents, done everything she could to convince them. I understood that if they left tomorrow morning, they would never come back.

Grandfather reached out his hand for Roza's. He locked eyes with her. In a low voice, he said, "You and I know my true fortune, Mistress. Here is my last request to you: Come to the event tomorrow."

I translated, knowing there was much below his words, things that passed between him and the Mistress of Destiny, things that unnerved me.

After a long while of gnawing on her pipe, she said something to the Duke. He protested, but she repeated it more firmly.

Finally, he nodded his head and barked out an order to his people. They stopped packing, puzzled. And then, shrugging and grumbling, they began to unpack.

Esma threw her arms around the Duke, and then around Roza. "We'll stay!" she said, doing three wild twirls. "We'll stay!"

And my heart rose with the smoke and sparks, up to the stars.

As Grandfather and I walked slowly back home, we were silent. Part of me was dancing inside at the good news; part of me felt off-balance with so many unsaid things just below the surface. *Grandfather's true fortune.* What exactly had made the Mistress of Destiny change her mind?

I didn't ask Grandfather about it. I said only, "Thank you."

He nodded, rested a hand on my shoulder. "You know, Teo. That was the first movie I've seen. And it makes me think. Life is like a movie."

"How?"

"We get so involved, we think that's all there is, what's on the screen. We laugh, we cry, we love. We forget that if we only moved our eyes away, we'd see so much more."

He squeezed my shoulder, said softly, "I'm near the end of my movie, son."

My chest clenched, making it hard to breathe. "Are you scared?"

"Not a bit. I've already been glancing off-screen all my life. And after I'm gone, you can, too. Just take a little break from your own movie, turn your head, and find me there."

So this was the unspoken, true fortune. That my grandfather's final credits were rolling.

Unlikely Thief

Fresh morning sunlight streamed into the classroom as Maestra María greeted the students in hesitant, broken Mixteco. At least it showed some effort. "*Yo'o naa yo.*" Good morning.

The students' eyes grew wide, and most said nothing, probably suspecting a trap. A few brave souls answered in Mixteco. "*Yo'o naa yo,* Maestra."

She offered a crooked upturn of lips, still far from a real smile.

No, she hadn't changed overnight. Throughout the day, after a few minutes of kindness, she'd forget and fall back into the usual hard-edged words. Then at some point, seeing a student's troubled face, she'd stop herself, take a breath, and say something in choppy Mixteco. She'd drop her voice, and her eyes would flick furtively toward the door, as if at any moment, her superiors would burst in and fire her on the spot.

Be brave, I silently urged her.

By the end of the day, two facts were clear to all the students. First, the ruler had not budged from its spot on the desk where Esma had laid it. And second, Maestra María, beyond all belief, was trying to be nice. Of course, not all her words were petals; not all her words were even understandable. But she was making patient baby steps toward kindness. And baby steps toward respecting our language and people.

After school, instead of racing home, or positioning themselves at a safe distance beneath the tree to talk, the students gathered just outside the door. They showered me with questions, peering at the maestra from the corners of their eyes. And their questions were in Mixteco, testing the new limits of our teacher.

Exhilarated, Marcos said, "She's changed because of the Gypsy curse, hasn't she, Teo?"

"Where did she learn Mixteco?" asked Benito.

And from the others: "Is she really different now?"

"Will she keep being nice to us?"

"How long will this last?"

I shrugged at the barrage of questions. I couldn't tell them about her visit with Grandfather; that was confidential. But my silence only drove them to further grill me.

"Hey, did your mother ever get her earrings back?"

"Did you guys find the thief?"

"It wasn't a Gypsy, was it?"

"The Gypsies are nice! No, it couldn't have been them, right?"

I stayed quiet and let them interrupt one another. I was still embarrassed that my mother had been exposed last night. It felt better with her shut in her room, involved in her own strange rituals.

"Who's the real thief?"

"Yeah, who is it?"

"Teo, come on, tell us, what do you think? Who could have broken in and stolen them?"

That, precisely, was the question that had been flitting in and out of my mind all day. If I caught the real thief, then I could prove Esma's and the Rom's innocence. Then maybe, just maybe, they'd return next year.

"My mother might have lost them," was all I said. Yet last night, after the movie, we'd looked everywhere for the earrings, with no luck. Even if my mother had misplaced them, we would have come across them.

I looked away from the kids' eager faces, inside to the maestra, packing up. And I caught a glimpse of gold poking out from the pocket on her bag. I squinted, watching carefully.

As she arranged her pens and pencils in the pocket, she removed a pair of large, dangling earrings. Lacy half moons. My mother's earrings. Just as quickly, the maestra tucked the jewelry back into the pocket with the pens.

I glanced at the other kids to see if anyone else saw. But no, they were still deeply involved in their own speculations.

Maestra María was the thief? It felt like a kick in the stomach. Before today, I would have welcomed the chance to see her carted off to prison. But today, today I'd actually started to *like* her. To *want* to come to school.

Yesterday evening, she'd disappeared into my mother's room and stayed there, alone with her for several minutes . . . supposedly to compliment my translation skills. Maybe she'd had other motives. And maybe she'd assumed my mother was too crazy to notice something was gone.

I leaned against the door frame, shaken to the core. I'd believed her heart had opened last night; I'd believed she liked using feather-soft words. But no, her kindness was only for selfish reasons, to avoid the curse. There was something even more heartless about pretending to open your heart. The betrayal was deeper.

The maestra walked toward the doorway, and we all backed up a little. The chattering stopped.

"It's fine with me if you speak your language," she said with a smile, a little less crooked than before.

The students looked relieved; they'd hoped for this, but it was good to hear from her mouth.

"So, what are you talking about?" She'd never shown any interest in our lives until today, but now she seemed genuine.

The boys looked at one another, gauging the situation. If they told her they watched a movie shown by the Rom, would she be angry? After all, it had been a Romani girl who cursed her. An older boy spoke. "We went to see the movie last night."

172

"A movie?" she asked, surprised. "In the city?"

"No, in Teo's village. The Gypsies showed it."

Maestra María sucked in a breath. "I see."

Encouraged that the maestra wasn't angry, the boy continued. "Teo's mother had something stolen from her last night. Earrings. In the middle of the movie, his uncle stood up and accused the Gypsies."

The maestra paled, blinked, clutched her bag. "Well, children, I must be going," she said quickly.

She glanced back at me on the way to her car. "I'll see your grandfather later this evening, all right?"

I said nothing, only stared at her climbing into her car. She dared return to our home? Was she going to steal something else from us? But why? She had enough money. She even had her own car! Maybe that car hadn't come from her dead husband. Maybe she'd stolen that, too.

Fleeing the students' next round of questions, I started running home.

Halfway there, I slowed to a walk, breathing hard. It felt good to run, to feel my blood zooming and my heart pumping. As I rested, doubled over, I remembered that this evening was the gathering for my sister, the Romani Business Appreciation Event.

My thieving teacher would show up right in the middle of a bunch of Rom, who she could easily blame for anything else she'd steal.

And this was to be my last night with Esma for a whole year. At this rate, maybe forever.

SECOND ANNUAL ROMANI
BUSINESS APPRECIATION EVENT

*I*n the silvery-blue twilight, our Romani guests stood before Grandfather's mosaic, oohing and ahhing. Beneath the tree, the rectangle of colored sawdust featured a girl with dark hair and a red skirt and purple flowers swirling around her. Golden rays surrounded her like an angel's halo—or bolts of lightning—depending on your perspective.

To the Rom, the girl was Esma, a gesture to show we didn't share in Uncle Paco's suspicions. A sign of solidarity.

To my people, it was Lucita dancing in heaven, bathed in beams of celestial light.

Soon my aunts were handing out hot cinnamon-chocolate and sweet tamales, commanding us, "Eat! Eat!"

They had spent all day cooking, and a good thing, too, because every inhabitant of the Hill of Dust was gathered here in the candlelight, together with the Rom. Words in broken

Spanish flitted around the nighttime courtyard. Feelings filled the spaces between words, between my people and our visitors. There was appreciation, as warm as steaming tamales. But there was also fear that the ugly scene from last night could repeat itself.

The villagers said, "Oh, how sad we are you're leaving tomorrow!"

And the Rom said, "How sad we are to leave!"

"You'll come back, won't you?" the villagers asked.

To this, the Rom vaguely nodded, casting nervous glances at Uncle, who was skulking around the shadowy edges of our courtyard.

Grandfather had made him promise not to contact the police and not to stir up trouble. Uncle knew he was outnumbered, but still, I cringed at the thought of him ruining this night. What if he'd disobeyed Grandfather? What if the police were on their way?

When I'd told Grandfather about the stolen earrings in Maestra María's bag, he'd nodded, eyebrows furrowed in thought, and said, "If Paco accuses the Rom again, you can tell everyone your suspicions of the maestra. Otherwise, let's keep this quiet for now."

I didn't want to keep it quiet. I wanted to shout it out to the entire Hill of Dust, clear the Rom's name for good. It was even harder to bite my tongue when, through the crowd, I caught sight of Maestra María.

She wore a pale pink skirt and a white cotton blouse, and

her hair was gathered in a girlish, pink-ribboned ponytail. She'd probably chosen her outfit to suggest innocence. And she'd brought her large white bag, perfect for stashing more stolen goods. It made my stomach turn.

Her face held a mystified expression as she looked around, her lipstick glittering in stray light from flames and stars. Her eyes landed on me.

"Buenas noches, Teo," she said, weaving through the crowd. "What's going on here?"

"I forgot to tell you," I said flatly. "It's a kind of party." I hesitated, unsure how to explain our annual event to an outsider. "A joint celebration to honor my sister's death and a Romani Business Appreciation Event."

"Romani?" she asked, confused.

"Gypsy," I said, an edge to my voice.

She squinted at the throng of Rom. She held her bag closer, as if she were afraid *they* would steal from *her*. "These are all Gypsies?" she asked in disbelief. "You invited them to your house?"

I leveled my gaze at her. I wanted to grab her bag and dump out the contents and reveal her as the thief. "You were wrong about our language," I said evenly. "You're wrong about the Rom, too." I couldn't help adding, "They're not the thieves around here."

She gave me a strange look, but before she could say anything, Aunt Perla came by and offered her a gourd full of chocolate and a sweet *tamal*.

176

"Tatsavini," the maestra said in awkward Mixteco. Thank you.

My muscles clenched at the sound of her speaking our language, pretending. She ate the food, drank the drink, even tried complimenting it. "Yeu." Good.

I watched her, wondering what she had planned. Because she *did* have something planned. I could tell by the way her eyes flickered around, the way she fiddled with the zipper of her bag, the way her eyebrows pressed together, the tips up like vulture wings.

Then she said, "Is your uncle here? The one who escorted me to my car last night?"

She had to be the only person in town who actually wanted to see Uncle Paco.

"Over there," I said, pointing with my chin.

The maestra headed over to Uncle. On seeing her, his face lit up. He tucked in the tail of his shirt and wiped his hands on his pants. He grabbed an empty chair and set it between them, gesturing for her to sit.

But she didn't sit. She stood tall. And in the evil voice she hadn't used all day—the Heartless Woman voice—the maestra called out, "I'd like everyone's attention, please."

Oh no oh no oh no. This could not be good.

Rom and Mixteco alike stopped talking and stared at her. There were murmurs of "la mujer sin alma" . . . "la devoradora" . . . the woman without a soul, the devourer . . . "María Félix, the movie star herself!" She was indeed a sight to behold, the flames illuminating her gorgeous face, casting dramatic shadows beneath her cheekbones, accentuating the long, curved eyebrows.

Her expression, at the moment, was as ruthless as I'd ever seen.

She kicked off her heels and climbed onto the chair. Towering over us all, she demanded, "Where is the Gypsy girl who came to my classroom yesterday?"

Oh no oh no oh no. The maestra was going to wreak vengeance on Esma. I had to do something. I had to protect her. I had to save her.

As Esma loped forward, I stepped beside her, wishing I were brave enough to hold her hand. Instead, I kept my hands on Flash, wriggling around my collar, in case I had to threaten the maestra with him.

"What is your name again, señorita?" Maestra María asked.

"Esma," she replied, chin high. "Queen of Lightning."

My heartbeat filled me like thunder. I whispered to Flash, "Get ready."

"Esma, Queen of Lightning," the maestra continued, "did your curse say anything about the tears of a grown man?"

I blinked, confused. This was not what I'd expected.

Esma tilted her head, curious, then shook it. "Only tears of a child."

The maestra smiled. She opened the side pocket of her bag and pulled out the golden crescent earrings. She raised a finger like a magic wand and pointed it at Uncle Paco in the same way that Esma had pointed at her the previous morning at school.

"I'd like to make it clear," the maestra said, "that this man gave me these earrings as a gift when he escorted me to my car yesterday."

Uncle stumbled backward as if he'd been hit.

A wave of shock, and then relief, washed over me. Once I found my voice, I translated to Mixteco, shouting so that everyone could hear.

"Is this true?" my other uncles asked.

Uncle Paco shook his head and sputtered, "She's crazy, I didn't . . ."

"Do not lie to me," the maestra commanded, pulling her ruler from the bag. Would she actually smack him with it?

Her eyes, beneath their arched brows, bored into his, until finally, he muttered, "I took them."

For several more minutes, the maestra yelled at him and shamed him. All the yelling and shaming she'd saved up in the past day of kindness burst out, straight at Uncle. On and on she raged, her words stronger and more vicious than any ruler.

And his tears came. His tears came and he sank to the ground, a salty, wet heap in the dust.

Grandfather whispered to me, "Sometimes a heart needs to be broken open, doesn't it?"

Later, after Grandfather led Uncle into the curing room, and after the earrings were safely back in my mother's box, and after Maestra María came down from the chair, she approached Esma. For a long moment the maestra stared at her. Then, with a frown, she said, "I suppose I should thank you."

"Me?" Esma's eyes widened.

"For showing me that trick of standing on chairs." The corner of Maestra María's mouth tipped up into the tiniest hint of a smile. And then, just as fast, went back to a frown.

"You're welcome, Maestra," Esma said, almost shyly.

At that moment, the maestra's ears perked up, and she turned in the direction of the toddlers. Da and Ba were stuffing their little cheeks with tamales, but Ga was looking at hers, which had just fallen to the ground. Flash scrambled over and dragged it away.

Ga's lip quivered, and her face scrunched itself into that look a face gets just before the wailing starts.

Maestra María flew over to Ga, grabbing a new tamal on the way, and just in time, stuck it in the child's hand. Ga's face rearranged itself into a smile, and she took a huge bite. The maestra stayed beside her, kneeling down, chatting with her and the other two. Tears averted. More links in the chain broken. And yes, from the way the maestra stroked the girl's tendril, she just might have been enjoying herself.

Late into the night, right before everyone left, Esma sang a song for Lucita. A song of longing and missing and hoping. I felt Lucita's presence strongly, as if she were beside me. As if Esma's voice were so powerful, it made me turn away from the movie of my life and look into the other realm where Lucita dwelled.

Esma's voice brought tears to other people's eyes, too; perhaps they felt their own loved and lost ones at their sides. I wished my mother could hear it, but she'd already disappeared into her room with the box.

No wonder Esma's songs had enchanted the music agent. No wonder he wanted to bring this voice to the rest of the world. Despite everything it would mean, I wanted other people to hear her songs, not just people on the Hill of Dust and other Mixteco villages, but people in far-off lands.

Tears streamed down Maestra María's face as she listened. Now there was no crookedness at all in her smile. It was pure and sweet and laced with salt water. And when she bid me and Esma good night, she sniffled and said, "Esma, Queen of Lightning, your voice can bring back the dead. At least for a few precious moments it can. I thank you for that gift."

UNCLE PACO'S STORY

*E*very tear holds a story. That's what Grandfather always said. Judging by the tears spewing from Uncle Paco, he must have been holding in a sea of stories.

Even more tears flooded out after Grandfather gave him a *limpia* to clean his spirit. That meant spitting on him with cactus liquor and beating him with bundles of herbs. And now, in the aftermath, tearstained and huddled in the corner of the healing hut, Uncle Paco looked like a half-drowned rat, soaking wet, shivering, small, and meek.

I paused at the doorway, unsure whether to enter. My animals trailed behind me, full and sluggish after so many scraps of tamales. The last of our visitors had just left, leaving ghosts of loved ones lingering among the chocolate-crusted drinking gourds and corn husks.

Grandfather sat in an exhausted heap beside Uncle, holding a limp, damp bundle of *ruda* leaves.

"Everything all right?" I asked, more concerned for Grandfather than Uncle. Grandfather was usually asleep by this time of night. It took energy to perform a limpia, more than he now had.

Grandfather nodded weakly. "Teo, will you sit with your uncle while he drinks the tea?"

I was not enthused about being alone with Uncle in his soul-shaken state. Patients could react in all kinds of strange and unexpected ways after a limpia—from sobbing to laughing to beating the ground. But Grandfather needed my help. And I remembered what he'd said about finding strength to help those you hate. Those you *think* you hate. With a sigh, I said, "All right."

After bidding Grandfather good night, I sat on his now empty chair. Spark, Thunder, and Flash curled up by my feet.

In the flickering candlelight, I watched Uncle sip his tea and wondered when I could leave to go to sleep.

My eyelids were just fluttering shut when he spoke, in slow, soft words.

"I left this village for the city three years ago, Nephew. I planned to work in construction, make money for a house, a big one, and a big piece of land." He flung out his arms in a gesture of hugeness, splashing his tea. "I was going to come back here in a big, fancy car. I was going to find a beautiful wife."

He paused, looking at his feet, which were now bare. He'd taken off his pointy shoes for the limpia, leaving them in the opposite corner, out of place in the earthen-walled, dirt-floored room.

"But you want to know a secret, Nephew?"

· "What?"

"People there taunted my goat-hide sandals, said my feet were like animal claws." He flexed his toes, spotted with oozing blisters. "They called me a backward indio, said I spoke Spanish like a fool. They cheated me out of my wages on construction jobs. When I complained, no one listened."

As he spoke, he stroked Spark's velvet ears, the first time he'd given my animals any affection. The calming powers of her ears were working their magic on Uncle, tapping into his own tender spots.

He leaned in closer and whispered, "I rooted through trash cans for food. I sat on the ground begging. Then I crawled back with my tail between my legs. Worst of all, I've treated my family the way I was treated."

Uncle reached down and picked up my skunk. He held Flash in the air, pointed the bushy tail at his own, tear-streaked face. "Go ahead," he said. "Spray me, I deserve it."

Flash thought Uncle was playing. He squirmed out of his grasp, climbed onto his shoulder, and nibbled at his collar.

"Why won't he spray me?" Uncle said miserably.

"He likes you now," I observed.

Uncle gave a quiet laugh, then ran his hand over Flash's

white stripe. "When I came back, I was ashamed I had nothing, nothing at all to offer a wife or anyone else. Then I saw that beautiful teacher with her fancy car, and I thought, *Maybe it's not too late.* But I needed to offer her something, so I took my sister's earrings." He buried his face in his hands. "I didn't think she'd notice."

Silence for a few moments. I had no idea what to say, so I tried to think of what Grandfather would say. "Do you want to change, Uncle?"

He paused, stared at the ceiling as Flash nestled into his neck. "Yes."

Again, I channeled Grandfather. I'd seen him with so many patients, it was easy to imagine his responses and questions. "Will you work hard at it?"

Uncle looked me in the eyes. "Yes."

"Then I will help you. Every day I will give you limpias and teas, and you must follow my instructions."

It felt strange hearing myself talk to Uncle this way, but it was how Grandfather spoke with all his patients, firmly, asking them questions, making sure they felt committed.

After bidding Uncle good night, I walked across the courtyard toward my room. Spark and Thunder wobbled sleepily behind me, while Flash, most lively at night, darted in spirals around my feet. Inside, my mother sat in the corner, the lantern casting eerie shadows over her face. She cradled her earrings in her hands.

I swallowed. "Are you all right, Mother?"

She rocked with her earrings. I wished she would touch me with such tenderness, gaze at my face the way she gazed into the lifeless silver and gold.

Kneeling at her side, I kissed her cheek. "I can help you, Mother. If you want to get better. Do you?"

No answer.

I put Flash into her lap, hoping he might make her laugh the way he did for Uncle.

But she only shrugged off the skunk.

I put her hand on Spark's magic ears, but she quickly moved it back to the cold metal.

Still on my knees, I begged, "Please, please, Mother. Let me help you."

Silence. I scooped Flash from the ground and gathered Spark and Thunder close and felt their warm, pulsing bodies, all feathers and fur and devotion.

I hoped they would be enough.

SCREAM STREAM

uenos días, Teo, my friend for life!" Esma's voice rang out across the courtyard, competing with the roosters' morning crows. And a moment later, she came into view on the path, waving and loping along, swinging a red bucket.

"Esma?" I sputtered. I'd been washing my face at the cistern, and now water dripped from my chin. I'd slept badly last night, knowing she'd be leaving today, Saturday. Now my grogginess vanished. I was suddenly alert and wide-eyed, as if a shooting star had just plopped in front of me.

"How did you get away?" A bewildered grin took over my face. "And where are the kids?"

"Back at camp. I'm free!" She spun in a joyful circle, and then grew serious. "I only have an hour before my caravan leaves. Let's go to the river." She tugged at my arm. "Come on!"

I wiped my face on my shirt, then grabbed some tortillas and salt and lime for breakfast. And we headed into el monte, with my animals following. Thunder whistled and huffed, annoyed that I'd interrupted her own washing routine in the irrigation ditch, but Flash scurried happily along, always up for adventure. And Spark ambled sweetly behind us, munching on weeds and shrubs.

As we walked, I couldn't help staring at Esma, memorizing every last wild lock of hair poking out from beneath her scarf, every shell woven into her braids. "How did you manage this, Esma?" I asked, breathless. "More creative storytelling?"

"Actually, no!" Her eyes lit up. "I woke up before dawn to someone hitting my head. I opened my eyes and there was my grandmother's nose looming over me. She whispered, 'Squash head, go out and fill this bucket with berries.'

" 'But what about the toddlers and packing up?' I asked.

"She tugged my braid. 'I'll handle it,' she said. 'You go.'

" 'But I've never even found berries before,' I said.

" 'Of course you haven't, squash head. Maybe you can find a local to show you some.'

"Again, she hit my head and stared at me, like we had a secret."

Gratitude toward the Mistress of Destiny filled me. "Your grandmother wanted you to find me," I said slowly. "She wanted us to be together. She wants to help our fortune come true."

🔹🔹🔹

When we reached the boulder beneath the tree, Thunder resumed her preening and fluffing in the river, while the other animals curled up with us.

Esma sang a tune beneath her breath as we squeezed lime and sprinkled salt on the tortillas. The melody of water was her instrument, and her voice mingled with its currents, as though her song came from a hidden spring inside the earth.

After we ate the tortillas, Esma brushed the salt from her hands and said, "Let's write our names in the dirt."

"I have something better," I said, and pulled out the fresh pencil and notebook that Maestra María had given me, which I'd stuck in the sack with the food. "This is for you."

Esma held the gifts like precious jewels, and then opened the first pages, beaming.

"I wrote the alphabet for you, see?" I pointed. "And some words with pictures beside them. The rest of the pages you can fill up yourself with practice."

"Thank you, Teo. You don't know how much this means to me."

She put the notebook and pencil in her deep dress pocket and pulled out the business card. "I'll have to hide these well. If any of my people knew I was learning to read . . ."

"What?" I asked. "What would happen?"

"Many years ago, before I was born, there was a Romani girl, back in Eastern Europe, the land my ancestors traveled. Her name was Papusza. Doll. She was a singer and poet, and she wanted to learn to read."

Esma stood up and began spinning. She didn't sit still much. Inside her whirled the force of storms, which she had to let out. Still swirling slowly, she said, "So Papusza gave food to gadjé villagers in exchange for reading lessons and books. Then her family caught her. Beat her. Destroyed her books."

Esma paused in her spinning and gazed grimly at the horizon.

My muscles tensed. "So what did she do?"

"She kept at it anyway!" Esma said, head high. "She wrote her poetry and sang her songs, and then, one day, a famous poet, a gadjo, discovered her talent."

My heart flew. "So it was a happy ending."

Esma shook her head. Her hand reached out for Spark's ear, and she rubbed it gently. "When Papusza entered the gadjé world, our people rejected her, declared her unclean. Marime. And the gadjé took advantage of her, used her songs for their purposes. Her sorrow was so deep, she lost her mind. Now she doesn't sing or write poetry. She's alone and abandoned, forgotten by the gadjé and scorned by my people."

Now Esma was rubbing both of Spark's ears, one with each hand. Then she sank down beside me and pulled out the notebook and pencil and business card, staring at them.

I shivered in the morning light. I wanted to grab back the notebook and pencil if they would lead Esma down the same path as Papusza. "Are you sure you want to do this, Esma?"

"I'll find a way to make my ending happy."

"But is that possible?"

"Anything is possible, Teo." She paused. "And I know that even if . . . even if I have to say good-bye forever to my people, you will be my friend. My loyal friend until the end of our long lives. And that makes me brave."

I reached out and tugged her braid. And then her other. "I'll always be here for you, squash head." Lightly, I tapped her temple.

Her face softened. "When I leave, I'll never see my grandmother again. So it will be up to you to remind me of her. How she taps my head and tugs my braid. How she calls me squash head."

"Sure," I said, my heart thudding, not from fear now but from the opposite. "Just don't make me start chewing on a pipe."

She laughed and leaned in to tap the brim of my hat. "Thanks, squash head." She gave me a sad smile, leaned in farther, and said softly, "There's more, Teo."

My breath caught in my throat. "What?"

"Remember how we were camped with other caravans for a time? And I saved everyone from the fire?"

I nodded and swallowed.

"Well, it caught the attention of a horrible, old, ugly, widowed man. And he decided he wants to marry me, even with my lightning-struck hand and leg. My father made a deal with him."

My mouth grew parched. I struggled for words. "A-a deal?"

"The geezer said he'll pay a bride-price for me. He wants to marry me next year."

Black stars filled the edges of my vision, moving in. "Will you do it?"

"Of course not, squash head! That man would suck the lightning right out of me. I'll leave long before that happens." She jutted out her chin, but her voice wavered, just a little. "I *will* be a famous singer."

"Esma," I breathed. Our faces were close. "How can I save you?"

"Just by being here," she whispered. "Being you. My loyal friend for eternity."

"I promise," I said. "I always will be." I moved my face even closer, till our noses were nearly touching, and then I didn't know what to do next, so I whispered, "Let's scream."

She smiled and stood up. "Let's scream."

And so we spun and screeched and spun. Thunder let out a disapproving whistle, and Spark just sat there, puzzled in her blindness, and Flash ran excited circles around us. The creatures and Esma soon became a patchwork blur as I grew dizzier and dizzier.

Finally, breathless and hoarse, we collapsed on the ground. "You know," I admitted, "sometimes I come out here and scream alone."

She smiled. "Scaring off the stream spirits?"

"They're long gone."

She tilted her head at me. "Why do you scream, then?"

I looked at the sky. "My mother. It's like she's already gone. A ghost. I've offered to heal her, but she's refused."

Esma was rebraiding her hair, and she paused to say, "Maybe you can only put the spark of life back inside someone who wants it."

"I wish she wanted it." I hesitated. "And my grandfather . . ." I forced myself to continue. "I don't know how much longer he'll be here." I shared my deepest fear. "I'll be alone, Esma."

She adjusted her scarf, then quietly said, "You're stronger than you think, Teo."

It was an echo of her grandmother's fortune to me—the false fortune. Or maybe not so false after all. "But, Esma, you have lightning in your blood. You have powers. I'm just a regular boy."

She finished knotting her scarf at her nape. Then, matter-of-factly, she said, "Teo, I wasn't struck by lightning."

A wave of something crushed me. Something sickening and heavy. Betrayal. "You lied to me?" I sputtered.

"Creative storytelling," she said sheepishly.

It was one thing to do creative storytelling with others. Not with her supposed best friend for life. I'd shown her the deepest, most hidden pieces of me—about Lucita and my mother and father—while she'd been *lying*? I'd even told her the burning-drowning words. Why had I trusted her?

Suddenly I was steaming with humiliation. Without a

word, I stood up and walked away. My animals made scuffling sounds as they followed me. At least they were loyal friends.

"Teo, wait!" Esma called out.

I didn't turn around. But I noticed my legs slowing, just a little, as her lopsided, running footsteps grew closer.

She gripped my arm with her good hand. "Let me explain."

Her fingers dug into my flesh, as though she'd hang on forever if need be. Still, I could probably tear my arm away if I pulled hard enough.

I didn't. I didn't because even though her lightning was a lie, it was there. It was there and it was zipping through her fingertips into my arm, through my blood, swirling and blazing in my chest.

Gritting my teeth, I stopped beside a boulder and turned to face her. "So how did you get lame?" I asked, knowing she hated that word.

With a sigh, she released her grip. She tapped her leg, held up her twisted hand. "Polio."

The word struck a deep fear, this disease everyone dreaded. My rage shifted to something else. "Then why . . . ," I began.

"I couldn't bear to be weak, Teo. I couldn't bear people calling me 'the Lame Girl.'"

I swallowed hard, wishing I could take back the word. This was Esma showing me her own deepest, most hidden spots—me, of all the people in the world. It was a gift for me alone, her friend for life.

"I made myself into the Queen of Lightning," she continued, fingering the coins at her neck. "And you know, after all this time talking about lightning in my blood, I've started believing it. I've started feeling it."

"Me, too," I admitted. She could work magic. One moment, I'd felt hurt and angry. The next, honored that she'd confided in me. And now, *inspired*, as though anything were possible, if I believed it enough.

She climbed onto the rock, raised her arms. "If you believe you're weak, you'll be weak. You're cursing yourself. Yet if you believe you're strong, you'll be strong. Give yourself a fortune and make it come true."

Her words lodged inside me, the way the lightning had. It didn't matter that lightning hadn't actually struck her. It was there, illuminating everything she did, and now it had flowed into the currents of my own blood.

In the distance, thunder rolled, a rumble through my bones.

We looked to the horizon, where strange, yellowish clouds had gathered. And suddenly, Esma said, "Oh, no! I'm such a squash head. It's been an hour, hasn't it? I have to get back to my camp."

She held up the empty bucket. "Any chance we'll find berries on the way?"

"I doubt it," I said. And then, with a smile, I climbed up beside her on the rock, spread my arms, and said, "Here is your fortune, my queen: In your bucket, very soon, there will appear berries!"

BERRIES

*E*sma's bucket was still empty as we approached her camp, bustling with people packing to leave. I slowed, breathing in the smoke and spice of their morning tea, not ready to say good-bye.

But instead of stopping, Esma suddenly yanked on my arm and pulled me in a wide arc around the cluster of wagons. She ducked behind a bush and, in an urgent whisper, said, "I have to say good-bye to your grandfather."

"But your people—they're about to leave."

"This is important!" she insisted, and took off running toward my house.

Soon we'd reached the courtyard, where Grandfather was sipping chamomile tea, slumped in a chair. He straightened up and brightened when Esma came over. "Buenos días, Queen. Have a seat and some tea!"

"I only have a minute," Esma said, pulling up a chair. "I want to thank you. For helping Teo and me. For the Romani Business Appreciation Event. For everything."

"Thank you, Queen," he said tenderly.

At that moment, a squabble broke out among Thunder and the turkeys. As I went to calm them, Grandfather leaned in to Esma, speaking softly.

I grabbed Thunder from the chaos of feathers, tucked her beneath my arm, and shushed her. Secretly, I strained to over-hear Grandfather's conversation. After some mumbling, I heard, "I have a favor to ask you, Esma." His Spanish was thickly accented, barely understandable.

"Anything," she replied.

I inched closer, ears perked, looking in the opposite direction and feigning interest in Thunder.

"After I'm gone, keep an eye on Teo's spark. If it leaves, put it back. Even if it seems impossible." He spoke slowly, deliberately, searching for the right words in Spanish. "You brought him back from the dead last year, Esma. Never doubt your power. Or your fortune. You two will be friends for the rest of your long lives."

A woman's voice rang through the morning air. "¡Buenos días!" And then, a greeting in accented Mixteco, asking how I was. "Nixi yo'o?"

Maestra María.

I raised my hand in welcome, and answered, "Yo'o sunii."

She was smiling, heading toward us, carrying a cloth bag.

"I came by to thank you for last night. I picked these up for you at the market."

She opened the bag to reveal hundreds of plump, red, glistening berries.

Esma and I exchanged wide-eyed looks.

When I could find words, I said, "Let's give them to Esma's people. As a farewell gift."

Grandfather and the maestra nodded in approval, and I dumped the berries into Esma's pail.

Grandfather smiled with his eyes. "Now there will be sweetness to add to the sorrow of their parting. All partings have a hint of sweetness, if you let them."

Along with the other folks on the Hill of Dust, Grandfather insisted on seeing off the Rom. I held one elbow while Uncle held the other, and we made our way down the dusty road to their camp. The horses were already hitched to the wagons, stomping their feet, ready to go. The toddlers were strapped onto women's backs, munching on berries, their faces stained and sticky and happy.

Esma and her grandparents approached us just before leaving. The Duke's mustache shone with fresh wax, spiraling up at the tips. Warmly, they shook Grandfather's and my hands good-bye.

Uncle stared sheepishly at the ground, muttering good-bye, and then whispered, "Sorry about everything."

The Duke grasped his hand and said, "Let us offer you a gift to show there are no hard feelings."

Esma translated this, her voice suspicious, unsure what her grandparents were up to.

The Duke slipped his hand into his jacket pocket. No raw onions, I silently pleaded.

But no, it was the little diosito statue that I'd given them last year, to ensure their return. He placed it in Uncle's hands.

"This did indeed give us good luck last year, and now we're passing it to you, so that you, too, may have good luck."

I wasn't sure what to make of this. It was a kind gesture of forgiveness, but there was something more to it. He was also ridding himself of the supposed curse, ridding himself of the need to return next year.

Worried, I looked at Esma. This was a surprise to her, too, judging by her scrunched-up expression.

"Will you come back, Duke?" I asked, steadying my voice.

He shrugged, twirling the ends of his mustache. "We go where the wind takes us. Of course, we do love your village, but you never know what the wind will blow away and what new things it will bring."

Translating slowly, stretching out our last moments together, Esma locked eyes with me. *Friends for life* were the unspoken words between us. No matter what, *friends for life*.

She held up her hand in farewell, and I held up mine.

Lightning zapped from her palm across the air into my own, an electric surge of confidence that only the two of us felt.

Yet, a few minutes later, as I watched the caravan wind down the valley, doubts crept in. What if Esma's people didn't return? What if other kids taught her to read, and she didn't need me anymore? What if she left to become a famous singer? What if Uncle's rudeness had made the Rom never want to come back? What if her father forced her to marry that man? What if she ran away to escape the marriage?

I filled my mind with little what-ifs to fend off the biggest ones: What if Esma left me? And Grandfather left me? What if I couldn't save either of them? What if I were left truly alone?

More dark yellow storm clouds rolled in after the Rom left. Zigzags of light ripped at the horizon. Far-off thunder moaned, low and sad. For a long time, I waited for a raindrop, but it never came.

HUSH

Mateo

THE HILL OF DUST,
OAXACA, MEXICO

Present Day

27

SECOND INTERMISSION

*Y*ou all right, Mateo?" The voice sounds far away.

"Huh?" I clear my dried-out throat. "Yeah, fine." It takes me a second to remember where I am . . . even *who* I am. It's like when you're so absorbed in a movie that when your friend says something, you feel like he's speaking a whole different language, even like he's on a whole different planet.

I force my mouth to form words. "Why, Grandpa?"

"You're squirming."

I bring myself back into my body, feel the wooden seat beneath me, the coin necklace in my hand.

Yup, I have to pee all right. My mind's been ignoring it, but my legs are shifting around like crazy. Just like at the movies, when you gotta go, but you don't want to leave the magic, so you just sit tight and hope the pee reabsorbs.

"I'm okay, Grandpa."

"You sure, mijo?"

Rain's dripping on the roof, which isn't helping me ignore the urge to pee.

"Yeah, you can finish the story." Then a fear strikes me. "But you did see her again, right?"

His lip quivers like a leaf, and his eyes fill, and I want to look away, but I don't. Oh, man, I've never seen Grandpa like this before.

I swallow hard, clench the coins in my hand. Grandpa told me he needed my help. And in order to help him, I have to know this story. Somehow, I have a role to play here . . . I just need to find out what it is. "Then what happened, Grandpa?"

He takes off his hat and looks up at the ceiling, wood and palm woven into a giant spiderweb pattern. He gathers a breath and holds very still, like the heavy silence before a storm. A hush falls over the room. Even my stomach quiets down.

I twirl the coins around my fingers, one way and the other and back again. Softly, I say, "Grandpa, did she come back?"

Finally, he speaks, and once again, I leave my body behind and let the movie suck me back in like a tornado.

BOOM

Teo

THE HILL OF DUST,
OAXACA, MEXICO

Long, Long Ago

CATCHING DEATH

*A*lone in the rain, I perched atop the highest point of the Hill of Dust. These days, it should have been called the Hill of Mud. In the rock shelter beneath me, my goats were huddled with Spark and Thunder and Flash, safe from the storm.

But there was nothing between me and the lightning stabbing the sky. I raised my face, willing it to strike. No such luck.

Rainy season had been here for weeks already. The third anniversary of Lucita's death had come and gone. Esma and her people had never arrived. And this year, more than any other, I needed my best friend for life.

Out of habit, my eyes went to the base of the hill, the curve where her caravan used to come into view, in all its colorful glory, at the end of dry season.

Nothing. Only the sluice of water down the mudslide of a road. No cars or horses, much less wagons, would venture through the rivers these valleys had become.

Was that why the Rom hadn't come? But they usually came before the rains started. Had Esma left them already? Had she learned to read and write, then contacted the agent? Was she already a famous singer? Or had they married her off to that old man? What had happened?

I'd let loose so many screams by the river, there were none left. Something about that scared me. Maybe that's why I was here, inviting lightning into my veins. Real, deadly lightning.

When the storm ended and the last flashes vanished and the booms faded, I was still alive. Soaked to the bone, but alive. I gathered my animals and trudged home through the mud, walking too close to the river, raging and wild.

But Thunder stopped me. She shrieked with alarm until I moved away to a safe distance.

I headed up the path toward home, past the dripping leaves, and then stopped. This was the hardest part, coming home without Grandfather to greet me. I gathered a long breath and what little strength I had, then forced my legs to walk past his closed-up healing hut. Rain drummed on the thatched roof. It had been empty and unused for five months now. Who knew if it even smelled like Grandfather anymore. I couldn't bear to open it up to find out.

Uncle Paco called to me from the edge of the bean field, where he was installing water pipes. After a year of trial and error, they actually appeared to work. "*Oye*, Teo! Want to help?"

I could barely muster energy to shake my head.

Lalo, playing ball with Chucho by the irrigation ditch, called out, "Teo! Come play soccer!"

I kept walking past Grandfather's room. That was where I'd found him that morning, five months earlier. I'd gone in his room to offer him a cup of atole. He hadn't responded to my voice, or to my gentle nudging, or to my desperate shaking.

He'd died in his sleep, a peaceful half smile lingering on his lifeless face.

"Teo!" Aunt Perla poked her head out from the kitchen, baby on her hip. "Come inside! Have some atole! You're soaking wet! You'll catch your death of cold!"

I didn't feel the cold. My belly was empty—I hadn't eaten all day—yet I didn't feel hungry or thirsty. And the idea of catching my death? Well, it didn't feel bad. It felt like relief.

My mother was inside the kitchen, an untouched cup of atole before her, its steam making her face ghostly. She studied the box of shiny things in her lap, not looking up as I entered.

Yes, catching my death would be a relief.

The next morning I woke up with a sore throat and sneezes and a cough. Aunt Perla fussed over me, the baby slung on her back. "What did I tell you about catching your death, Teo?" she scolded. "Now stay inside and rest," she ordered, tucking the wool blanket around my chin.

Any other time I would have shrugged her off and gone to pasture the animals anyway, but not this time.

I didn't touch the new notebook that Maestra María had given me to use as a journal. Every page was blank. She'd helped me apply for a scholarship to the secondary school in the nearest town. During the last months of the school year, after Grandfather's death, I'd held myself together, barely. I'd focused on schoolwork, hung on to the daily comfort of Maestra María.

Over the year, she'd become a beloved teacher to all the students, especially me. After Grandfather's death, she stayed after school to talk, soothing me with the very words in Mixteco that he'd taught her. Taxiini . . . sikita'an . . . kuu ini. She even came by our house on weekends to check up on me and bring us fruit, or vegetables, or beans.

But for the past two months that school had been out, she'd been away visiting her relatives. Now every day had become an empty page of an empty book.

I picked up one of the books she'd lent me—poetry by Gabriela Mistral.

If they could, the trees would lift you
And carry you from valley to valley . . .

My eyes couldn't focus on the words. No, not even the maestra's precious books held my interest. Instead, I stared at the bits of corncobs and dried leaves poking out from the adobe walls. What a relief it would be to join Lucita and Father and Grandfather. Was this how my mother had felt for the past three years? I buried my face in the crook of my elbow and burrowed beneath the blanket.

No, I couldn't live the rest of my life like her, mostly dead.

No, death would be a relief.

I walked toward it with open arms.

The days and nights blurred together, with my aunts bringing me atole and soups and helping me walk to the outhouse, my eyes half-closed because it was too bright outside.

"Oh, Teo," they said, in worried, distant voices, "your fever's so high."

They forced me to sip teas, asking desperately, "Teo, what would your grandfather have given you for your illness? Which herbs?"

I shrugged and rolled over.

Lalo cared for Flash and Spark and Thunder, who were often at my side, whistling and *baahing* and scuttling and trying to make me play. I ignored them.

One day, Uncle Paco came in and said, "Teo, there are some people who traveled far to see your grandfather."

I kept my eyes closed, said nothing.

"Teo, talk to me."

"Turn them away," I murmured.

"I think you could take a look at the patient. It's a girl your age, Teo."

A crazy hope. My eyes flew open. "Esma?"

He shook his head slowly. "No, not the Gypsy girl. A girl from a village three days' walk west over the mountains. No other doctor has been able to help her. The journey was hard on her." He paused. "Teo, your grandfather taught you everything he knew. You can help her."

I shook my head. "I'm too weak. I'm not wise."

Uncle Paco put his hand on my forehead. "You healed me, son."

"Grandfather did."

"You did. And you can heal yourself, too. You can heal this girl."

At the door appeared Aunt Perla, leading the girl inside. She shuffled slowly, hunched over, thin and sickly, a wilted flower supported by a couple who must have been her parents.

"I'm sorry," I said. "I'm not my grandfather. I can't help you. I can't even help myself." Inside, I thought, *And I don't want to.*

I turned over and shut my eyes tight.

TURNING AWAY

*T*ime passed. Snatches of conversation drifted in and out of dark dreams. It was mostly my aunts and uncles, fretting that they couldn't fetch a doctor; mudslides had blocked the roads. One voice I never heard was my mother's.

One day, a husky, elegant voice stood out from the rest. Maestra María, murmuring sweet things in Mixteco and stroking my cheek. "Taxiini, sikita'an, kuu ini."

I opened my eyes, and there she was, like an angel.

But she was swimming in and out of focus, her lovely eyebrows waving like wings of a distant bird, lost in a cloud of rose perfume. Her voice was far away, but I tried to listen.

"Teo," she said, her eyes shiny. "I had no idea you were sick . . . I'm so sorry I didn't come sooner . . . your uncle Paco came to find me . . . oh, Teo."

She kissed my forehead, then wiped away the lipstick mark with delicate fingertips. In my ear she whispered, "You need a mother, sweet boy."

She read me books as I drifted in and out of consciousness, grasping at her words like darting silver fish. But they were too slippery, and I was too far gone. I sank into darkness.

At one point, Uncle's voice said, "What do you think, Maestra?"

I struggled to catch their minnow words.

"He needs a doctor now," she said, her voice trembling. "I'm driving to the city to fetch one."

"But the roads are closed, Maestra. It's too dangerous."

"Paco, your nephew could die."

Uncle sighed. "What doctor would risk his life to come out here? What doctor cares that much about a poor family of indios?"

"I have money," she said. "I'll say Teo is my own son."

"I'm coming with you," Uncle said after a pause. "I'll bring shovels to dig out the car."

Maestra María gave me another cool kiss on my forehead. More comforting murmurs in Mixteco. "Taxiini, sikita'an, kuu ini." Grandfather's voice spoke through her, feathers and petals that floated around me like spirits, like echoes. Perhaps he'd known that one day I'd need them, and she'd give them.

More time passed. Worried whispers of uncles and aunts.

"He's not moving."

"He's burning up."

"*Dios mío*, his pulse is weak."

"Ay, no! His breathing is so slow."

And then, the voices faded, and there were hands shaking me, but not me . . . my body . . . I could see it there below. How it shook as the hands moved it, but then flopped still, as if empty.

I was drifting outside my body, near the ceiling. I could see every detail of the room, the people in it, their faces distraught in the lantern glow. The frantic eyes of Aunt Perla with her baby on her back, the child's fingers in his mouth, shiny with saliva. Aunt Perla was the one shaking my body. My other aunts and uncles were huddled around, watching, their hands on my neck, my wrist, my chest, searching for signs of life.

I turned away.

I turned away from the movie of my life.

I saw another world, a world that had always been there, if I'd only turned around. A place of greenness and lushness, a thousand colors, an infinity of petals, sparkling water, dazzling reflections off leaves and stones, a sky the deepest blue . . . music that was really water and birdsongs and violins and voices dancing together . . . and it made me think of Esma and her caravan.

I moved toward the beauty.

There was Lucita. Beautiful Lucita, with her dazzling smile and her arms outstretched as if she wanted me to come play, as if we were still little children.

Behind her appeared Father, his strong hand resting on her shoulder.

And at her other side, Grandfather, his own wrinkled hand on her other shoulder. My powerful grandfather, before he'd grown sick. He bent down, whispered something to Lucita. Her face fell and her hands lowered.

Grandfather put up a hand as if to say stop. *Wait.*

But no, I wanted nothing more than to race into his arms.

I floated toward him, and he waved his hands, insisting, "No, Teo, go back."

Still, I flew to him, taking one last glance behind at my weak little body. It grew faraway, so tiny, a sad little heap of flesh and bone beneath my sobbing aunts and uncles and cousins.

There was the thinnest, silvery, spiderweb thread connecting me to that body. It stretched thinner and thinner the closer I moved to Grandfather and Lucita and Father. In a moment, just a moment, it would snap and I would be free.

THE SILVER THREAD

From behind me, light glinted. It was just enough to make me look back at the little adobe room. The source: the warm glitter of candlelight on coins.

There, at the doorway of the room, was Esma.

Esma in her flowered dress, a garden spilling over with petals, a treasure chest overflowing with gold, a bolt of lightning.

Esma, loping across the room, pushing others out of the way, throwing herself over my body.

Esma, clutching my face between her hands.

Esma, shouting, "Come back, Teo! Come back! My friend for life! Come back!"

Her shrieks were ear shattering. The howl of wind during the wildest of storms. She threw back her head and opened her mouth and screamed, as if she were at the river. As if all those screams had been building up to this moment. Her howls filled the room, bounced off the walls. "COME BACK, TEO!"

There I hovered, attached to my body by the thinnest sliver of thread, looking between Lucita and Father and Grandfather and Esma.

Grandfather's voice resounded, deep and rich. "You're needed there, Teo. You need to be the healer. You need to fill my place."

"I can't."

"Look," he said. "You made a promise to Esma. Even death cannot break it, Teo."

"Life is too hard," I said. "Without you, without my mother."

"Maestra María will be your mother. Esma will be your friend forever. Your cousins and aunts and uncles will always love you. As will your animals. They all need you, son."

"But I miss you, Grandfather!" I wanted to run into his arms.

Still, he kept his distance, his palm raised to stop me. "You can visit me when you like. Simply turn away from the movie of your life for a bit. There's no need to die, dear boy."

He didn't understand the emptiness inside me. "There's nothing to live for. Nothing to look forward to."

Grandfather sighed. "In your world, you're walking along a mountain path, only seeing what's in front of you. The present moment. But in this world, I'm a bird, seeing the entire mountain range from above—past, present, future. And, Teo, I see that not only will you and Esma be friends for life. So will your grandchildren."

Our grandchildren? Something shifted inside me. Something filled my emptiness. The possibility of my future, and my grandchildren's. I couldn't imagine myself as an old man, but the idea of it made me look back again.

Now the little adobe room was emptied of everyone but Flash and Spark and Thunder, huddled in Esma's lap. My aunts and uncles and cousins must have gone to sleep. But Esma remained, aglow in the candlelight. Her hand clutched mine.

"I'm so sorry, Teo," she said softly. "So sorry we came late. My stepmother had a baby and then there were mudslides . . ." Her voice broke. "Everyone else wanted to turn back, but my grandmother insisted we come. She knew, Teo. She knew you needed me."

Silence except for small whimpers; stillness except for her shaking shoulders.

And then, "Oh, Teo! What would I do without you?" She paused, took a long breath, collecting herself, steadying her voice. "Your uncles and aunts are worried the priest can't come to bless your body before . . . before the burial. But I know you'll come back. Won't you? You have to! You promised!"

All this time, I felt the strain of the silvery thread pulling me toward my body. At the same time, I felt the tug of the other world, so easy and glittering and colorful, the promise of an eternity playing with Lucita, basking in the warmth of Grandfather and Father.

And then, into the adobe room strutted Roza, Mistress of Destiny. She set down a burlap sack and plopped beside Esma, taking in her red and tear-streaked face. Roza tugged her granddaughter's braid gently, tapped the side of her head, and said something in Romani.

"Squash head."

In this in-between place, I could understand their language. Or perhaps I could simply understand all the feelings between the words. What mattered.

"My impossible squash head," Roza said quietly. Her nose held perfectly still. "Your grandfather is making us go. There's too much rain here to show movies. Everyone wants to leave. I can't change their minds."

"I'm staying with Teo," Esma said.

Roza pulled her pipe from a deep pocket, chewed on it for a while. "I know you are, squash head," she said gently. "I've always known."

From her sack, she pulled out a bundle wrapped in twine and a worn black violin case. She set them at Esma's feet. Then she removed a necklace of gold coins that reached down to her waist and draped it over Esma's head. It mingled with Esma's own strands of beads and coins and shells, shining brighter than the rest.

"Thank you," Esma said, wrapping her fingers around the necklace.

"Go make your own fortune, child. Your future is here. Now is the time."

Esma threw her arms around her grandmother and sobbed. "I don't know if I can."

"Make sure this boy lives," Roza said. "And he'll make sure your fortune comes true."

Her words entered me, etched themselves into my spirit. This echo of a promise I'd made, to be Esma's friend for both of our long lives. A promise that only death could break . . .

Or perhaps not.

Esma moved her grandmother's hand to the forehead of my limp body. Her voice was a hoarse whisper. "He's already cold, Grandmother. No pulse, no breath."

Munching on her pipe, Roza surveyed my body. Then she tugged at Esma's braid again. "What is it you always say, child?"

"Nothing is impossible," Esma whispered.

"Well then, work your magic, Queen of Lightning." A tear streamed down Roza's mountainous nose, trickling through its valleys and nooks like a tiny river.

After a long breath, she stuck her pipe back in her pocket, stood up, and headed toward the door.

"Wait, Grandmother! How? How do I bring him back?"

Roza's nose danced to an invisible melody. "Sing, my dear squash head. Sing."

A Tickle, a Nibble, a Song

*M*y soul string was stretched to a single, quivering, delicate strand.

Esma took a deep breath and opened her mouth.

The song swirled out like silver ribbons.

She rose and spun and more ribbons spiraled out from her outstretched fingertips, the rippling hem of her dress, ribbons of lightning and pure, raw power.

She swirled and sang and the ribbons braided themselves into my soul string, more and more and more until the cord was solid and thick as a tree trunk.

When I remembered to look back at Grandfather and Lucita and Father, they were far off, growing smaller and fainter and dissolving until they were only hands waving in a kind of mist.

And then nothing.

I turned back to Esma, felt her song pull at me, tugging me closer and closer to my body.

As I floated downward, Flash's ears perked up. He skittered onto my chest and nibbled at my ear. I could feel the gentle little teeth that always drew out laughter.

Then there was Spark's tongue, velvety soft and licking my arm, up and down, covering every last patch of skin. It tickled.

Then there was Thunder, biting at my ankle, so hard it hurt.

In a rush, I felt the beat of my heart and the flow of my blood and the whoosh of my breath.

I opened my eyes and saw Esma, twirling, and though I could no longer see the ribbons, they were there, making my soul string stronger and stronger with every note.

And then, all at once, Flash's nibbling and Spark's tickling and Thunder's biting made me laugh. A dry, hoarse, rough cry of a laugh.

Esma heard. She slowed her spinning, paused her singing, and stood, dizzy, meeting my open eyes. Hers were the color of my soul string, raindrop silver.

As she took my hand, a bolt of lightning shot through, right into my center.

A sudden commotion broke out. Beyond the door, in the courtyard, voices and cries and sobs shattered the night.

It was Maestra María's voice, yelling, "No, no, no, it can't be! He can't be gone!"

She stumbled into the room, and when she saw me with my eyes open, she crumpled to her knees at my side.

I felt her love, something warm and real and solid that I could hold in my hand, in my heart. The love of a mother. She covered my face with kisses and sobbed prayers of thanks, and when she finally caught her breath, she said, "Oh, Teo, they told me you'd died."

By this time, the doctor—a stout, bald man in a damp suit—had taken out his black bag and was pulling out a stethoscope.

Half-asleep, my aunts and uncles and cousins rushed over, touching my face, my hair, my flesh in disbelief.

"He's warm again!"

"His heart's beating!"

"He's breathing!"

"His eyes are opened!"

"But how can this be?"

"He was dead."

"He was cold."

"He had no pulse."

"No breath."

"I came back," I said.

Everyone gasped.

"Esma called to me," I said. "She saved me."

Esma shrugged a shoulder. "He saved himself. I just gave him a little nudge."

Maestra María threw her arms around Esma. "You sang," she said. "Your song brought him back from the dead."

I nodded.

Esma reached out to stroke Spark's ears. "Really, it was his animals," she said. "They tickled him back to life."

"Well," I said with a feeble laugh, "Thunder's bite is a little more painful than a tickle." Weakly, I reached out my hand, tapped the side of her head, and added, "One day I'll save you, too, squash head."

And then, Maestra María threw her arms around me again and kissed me twenty more times.

HEAD OF A LION,
WINGS OF A BIRD

$\mathcal{T}$he boy's in stable enough health," the doctor announced after examining me. "His vitals are strong."

"But he was dead!" Aunt Perla said, hand over her mouth.

The man scratched his hairless head, mystified. "Perhaps he fell into a coma, or a near-death state in which his organ function slowed down. You might not have detected a heartbeat or breathing. His temperature would have dropped."

As Uncle Paco translated the best he could, my relatives looked at one another, puzzled, and rested their gazes on Esma, as if she held the secret.

The doctor shrugged as he packed his equipment away. He patted the maestra's shoulder and said, "Your son should recover soon."

My relatives looked even more confused at the doctor calling me the maestra's son.

"Give him rest and plenty of food," the doctor added. "He'll be fine."

At the mention of food, my aunts scurried out to prepare me atole and soup and tea. Meanwhile, my uncles volunteered to drive the doctor home since Maestra María refused to leave my side.

She turned to Esma, eyebrows soft with compassion. "We saw your people leaving as we came here. Maybe you can ride with Teo's uncles and catch up."

Esma shook her head. "I'm going my own way now."

Maestra María's eyebrows furrowed in concern. "I don't understand, dear."

Esma raised her chin. "My grandfather always says, 'Better to be the head of a mouse than the tail of a lion.'"

"I'm not sure I follow you," said the maestra.

"Even though the Duke lives life on the outskirts, at least he's his own master. He decides where and when to travel. He answers to no one." She wrapped her grandmother's coin necklace around her wrist, then unwound it. "But if I stayed with my people, I'd always be the *tail* of a mouse."

"And what is it you want to be?" Maestra María asked.

Esma stood up and tore off her scarf, letting her shell-woven braids and waves of hair tumble wildly over her shoulders. "The head of a lion!"

Maestra María laughed. "I can see you as a lion's head."

I grinned. "Esma has the chance to be a famous singer."

"I can see that, too," the maestra said.

Esma pulled the business card from her pocket. It was well-worn, the edges soft and rounded.

"I can read it now," she said, handing it to the maestra.

From the other pocket, Esma pulled out the notebook that Maestra María had given me a year earlier.

The maestra and I took turns looking at both items, clearly precious to Esma. The notebook was filled with writing, every last space crammed with letters. In the early pages, the writing was big and uneven and the words ran together. Yet by the end, the writing was neat and small and well spaced. They were poems—maybe song lyrics—about dreaming and longing and missing. And, I noticed with a blush, the word *Teo* was on almost every page. How could I ever have thought she'd forget me?

I found I could read the business card now, too.

Antonio Reyes Salazar, Agente de la Música

Calle Morelos No. 20, Coyoacán, México, D.F.

Impressed, Maestra María asked, "He's interested in starting your singing career?"

We nodded.

Her left eyebrow arched with an idea. "Once Teo is better, we'll drive you there, make sure this man is legitimate."

"And if he is?" Esma asked tentatively.

"Why, then we'll help you settle in!"

Esma gazed adoringly at the maestra.

And I thought, *This is exactly the mother I want. The mother I need.*

The next time Maestra María drew me in for a hug, I whispered one word.

"*Mamá*."

And then, just like that, she was.

During my weeks of recovery, Esma stayed in Grandfather's old room. Her dresses and scarves and hair absorbed the scent he'd left behind—an earthy, smoky, copal scent. Sometimes, as she breezed by, I breathed in the pieces of Grandfather that lingered in her.

Every evening, she read to me from the maestra's books in a lilting singsong voice that I could have listened to forever. Sometimes she cried there in the darkness, whispering that she missed her little cousins and grandparents. She told me funny stories about them, recounted their favorite sayings, their quirks and antics. She told me how she'd convinced her old-geezer fiancé that the lightning had zapped her brain, too, and made her crazy. And her laughter turned to tears as she confided that after she'd scared the man away, her stepmother and father treated her worse than a rat.

I held her hand and tried to comfort her. I told her to look at the whole mountain range of her life, to remember that on one of the nearby peaks, she would become the head of a lion. I told her that on one of the distant peaks, our grandchildren would become friends. And as I told her this, I secretly wondered: If our grandchildren were friends, could they also be brothers and sisters and cousins? I felt her warm hand in mine, and a secret part of me imagined us getting married on one of those peaks.

During the days, Esma's spirits were higher as she loped and swirled around the Hill of Dust. She took good care of Flash and Spark and Thunder, and helped my cousins pasture the goats in el monte. With my aunts, inside the smoky kitchen, she learned to make tortillas and atole and salsa.

My relatives remained in slight awe of Esma. They were friendly toward her, and respectful, but almost too respectful, treating her like the Virgin María, a miracle worker not entirely of this earth.

Once, Esma sighed and said, "It would be good to be some-one's granddaughter or daughter or sister, wouldn't it?"

I saw the longing in her eyes. I couldn't tell her she was like a sister to me. No, she was something else, something more. So I simply nodded. "It would be."

A month after my time with death, during a lull in the rains, Esma came into my room and said, "Let's take a walk today!"

Slowly, supporting me with her arm, she led me down the muddy path to my mother's abandoned fruit grove, where rot-ting oranges and mangoes littered the ground. We walked among the trees, picking fruit from low-hanging branches and dropping it into our sacks. Sunlight fell through the leaves, wandering over Esma's skin, gleaming off her coins. Spark and Flash poked at the fallen fruit, scavenging bits here and there, while Thunder found small puddles to splash around in.

"What are you going to do when I leave?" she asked.

"Keep pasturing the animals, I guess." I kept my voice steady, tried to ignore the pain in my chest. "Eventually plant my own fields like my uncles."

Esma squinted at me. "Maestra María told me about the scholarship. Your chance to go to secondary school. I think you should do it."

I sat down, leaned against a tree trunk, hugging my knees. I still lost my breath easily and had to rest often. Flash nestled in the space beneath my legs, and I stroked his tail, thinking. "Esma," I said finally, "I can't just go to school. I have to contribute somehow—with work or money."

She picked up an orange, tossed it from one hand to another. Then she picked up two more and juggled them. "You could be a healer, like your grandfather."

I turned an orange over in my hand, breathed in the sweet, tart scent. Broke it open and fed it to Flash. "You really think so?"

"Yes!" Oranges in midair, she spun around, caught all three, then picked out the biggest and dug her fingertips into its liquid center. She popped a few sections into her mouth, letting juice spill down her chin.

I wondered if one day, oranges would remind me not of my father's unjust death, but of Esma, juggling and spinning and licking sweet nectar from her lips. Just as her swirling screams by the river had replaced Lucita's cries.

"I *know* you can, Teo." She wiped off the drops, took another bite. "And after you graduate, you could train with doctors in hospitals, too. So you'll know how to heal in your Grandfather's way and their way, too."

I rubbed my face. "I'm not the head of a lion, Esma."

"True," she said, wiping away more trickles of juice. "You're not."

Spark settled in my lap, and I rubbed her silky ears. "What if I'm just the tail of a mouse?"

"Know what you are, Teo?" Esma looked around, probably for a boulder to stand on. Seeing none, she hoisted herself up onto a low tree branch, then climbed upward. From the topmost branch, she said again, shouting this time, "You know what you are?"

"What?" I called up.

Through hundreds of sunlit leaves, her coins flashed, and her voice sang out, "The wings of a bird, my friend! A whole flock of birds! You lift everyone up!"

The truth is, her words lifted *me* up, until I was flying inside, right up there with her.

JOURNEY

*I*n the morning sunshine, when Maestra María's light blue car reached the top of the Hill of Dust, Esma and Uncle Paco and I were waiting for her in front of the church. Now, after another couple weeks of recovery, I was strong enough to hold Esma's satchel packed with all her belongings in the world. The bundle was no bigger than a melon. Beside me, she held her violin in its case, swinging it nervously back and forth.

I tugged at the stiff new suit the maestra had bought me. Hopefully, the new shoes wouldn't get muddy, but in case they did, Uncle Paco had lent me some polish and a rag to bring along. Now he was kneeling at Esma's feet, shining the pair of heels the maestra had bought her. Without raising his head, he said, "We'll miss you, Queen." And then, still polishing, he added, "You and Teo, you changed my thinking about things. About your people and our people. You changed the maestra's thinking, too. And I bet you'll change lots of other folks' thinking."

He stood up, wiping his hands on the rag.

"Thank you," Esma said, reaching out to take his hand, even though it was stained with black.

Uncle was not the only one sad to see her go. Earlier that morning, after my other uncles and aunts had tearfully wished her well, I'd leaned over my mother's petate, kissed her forehead, and said, "Good-bye. I'm taking a trip to the city." To my amazement, her eyes opened, and she croaked, "My box." I brought it to her, and she dug around till she found the gold earrings, the swirling half moons. "For the lightning girl," she said. I held them in my hands, watching my mother in wonder.

She must have been paying attention these past years, at least a little, through her fog of sorrow. She must have known, somewhere inside, how important Esma was to me. Maybe I couldn't fix my mother, but I could love her and treasure the pieces of herself that shone through, little by little, here and there.

Now, beside the maestra's car, I held the earrings in my free hand, waiting for the right time to give them to Esma.

The maestra stepped out in a sky-blue dress that matched her car perfectly. She kissed us both. "You two ready?"

Esma took a long breath and nodded.

I forced my chin to nod. "Yes, Maestra." I usually called her Maestra when she came to visit—nearly every evening. It was only when she'd hug me good night, when her face was close to mine, when my eyes were closed, that I shyly whispered *Mamá* in her ear, and she shyly whispered *mijo* to me. My son.

Esma climbed into the front seat, and I climbed into the back and set her satchel beside me on the creamy white upholstery. The car smelled faintly of leather and the maestra's sweet perfume.

She smiled at Esma. "You look lovely!"

She did. She'd washed her best of two dresses—the one covered in roses of all shades of red—and scrubbed herself pink and washed and freshly braided her hair. She shone.

Still gazing at Esma, the maestra arched her left eyebrow, suddenly inspired. She pulled out her purse, which looked cut from the same creamy leather as the car seats, and took out a handful of makeup. "May I?"

Beaming, Esma nodded.

"Close your eyes, dear."

Esma obeyed, and the maestra outlined her lids with black, sweeping the corners upward. Gently, she traced Esma's brows, bringing the arcs into relief. Brushed more black onto the lashes with a tiny brush. Swept rosy powder over Esma's cheekbones and berry-red cream on her lips. Finished it off with puffs of powder over her nose and forehead and chin.

"Gorgeous!" the maestra said. "Let Teo see you!"

Esma turned around in her seat. "What do you think?"

I blushed right down to my toes. When I found my voice, I stammered, "Nice."

But it was more than nice. Esma had transformed into a star, in just a few minutes, right there in the car. Her face held the magic of her songs, evoked caravans trailing up mountains, candlelit fortune-telling, bonfires and violins in the moonlight, films beneath stars, mysterious spices and stories. She looked like herself . . . only *more so.*

I handed her the earrings. "From my mother."

Esma's brow rose in surprise, and stayed that way as she fastened the earrings. Then, in a kind of daze, she collected the makeup from her lap and held it out to the maestra. "Thank you . . . both. Thank you."

"You know what?" the maestra said. "Just keep the makeup, dear. Practice a lot before you wear it out anywhere. But you'll get the hang of it soon. Dios mío, you're beautiful!"

Esma stretched her neck to look in the rearview mirror. She stared and smiled in disbelief. Tears filled her eyes.

"Oh, no, no crying," the maestra scolded, dabbing at the corners of Esma's eyes with her hankie. "I won't have you messing up that makeup now!"

She spritzed a mist of perfume on Esma's neck, and then, satisfied, tilted the mirror away, stuck the key in the ignition, and drove us, ever so slowly, down the Hill of Dust.

It wasn't until we were halfway down that I noticed my skunk had somehow snuck in and hidden beneath the front seat. "Flash?" I yelped. He leapt and hopped around the car on his three little legs as I tried to catch him.

Peering into the rearview, looking puzzled and amused, Maestra María pulled to the shoulder and stopped the car.

"Sorry, Maestra," I said, opening the door. "I'll let him out here. He'll find his way back."

"No," Esma said. "What if he doesn't? What if he gets lost or eaten?"

"Oh, he can come with us," Maestra María said, laughing.

I was just closing the door when I noticed Thunder, half-flying, half-waddling down the road in a fury of feathers and whistles. Close at her heels, a frantic Spark stumbled down after her.

Maestra María's eyebrows softened in surrender. "Let them all in," she sighed.

"Really?" I asked.

She nodded. "Just keep them off the upholstery."

I settled them at my feet, and Thunder chirped some satisfied whistles, and we were off.

For most of the drive, my jaw hung open in wonder. I'd forgotten how many mountains and villages were scattered around my own humble little Hill of Dust. The world was huge beyond belief . . . and all this was less than a day's drive from home.

The last times I'd been on these roads were back when my father was alive. We used to load up the donkey cart with baskets and hats and walk alongside it to the city—a long, hot, dusty trek that spanned days and nights.

Now, as the looming buildings of Mexico City came into view, I grew nervous. Exhaust smells replaced fresh air. Cars and trucks multiplied, rushing by like a river. An old fear clutched me, and through dark puffs of exhaust, I caught a glimpse of that orange rolling across the street and Lucita's pudgy hand slipping from mine and reaching for it. I could almost hear that thud of steel against flesh, and see the blood and tears on my father's lashes. And beside him, that perfect, glistening orange that had somehow survived.

I blinked, shook myself, then let my gaze rest on Esma's hand on the open window. I wanted to hold on to it, tightly, so tightly I'd never let it go. I wanted endless days of eating oranges and mangoes with her in the cool shade of trees.

I looked past her hand, outside the window, and saw we were leaving the wide street flooded with cars and turning onto a peaceful, cobblestoned lane, as narrow as a trickling stream, and dappled with sunlight through leaves. We passed flower-filled parks and gardens and gurgling fountains. Delicious scents poured through our open windows—jasmine and rose nectar, steam from spicy sauces simmering on corner stands. Lining the streets were emerald-canopied trees and houses painted lemon yellows and rich blues and petal pinks, a rainbow stretching before us.

This neighborhood wasn't the crushing, suffocating city that loomed in my memory, the place echoing with those words that had set me on fire years ago. *What's one less indio . . .*

I waited for the burning-drowning wave to hit me.

It didn't. Instead, I looked at Esma and the maestra in the front seat, both glowing with excitement. Both so confident in my own powers, my own future.

My spirit flew above the flames and floods, and from up here, I felt as strong as Esma and Maestra María thought I was. From up here, I knew that somehow, I could make any fortune come true. Lightning now lived in my blood, and I would use it to lift up those who needed me.

Soon, the maestra announced, "Coyoacán!" reeling my mind back into the car. "This is Señor Antonio's neighborhood. Chock-full of writers and actors and artists. He must be a bohemian type." She turned onto another street and pointed to a brilliant blue house. "Look, that's where the artists Frida Kahlo and Diego Rivera lived. Oh, and keep your eyes out for movie stars like María Félix!"

My eyes soaked in everything. Ladies strode by in skirts long and short, and even some in pants. The men wore all manner of hats—leather and reed and felt—and their shoes ranged from boots to sandals to the shiny, narrow kind Uncle Paco wore.

I peered at Esma's profile as she gazed out the window. This wasn't new to her. She'd been to the city before to stock up on supplies and rent movies. Still, she looked stunned. Her entire life was about to change, even more than it already had.

Checking her map, the maestra slowed the car and parked at the side of a quiet street. "And here we are!"

Esma glanced back at me, gave a nervous smile. We climbed out of the car, making sure my animals stayed inside with only their noses and beak poking out the window crack.

"So much for the upholstery," the maestra murmured, putting one arm around each of our shoulders.

"I'll clean it," I assured her.

She gave a slight shrug and a half grin, then kissed the top of my head.

We walked a few blocks and slowed at the sign reading 20. It was posted on a wrought-iron gate leading into a lush courtyard bursting with flowers and fruit trees and chirping birds. I'd never seen so many shades of bougainvillea—reds, oranges, yellows, pinks, purples. Beyond the courtyard was a pink three-story house, trimmed in white like icing and half-hidden by flowers and leaves.

Maestra María smoothed Esma's hair, freshened up her lipstick, dusted more powder on her face. Then she rang the bell, looking back and forth between me and Esma, smiling, excited.

An older lady in a checked apron came to the gate and gave the three of us a curious look. "May I help you?" she asked politely.

Thankfully, the maestra spoke; my mouth was too dry to say a word. Even Esma—bold, brave Esma—seemed struck silent.

Once the maestra explained that Señor Antonio had offered representation to Esma, the woman nodded with understanding. "Come inside, please."

Under the trees of the courtyard, she offered us glasses of bright-red agua de jamaica and told us to make ourselves at home and relax on the blue chairs.

She must have been a servant, because soon she returned with three elegant young women who looked to be in their teens, not much older than Esma and me. They wore pretty, fitted dresses, much like the maestra's, only more somber colors—pale gray, black, and brown.

The servant ducked back inside, excusing herself.

Extending their hands, the women introduced themselves as Margarita, Carmen, and Dolores. Their hands were cool and smooth, while mine were damp with sweat. Even after sipping the agua de jamaica, my mouth was still too dry to speak; I could only nod in greeting.

And then, Carmen spoke the words that made my heart stop. "We're so sorry," she said, "but our father—Señor Antonio—he cannot see you."

34

A Dream, Dead

J swallowed hard and glanced at Esma. Her face was frozen.

Unruffled, Maestra María smiled. "Oh, of course, señorita. He wasn't expecting us. We'd be happy to return tomorrow, or make an appointment for another day."

The girls exchanged meaningful looks. "Well, you see, señora," Dolores said softly, "our mother passed several months ago."

"Oh," Maestra María murmured. "I'm so sorry to hear that, señorita."

Dolores continued. "Our father hasn't—he hasn't been well enough to see anyone since then."

Esma spoke up, her voice trembling. "I'm sorry about your mother, señorita." She paused, gathering herself. "But we've traveled so far, and I've tried so hard, waited so long . . . given up so much. Please, is there any way we can see him?"

Carmen gave her a kind look. "I'll ask. Please wait here."

We stayed in the courtyard, holding our glasses of cool, sweet liquid. I couldn't take another sip, afraid I'd choke on it. Esma couldn't either. She was blinking back tears, trying not to smear her makeup. I was grateful for that makeup. I didn't know what I'd do if she started crying.

I strained to hear the voices coming from an open window above us. It was Carmen's voice, speaking with a lower, man's voice, grim and weak.

But I couldn't make out any words, especially not over the chattering of the other sisters' small talk. They inquired politely about where we were from and kept offering us food, insisting we must be hungry after our journey. "No, thank you," we assured them, too nervous to eat.

The women were enchanted when they discovered Esma was a real, live Gypsy. Thankfully, they showed none of the distrust that others in the city supposedly had. Perhaps as the daughters of a music agent, they'd met talented musicians from every walk of life. Perhaps they were used to all different kinds of people in this colorful neighborhood of artists. Perhaps they'd simply learned to keep their minds and hearts open.

"May I touch your jewelry?" the youngest sister, Margarita, asked, marveling at Esma's beauty, asking question after question about her people's way of life.

In any other situation I would have liked these girls, appreciated their curiosity, their warmth, their respect for Esma. Now my mind went to Señor Antonio. I couldn't help feeling angry with him . . . but also sad for him. After Grandfather had died, I'd been so lost, I couldn't imagine going on. I'd even refused to see that sick girl who'd traveled so far. I wished I could go back in time and treat her more kindly.

Back then, I didn't think I wanted to be saved, but Esma—and our fortune—showed me otherwise. I thought of Uncle, humbled and shamed last year, and how he wanted to be healed, and let me help him.

Suddenly inspired, I interrupted Margarita. "Excuse me, señorita, but perhaps I could heal your father."

"Excuse me?"

"I'm a healer. If your father would like to be healed, I could help him."

Margarita cocked her head. Hope brightened her eyes.

Dolores looked at her sister, shrugged a shoulder, as if to say, *Why not?* "Hold on, let me ask him," Dolores said.

More time passed, and now Margarita peppered me with questions about my healing rituals. I answered as best I could, trying to sound confident yet humble, as Grandfather always had.

While we spoke, dark clouds pooled in the sky and the wind picked up and moisture filled the air. I shivered, shoved my hands into my pockets to warm them.

Margarita frowned at the sky. "Oh, these afternoon storms!" she sighed. "So good for the plants, but not for much else."

244

"Certainly not the roads," Maestra María agreed.

"Would you care to come inside?" Margarita asked, hugging herself in the cool breeze.

But just then, the other two sisters came outside, their faces long. "We're so sorry," Carmen said. "Our father—he sends his apologies—but he's mourning, you see. He says he's not able to see you."

I thought of my mother, how she was still lost in mourning, unable to find her way back. Not *wanting* to find her way back, even though I'd tried to guide her. Maybe Señor Antonio was like her, too far gone. A deep ache filled me, heavy as a boulder.

Dolores continued, wind whipping her hair. "My sisters and I—of course we'd love you to heal him—we're desperate to get our father back. But he's not interested. I'm so sorry."

Rubbing her goose-bumped arms, Carmen beckoned us inside. "Please do come in for a bite to eat, though. Do you need a place to stay for the night?"

Maestra María was just explaining that we had to tend to the animals in her car when I noticed Esma's red lower lip tremble. Tears welled up. Suddenly, she bolted to the gate, running in that lopsided way that shot a little pain through my chest. The gate clanked, she was outside on the sidewalk, and her sobs let loose.

I ran after her as she stumbled toward the car.

Behind me, Maestra María gave quick apologies and farewells and thanks before following us out.

When I caught up with Esma, the sky opened and poured out a sudden waterfall of rain that mixed with her tears and made black rivers over her face. Her entire body shook. The only time I'd witnessed her sob this deeply, straight from her soul, was when I'd died.

That's when I understood: Her dream was dead. Her fortune, her destiny, her hope.

Dead.

There in the rain, for the first time ever, I hugged her. I wrapped my arms around her and pulled her close, and felt her sink into me. I had to save her. But how?

"Esma," I whispered into her ear. "Let's get married. We'll make a good life together, you and me. You can be my wife."

She didn't answer.

I kept talking. "Well, we wouldn't have to do it now. Maybe in a few years? But I want you to know—I love you. I—I want to marry you."

Sniffling, she pulled away to look at me. "You would want to marry me?"

I wiped her black-streaked tears away. "Of course."

Her lips turned up in a sad smile.

SING

A heartbeat later, lightning flashed, illuminating the entire sky.

I squeezed my eyes shut.

Behind my lids, I saw the silver glint of Esma's eyes.

I saw her swirling and flashing and singing.

I saw the head of a lion, wild and fierce.

Then it hit me with a jolt: The Queen of Lightning was too big for the Hill of Dust. She had to fulfill her destiny. And it was up to me to make sure she did. That's when the deeper truth struck me. Saving her meant losing her. Letting her go. *Helping* her go.

Yet I wanted to hold her tightly, forever. I dug down to find the strength to do just the opposite.

The sky shuddered with white electricity, and thunder roiled, and I whispered, "But first, Esma, let's make you a famous singer."

She breathed out. "Oh, Teo, the man won't even see me."

"Nothing is impossible," I said, taking her cold hands, letting lightning flow through mine into hers.

I looked up and saw Maestra María hovering beside us, face full of sorrow. She dabbed at Esma's eyes with her hankie, a kind but futile gesture in the rain. "Ready to go home?"

"No," I said, tugging at Esma's hands. "Come on."

"What?" Esma said, resisting. "Why?"

I pulled her, the way she had pulled me back to life.

Down the street, the gate was still open a crack. I pushed it open and led Esma inside.

"We can't," she protested. "He said no, Teo."

"Maybe a part of him wants to come back to the world of the living. And if anyone can bring him back, you can." I positioned her in front of the open window of Señor Antonio. "Sing, Esma."

She wrinkled her eyebrows. "I can't."

"Sing!" I shouted, tears streaming down my own face now.

Esma drew in a long breath, raised her arms, tilted back her head.

And she sang. Raindrops fell over her eyelids and lips . . . and she sang. Her voice rang out and the raindrops accompanied her and the lightning danced.

Esma sang and it was glorious. She took all the sorrow and hope and love and longing and missing inside her and transformed it into song, pure and raw and breathtaking, straight from her center, from the center of everything.

She sang and I felt Lucita and Grandfather and Father beside me, and other spirits, too—Señor Antonio's wife, the maestra's husband.

Esma sang her own fortune back from the dead.

Silver ribbons swirled around us in the rain. I felt them inside my chest, saw them from the corner of my eye.

A face appeared at the window above, a man's face, rapt with wonder.

The sisters ran outside, into the rain, and huddled there, listening, tears trickling down their cheeks with rainwater.

After Esma's song ended, there was silence. The pitter-patter of rain, the chirp of a bird.

Dolores's eyes were closed and a smile was spread over her face and she said, "I feel Mamá, right here with us."

"Esma!" Margarita cried. "Your song brought our mother here."

Moments later, Antonio appeared at the door to the court-yard, weak but joyful. Carmen took his arm, led him to a chair, wiping it off with her hankie before settling him into it.

"Please, señorita," he said hoarsely, "please sing another."

The afternoon passed, and the rain stopped as dusk came. The girls insisted on fetching my animals and feeding them kitchen scraps. They cuddled with Spark and giggled at Flash dashing around the courtyard.

Again, the sisters invited us inside. This time we accepted. The maid served a warm, filling dinner of chicken mole, rich with chocolate and chile, and as we thanked her, she said, "No, thank *you*. You've brought life back into this home."

After dinner there was more music. The sisters played instruments expertly—piano and violin—and were delighted to see that Esma, too, played violin. They offered us soft beds and even set up crates piled with rags for my animals.

The next morning, over a breakfast of *huevos estrellados* and *pan dulce* and cinnamon coffee, Antonio announced, "Esma, I would be honored to manage your career. My daughters would like to offer you a place to stay, here with us, as our guest, for as long as—"

"You can share my room!" Margarita interrupted, unable to contain her excitement.

Antonio smiled indulgently. "I can begin setting up shows for you this week, Esma. You would not only be my client, but a member of the family. Do you accept, my dear?"

Esma looked around the table, at these girls who treated her like the queen she was, and at the same time, like a sister. Then she looked at the maestra, who gave her a smile and a little nod. Finally, she looked at me, sitting beside her.

I wanted to pull her in again, hold her tightly, be with her every moment of forever.

Instead, I tapped her head. Tugged her braid. "Go make your fortune, squash head."

Beaming, she turned to Antonio, and said, "Yes!"

And just like that, Esma's destiny unfurled like a brand-new leaf; like a royal red carpet; like a ribbon, silver and strong and flying on the breeze.

Later that morning, Esma came to the maestra's car to see us off.

She gave the maestra a long hug good-bye. "Thank you for everything."

"Thank *you*, my dear girl," the maestra said, kissing both cheeks. "You were the spark that set off everything."

With a sad smile, Esma buried her face in the fur and feathers of my animals. "Take care of Teo," she told them.

The maestra took the animals and started settling them in the car, leaving Esma and me alone to say good-bye.

Esma threw her arms around me. Chin wedged onto my shoulder, she whispered, "Thank you for wanting to marry me." She held me tighter still. Her necklaces and beads pressed against my chest; her scarf brushed my cheek. "Maybe someday," she said. "Who knows. We have our whole, long lives ahead of us."

I took her hand. I never wanted to let go. "One day I'll save you, Esma."

"You already have." Her gaze swam over my face, so close to hers. "I thought I'd never need anyone to rescue me. But all along, I needed you, Teo. You've saved me . . . just by being my friend."

Her silver eyes locked with mine. She touched my cheek, lightly, her fingertips leaving a trail of sparks. Slipping her other hand from mine, she removed a coin necklace and held it up for a moment so it flashed sunshine. Then she pooled the shimmering strands into my palm and covered them with her other hand. Pressed together, our hands were alive with sparks and tingles and crackles of lightning.

I breathed, "Good-bye, my queen."

"Good-bye, my friend for life."

Our lips touched like two bird wings brushing against each other for the tiniest moment, then flying apart on their own separate journeys.

And then, I was in the car and waving and Esma was growing smaller out the window, and we turned a corner and she was gone.

My animals settled at my feet and I felt their warmth, their tiny movements of pulse and breath. A dam blocked my throat and a tightness squeezed my chest.

I didn't talk on the way back to the Hill of Dust.

But the maestra did. The whole way, she murmured the sweetest, softest words in Mixteco, words from Grandfather that floated here and there like feathers.

And as the mountains spread around us like our past, present, and future, I dangled the coin necklace in front of it all and saw Esma in every glitter of sunlight.

BURST

THE HILL OF DUST, OAXACA, MEXICO

Present Day

HIDDEN THINGS

*G*randpa Teo's far-off gaze focuses back on me, onto the necklace in my open palm. The old coins are still zinging in my hand, sparks shooting out.

I rub my eyes and stretch my arms and stamp my numb feet. It's that feeling you get at the end of a movie, when the credits start rolling and you take off your 3-D glasses and blink, totally shocked to return to the regular world. Only this movie hasn't finished yet, not really. Grandpa said it was up to me to make the ending. But how?

I raise the necklace in front of me. Like a ghost of Esma, it's dancing and swirling in the air, even though there's no breeze in the healing hut.

I let it fall back into my hand. My voice creaks out, rusty. "Ever see her again, Grandpa?"

He reaches into a small pine box behind the altar and pulls

out a yellowed envelope and a postcard with wavy, worn edges. I take a closer look. They're addressed to him on the Hill of Dust, in fancy, old-fashioned handwriting.

"We wrote to each other for five years," he says with a sigh. "Esma was performing for big, adoring crowds. I was so proud of her."

"Really?" I'm actually on the edge of my seat. "Then what?"

"Well," he says, "at that time I was studying in high school, then interning at a hospital."

"The one where you met Grandma?"

He nods. Very carefully, as if handling a baby animal, he takes out the letter and unfolds it. "Here, mijo, read it."

"Um, okay." I hold the crinkly paper to the candlelight and read slowly, since it's in Spanish and written in superflowery lettering that's hard to make out.

> *Dearest friend for life,*
> *I am in America now! Oh, how I love it here!*
> *I make enough money to live in a nice little house,*
> *and I even have a car—the same color as the*
> *maestra's! The only thing missing from my life is*
> *you, Teo. Please come live with me . . . will you?*
> *Love,*
> *Esma*

I swallow hard, flushing, like when a romantic scene sneaks into a "family" movie I'm watching with my parents. This is a *love* letter. I mean, Esma's practically asking Grandpa to marry her. I fold up the paper, hand it back to him. Awkwardly, I ask, "You were already in love with Grandma by then, right?"

He nods. "For days I could barely eat or sleep. I didn't know what to do. And then a sick little boy came to be healed. So sick he was nearly dead. I stayed up all night, tended to him for days with teas and herbs. And he recovered. That's how I knew, Mateo. I belonged on the Hill of Dust. I was the head of a mouse here. If I hadn't been here, the boy would have died. I asked myself, How many animals and people would suffer if I left? Yet I couldn't ask Esma to come here. She was already the head of a lion in America." He sighs. "And then there was your grand-mother. I loved her, and she was happy to live on the Hill of Dust with me. That day, I wrote Esma the hardest letter of my life."

He gets quiet, so I nudge him. "And what did she say, Grandpa?"

He takes the postcard from the altar and hands it to me. There's a photo of the New York City skyline of long ago, black and gray and cream.

On the back, there's one handwritten line.

I suppose some things are impossible after all.

My insides sink. What a gigantically massive bummer. I stare at the postcard, imagining how crushed Grandpa must have been, imagining how this letter cut their bond of friendship with a single snip. And I don't know much about girls, but it doesn't take a genius to see why Grandma didn't like hearing stories about some miraculous, beautiful Gypsy girl who was in love with Grandpa. No wonder my grandparents never talked about her before.

I remember the impossible fortune the Mistress of Destiny gave to Grandpa, something like this: *You and Esma are on the path to being friends for life. If you fulfill this destiny, you will save each other when no one else can.*

A wave of sadness rushes over me. A feeling that the fortune is *supposed* to come true. A feeling that something is wrong, very wrong.

"Grandpa," I say. "You said you needed my help."

He looks at me closely in the darting candlelight. "Will you look for her?"

The necklace jolts and leaps in my hand. "Yeah. Of course."

"Gracias." He tilts his head, smiles. "It won't be easy, but if anyone can help me, you can, Mateo."

I have a zillion questions, but I'm growing more desperate for food and a bathroom by the second. I settle on, "Why now, Grandpa?"

"Lately I've been hearing Esma's voice . . . in crackles of lightning, rumbles and booms of thunder, gusts of wind, bursts of rain. She needs me, Mateo. Now."

And in the pocket of silence that follows, I swear I hear a whisper in the rain drumming outside.

"You know," Grandpa continues, "a few months ago I spoke with your grandma's spirit. She offered me her blessing to find Esma. So I gave your cousins her name and had them search online. They found nothing." Suddenly, Grandpa looks vulnerable, like a lost little boy. "Mateo, don't feel bad if you can't find her either."

I hold up the coin necklace to the light, watch it swing back and forth, imagine the Romani girl's eyes flashing, the lightning zipping through her veins, and her words: *Nothing is impossible!*

The coins buzz with electricity. Something zaps through my fingers and pumps through my blood. Esma's words echo in my head. *Give yourself a fortune and make it come true.*

"Grandpa, I'm gonna find her for you." I stand up, the force knocking my chair backward. In a voice that seems to come from outside me, or maybe from some hidden place inside me, I say, "Nothing is impossible!"

TALES FROM THE OLD PEOPLE

A knock at the door. Mom peeks her head inside. "Mateo? Papá? You guys have been in here for hours! Aren't you hungry?"

"Starving," I admit. So starving it overpowers my urge to take out my cell phone and start searching for Esma. But just barely.

Grandpa stands up. "Let's eat," he says, leaving the letter and postcard on the altar and resting his hand on my back. On the way out, he rests his other arm around Mom, his oldest daughter.

Outside, I'm startled to see it's already nighttime. I jog through the silver drizzle, across the patch of mud to the bathroom. Sweet relief. After that detour, I head to the kitchen hut, stomach growling. Bits of wet straw poke out from the adobe walls and the thatched roof. The door's open, welcoming, revealing an orange hearth fire in the corner and a little wooden table surrounded by *los viejitos*. The old people. That's what we call all the great-great-uncles and great-great-aunts who still live here in the village. I can't even keep track of how many *greats* there are.

Most of the younger relatives live in Mexico City or Chicago now, except for us in Maryland. Sometimes, my cousins come to the Hill of Dust on the weekends, and it's cool having kids my age to hang out with. But secretly, I like los viejitos the best. And now, after hearing Grandpa Teo's story, I see them in a new light. They weren't always ancient and shriveled and wise.

Grandpa and Mom and I squeeze in beside them, and his latest rescued animal—a deaf baby fox—curls at our feet. It's supercozy in here, with that fairy-tale feeling, and rain pitter-pattering the roof and chamomile tea bubbling on orange wood coals. We dig into the heap of pink-sugared sweet rolls and sip warm atole.

Everything is exactly how it's been every summer of my life, the same faces around the table, growing more wrinkled by the year. For the past two years, though, Grandma's face has been missing. Sadness gets me right in the chest, like a hole's ripped through it. I think back to her funeral, so many crying, sniffling people packed into the cathedral. Even Dad was here on that trip, comforting Mom and me.

I glance at los viejitos, glad that Grandpa wasn't left alone here on the Hill of Dust. Uncle Paco, who's technically my great-great-uncle, is shining a black shoe in his lap with a rag, and the smell of polish mixes with the wood smoke. I try to imagine him as some arrogant jerk hurling insults and stealing, and later, sniveling with shame. But I only see the gentle, funny, smart man who has offered to shine up my sneakers and flip-flops every evening of every summer I've spent here.

The Maestra—my great-grandmother—leans over and kisses my cheek, leaving a cloud of old-lady perfume. I can't help wondering if it's the same stuff she wore decades earlier. "You're getting so handsome, Mateo. Your eyelashes are just like your grandpa's when he was young, you know. Oh, the girls better watch out for you!"

I shrug and smile weakly, because what are you supposed to say to that? I have yet to see any girls stricken by my lashes.

The Maestra clasps her hands together in delight, then leans in to kiss my other cheek. Until today, I never knew why everyone calls her the Maestra; I just went along with it since I was little. When the Maestra's not looking, I wipe her lipstick from my cheeks.

I mentally erase her sags and wrinkles and age spots, and picture her as a stunning and stylish young woman. Who knows, maybe she still could be if she laid off the makeup a little. She always wears fancy dresses and heels and a perfect bun in her hair and sits up really straight. As usual, she's holding a book now, her manicured fingers smoothing the pages. Poetry, probably. She's the only one who speaks perfect Spanish besides Grandpa, and she's always trying to get me to read Spanish poetry with her, which I secretly don't mind so much.

My other great-grandmother, who I've always called *la Otra Abuela*—the Other Grandmother—hardly speaks at all, and when she does, it's in a soft mix of Mixteco and Spanish. Right now she's poking around in the cardboard box on her lap. I always figured it was like her security blanket or stuffed animal or something. I never guessed it was connected to the death of her daughter, ages ago. I just get excited that on every trip, she lets me choose a shiny old treasure as a present. Over the years, I've picked out a mirror, a knife, a picture frame . . . and this year, there are only two things left—a candlestick and a silver hairbrush.

"Choose something, Mateo," she whispers, softer than the crackle of the fire. Her voice sounds creaky and out of practice.

I take the candlestick, wondering what I'll do with it. I feel kind of bad; I mean, now the Other Grandmother only has that hairbrush to look at all day. "Thanks," I say, really looking at her for the first time, at all the sorrows behind the curtain of her eyes. "What'll you do when the hairbrush is gone?"

She moves her dried, wrinkled lips to my ear and whispers, "Why, then I'll be free."

Aunt Perla pats her shoulder, then scoops up another cup of atole for me and changes the subject. She's used to the Other Grandmother's quirks. "Teo, did you know your uncle Paco won an award for lasting contributions to the Hill of Dust?" She speaks Spanish in the choppy way of old people who spent most of their lives speaking only Mixteco. Tossing a white braid over her shoulder, she pulls out a plaque from the shelves of spices, shines it with the hem of her blue-checked apron, and holds it up proudly.

"Congratulations!" Mom says.

Uncle Paco waves away the compliments and starts in on his other shoe.

Aunt Perla explains that the award was for installing the community water system nearly single-handedly, years ago, long before any villages in the area had plumbing. Some still don't. Every time I take a shower with hot water here I feel grateful, knowing that people in nearby villages are taking cold bucket baths and peeing in an outhouse.

Grandpa Teo pats him on the back. "What would we do without you, Uncle?"

"What would we do without *you*, Doctor?" Uncle Paco says with real fondness.

It's true, Grandpa is the real celebrity around here. "El Doctor Teo," everyone calls him, with voices full of respect. Whenever people around here find out I'm Doctor Teo's grandson in *el Norte*, they tell me stories of how he saved their kid or brother or mother . . . seems like he's saved everyone in a hundred miles of the Hill of Dust. He is definitely the head of a mouse in these parts.

Modestly, Grandpa shifts the conversation to the weather—specifically, the storm today, and how Mom and I had to slip and slide up the Hill of Dust, which should be called the Hill of Mud, he jokes.

Then Aunt Perla tilts her head at Grandpa and says, "Remember the mudslide that summer you died, Teo, dear? How terrible it was?"

The other viejitos nod and murmur in agreement. Mom frowns and shifts in her seat. She's a scientist, through and through, and doesn't know how to react to these stories. But I've always soaked them up like a dried-out sponge.

For the hundredth time, they tell the story of Grandpa Teo's death, and the Gypsy Queen who sang him alive, because for her, *nothing was impossible*! And then they launch into stories about the Gypsies' fortune-telling and movies. Every summer, I've heard stories about the Gypsy Queen from the viejitos, but until my talk with Grandpa today, she just seemed like a fairy-tale heroine, not a real, live girl. I mean, I always used to picture her like some kind of superhero or goddess, living in the sky and shooting out lightning from her fingertips.

I glance at Grandpa. Usually, when the viejitos tell these tales, his face never reveals any clues. But now, he gives me a secret wink.

I keep my hand in my pocket, holding on to the electrified coins, and it's all I can do not to take them out and tell everyone, "Esma's real! Somewhere she's alive!" But Grandpa must want to keep this quiet, so I just let the necklace buzz and hum in my hand.

When Grandma was alive, she didn't like hearing these Gypsy stories, even less than Mom does. Grandma came from a town a couple hours away, where Grandpa was interning in a hospital. She was doing midwifery training there, learning how to deliver babies. I always figured that since she was from a bigger town, she just didn't believe in hocus-pocus stuff from the village. Now I get it: She felt threatened by this real, live Lightning-Queen-Goddess-Superhero, her husband's first love and supposed friend for eternity.

I used to tell my friends back home about the Queen of Lightning, and they made faces and said, "Dude, those old people are *nuuuuuts!*" Over the years, I learned to keep the mystical parts of the Hill of Dust to myself. But I wish I had someone to share them with, to *wonder* with, especially now that I've promised to find Esma, especially now that magic and real life have collided.

Once los viejitos grow too tired to continue the storytelling, they yawn and drain their last drops of atole and tea and say good night. Soon enough, I walk outside, too, where the moon is a bright, fuzzy circle, and the air is damp and cool. The mist wraps around me like a blanket.

Mom disappears into the bathroom to brush her teeth, and Grandpa brings the baby fox into his room to tuck it into its crate of rags. I linger outside, watching the cornstalks that look like people waving their leaf-arms to say good night.

A hand rests on my shoulder. It's Grandpa. I turn to face him, noticing we're the same height this year. He looks closely at me. Although his lashes have thinned and grayed, it's true we have the same eyes. Like mud puddles in reeds, he always says.

When I tell my buddies about my trips here, they get impressed with the scorpions and ancient artifacts and machetes . . . but that's not the thing that makes it so awesome. It's the hard-to-capture details—how my hair smells like wood smoke for weeks, how the tortillas taste when they're cooked over a fire, how mysterious los viejitos' voices sound when they talk about the Gypsies. And most of all, it's being with Grandpa Teo, collecting herbs by the river, wandering in el monte, and sometimes—thanks to his creature-in-trouble radar—even saving animals.

Mostly I'm okay with being an only child, but I wish there were someone back home—some *kid*—who got my new mission to find the Queen of Lightning, who got this part of my life, who got the magic of the Hill of Dust, who got that my grandpa isn't just some old geezer in the boondocks of Mexico, but more like—I don't know, a knight or king or someone really noble and important.

Someone I'd do anything for. Like find his long-lost friend for eternity.

I hug him good night, then take out my phone and start searching.

A PIECE OF MAGIC

A month later, on the ripped-up backseat of an ancient bus, to the annoyingly cheerful blare of *ranchera* music, I watch the Hill of Dust grow smaller. Swallowing the lump in my throat, I pull the coin necklace from my pocket and let it dangle in front of the storm clouds. Once the hill has vanished from view, I tuck the necklace back into my pocket, carefully, like a piece of magic I'm bringing home.

My forehead falls against the window. Saying good-bye to the Hill of Dust always sucks something out of me and leaves a lonely space. And now there's the added disappointment of not finding Esma. It was a bummer saying good-bye to Grandpa Teo this time, even bigger than usual, knowing something important was left unfinished.

Last month, the night of our arrival, I'd felt sure I could find out something about Esma online. I figured my cousins had spelled her name wrong when they searched for it, since it's pretty long and confusing. But when I typed in Esma's full name, I got nothing but a bunch of random links. Nothing about a singer. Dejected, I realized she probably uses her married name now, and who knows what that could be. For hours, I kept searching, but the cell connection was so spotty, it took forever and turned up nothing useful.

Then, on the second day, my phone dropped in the stream and stopped working. Even though Mom let me use her phone, it was so old and grumpy, I got nowhere. I tried a couple Internet cafés around here, but the computers were so slow I nearly bashed my head into the screens. I'd just have to wait till we got back to Maryland to make any real progress. If only Grandpa and I could get together in front of our superfast computer at home with high-speed wireless.

"Hey, Mom," I say suddenly, lifting my head from the window. "Why hasn't Grandpa ever visited us in Maryland?" It's never occurred to me to ask before; he's always seem tied to the Hill of Dust, like a kite on a string that could only go so far.

"Well," she says, glancing up from her ebook, "I used to ask him and my mom to come, but she was scared of flying and he'd never leave his animals. And he worried someone would get sick and there'd be no one to heal them."

"But now there's that new clinic nearby, right?"

"Yup. And you know, today when I was saying good-bye, he mentioned he might visit us sometime."

My eyes bug out. "No way!"

She taps her ebook screen, distracted. "I told him we'd pay for him to come with one of my cousins. Of course I wouldn't feel comfortable with him flying alone. He's never even been on a plane before."

"That'd be awesome, Mom." My heart speeds up, new possibilities exploding inside me. If I can find Esma, Grandpa could come to the United States and see her . . . and me. It would be like bringing the ultimate, giant piece of magic back home.

Mom goes back to reading, and my hand grazes the old silk string and silver coins of the necklace. *Zap.* Something's rushing in to fill the emptiness—a lightness, a liquid gold. My hands tingle and my blood screams the words: *Nothing is impossible!*

I close my hand over the necklace.

Silently, I tell myself my fortune.

I will find Esma.

ZAP!

SUBURBAN MARYLAND

Present Day

RAINDROP, FLAME, AND
ESMERALDA RAYOS

*B*ack in Maryland, a few weeks after our Mexico trip, I'm lying on my bed, covered in dried sweat from soccer camp, messing with my new phone. Esma's necklace is hanging from the end of my curtain rod, and a breeze through the window is moving the coins, making a weird, tinkling music. Most of my weekdays are filled with camp, and my weekends with the pool and Xbox with friends, but in the in-between times—like now—I search online for clues about Esma.

So far, no luck.

Last week, I mentioned Esma to my buddies because it seemed like a cool mystery, detective stuff they could get into. But they were all, "Dude, you're, like, obsessed with these old people. Give it up." And for the next few days, "Gramps" was my new nickname. Luckily they forgot about it, and I haven't reminded them.

I flip onto my back and, for the thousandth time, tap in *esma romani singer* and scroll through link after link, but it's all the same—hundreds of entries on some *other* singer named Esma, from Macedonia. I'm ready to throw my phone across the room. There has to be *something* about my Esma online, even if she ended up taking her husband's last name or failing at her career or even dying young. After all, she was on her way to fame when she wrote that letter.

Dully, I check my e-mail, eyes glazing over at the usual celebrity headlines on the home page. Musicians and actors, most of them with crazy names. In the corner of my room, the coin necklace is making a strange, light melody in the wind, like a secret song just for me. It's as if the notes seep into my brain and zap new electrical paths from cell to cell.

I'm staring at a freaky photo of Lady Gaga on my phone when it hits me—maybe Esma has a stage name. Actually, she sort of already had a stage name back when Grandpa knew her.

I type *gypsy queen of lightning.*

The results pop up.

And my mouth drops open.

No *way.*

I sit up, tuck a pillow behind my neck. My heart is thudding like crazy. The first website that comes up is a Wikipedia entry for "Esmeralda, Gypsy Queen of Lightning."

There's a black-and-white photo of a beautiful woman in some kind of coin headdress, with more coin necklaces covering her shoulders and neck. She's standing on a chair, holding a violin. Her chin is raised proudly, and her eyes are piercing, traced in black lines that curve up at the corners like Cleopatra's.

With shaking hands, I scroll down, reading more.

> ESMERALDA RAYOS, *best known as Esmeralda, Queen of Lightning, is an acclaimed singer/songwriter of Gypsy, or Romani, origin, known for her soul-searing music. Born in 1947, she spent a nomadic childhood in rural Mexico as part of the* cine ambulante, *or traveling cinema, popular in rural Mexico in the mid-20th century. At age thirteen, she left her family and signed with well-known music agent Antonio Reyes Salazar, who is credited with beginning her successful and long-lived career. She has produced seven critically acclaimed albums, and continued live performances until the early 2000s. Known for her colorful life, she has married and divorced four times, and performed internationally.*

I click on a link to hear one of her songs. The first notes are sad and fierce and beautiful, a warbling, passionate, wordless song-cry.

The air fills with a kind of electricity, speeds up my heart and tingles a place inside my chest. It's a strange feeling, deep as a cave and towering as a mountain and wide as a starry sky.

For some reason, it makes me think of Grandma.

Afternoon sunlight streams through the window, sparking off the coins, and I can almost feel my grandmother here with me, as though Esma's song has opened a path to somewhere hidden. A pathway to another world, right here in Maryland.

I have to tell Grandpa. I wipe my sweaty hands on my shorts, then scroll through my contacts, looking for his number. Hopefully he'll answer. He never set up voice mail, and couldn't care less about texting or e-mail or the Internet in general. Half the time he forgets his phone somewhere random, like the grain storehouse or the turkey coop.

But the number's not even here. Why would it be? Mom's always the one who calls him. I'm just about to text her at work for the number when my phone rings.

MOM appears on the screen.

Quickly, I answer. "Hey, Mom, this is so weird—I was just—"

"Teo, hon, are you at home?" She sounds shaken up, her voice on edge.

"Yeah. Why?"

"My dad just called me. He's at the airport."

My forehead wrinkles. "Huh?"

"I could kill him! He came all the way here, all by himself, without telling me. Said he knew I wouldn't let him come otherwise. Can you believe it? Good thing we're even in town. I mean, this isn't like the Hill of Dust, where you can just drop in and everyone's waiting for you with atole and . . ."

She rambles on for a while, and I let it sink in. Grandpa Teo . . . *here*? *Now*? Why the urgency? And so soon after we saw him? It has to have something to do with Esma. Of course, that's not something he'd tell Mom about. Too irrational.

"Listen, Mateo, I'm coming to pick you up now, then we'll go get Grandpa together, okay?"

"Sure," I say, jumping off the bed. And then, "Hey, did he say why he was coming?"

She makes a *pfft* sound. "I asked him, of course, and all he said was, 'It's time.'"

An hour later, beneath the fluorescent lights of baggage claim, I spot Grandpa Teo in his palm hat. The little kid in me escapes, and I run toward him, hurling myself into his arms.

"Careful, Mateo!" he says, laughing.

Once I loosen my grip, he sticks his hand in his suit pocket and pulls out a tiny bird. A *live* bird.

A sparrow? Now *I'm* laughing. Of course he'd have a live sparrow in his pocket.

But Mom, clicking toward us in her heels, gasps. "Papá! You brought a bird? All the way from Mexico? That's illegal! How'd you make it past customs?"

He smiles in that soothing way that makes you feel like you're sipping hot chocolate by a fire.

"Oh, mija, I found her here in the airport." He presses his cheek to her feathers. "She must've snuck in somehow. Raindrop, that's her name. Tiny as a raindrop, fallen from the sky. She hurt her wing, probably slammed into a window."

"Ay, Dios, Papá," Mom sighs. "This is so like you!" She gives him a long hug, careful about the sparrow.

On the highway, inside the car, as Raindrop lets out tiny peeps, Mom grills Grandpa about why he came, and if everything's all right back in Mexico, and whether he's going senile. Calmly, he reassures her, stroking Raindrop the entire time. His calloused fingertips ease her shivering like a magician's spell.

Mom takes the exit to our suburb, passing clusters of big gray and beige houses, interspersed with giant block stores and parking lots. I watch Grandpa Teo look out the window, sunlight flashing over his face like a strobe. I wonder what he thinks of our neighborhood with its rectangular lawns and neat hedges. His eyes don't reveal anything; they just have their same relaxed, curious expression.

We're nearing our cul-de-sac when Grandpa Teo raises a hand and says, "Stop, please."

Mom slows down, puts on her blinker, pulls to the roadside. "You okay, Papi?"

Nodding, he says, "*Momentito*," then opens the door and walks back along the curb, shaded beneath the tree canopy.

"Go see what he's doing, Mateo," Mom says, squinting at the rearview.

I hop out and see Grandpa Teo bending over something . . . a baby box turtle, mottled orange and yellow and black. It's

278

struggling to climb up the curb. Grandpa picks it up, examines it, then searches the underbrush near the sidewalk.

"See his mother around, Mateo?"

I shake my head. For a while, we look through brambles and sticks and bushes and leaves, with no luck. The air's steamy hot, even in the shade, and within minutes, I'm sweating in my shorts and T-shirt. Grandpa's dripping in his suit.

Mom honks, impatient, and calls out the window, "Let's go!"

"*¡Ahorita vengo!*" Grandpa Teo responds. Be there in a sec. With a wink, he sticks the baby turtle in the suit pocket that's not occupied by the sparrow.

"What should we name this little guy?" he asks, wiping his forehead with a handkerchief. "How about Flame? See how his head sticks out, orange and yellow?"

"Yeah, sure," I say. And then, heart hammering, I ask, "Grandpa, why'd you decide to come here? Why now?"

"Last week," he says, "the lightning in my blood started screaming. Shouting that there was no time left. 'Find her! Save her!'" He gives a little shiver. "Any leads, mijo?"

A grin spreads over my face. "Just found her online, Grandpa." I pull out my phone, open the Wiki page, zoom in on her photo.

Grandpa fumbles with his glasses and squints at the tiny screen. For a long time he drinks in her picture, cradling the phone in his palms like a long-lost treasure. Raindrop flaps and chirps in his right pocket, and Flame tries to climb out of the left one, but Grandpa is oblivious to everything but Esma.

"She did it," he says finally, under his breath.

I take the phone and scroll down, reading the Wiki entry aloud, translating awkwardly to Spanish. When I click on the link to her song, it rises up like a wild storm over the beige houses and identical lawns. Suddenly, there's a rain shower of magic over my neighborhood.

Grandpa must feel it, too. His eyes are closed and his face is leaning back to the sky, blissed-out.

Mom honks the horn again and calls out, "What's going on, guys?"

Grandpa puts a finger to his lips, gives me a secret grin, and we return to the car as if nothing happened. Well, except for the new baby turtle in his pocket.

CONTACT

*G*randpa Teo and I don't get a chance to talk alone until the next morning after Mom and Dad have left for work. I've convinced them to let me skip soccer camp today, told them Grandpa and I would probably spend the day on nature walks. Mom frowned and said, "No more rescued creatures, okay? We're not an animal shelter here."

Grandpa promised, "We'll be good, mija."

Our real plan, of course, is to spend the whole day looking for Esma. I'm sitting with him at the sunny kitchen table, just the two of us, munching on bagels with cream cheese and feeding Flame in one cardboard box and Raindrop in another. Flame shuffles around, picking at bits of lettuce, while Raindrop peeps and pokes her tiny beak into a dish of oatmeal.

It feels comfortable with Grandpa here, even though it's weird he's never had a bagel with cream cheese before. He's brought the ancient smell of wood smoke and incense into our home, a piece of the Hill of Dust. If magic had a scent, this would be it. And he's brought the cute-magic of Flame and Raindrop, rustling and flapping around on the table.

But most of the magic is coming from Esma's music, blasting on the stereo. I've downloaded all her albums, but the one called *The Impossible Caravan* is my favorite. I keep catching the word *Teo* here and there, at least I think I do—the songs are in Romani.

Grandpa sways to the melodies, peering at an image search of Esma on my phone. In the black-and-white pictures, she's a young woman, so beautiful with those exotic eyes. The later color photos show her as a middle-aged woman with wrinkles fanning over her cheeks, decked out in bright scarves and gold jewelry and sparkling coins that make her look like a queen.

After the fourth song, Grandpa Teo closes his eyes and shouts over the music, "Is she alive?"

"I think so, Grandpa," I shout back, then turn down the stereo. "I mean, I'm not seeing a date of death anywhere."

He breathes out in relief. "Can you find out where she lives?"

"That's trickier," I admit, spreading cream cheese on a second bagel.

His face falls.

Quickly, I add, "But hey, nothing's impossible, right?"

It does require some detective work, but nothing my phone can't handle. Within an hour, I've found the number of Esma's music agency, called, and explained the situation. Thankfully, the agent's friendly, because talking to random strangers on the phone freaks me out a little. When I mention that my grandfather is the Teo in Esma's songs, the lady gets superexcited and starts talking really fast. She says that years ago Esma instructed her agency to give her phone number to Teo if he ever called.

"Awesome," I say, jotting down the number with a nearly dried-out pen.

In a hesitant voice, the agent adds, "You should know that Esma hasn't been performing for several years."

It sounds like she's about to say more, but then she stops herself and just adds, "She lives in Pennsylvania. Good luck. Send her my best."

"Where's Pennsylvania?" Grandpa asks eagerly after I recap the conversation.

"Just one state away from here," I tell him, my pulse zooming.

"Let's go, Mateo!"

"Now?"

"Yes!" He stands up, puts on his hat and suit jacket. "She needs me. It's my turn to save her."

"Um, we have to call first. To get the address."

Grandpa looks about to burst. "Go ahead!"

Bagels churning in my stomach, I call, getting ready for the weirdest phone conversation ever.

A girl answers.

"Um, hi," I begin, picking at the wood grain of the kitchen table. "Is Esma there?"

"She's still at the rehab center." A pause. "Can I ask who's calling?"

"Um, yeah, I'm Mateo. I'm Teo's grandson. He used to be friends with her and—"

"Teo!" the girl shrieks. "Did you say Teo? Her loyal friend for life?"

Ouch. I move the phone away from my ear. "Yeah."

Who knows if she hears me, though, since she's still squealing like a hyper puppy. "Really? Teo's looking for her? Oh my gosh, I've heard so much about him! She always said he'd find her one day. When he was ready. So he's ready?"

"Yeah, definitely." I try to stay cool, but I really feel like jumping up and down. "He wants to see her."

"Oh my gosh, yes! I'm there with her every afternoon during summer break. I'm her granddaughter. My name's Ruby. I'm thirteen, so I just bike over, but it's not too far. Ready? I'll give you the address, okay?"

"Uh, let me get a pen." I rush over to the junk drawer, sifting through pens for one that works. I'm actually sweating with the craziness of this, trying to wrap my head around it. *I'm talking to Esma's granddaughter. And we'll be meeting the Queen herself soon. This is it.*

The whole time, Grandpa is watching me, wide-eyed.

I find a pencil stub and copy down the room number and

address. This is all moving so fast, my hand is shaking and so sweaty I keep losing my grip on the pencil.

"Okay, cool," I say, collecting my thoughts and folding the paper into a tiny, tight square. "I don't know for sure when we'll be there—I mean, I guess my mom could drive us, maybe this weekend or next." I look at Grandpa, so hopeful. He'll want to know how she's doing. "And, uh, what do you mean, rehab center?"

Ruby gets quiet. "It's like a hospital, sort of. Sort of an old folks' home." She sighs. "My grandmom's been there a couple months now. It's like a place where people go to get better. Or to die."

Silence. "Is Esma okay?" I glance at Grandpa's beaming face, glad he doesn't understand English.

"She got cancer."

Sucking in a breath, I grip the pencil and shut my eyes. When I open them, Grandpa knows something's wrong. A dark cloud drifts over his face. He might not understand English, but he's an expert at seeing feelings in the spaces between words.

Ruby goes on. "She had chemo and it was awful, but the cancer's gone now. Or at least in remission."

The tightness in my chest lets up, but only a little, because of the somber tone of Ruby's voice. "The chemo damaged her vocal cords. She can barely even whisper now. That's why there's no point in me giving you her phone number. And . . ." Her voice grows quiet. "She can't sing."

I swallow hard. "Oh, man. Bummer." And then I flush, because what kind of stupid thing is that to say?

"It is a bummer," Ruby agrees. "The doctors said she might get her voice back with therapy, but she's been really weak and depressed and . . . I don't know. We don't know. She says she's no one without her voice." There's a pause, and then she adds, "It's like she's on the verge of giving up. On everything. On life. It scares me."

Silence. I study the pattern on the tile floor, black-and-white linoleum squares, speckled with bagel crumbs. I wish Mom were making this phone call; she'd know how to handle it.

Ruby speaks again, forcefully. "You need to come soon. Like, today!"

"Today?" I sputter. "But—"

"Nothing's impossible!"

I glance at Grandpa's stricken face and draw in a deep breath. Pennsylvania's just a state away, right? It can't take that long to get there. "Okay," I say, "um, I guess we'll be there this afternoon."

THE MISSION

*M*om freaks out when I text her to say we're in Dad's beat-up old truck, on the highway, halfway to Pennsylvania, on the way to see the Queen of Lightning.

She calls me immediately.

"Mateo! What the—? Does that truck even run? And is your grandpa even allowed to drive without a U.S. license?"

"Yup and yup. We looked it up. For the short-term, he can use his Mexican license."

"¡Dios mío! How on earth do you know where you're going?"

"The GPS on my phone." I finger the ripped brown vinyl seat. "We're fine, Mom."

"Mateo, put me on speaker. No wait, don't! I don't want to distract my dad and cause an accident. Has he ever driven on anything bigger than a one-lane road? Or over thirty miles an hour?"

I grin. He's grasping the steering wheel, knuckles white, eyes squinting in concentration. "Well, he's not driving much faster than that now." Cars zoom by as we chug along in the right lane.

Mom does deep yoga breathing. "Tell him to pull over to an exit. I'll pick you guys up."

I suck in a breath of sun-baked vinyl, roll down the window for fresh air. "Mom, we're fine."

"Oh, Mateo, why couldn't this wait till tomorrow?"

Unsure how to answer, I pull the coin necklace from my pocket, watch it glint and whip in the wind. I've brought it along for good luck.

"Mateo?" Mom says. "You still there?"

There's only one way to say this. "Tomorrow could be too late. Esma's been sick. She needs us now."

Silence. "She's real? You're sure of it? I mean, my dad hardly talked about her. And all the aunts and uncles made her sound like a fairy tale. And your grandma said it was just imaginary nonsense."

"Esma's real. Look her up, Mom. Esmeralda Rayos, Gypsy Queen of Lightning." Saying the words sends a little shiver up my spine. A shiver of anticipation and dread at once. Who knows how this trip will turn out? I gather the necklace into my palm, let it give me courage, then slip it back into my pocket.

More deep breathing on the other end of the phone. "Okay, be safe. Text me when you get there. You have your seat belt on, right, hon?"

From the floor by my feet, Raindrop suddenly flutters up, chirping, and I drop the phone to catch her. Grandpa swerves and then reaches out his hand for the bird. A car in the next lane over honks.

I grab the phone, which has fallen into Flame's box. Fumbling, I press it to my ear.

"What's going on there?" Mom screeches. "Are you okay?"

"Just dropped the phone for a sec."

"But what was that honking and chirping? You didn't bring that bird, did you?"

"Look, I have to give Grandpa directions. Bye, Mom. Love you." I hang up, silence the phone, stick it in the glove compartment.

"Everything all right?" Grandpa asks, stroking Raindrop's head, now happily poking out of his pocket.

"Great." I look at him, his neck straining forward like a turtle's, focused on the highway. I should prepare him for what we might find. But I still can't bring myself to tell him that Esma's giving up on life. I think that, somehow, he already knows.

According to my phone's directions, we should have arrived in two hours, at three o'clock, but since we went about thirty miles below the speed limit, we don't get there till five.

The rehab center is a low brick building with a fountain in the front and woods in the back. Not too bad from the outside, but when we step inside, I nearly gag on the mix of cleaner and pee smells. I try to hold my breath while I ask the lady at the front desk how to get to room 21. But I have to breathe as we walk down the hallways—we could be in here a while.

The patients freak me out, big-time. They're scattered in wheelchairs along the hallways, just watching us go by, some drooling, some muttering. One old lady is clutching a baby doll. Creepy. If the *opposite* of magic exists, this place is it.

Grandpa senses my discomfort and keeps one hand on my shoulder as we search for room 21. His other hand moves between Flame and Raindrop in his suit pockets. Birds and turtles have to be against the rules, but Grandpa insisted that they'd get heatstroke inside the parked truck. The nurses are too busy to notice the creatures' beaks poking out, even when the patients point and exclaim.

Grandpa Teo pats my shoulder. "Mateo, just wait till you hear Esma's voice in real life. It'll make everything better."

My gut twists around with guilt. I'm in over my head. He came all the way from the Hill of Dust, dreaming of Esma's voice, hoping to save her, and now I've brought him to this horrible, stinky place. And when he steps into room 21 and sees what's happened to her, his heart will break.

I weave my fingers through the necklace in my pocket. "Grandpa, there's something I didn't tell you. Esma—she can't talk anymore. Or sing. Cancer treatments messed up her voice."

He stops in the middle of the hallway, his hand to his mouth.

Being the bearer of bad news is the worst, but I force myself to tell him exactly what Ruby told me. I stare at the pastel pictures of sailboats and seashells on the wall because I can't meet his eyes.

Afterward, he nods grimly and pats my shoulder. "Let's go, mijo."

We start walking again and within seconds run into a girl about my age, striding down the hallway like a breath of fresh air. She has chin-length dark hair and silvery eyes lined in black. She looks a little goth, with a ripped black tank and a short black skirt. But there's a silky pink flowered scarf wrapped around her hair that makes her look like an old-time movie star.

All our eyes meet and she ventures, "Mr. Teo?"

I point with my chin to Grandpa, and she throws her arms around him.

"I'm sorry, sir, it's just that I feel like I know you. I'm Ruby. I gave up on you coming today, but look, here you are! Come in!"

I translate her words as she tugs on Grandpa's hand and pulls him into room 21.

And there, beside a hospital bed, in a wheelchair, face silhouetted against the window, is Esma, Queen of Lightning. Oxygen tubes trail like vines beneath her nostrils, over her ears, and tangle with an IV taped to her hand. She's wearing a dress covered in red roses, and necklaces of beads and shells and coins, and a scarf over her head. Just a few short wisps of hair poke out. Her face is made up, and for some reason, it makes me want to cry.

Yup, she is real, so real I want to run from the room.

"Esma?" Grandpa says.

She turns to face him, straightens up, raises her chin.

Warily, I wait to see what will happen. Will he run to her, drop to his knees, embrace her? It's been fifty years. Ruby, too, is watching expectantly.

But there's only awkwardness, the drone of the news on TV, the beeping of machines, the calls of nurses in the hallway, the rambling of patients in rooms next door.

Self-consciously, Esma tears the tubes from her nose, rips the IV from her hand. She straightens the scarf on her head. On a pad of paper on a TV tray, she writes something, passes it to Grandpa.

I look over his shoulder; I can't help it. It's in Spanish, in the same old-fashioned handwriting from the postcard and letter she wrote years ago.

> *Ruby said you'd be here a while ago. I thought*
> *you'd changed your mind.*

Grandpa Teo puts on his reading glasses and studies the paper. He seems to have lost his voice, too. And it's like he forgets she can still hear.

I answer for him, in Spanish so he can understand. "My granddad's a pretty slow driver," I say over the TV newscaster's voice. "I'm Mateo." Mustering up courage, I reach out and shake her hand, spotted purple from the IV.

"Grandmom," Ruby says, picking up the remote and muting the TV, "you should probably keep those tubes in, right?"

292

I DON'T CARE! Esma writes, pressing hard with the pen. She looks at Grandpa, then scrawls more.

Grandpa gestures for me to read the paper alongside him, leaning on my shoulder, like he needs my support. Poor guy, I'm not the right one to do this. This is a colossal mistake. Why didn't I just let Mom handle it all?

> *It's too late. I don't want you to see me like this. I wish you'd seen me onstage for thousands of people, singing my heart out. Not like this.*

Finally, Grandpa speaks. "But this is when you need me, isn't it?"

Something is passing between the two of them. Still, Grandpa seems unable to step forward and touch her.

And it's suddenly so sad and awkward, I can hardly stand it. It's painful, seeing this reunion with the mythical, miraculous girl who turns out to be real and sick and old.

Uncomfortable small talk fills the silence, started by Ruby and translated by me, the usual boring questions about marriage and children and jobs and weather. It's not the kind of conversation you'd wait fifty years for, not the kind of conversation you'd even drive a half day for on the highway at thirty miles an hour. During pauses, everyone's eyes drift toward the TV.

The small talk topics are nearly exhausted when, thankfully, a nurse pops her head in. "Last call for dinner! Should I wheel you to the dining room?"

Grandpa shifts to his other foot and says, "We'd better head back now. We should get home before dark."

As I translate, tears fill Ruby's eyes, and the black makeup smears as she wipes them. It makes me feel terrible, so terrible that I mutter to Grandpa in Spanish, "Hug Esma good-bye or something."

Tentatively, he steps toward her, bends down, and gives her a stiff pat on the shoulder.

She gives his hand an equally stiff pat in return.

Quickly, he steps back. "*Pues, adiós*, Esma," he says, not meeting her eyes.

She offers a half-hearted wave, her eyes already flicking back to the muted TV.

I'm not big on sappy scenes, but even the sappiest, pukiest scene in the world would be better than this.

Waving a limp good-bye to Ruby, Grandpa and I trudge back down the hallway.

"You can only save people if they want to be saved," he says, catching a tear from the corner of his eye. "Nearly my whole life, I tried to save my mother. Your Other Grandmother. I never could. Looks like I can't save Esma now either."

"Bummer," I say under my breath in English. "Major bummer."

"What?" he asks hoarsely.

"Nada, Grandpa." Nothing.

42

RIBBONS

*W*e're just passing the lady with the baby doll when Grandpa blows his nose, then says, "You know, Mateo, all my life I believed you'd be friends with that girl, Ruby."

I stop, turn to face him. Lite rock music trickles faintly from ceiling speakers. A nurse wheels an empty chair past us. The lady with the baby doll coos.

I find words. "Uh, what are you talking about, Grandpa?"

Leaning against the wall, he rubs his face. "You know that time I died?"

I nod, as if that's a perfectly normal question.

"Remember what my grandfather's spirit told me?" he says slowly. "The thing that made me want to live again."

I scan through that part of his story, and then, with a jolt, I remember. The thing about the grandkids! "He said Esma's and your grandkids would be friends. For life."

I nearly slap my forehead. How did I not realize this sooner? Like back when I was on the phone with Ruby? Or when we met in the hallway? I was so caught up in reuniting Esma and Grandpa, I forgot about the grandkid thing.

It hits me hard in the gut, like I've just belly-flopped off a high-dive . . . how much *sense* it makes. Ruby's the only other kid in the world who understands our grandparents' impossible fortune, who wants to bring that magic into our world, here and now. Of course I'm destined to be friends with her. It's what I've wanted all my life.

Suddenly, everything shines in a new light—the pale flowered wallpaper, the nubby purple carpet, the baby doll's plastic head. Everything is *possibility.*

The coin necklace is practically dancing in my pocket, alive with crazy electricity. I pull it out and let it wind around my fingers. And now I'm buzzing with lightning and the feeling that nothing is impossible.

"Grandpa," I begin, figuring things out as I go. "What if Esma does want to be saved? I mean, you could've tried harder back there, right? Listen, I can help you. Together—"

He pats my shoulder. "Oh, Mateo, many things happened over the past fifty years. Things—"

A sudden flutter of feathers interrupts him. Something brown and tiny flits in the air between us.

It's Raindrop. She's flown out of Grandpa's pocket. With her injured wing, she hangs crookedly above our heads for a moment, gives us a look of impatience. Then she makes a lop-sided flight back down the hallway.

No nurses notice, but the lady in the wheelchair props up her doll to give it a better view.

Grandpa and I follow the bird down the blue carpet as she darts into Esma's room. On the way in, I whisper, "Try harder this time, Grandpa."

A fresh look of determination sweeps over his face.

Inside, the bird rests on the windowsill beside Esma.

Stunned, Esma looks at the sparrow and then at Grandpa Teo, hovering in the doorway beside me.

And for the first time on our visit, Esma smiles.

"Esma, meet Raindrop," Grandpa says, laughing. "Looks like she doesn't want to leave you. Want to keep her?"

I translate for Ruby, adding in Spanish and English, "I doubt this place allows birds." Great, I sound like Mom.

Grandpa pulls Flame from his pocket. "Then how about a turtle?"

Esma smiles bigger. A hoarse whisper, like the echo of a laugh, creaks out. On her notepad, she writes, *Let's get some fresh air.*

Yes, I think. *Let's get out of here.* I translate for Ruby, who nods with relief, tucks the notepad beneath her arm, and maneuvers Esma down the hall.

Outside, I gulp the early evening air. It's still sunny and humid, and the roses give off a sweet, hopeful scent. We head down the paved path, into the woods behind the building. Ahead, Grandpa insists on pushing Esma in the wheelchair, talking to her softly in Spanish as they go.

I can't help sneaking glances at the girl destined to be my lifelong friend. That silky scarf in her hair is really cool. And she kind of bounces on her toes as she walks, like the world is her inflatable castle.

She catches me staring, and for a second, our eyes meet. I panic, because it's not every day that a pretty girl looks at me this way, so open and curious. A pretty girl I'm *destined* to be friends with.

Unsure what to do, on an impulse, I hand her the necklace from my pocket.

"Cool," she says, holding it up, staring at its silhouette against the blue sky, listening to the music of the breeze through it. Maybe it's the necklace, but something releases a river of words pent up inside her.

"Okay, Mateo, that's your name, right? Well, I have so many ideas, and none of my friends get them, but maybe you will, 'cause, well, you know . . . but listen, wouldn't it be cool to make a Romani caravan and paint it amazing colors and hook it up to a truck and drive it all the way down to the Hill of Dust? Like you and me and my grandmom and your granddad? And oh, another thing is I'm starting this Gypsy rock band and I can sing and play violin, but I need someone else, and do you play an instrument? Wouldn't that be awesome? And also, I really want to taste homemade tortillas and maybe learn how to make them, the ones ground on stone and cooked over a fire, because my grandmom always talks about them and we've been to, like, a hundred Mexican restaurants looking for them and we even went to Cancun but they're never as good as the ones on the Hill of Dust, 'cause it's, like, the Hill of Dust is pure magic, you know?"

Ruby bites her lip, suddenly embarrassed. "Oh, gosh, Mateo, I never talk this much, it's just that I've been saving up all my ideas for someone who actually cares and now you're here and I can't stop blabbing!"

She slaps her hand over her mouth. Above, her black-rimmed eyes are smiling.

I clear my throat and say quietly, "I took a woodworking class. Made a stool." I shrug. "How much harder can a wagon be?"

A happy squeal pops from behind her hand.

I keep going. "I've played drums since second grade. And I'm learning guitar."

Another squeal.

"And it's true," I say, "there's nothing like the tortillas on the Hill of Dust. They'll taste extra good after a superlong caravan ride there."

Her eyes widen to twice their normal size. If eyes could scream with laughter, that's what hers are doing now.

I feel my own eyes grow big with excitement. "My aunt Perla could teach you to make tortillas in her little kitchen hut. The best part's how your hair smells like wood smoke the whole time."

Ruby removes her hand from her mouth, revealing the world's biggest grin. Her teeth are straight and white, and her lips very pink. "That's it! That's what I want! Exactly! Tell me more about the Hill of Dust, every tiny detail."

As we walk down the path through the woods, I tell her.

And she listens.

And she gets it.

Afterward, she gives me a sideways glance. "Anyone ever tell you your eyelashes are amazing?"

Heat spreads from my cheeks to my toes. Then I whisper, "Anyone ever tell you that for fifty years we've been destined to be friends for life?"

Once we're deep in the forest, with only bits of golden sunshine sprinkled through the leaves, Esma raises her hand to say stop. We're on a bridge over a small stream. I wipe sweat from my neck and watch the water trickle by, spots of light swimming over the surface.

Shakily, Esma stands up.

Grandpa takes one elbow, and Ruby takes another. "Sure you can stand, Grandmom?"

Esma straightens up, tilts back her head, and opens her mouth. A raspy sound emerges.

Some kind of seizure? Or a stroke? I'm about to ask Ruby whether we should call 911 when Grandpa Teo throws back his own head, opens his mouth, and screams. It makes my heart jump, this thundering sound, incredibly loud for an old man.

Still screaming, he wraps his arm around Esma's shoulder. Looking strangely satisfied, Ruby sits down on a nearby log. I sit beside her, my heart beating like crazy. "What's going on?"

"Screaming at the stream!" she declares.

"Oh, right." The corner of my mouth turns up in a bewildered smile. "My grandpa told me about this."

The screaming freaks me out at first, but soon I relax. They seem so happy with their screams—Grandpa's loud, Esma's nearly silent. For a while I watch them, and then my eyes move to the reflections off the river, flashing like tiny bolts of lightning.

It's a strange thing, how their screams eventually fade into laughter, his loud, hers breathy.

Ruby turns to me. "Know what my grandmom always said? That Teo helped her discover her true power. That she owes, like, every success in life to him."

I think about this. "She helped my grandpa discover his power, too. I mean, he probably wouldn't have become the famous Doctor Teo without her."

Ruby's voice drops to a whisper. "Know something crazy? My grandmom was married and divorced four times."

I don't want to admit I already know it from Wiki, so I just say, "Wow."

"She was looking for Teo in every man. She could never find him. Not till now."

In front of us, Esma and Grandpa stand close. She leans into him, and he lets his arm settle on her hip. I can't help listening to their conversation.

"So, my friend for life," Grandpa asks, "how has life as a lion's head been?"

Pressing her lips in a girlish smile, she writes something on her paper, hands it to him, chuckling in her wheezy way.

He reads it and nods. "When you're old, you don't need to be the head of anything, do you? You can just grow like a tree, something with feet in the earth and hands in the sky and water flowing through it." Grandpa Teo pulls her closer, gives her head a light tap with his fingertip.

I can barely hear him whisper, "Oh, squash head. Let's be trees together."

Ruby elbows me, whispers, "Translate!"

I obey, and she gets a melty look in her eyes. "They do look like trees, leaning against each other, don't they?"

I nod. "It's like, even though they lived so far from each other, they were holding each other up this whole time. Like their roots were all tangled together."

"Yes!" Ruby says, giving me another sideways look that sends shivers through me, the good kind. Her arm brushes mine. It feels like there's something alive, buzzing and sparking in that tiny, warm space between our skin. "Guess we'll be seeing a lot of each other this summer," she says. Her eyes flash, silver and playful.

"Guess so," I say, feeling something big welling up inside me. "Building a caravan's a lot of work."

Suddenly, Ruby's hand flies up to my shoulder. "Look!" she whispers, her voice full of wonder.

I follow her gaze and see Esma raising her arms like branches of a tree, slowly turning in a circle.

Grandpa reaches up to take her hand and twirls her, ever so slowly, in a strange, slow dance.

Together, they spin like ancient planets.

Then Esma's song emerges, rising over the trees and into our cores. It's a single, warbling note, without words, raspy and soft.

Still, it's a song.

And as the two spin together, sunshine dances on the water, and I could swear I see two silver ribbons of light, one from her chest, the other from his, weaving together and swirling into the sky.

Author's Note

INSPIRATION

I felt fortunate to form meaningful friendships with Mixteco people when I took a teaching position in the remote mountains of Oaxaca, Mexico. For two years, I was welcomed into Mixteco communities, first as a teacher and later as an anthropologist studying their culture. During this time, I heard stories about the beloved *gitanos*, whose caravans had shown movies in this region years earlier. I knew that gitanos (also known as Rom or Gypsies) have been misunderstood throughout the world, so I was intrigued by how fondly local people spoke of them. Like the Rom, the Mixteco have also faced prejudice and racist treatment for centuries. I felt drawn to explore the fascinating relationship between these two cultures.

As I developed this story, I wove in realistic and mystical elements of oral histories I heard in Mixteco villages. The initial spark for this book came from the experiences of a ninety-six-year-old healer named María López Martinez (lovingly nicknamed María Chiquita—María the Little One). When she was a young girl, a *gitana* fortune-teller told her she would live a very long life. Shortly after her fortune, she grew ill and appeared to die. Inside their hut, her family held a candlelit vigil over her apparently dead body. At one point during the mourning, a drop of candle wax fell onto María Chiquita's body. Somehow, it woke her from death!

She told me that her time in the other realm gave her powers to become a healer. She lived to age ninety-seven, and near the end of her life, she proudly pointed out that the gitana's prediction had come true. I returned to María Chiquita's village for her cabo de año—the candlelit one-year anniversary of her death. I'm grateful to continue a friendship with her daughter, granddaughter, and great-granddaughter.

THE MIXTECO PEOPLE

In my novels, it's important to me to include not only the mystical parts of a culture, but also the tough realities that have shaped its experiences. Before living in Oaxaca, I had focused on indigenous—or native—rights issues for my anthropology studies. Once I moved there, I got a firsthand look at the injustices these cultures have faced for centuries.

As of the 2010 census, indigenous people made up 13 percent of Mexico's population. They speak a total of sixty-two different native languages. Oaxaca, the state where I lived and where this story is set, has the second-highest indigenous population (at 58 percent). (*Comisión Nacional para el Desarrollo de los Pueblos Indígenas, México, cdi.gob.mx.*)

There are over a dozen indigenous groups within Oaxaca, the Mixteco culture being most common where I lived. In rural communities, some people still speak Mixteco, close to the language spoken in pre-Hispanic times. Many of my friends have kept alive not only their ancestors' language, but also their traditions, adapting them to modern life. I studied these practices in my fieldwork on Mixtecos' ideas about illness and healing, some of which appear in this book.

In the 1500s, after the Spaniards arrived in what is now Mexico, over 90 percent of the indigenous population died from violence, forced labor, and disease. The colonial government imposed a caste—or rigid class—system. They placed the indigenous people at the bottom and those with Spanish ancestry at the top. Over the years, these groups mixed, and the ethnic category mestizo—or mixed race—was born. Mestizos, too, had more privilege and prestige than indigenous people.

During the early to mid-twentieth century, with the Mexican Revolution, the general population began to view indigenous people as the true foundation of Mexican society. Artists like Frida Kahlo and Diego Rivera honored native cultures. In the later part of the century, indigenous rights movements led the government to take more measures to respect indigenous languages and cultures. One such governmental effort was the creation of bilingual education (Spanish and the local indigenous language) in the 1970s.

Unfortunately, despite some progress, indigenous people are still marginalized—unjustly pushed to the edges of society.

In most communities, indigenous Mexicans live with higher poverty rates, much lower literacy rates, and much higher infant death rates than the general population. They have less access to quality education and health care, and often experience discrimination and racism.

During the mid-1900s—the setting of Teo's story—indigenous students could be physically punished for speaking their native language at school. Some of my middle-aged friends in Oaxaca described to me how the teacher smacked their hands with rulers when they were children. This made them feel ashamed of their native tongue, discouraging them from later speaking Mixteco as adults. Even in the late 1990s, when I lived in Mexico, I noticed that the word *indio*—Indian—was used as an insult, often together with words like *dirty*, *poor*, or *ignorant*. I've noticed hypocrisy in how indigenous people are treated. Pre-Hispanic cultures are highly valued, yet their modern-day descendants are marginalized.

My Mixteco friends are intelligent, hardworking, warm, fun, welcoming people who often speak several languages and hold a wealth of fascinating knowledge. Some of the stories they've told me feel enchanting—like María Chiquita's. Others upset me—like stories of being punished for speaking their native language. In writing this book, I've tried to balance the magical parts with the gritty reality. Ultimately, I want to honor the way that many indigenous people—including children—have resisted oppression and created positive change for themselves and future generations.

THE ROMANI PEOPLE

For centuries, the origin of the Rom was a mystery. Now, based on linguistic and genetic evidence, we know that about a thousand years ago, the Rom first left India and spread across Europe.

There is no accurate data for the number of Romani people in the world, in part because the Rom often choose not to register their ethnicity in official censuses. In Europe alone, Romani population estimates range from between four million and fourteen million. Several million more Rom live in the Americas.

Traditionally, the Rom traveled by caravan in groups that specialized in certain skills, from musical entertainment to metalworking. Today, some are still nomadic, and some have settled. It's remarkable that although Rom on different continents have adopted certain practices of their host countries, they have kept a core cultural identity and language for so long.

Unfortunately, over the past millennia, most Rom across the world have also suffered from misunderstanding and discrimination. Europeans thought they came from Egypt and began calling them *Gyps*ies, spreading rumors that they were thieves and child stealers. During the Middle Ages, they were enslaved, and over the past several centuries, persecuted. Many people don't know that the Rom were among the millions of people massacred in Nazi concentration camps.

In Europe today, the Romani people are still mistreated. Many are forced to move their camps or settle in substandard homes. Many have access to only poor-quality education and health care. Many face discrimination in jobs and are victims of race-related hate crimes. Meanwhile, most governments do little to protect Romani people's basic human rights.

Sadly, many non-Rom around the world aren't aware of these injustices. Instead, they have only a romantic idea of gypsies (lowercase) as simple, carefree, happy-go-lucky wanderers. International human rights movements are trying to raise awareness and promote social justice for Romani people.

Largely to escape persecution, many Rom have immigrated to the Americas over the past five hundred years. The greatest waves of Rom came between the late 1800s and mid-1900s. These subgroups of Romani people came mainly from Romania, Yugoslavia (Bosnia), Hungary, Poland, Russia, Greece, France, Turkey, and Spain. Some groups first settled in the United States or South America, and then migrated to Mexico.

Although I easily found information about the Rom in Europe, it was much harder to find sources on their presence in Mexico. The Rom have been dehistorified, as described by David Lagunas of the National School of Anthropology and History in Mexico. "They do not appear in the history of Mexico," he says. "We know very little about them." ("Gypsies, or How to be Invisible in Mexico," *IPS News Agency*.)

After much searching, I finally came across several works about the Romani culture in Mexico. I was fascinated to learn more about the traveling cinema (cine ambulante), which was popular work for the Rom in Mexico in the mid-1900s.

Since the spread of VCRs in the 1980s, few groups still practice cine ambulante (now traveling in trucks and campers). As alternatives, many Rom have turned to machine repair; buying and selling vehicles; and performing theater, magic, and clowning.

I was especially thrilled to come across several narratives by gitanos in Mexico. In one, Alfredo Yovani reminisced about his days of cine ambulante: "In the forgotten villages where nothing [new] ever came, the people would become happy [to see us]. We knew just what films they liked . . . Wherever we'd go, it was a novelty. Everyone was excited about the films. It was wonderful work . . . and we traveled around, very content." (*Piel de Carpa: Los Gitanos de México*, p. 66.)

I was happy to discover that the Mixteco villagers' fondness for the Rom was mutual. In the midst of so much prejudice, these two groups embraced each other with appreciation and respect. Now if only the rest of the world could follow their lead . . .

Mexican Spanish-English
GLOSSARY AND PRONUNCIATION GUIDE

agua de jamaica (AHG-wah day hah-MY-kah): sweet hibiscus water

agua de papaya (AHG-wah day pah-PY-ah): sweet papaya water

ahorita vengo (ow-REE-tah VAYN-goh): I'll be there in a second

amigo (ah-MEE-goh): friend

atole (ah-TOH-lay): traditional indigenous Mexican corn drink

brujo (BROO-hoh): witch (male)

buenas noches (BWAY-nahs NOH-chays): good evening/good night

buenos días (BWAY-nohs DEE-ahs): hello/good morning

cabo de año (CAH-boh day AHN-yoh): ceremony for the first anniversary of a person's death

centavos (sayn-TAH-vohs): cents

chile (CHEE-lay): chili

cine ambulante (SEE-nay ahm-boo-LAHN-tay): traveling cinema

curandero (coo-rahn-DAY-roh): healer

Dios mío (dee-OHS MEE-oh): my God

diositos (dee-oh-SEE-tohs): "little gods," statues from pre-Hispanic cultures

el monte (ayl MOHN-tay): the countryside/hilly pastures outside of town

gracias (GRAH-see-ahs): thank you

huevos estrellados (WAY-vohs ays-tray-AH-dohs): fried eggs

huipil (WEE-peel): traditional, handmade indigenous women's tunic

indio (EEN-dee-oh): Indian. Can be an offensive term, used as an insult throughout Latin America. The respectful alternative is *indígena* (indigenous person).

La Devoradora (lah day-vohr-ah-DOHR-ah): the devourer/the man-eating woman (a classic Mexican film)

La Mujer Sin Alma (lah moo-HAYRR seen AHL-mah*): the woman without a soul / the heartless woman (a classic Mexican film)

limpia (LEEM-pee-ah): spiritual cleansing ceremony

los viejitos (lohs vee-ay-HEE-tohs): the old people (affectionate term)

maestra (mah-AYS-trah): teacher (female)

Mamá (mah-MAH): Mom

más o menos (MAHS oh MAY-nohs): so-so, more or less

maza (MAH-sah): tortilla dough

mija (MEE-hah): my daughter (contraction of "mi hija")

mijo (MEE-hoh): my son (contraction of "mi hijo")

milpa (MEEL-pah): cornfield

mole (MOH-lay): chocolate-chili sauce, a traditional food in Oaxaca, Mexico

momentito (moh-mayn-TEE-toh): just a moment

nada (NAH-dah): nothing

314

Nosotros los Pobres (no-SOH-trohs lohs POH-brays): We the Poor (a classic Mexican film)

oye (OH-yay): hey

pan dulce (PAHN DOOL-say): sweet roll

panela (pah-NAY-lah): raw, whole, brown cane sugar

Papá (pah-PAH): Dad

petate (pay-TAH-tay): woven palm mat

pobre (POH-bray): poor

pobrecita (poh-bray-SEE-tah): poor thing (female)

pobrecito (poh-bray-SEE-toh): poor thing (male)

por favor (pohrr fah-VOHRR*): please

pues, adiós (PWAYS ah-dee-OHS): well, good-bye

querido (kay-REE-doh): dear

ranchera (rrahn-CHAY-rah*): a traditional style of Mexican music

ruda (RROO-dah*): rue, an herb used in spiritual cleansing ceremonies

señor (sayn-YOHRR*): sir, mister

señora (sayn-YOH-rah): ma'am, lady

señorita (sayn-yohr-EE-tah): miss (young lady)

tamal (tah-MAHL): tamale (singular form)

* *"rr" represents a rolled r*

Mixteco-English

GLOSSARY AND PRONUNCIATION GUIDE

Note that Mixteco includes several dialects, and can vary even from village to village; spelling can vary as well. The dialect I've used is spoken in the village of San Agustín Atenango, in the Mixteca Baja region. Mixteco is a tonal language, so the meaning of a word can change depending on whether your voice goes up or down.

yo'o sunii* (joh-oh soo-neee): I'm fine

yo'o naa yo* (joh-oh naah joh): hello/good day/good morning (formal)

taxiini (tah-sheee-nee): calm down

kuu ini (kooo ee-nee): love

sikita'an* (see-kee-tah-ahn): hug

ñamani (nyah-mah-nee): please

nixi yo'o?* (nee-shee joh-oh): how are you?

tatsavini (taht-sah-vee-nee): thank you (formal)

yeu (jay-oo): good

* The apostrophe represents a glottal stop, similar to the sound represented by the "-" in "uh-oh." You stop airflow in your windpipe for a split second.

Romani-English
GLOSSARY AND PRONUNCIATION GUIDE

Romani dialects vary from country to country, and even from group to group within a country. Most Rom in Mexico nowadays speak Spanish and/or some form of Spanish-Romani, which includes some Spanish words interspersed in the traditional Romani language. Spelling can also vary widely; I've chosen to use the most standard.

boria (bo-ree-ah): women who have married into a family (daughters-in-law, sisters-in-law)

gadjé (ga-jay): non-Romani people

gadjo (ga-joh): non-Romani male

marime (ma-ree-may): unclean, polluted, impure, contaminated (a cultural concept)

Rom (rrom*): noun form for Gypsy**

Romani (rro-ma-nee*): adjective form for Gypsy

* "rr" represents a rolled r
** There are many different terms that the Rom use to refer to themselves, including Rrom, Řom, Roma, Rroma, Romani, Rromani, Řomani, Romany, Řomany, and Rromany. After weighing various expert opinions, I have chosen to use the term Rom as the noun form and Romani as the adjective form in this book. This was apparently the most common terminology among the Rom in the Americas in the mid-twentieth century, the setting of this story. Non-Romani Mexicans usually refer to the Rom as gitanos or húngaros (Hungarians), even though only one subgroup immigrated from Hungary.

Acknowledgments

With every new book there are even more wonderful people to thank! I've been thrilled to work with the enthusiastic team at Scholastic, who have been a burst of sunshine in my life. My talented and dedicated editor, Andrea Davis Pinkney, has been the brightest sunbeam of all. Andrea, I can't tell you how honored I feel to be creating with you. I also offer a heartfelt thanks to my brilliant agent, Erin Murphy, for connecting me with Andrea, and for being so much fun to work with over the past decade, along with Tara Gonzalez, Bon Vivant Dennis, and the other shining stars at Erin Murphy Literary Agency.

Mountains of gratitude go to early readers Carrie Visintainer, Chris Resau, Dana Masden, Janet Freeman, Jeannie Mobley, Karye Cattrell, Laura Pritchett, and Tara Dairman. *Abrazos* and gracias go to Gloria García Díaz, magnificent writer friend who offered valuable feedback on Mexican culture and Spanish language elements. My spirited tribe of Colorado writer friends and my beloved EMLA gang provided me with plenty of support and laughter along the way.

Laurie McMahon, an extraordinary teacher in Half Moon Bay (who knows my books better than I do), offered me precious feedback on this manuscript. I started writing this book in my head while walking along the succulent-covered sea cliffs of Half Moon Bay, feeling elated from a visit with Laurie's students and conversations with exuberant librarian Armando Ramirez (who shared some gitano memories from his own childhood). Thank you, fantastic Half Moon Bay community!

I couldn't have written this without inspiration from Fidelina López López and the late María Chiquita López Martinez, Oaxacan women who shared tales of the queridos gitanos, welcomed me to a beautiful cabo de año, and brought magic into my life. Other generous friends in the Mixteca—Melissa Ferrin and Marcelino Ramírez Ibañez—reviewed the manuscript and offered excellent suggestions. Their extended family, including Francisco Ibáñez Martínez and the late Catalina Ibáñez Martínez, graciously shared their memories of the gitanos and answered *un montón* of detailed questions about Mixteco villages in the mid-twentieth century. I am eternally grateful for your help.

Thanks, also, to Sonia Castro Pozos and her family for Mixteco language assistance and years of friendship. A giant gracias to Baruc Cruz Blanco and my other friends in Oaxaca who have welcomed me into their families' homes and shared their stories with me over the years. This book truly would not exist without you all.

A big thank-you to Baby Goose Grape, who sparked the idea for the rescued animal characters after becoming a brief but meaningful (and very cute and poopy) part of my life. Thanks, also, to Ronald Cree and Alexis Gerard, who kindly shared some fun and quirky animal stories of their own. Rob

Sparks, birder extraordinaire, was my awesome go-to guy for Mexican waterfowl questions. And I have Les Sunde and Kathleen Pelley to thank for their words of wisdom that found their way into this story. I'm also grateful to my creative young friend Roxi for her thoughtful title feedback.

A huge thanks to Charlie Cox, who, after our serendipitous encounter at the farmers' market, took the time to show me his gorgeous vintage caravans and share his knowledge of Romani culture. I'm indebted to Matt Salo of the Gypsy Lore Society for directing me to little-known academic sources and patiently answering my many questions about Romani culture, history, and language in Mexico.

My extended family has been an essential part of my writing journey since I was a young girl. Thanks to you all for your endless encouragement, especially Mom, Dad, Mike, Aunt Liz Neal, Susan and Bruce Hansen, Wolfger Schneider, Gertrude Vuynovich, and Grandmom Winnie, who recently passed away. Thanks, also, to my wildly creative friends (since middle school)—Andrea, Megan, and the Amandas—who spent summer afternoons with me at the Scream Stream long, long ago.

As for the two biggest treasures of my life, Ian and Bran, thank you for inspiring me to laugh and love and feel so happy to be alive. As Bran says nearly every day, "This is the best day EVER!"

Finally, I want to thank you, dear reader—whether you're young or old, a teacher or student, a librarian or patron—for letting me do this job, which I love with all my soul.

About the Author

Laura Resau is the author of several highly praised novels, including *Star in the Forest*, *The Queen of Water*, *Red Glass*, and *What the Moon Saw*. She is also the author of the acclaimed Notebook series, which includes *The Indigo Notebook*, *The Ruby Notebook*, and *The Jade Notebook*. Laura's books have gathered many state and library awards as well as multiple starred reviews. *The Lightning Queen* is drawn from Laura's experience of living in rural Mexico. She now lives in Fort Collins, Colorado, and donates a portion of her royalties to indigenous rights organizations.